The Organic Directory
2007-8

The
Organic
Directory
2007-8

Edited by Clive Litchfield

Published by Green Books
with
The Soil Association

ACKNOWLEDGEMENTS

Ever since I started work on the first edition of this Directory in 1991, I have had enormous amounts of help and encouragement from a variety of people and organisations: thanks especially to my wife Annie, our daughters Sophie, Lydia and Ella, Mark Redman, Paul Adams, Tom de Pass, Martin Trowell, Sam Platt, everyone at the Soil Association, Basil Caplan, Alan and Jackie Gear, Robert Sculthorpe, James Anderson at the BDAA, Dr. Mae-Wan Ho, G.P. Lawson for Mac and website help, Jan Hurst for introducing me to organics twenty-odd years ago, and John Elford at Green Books for taking on this project.

This edition published in April 2007
by Green Books Ltd, Foxhole, Dartington, Totnes, Devon TQ9 6EB
sales@greenbooks.co.uk www.greenbooks.co.uk
www.theorganicdirectory.co.uk

with the Soil Association
South Plaza, Marlborough Street, Bristol BS1 3NX
info@soilassociation.org www.soilassociation.org

Copyright © Clive Litchfield 2007
Design by Julie Martin
Cover by Rick Lawrence
Typeset at Green Books

Printed and bound by Butler & Tanner, Frome, Somerset, UK. The text is printed on Emerald FSC (75% post-consumer waste paper + 25% FSC-approved paper) and the cover on GreenCoat Velvet 80% recycled board.

First edition published October 1992; Second edition October 1996
Third edition October 1998; Fourth edition May 2000
Fifth edition June 2002; Sixth edition June 2004
Seventh edition October 2005

A CIP record for this book is available from the British Library.

ISBN 978 1 903998 83 0 (10–copy counterpack for retailers: ISBN 978 1 903998 84 7)

CONTENTS

LOCAL DIRECTORY including shops, box schemes, 19
accommodation and farm visits, listed by region and by county

CONTENTS (continued)

INTRODUCTION

What does organic mean?

Organic agriculture is a safe, sustainable farming system, producing healthy crops and livestock without damage to the environment. It avoids the use of artificial chemical fertilisers and pesticides on the land, relying instead on developing a healthy, fertile soil and growing a mixture of crops. In this way the farm remains biologically balanced, with a wide variety of beneficial insects and other wildlife to act as natural predators for crop pests, and a soil full of micro-organisms and earthworms to maintain its vitality. Animals are reared without the routine use of the array of drugs, antibiotics and wormers which form the foundation of most non-organic livestock farming.

How do I know if a product is organic?

'Organic' is a term defined by law, and all organic food production and processing is governed by strict standards. Producers, manufacturers and processors of organic foods have to be registered with one of the approved certification bodies and are required to keep detailed records ensuring a full trail of traceability from farm, through any processing operations, to table. Any major infringement of this results in the suspension of their licence and withdrawal of products from the market. All organic farmers, food manufacturers and processors are inspected annually, as well as being subject to random inspections.

The standards are stringent and cover every aspect of registration and certification, organic food production, permitted and non-permitted ingredients, the environment and conservation, processing, packaging and distribution. The standards are regularly updated and are then enforced by certification bodies.

To avoid any confusion with non-organic produce, most organic food is sold pre-packaged. Always check for the symbol and/or number of recognised certification bodies. Where produce is sold loose, proof of certification must be available to consumers. If the retailer cannot prove certification of the produce being sold, then find out who their supplier is and contact them to find out about their certification. All manufacturers must be registered with a certification body. Some shops pay a certification fee to register as organic in their own right. This gives an added assurance to customers. Any shop that repackages goods out of sight of customers, or cooks its own food and labels it 'organic', must also have its own licence to do so.

Is organic food healthier for me?

"Many research publications have shown that organically produced foods have higher amounts of beneficial minerals, essential amino acids, vitamins and lower potential risks from food pathogens and mycotoxins." – Carlo Leifert, Professor of Ecological Agriculture, Director of the Tesco Centre for Organic Agriculture.

Over 400 chemical pesticides are routinely used in intensive farming, and residues are often present in non-organic food. So-called 'acceptable levels' are calculated for each of these chemicals, and their risks to human health evaluated. However, surveys consistently show high and multiple residues occurring in a proportion of food samples such as baby food, spinach, dried fruit, bread, apples, celery and chips. There is also little knowledge of the long-term effects of these compounds, or of the 'cocktail' effect (the way in which their toxicity may be increased by mixing them together). The routine use of synthetic pesticides is not allowed under organic standards. Only four chemicals are allowed in restricted circumstances under Soil Association regulations.

Research has also shown that on average, organic food contains higher levels of vitamin C and essential minerals such as calcium, magnesium, iron and chromium, as well as cancer-fighting antioxidants. Even organic processed food is different – hydrogenated fat and artificial flavourings and sweeteners are banned, along with other food additives that can cause health problems.

Why should I buy local?

Buying locally produced food helps to support the producers in your region, maintaining a well established rural way of life. It gives the local economy a boost by keeping money within the community, sustaining local businesses and creating jobs for people who live in the area. Food that is grown closer to us has travelled less distance to reach us – this means less environmental pollution. Locally produced food can also be fresher, healthier and more nutritious, having been spared lengthy periods of storage, chilling and travel. And culturally, local organic food has its own 'story', bringing a shared meaning at mealtimes and a deeper connection to the land.

What is a box scheme?

A box scheme is a box (bag, sack or net), containing freshly picked, locally grown produce, delivered weekly to your door or to a local drop-off point. Box scheme operators usually offer small, medium and family-size boxes, with prices ranging from £5 to £15. The operator decides what vegetables go into the box, and this will vary each week depending on the seasonal vegetables available – healthy, tasty vegetables, just as you would want to grow them yourself!

Organic box schemes are now one of the fastest growing forms of direct marketing in the UK: that is, getting food straight from the farmer to the consumer. The original concept was developed by vegetable growers to shortcut the extended food supply chain in order to sell their fresh produce direct to local consumers. Not surprisingly, a number of variations on the basic model have evolved, and there are an increasing number of home delivery businesses that buy their produce from farms and wholesalers. They may also supply fruit, dairy produce, meat, wines and wholefoods. Most schemes operate locally or on a regional basis, but some also deliver nationally. Box schemes usually source produce locally, keeping unnecessary packaging, storage and transportation to a minimum, which ensures it's fresh when it arrives at your home.

What is a farmers' market?

Farmers' markets help local producers and processors to sell their goods direct to the public, near the source of origin, creating benefits to them and the local community. Usually held on a weekly basis, farmers' markets place an emphasis on added value, quality and freshness. They aim for an atmosphere that is vibrant, upbeat and fun, helping to revitalise urban centres and to make shopping an enjoyable experience. Although the concept is not a new one, farmers' markets are becoming increasingly popular – more and more people are demanding quality, locally produced food, sold at a fair price to both consumer and producer.

Is organic farming better for the environment?

Extensive research has shown that organic farming can be better for the environment than conventional agriculture. Surveys by, among others, the Ministry of Agriculture and the British Trust for Ornithology, have shown the beneficial effects of organic farming on wildlife. It's not difficult to see why: the pesticides used in intensive agriculture kill many soil organisms, insects and other larger species. They also kill plants considered to be weeds. This means fewer food sources available for other animals, birds and beneficial insects, and the destruction of many of their habitats.

By contrast, organic farming provides a much wider range of habitats: more hedges, wider field margins, herb and clover-rich grassland, and a mixed range of crops. Wildlife is not a luxury for the organic farmer, but an essential part of the farming system, and conservation is an integral part of the Soil Association's standards.

The avoidance of artificial chemicals means organic farmers minimise health and pollution problems. They also reduce the use of non-renewable resources such as the fossil fuels which are used to produce fertilisers and other agrochemicals.

What are biodynamic farming standards?

You will notice that some of the producers listed in this directory are certified as biodynamic. Biodynamic farmers apply organic standards, but in addition use special preparations for field sprays, and for compost and manure treatments. Close attention is also paid to practical rhythms in husbandry, concentrating on closed systems. Biodynamics is a contemporary organic philosophy, following the ideas of Rudolf Steiner; it sees the whole earth as a living organism interrelating with the universe. Biodynamic produce is certified by the Demeter Standards Committee and carries their symbol, which is their trademark.

What about farm animals – how well are they looked after?

"Organic farming has the potential to offer the very highest standards of animal welfare. The Soil Association's welfare standards are leaders in the field." – Joyce de Silva, Chief Executive, Compassion in World Farming, 2003

Organic standards place a strong emphasis on animal welfare. Animals have access to fields and are allowed to express their natural behaviour patterns. They always have comfortable bedding and plenty of space when they are housed. Organic livestock farmers can manage their animals without the routine use of antibiotics and other drugs because they run a healthy, balanced system: not keeping too many animals on a given area, keeping a mixture of species wherever possible, and using natural organic feedstuffs. Grazing animals such as cows and sheep are fed mainly on herb and clover-rich grass. Homeopathy and herbal remedies are used widely in organic livestock management. In a case of acute illness, where the animal might otherwise suffer, a conventional drug treatment would be used.

The Soil Association is one certification body that has chosen to set higher standards for animal welfare in certain key areas, to ensure that the highest possible standards are being met. These standards are constantly under review by a group of experienced organic farmers, vets and scientists, to ensure that all the farm animals are reared in optimal conditions on organic farms.

What are genetically modified organisms (GMOs)?

Genetic modification involves the artificial insertion of a foreign gene into the genetic material of an organism in an essentially random way. There are currently two main types of genetically modified crops: those engineered to be resistant to herbicides in order to kill weeds, and those engineered to produce toxins to kill pests.

Though GMOs have been marketed for several years, scientific knowledge of the processes involved is actually at a very early stage. Very little is known about the side effects of the inserted genes' random location, how gene location is controlled, and gene transfer into other micro-organisms such as bacteria in the human gut. In addition, evidence set out in the Soil Association's 'Seeds of Doubt' report illustrates that GM crops have no economic benefits and can actually harm the environment.

Organic standards prohibit the use of GMOs and GM derivatives in organic food production and in animal feed.

What about organic imports – just how 'organic' are they?

Each EU member state has its own national organic certifying authority that applies the EU regulation in that country. These approve private certification bodies, or in some cases take on the role of certification themselves. As in the UK, each certification body may apply additional specifications on top of the EU standards.

Food imported from outside Europe into the EU is subject to similar rigorous checks and standards. Imported produce must come either from countries recognised as applying equivalent standards and inspection procedures, or from identified supply chains where it can be verified that equivalent standards and certification criteria have been permanently and effectively applied at all stages. Importers and their storage facilities are also inspected and certified to ensure all their importing activities comply with the above.

Is it possible to visit an organic farm?

Yes! The Soil Association's Organic Farms Network was set up in 1998 to help the public and schools connect with organic food and farming. The project supports organic farmers who want to welcome the public and schools on to their farms. These farms play a key role in forging a bridge of knowledge and understanding between rural and urban communities, inspiring visitors through the 'seeing is believing' principle to inform them about farming practices and their relationship with the countryside. This will help to encourage a life-long commitment to supporting organic food, local farms and the environment.

The farm network promotes 'green tourism', developing a national network of working farms with informal access to way-marked farm trails; opportunities to buy fresh food from farm shops and box schemes; and the potential for longer stays through camping or bed and breakfast accommodation.

Open days and special events recreate the link between the consumer, the land and the cultural aspects of farming that have for centuries been at the heart of rural life. During Organic Week in September each year, we encourage farms to open their gates as part of the special Organic Experience weekend.

The farms also provide a platform for more structured education, both for groups seeking guided tours, and schools wishing to enthuse their pupils with a visit to a working organic farm.

The Soil Association aims to give every child of primary school age the opportunity to visit an organic farm to discover where their food really comes from. They believe the development of demonstration farms will enhance the education of the public and farmers, but more importantly will reach thousands of children in their formative years, providing them with interesting and stimulating first-hand experiences of food, farming, wildlife and the countryside.

The Soil Association aims to ensure that membership of the Organic Farms Network fits in with the farming enterprise concerned. There are three types of farm:

- those which are open to groups 'by arrangement', or have a farm trail
- local centres where the farm may, for example, have a farm shop and staffing to enable them to be open all the time, and
- regional centres that provide dedicated visitor centres, conference facilities and sometimes an education officer

All members of the Soil Association Organic Farms Network are highlighted in *The Organic Directory*. For more information about the network, visit the Soil Association website www.soilassociation.org/farmvisits or call 0117 914 2440.

How easily can I find organic food and drink in restaurants and cafés?

The market for food eaten outside the home grew to over 30% of food spend in 2004 and now stands at £36 billion. Yet there's been an even more noticeable shift in what people are buying.

There has never been such an interest in organic food, slow food, local produce, seasonal menus and traditional recipes. People are rediscovering food culture and demanding good quality food, and this has a positive effect on the number of restaurants, hotels and cafés serving local, organic and seasonal food.

Applications from restaurants for Soil Association certification have doubled in the past year, and the new Soil Association 'catering code of practice' helps restaurants that do not have full organic certification to back up their claims when using organic ingredients. It also supports them in finding suitable organic producers and suppliers. Fully certified organic eateries in this Directory carry the Soil Association symbol next to their entry.

You'll find many organic eateries in this Directory, and we expect many more in future. Newly certified venues include the first wholly organic restaurant in Cornwall, based at the first Soil Association certified B&B establishment, Bangor's House.

Local, fresh organic produce used to be a bonus – now it's an expectation, so remember to ask for it!

What about other products like health, beauty and textiles?

So you are convinced of the benefits of eating organic food – no nasty pesticides, benefits for the environment and high animal welfare standards – but what about the health and beauty products you use and the clothes you wear? Maybe it is time to consider going organic in other areas of your life.

Are all 'organic' beauty products really organic?

It is estimated that our skin absorbs over half of what we put on it: a worrying fact, when you consider that most of today's skin care products contain a toxic cocktail of parabens, petrochemicals and hydrogenated fat. In addition, non-organic beauty products can contain harsh surfactants that literally strip oils away from skin and hair, leaving them dry, dull and flaky. Extra care needs to be taken with babies and children: their bodies are still developing, so they are a lot more susceptible to chemicals and fragrances present in cosmetics.

Many people are turning to 'organic' cosmetics to avoid the risks associated with these chemicals. But how can you be sure that what you are buying really is organic? There is currently no national legislation governing organic beauty products – a product labelled 'organic' may only contain a tiny amount of an organic ingredient, and could still contain ingredients that are linked with health risks.

However, a product bearing the Soil Association symbol means that it has been independently audited and checked under rigorous organic standards, which aim to provide you with cosmetics that are as natural as possible. This means eliminating chemicals and replacing them with natural preservatives and antibacterial agents such as honey, sugar and alcohol. The standards work on a precautionary principle. and do not permit ingredients or processes that have been linked to health risks, such as parabens and phthalates, or do not have enough evidence to support them yet, such as nanoparticles. Plant extracts can also be used, such as rose, cinnamon, cloves, calendula and vanilla. So to feel beautiful on the outside as well as the inside, check the product label for organic certification as well as the word 'organic'.

Why would I buy organic textiles?

Sales of organic cotton have reached an estimated £20 million in the UK. The environmental and ethical benefits of organic textiles are being increasingly recognised by consumers – even a leading supermarket has introduced an organic baby wear range – and who can blame them? Take a look at the harmful effects of producing non-organic T-shirts:

- Non-organic cotton production is the biggest user of insecticides in the world – over 20 per cent of the world's insecticides are sprayed on cotton crops
- Around 30 teaspoons of pesticides are used to grow the cotton for each T-shirt
- The World Health Organisation estimates that at least 20,000 people die each year in developing countries as a result of sprays used on non-organic cotton

- Large-scale non-organic production uses irrigation, which can put pressure on scant water resources

The Soil Association has licensed manufacturers to produce textiles to its standards, covering every aspect of production including the way in which animals are reared, the growing of natural fibres and the processing and manufacture of the end product. They are also working with suppliers to develop more certified organic clothing, bedding and cotton-based products – so watch this space, and wear it with pride!

The Soil Association's Organic Food Awards 2007

The Organic Food Awards are held very year, and aim to celebrate the very best of organic fare. In 2006 the judging of the Awards took place in the spring, moving them from their previous autumn date. This means that winners were able to showcase their winning products to the public at the annual Organic Food Festival in September 2006.

The product categories and closing dates for the next Organic Food Awards will be available early in 2007, and full information will be published on the Soil Association's website (www.soilassociation.org).

The awards regularly attract over 1,000 entries, and involve a team of 90 judges, including well-known chefs and food writers, to ensure that the exceptional quality of winning products is maintained.

Categories in previous years have ranged from 'food to go' and 'local food initiative of the year' to the best organic sausages! Businesses that win an award can then go on to use the Organic Food Awards logo on their winning products. So if there's an Organic Food Awards logo on a product, you know it comes well recommended!

In 2006 'Organic Restaurant of the Year' became part of the Organic Industry Awards, which were judged in March 2006 and announced at the Organic and Natural Products Show in April 2006.

Businesses in this Directory that have won a 2006 Organic Food Award for one of their products are marked with the Organic Food Awards logo.

What do the UK organic certification codes mean?

Each certification body within the UK is given a UK code – the Soil Association's is UK5. The number awarded has nothing to do with stringency standards, but reflects the order in which DEFRA received applications from the certification bodies. Legally, a company does not need to show a certification symbol on a pack, but if the product has been pro-duced and/or processed in the UK they must show the UK code. The Soil Association standards are among the highest in the world.

The UK certification bodies and their codes are listed on the next page.

THE UK ORGANIC CERTIFICATION BODIES

The organic food sector in the UK is expanding rapidly. Although over 70% of all organic products in the UK carry the Soil Association symbol, there are a number of other certifiers who, unlike the Soil Association and Demeter, operate on a profit-making basis. The certification bodies are:

 Soil Association Certification (SA Cert) – UK5

 Organic Farmers and Growers Ltd (OF&G) – UK2

 The Scottish Organic Producers Association (SOPA) – UK3

 The Organic Food Federation (OFF) – UK4

 Demeter (BDAA) – UK 6

 The Irish Organic Farmers and Growers Association (IOFGA) – UK7

 Organic Trust Ltd – UK9

 CMi Certification – UK10*

 Quality Welsh Food Certification – UK13

 Ascisco Limited – UK15

* CMI ceased issuing certification licences after 30th November 2006

THE LABELLING OF ORGANIC FOOD

Strict EC regulations cover the labelling of organic foods, with the aim of ensuring that consumers are not misled. Natural products such as potatoes and lettuce may only be described as 'Organic' if they have been grown by a registered organic producer; they will probably be labelled 'Organically Grown Lettuce' or just 'Organic Lettuce'. The inspection system for organic producers is covered in the Introduction to this book. Manufactured goods such as bread are covered by the same regulations, and will probably be labelled, e.g. 'Bread baked from Organic Flour'. Where it is not possible to manufacture goods from wholly organic ingredients, the manufacturer can use up to 5% non-organic minor ingredients – these are specified in the regulations, and are recognised as not being available in sufficient quantities in organic form. So products labelled 'Organic' will be between 95% and 100% organic.

Products containing between 70% and 95% organic ingredients cannot be labelled 'Organic'. These products may use the term 'Organic' only in their ingredients list in descending weight order, e.g. Organically grown wheat (55%), Organically grown barley (15%), Organically grown oats (7%).

Products containing less than 70% organic ingredients may not use the term 'Organic' or any derivative of the term anywhere on the label. Percentages refer to agricultural ingredients; non-agricultural ingredients (e.g. water and salt) are not included in the calculations. No genetically modified or irradiated organisms are allowed in organic food products.

In the UK registration issues are advised by ACOS *, which also recognises all other EC certification bodies and a limited number of non-EC certification bodies that have an equivalent standard and inspection system. For all other countries, importers must demonstrate, either to ACOS or an equivalent body in another EC country, that the food has been produced to equivalent standards and inspection systems in order for them to be allowed to use the term 'Organic' or its derivatives. A list of worldwide organic logos is available from the International Federation of Organic Agricultural Movements (IFOAM) – see under Associations listing.

Details of UK legislation with regard to organic standards can be found at: www.defra.gov.uk/farm/organic/standards/index.

* The Advisory Committee on Organic Standards (ACOS) is a non-executive non-departmental public body which advises government on organic standards, approval of organic certifying bodies and R&D. It was preceded by UKROFS.

HOW TO USE THIS DIRECTORY

This edition of the Directory has been organised into four main sections:

LOCAL

This section, laid out regionally, contains retail shops, box schemes, accommodation, farms open for visits, farmers' markets, restaurants, cafés, and other facilities that can be visited in person or that supply a local service. Many of these entrants may also supply via mail order, catalogue or online ordering. The symbols for the various types of entry are shown alongside each company name.

NATIONAL MAIL ORDER

This section contains an alphabetical list of businesses supplying to the public via mail order, purchasing through a catalogue or online shop. These do not usually have facilities for personal visitors, although some may also have retail outlets which will be detailed on their website. The symbols for the various types of entry are shown alongside each company name.

BUSINESS-TO-BUSINESS

This section, laid out regionally, contains producers, manufacturers, processors, importers, exporters, wholesalers, business advisers and consultants, etc., that deal primarily with other businesses, rather than with the general public, although they will happily advise the general public of the availability of their products. The symbols for the various types of entry are shown alongside each company name.

ASSOCIATIONS

This section contains an alphabetical list of associations, organisations including certification bodies, education, clubs, R&D, publishers and publications, and other services.

Some sets of symbols (see opposite page) with their meaning are scattered throughout the Directory, depending on available space.

In order to avoid potential disappointment please telephone suppliers (especially farmers) before making a special journey to visit them!

The world of organics is changing fast. Inevitably, some companies in the Directory will move premises, or even go out of business. New businesses will open – please let us know of any not listed. There have been changes in recent years with regard to the naming of Welsh and Scottish counties. We have used county names in this book, not unitary authority names.

DISCLAIMER

The information in this Directory regarding the producers, retailers etc. and the products they grow and sell has been gathered primarily from the entrants themselves. We have not verified any claims as to whether any produce described as such is 100% organic. Please note therefore that we cannot be held responsible for any claims made as to the quality of the produce or goods offered. There has recently been a proliferation of 'Green' labelling schemes, and we advise you to satisfy yourself as to the validity of any such claims.

WHAT THE SYMBOLS MEAN

See page 14 for the symbols of the organic certifying bodies.

 Accommodation: this can be anything from a field for camping to a hotel with full board.

 Alcoholic drinks.

 Baby goods (food or non-food items).

 Box schemes & local deliveries: local box schemes and/or delivery services. Boxes may be delivered to the door, or to a central pick-up point.

 Cosmetics and toiletries.

 Day visits: generally farms open to visitors. Some may require prior booking.

 Farm gate sales: sales of produce from the farm (may need prior notification).

 Farmers' market stall: sales of produce from local farmers' market stall.

 Garden and farm sundries: composts, seeds, tools, etc.

 Household products: non-food items, cleaning and decorating materials, etc.

 Manufacturers & processors: mainly food manufacturers and/or processors, but can be any manufacturing process.

 Importers and/or exporters.

 Mail order suppliers, including internet suppliers.

 Pet supplies.

 Producers: farmers, growers etc.

 Restaurants, cafés & caterers. All claim to serve some organic produce.

 Retail shops.

 Textile suppliers: clothes, nappies, mattresses, bed linen etc.

 Wholesalers and distributors.

Local Directory

LONDON & THE SOUTH-EAST
ESSEX

ASHLYNS ORGANIC FARM & SHOP

High Laver Hall, High Laver, Ongar, CM5 0DU
Tel: 01277 890157 info@ashlyns.co.uk www.ashlyns.co.uk
Soil Association G2401, P5815. Home grown produce available in our Organic Farm Shop, offering home-grown vegetables, fruit, meat, dairy, eco products, cosmetics, toiletries, and home-made delicatessen. Member of the Soil Association Organic Farms Network. Schools and other educational groups' visits arranged. Shop address: Ashlyns Organic Farm Shop, Epping Rd., North Weald, Essex CM16 6RZ. Shop 01992 525146, educational visits 01277 890821.

BEATBUSH FARM

Brook Hall Farm, Steeple Road, Latchingdon,
Chelmsford, CM3 6LB
Tel: 01621 741470 Fax: 01621 741474
nicola@beatbushorganicfarm.co.uk www.beatbushorganicfarm.co.uk
Producer, retailer and wholesaler of organic beef, lamb and poultry. Visit our website for a list of local farmers' markets that we sell through.

BUNTINGS

89 High Street, Maldon, CM9 5EP
Tel: 01621 853271 www.buntingfoods.co.uk
Retail fine food shop specialising in butchery, delicatessen, home-made pies, cooked meats, patés. Delivery areas CM8, CM9, CO6.

BUNTINGS

18 Church St., Coggeshall, CO6 1TU
Tel: 01376 561233 www.buntingfoods.co.uk
Retail fine food shop specialising in butchery, delicatessen, home-made pies, cooked meats, patés.

CORNFLOWER WHOLEFOODS

49 High St., Brightlingsea, CO7 0AQ
Tel: 01206 306679 chrysalis@homecall.co.uk
A family run independent retailer or organic foods and toiletries. Organic fruit and vegetable boxes tailor-made to your requirements with free local delivery.

FARMER KIT ORGANICS

Little Bowsers Farm, Bowsers Lane, Little Walden,
Saffron Walden, CB10 1XQ
Tel: 01799 527315 Fax: 01799 527315 sales@farmerkit.co.uk www.farmerkit.co.uk
Soil Association G2143. Little Bowsers Farm produces organic free range eggs and organic top fruit, apples, pears, plums. Also organic soft fruits. We deliver regularly to London wholesalers.

GARDEN ORGANIC

The Organic Kitchen Garden, Audley End House, Saffron Walden, CB11 4JF
Tel: 01799 522148 Fax: 024 7663 9229 enquiry@hdra.org.uk www.gardenorganic.org.uk
HDRA, the organic organisation, runs the walled kitchen garden at Audley End House, an English Heritage property. The 2-acre walled gardens include heritage vegetables, vinery and fruit house. For opening hours please see website.

ESSEX

HEPBURNS OF MOUNTNESSING

269 Roman Road, Mountnessing, Brentwood, CM15 0UH

Tel: 01277 353289 Fax: 01277 355589

Traditional butcher and grazier with a reputation for quality and service. Established 1932. Highgrove organic beef, lamb and pork when available. Deliver locally and to London (over £50 free).

LEGG, ROGER

Heards Farm, Heards Lane, Shenfield, Brentwood, CM15 0SF

Tel: 01277 211883

Local grower and producer of vegetables, fruit, herbs, plants, cut flowers & eggs, marketing through Blackmore and Stock farmers' markets, Shenfield Country Market and seasonal local box scheme in Brentwood/Shenfield area.

ONLYFINEBEER

37 Broomfield Road, Chelmsford, CM1 1SY

Tel: 01245 255579 chelmsford@onlyfinebeer.co.uk www.onlyfinebeer.co.uk

A retailer of 39 different organic beers, ciders and Perrys. This range will continue to increase as more and more brewers are turning to using organic ingredients. You can use www.onlyfinebeer.co.uk to search for the word 'Organic', in the brand title, or use the advanced search facility to find the word 'Organic' when it is used in the description.

ORGANIC CHOICE

60 High St., Halstead, CO9 2JG

Tel: 01787 478471 Fax: 01787 478457 info@organicchoice.net www.organicchoice.net

Organic delicatessen offering fresh fruit & vegetables, traditional & speciality cheeses, paté, hand-carved ham, award-winning breads, wine, groceries, dairy, chilled & frozen foods, environmentally friendly products. Free home delivery throughout Essex and Suffolk borders. Price list available. Credit cards accepted.

THE ORGANIC COUNTRY STORE

159 Little Wakering Rd., Little Wakering, Southend, SS3 0JQ

Tel: 01702 219037 Fax: 01702 217750

sales@theorganiccountrystore.co.uk www.theorganiccountrystore.co.uk

The Organic Country Store is based in Southend, Essex. We have a free delivery box scheme which covers the whole of Essex, Hertfordshire and areas of NE and SE London. You can even make your own personalised box! Ring 01702 219037 or visit our website.

PILGRIM'S NATURAL

4 King Georges Place, High St., Maldon, CM9 5BZ

Tel: 01621 858605

Retailer and packer of a wide range of organic food including butter and yoghurts, ice cream, bread and cakes.

RIVERFORD HOME DELIVERY

No 11, The Oakleighs, 630 High Road, Woodford Green, IG8 0PU

Tel: 0845 600 2311 Fax: 01803 762718 boxscheme@riverford.co.uk www.riverford.co.uk

Award-winning organic vegetable box scheme operating in Enfield and surrounding areas of north London. Various box sizes to suit all households from a single occupant upwards. A wide selection of fruit, dairy products, wine, eggs, chocolate, fruit juices etc. are also available. Order weekly, fortnightly or whenever you like. You can order online at www.riverford.co.uk or by telephone on 0845 600 2311. BBC Radio 4 Farmer of the Year 2005.

SALLY GREEN'S

74 High St., Maldon, CM9 5ET
Tel: 01621 854727 greens@tillinghamfarm.fsnet.co.uk
Retail shop selling Sarah Green's locally grown seasonal organic vegetables.

SARAH GREEN'S ORGANICS

Tillingham Hall Farm, North Street, Tillingham,
Southminster, CM0 7ST
Tel: 01621 779500 Fax: 01621 779500 sarahgreen@farming.co.uk
A family-run farm growing a variety of fresh seasonal vegetables all year round. There is a farm shop in
North Street, Tillingham, open Thurs, Fri and Sat 9am–4pm. We also supply Sally Green's, 74 High
Street, Maldon (01621 854727) with fresh seasonal organic vegetables, as well as attending Burnham-
on-Crouch Farmers' market. We plan to start producing a range of home grown fruit. All our produce is
organically grown in Tillingham and sold fresh from the field.

SUNRISE HEALTHFOODS LTD

31 Spa Rd., Hockley, SS5 4AZ
Tel: 01702 207017
Modern healthfood shop offering 2,000 products including many organic lines, frozen and chilled foods,
special diet foods and supplements. Friendly service and competent advice always available.

SUNRISE ORGANICS

High Laver Hall, High Laver, Ongar, CM5 0DU
Tel: 01277 891310 info@sunriseorganics.co.uk www.sunriseorganics.co.uk
Soil Association certified organic veg box home delivery service. We provide tasty, seasonal, locally grown
produce, sourced from local organic farms. We cover Essex and provide a great range of boxes to choose
from. You can order weekly, fortnightly, or just when you want.

TEY BROOK FARM

Tey Brook Farm, Brook Rd., Great Tey, Colchester, CO6 1JE
Tel: 01206 212467 Fax: 01206 212597 info@teybrookfarm.co.uk www.teybrookfarm.co.uk
Organic producer of vegetables for sale through local retail outlet, restaurant and box scheme. Farm shop
open Tuesday–Saturday 10-4.

THE WHOLEFOOD STORE

26 High St., Manningtree, CO11 1AJ
Tel: 01206 391200 jondyvig@hotmail.com
We are an independent and friendly wholefood store selling an extensive range of organic dried foods,
fresh fruit and vegetables, dairy products, drinks, bread and pastries.

WILLOW HALL ORGANICS

Willow Hall, Wix, Manningtree, CO11 2UH
Tel: 01255 870349 hamptwix@fwi.co.uk www.willowhall-organics.co.uk
Sales of biodynamic beef and pork, also selling biodynamic feed wheat. Not a box scheme but local deliv-
ery available.

FOR DETAILS OF
SYMBOLS USED
IN THE ENTRIES,
SEE PAGE 17

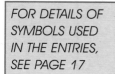 

KENT

BROCKMAN, AG & CO

Perry Court Farm, Garlinge Green, Canterbury, CT4 5RU
Tel: 01227 732001 Fax: 01227 732001 agbrockmanco@farmersweekly.net
Producers of Demeter certified organic foods since 1953. Beef, milling wheat, oats, wheat flour, vegetables, salads and herbs. Sales through farm shop, box scheme, farmers' markets, local shops and wholesalers.

CANTERBURY WHOLEFOODS

1 & 2 Jewry Lane, Canterbury, CT1 2RP
Tel: 01227 464623 Fax: 01227 764838
info@canterbury-wholefoods.co.uk www.canterbury-wholefoods.co.uk
Soil Association R1676. We are a large, traditional wholefood store and café specialising in organics, fresh fruit and vegetables, bulk sales and discounts.

CHUN FARM

Churn Lane, Horsmonden, Tonbridge, TN12 8HL
Tel: 01892 722577
Soil Association G4567. Seven-acre smallholding producing salads, vegetables, fruit and nuts sold through local farmers' markets.

CHURCH VIEW FARM

Ightham by-pass, Sevenoaks, TN15 9AZ
Tel: 01732 886680 churchvieworganicfarm@hotmail.com
Soil Association G6051. Local organic box delivery scheme including vegetables, fruit, eggs and juice supplying Tonbridge and Sevenoaks.

CROWN COFFEE

1 Church St., Wye, Ashford, TN25 5BN
Tel: 01233 812798 Fax: 01795 890430 Contact: Lorraine Stevens
crowncoffee@btinternet.com www.crowncoffeeandgifts.com
We are a coffee shop, delicatessen and bistro. Our menu is predominantly organic. We sell organic baby food, and a completely organic children's lunch box. Our house blend coffee and tea is organic, as is our house wine. There is always an organic option, and we are constantly sourcing suppliers to replace non-organic products with organic free range without compromising on taste.

CUCKOO'S PIT ORGANIC FARM

Kippington, Redbrook Street, Woodchurch, Ashford, TN26 3QU
Tel: 01233 860199 thebugdengang@aol.com
We are an expanding organic farm in the heart of the Kent countryside. We produce and sell all our own home-reared livestock. We sell organic beef, lamb, pork, sausages, ham and bacon. Several of our livestock breeds are rare breeds, e.g. Gloucester Old Spot pigs and White Park cattle. We sell at our gate or can deliver locally.

DABBS PLACE ORGANIC FARM

Cobham, Gravesend, DA13 9BL
Tel: 07712 439304 mail@organicveg.net www.organicveg.net
Soil Association F165. Local box scheme, vegetables, arable farm.

ESPECIALLY HEALTH

119 High Street, Sevenoaks, TN13 1UP
Tel: 01732 741181 Fax: 01732 740719 info@especiallyhealth.co.uk www.especiallyhealth.co.uk
Wholefoods and healthfoods including sprouted wheat (essene), spelt and other non-wheat breads.
Dietary consultations, blood group advice, allergy testing, vitamin and mineral testing, massage, flower
therapy and medical herbalism.

FOOD FOR LIVING

Market Place, Dartford, DA1 1EX
Tel: 01322 278790 Fax: 01322 278790 john@foodforliving.co.uk www.foodforliving.co.uk
Health food shop with a wide range of organic foods. Vitamins and supplements also supplied.

GARDEN ORGANIC

Yalding Organic Gardens Benover Rd., Yalding,
Nr. Maidstone, ME18 6EX
Tel: 01622 814650 Fax: 01622 814650 enquiry@hdra.org.uk www.gardenorganic.org.uk
Yalding Organic Gardens trace the course of garden history through 16 landscaped displays, illustrating
the organic techniques used to maintain them. Shop for browsing and organic café for refreshments.

THE GOODS SHED

Station Rd West, Canterbury, CT2 8AN
Tel: 01227 459153

A permanent farmers' market, open six days a week and including a restaurant which sources seasonal
ingredients from the local and regional producers who run the stalls. Converted from an industrial coal
store, it opened in 2002 and now has its own on-site bakery, and an on-site retail butchery selling well-
matured meats from five local and organic producers. Organic Food Awards 2004: Local Food Initiative
Joint Winner.

HEALTH MATTERS

28 Royal Star Arcade, Maidstone, ME14 1SL
Tel: 01622 691179 Fax: 01622 691179 www.maidstonehealthfoods.co.uk
We offer a wide range of organic wholefoods and also offer food intolerance testing.

IVY HOUSE FARM

Ivy House, Sandhills, Ash, Nr. Canterbury, CT3 2NG
Tel: 01304 812437 Fax: 01304 812437
Our farm, registered with the Soil Association, produces a range of organically grown vegetables for
wholesale and retail. Our farm shop also sells organically grown produce from other certified producers.

JONES & GARRATT

Burscombe Cliff Farm, Egerton, Ashford, TN27 5RB
Tel: 01233 756468 Fax: 01233 756468
Soil Association symbol no. G683. Organic beef, sheep and pig farmers offering beef, lamb, pork, bacon,
sausages. WWOOF host open farm. Always telephone for availability. Most produce sold via local farmers'
markets or occasionally via farm gate.

JUBILEE FARM

Rhodes Minnis, Nr. Canterbury, CT4 6YA
Tel: 01303 862317 Fax: 01303 864257 jubilee@farmline.com
Soil Association G7668. Mixed farm, livestock including Aberdeen Angus herd, sheep, poultry, free range
eggs, vegetables, cereals, top fruit and soft fruit.

KENT

LOWER THORNE FARM

Lower Thorne, Smarden Rd, Pluckley, TN27 0RF

Tel: 01233 840493 info@lowerthorne.com www.lowerthorne.com

Lower Thorne is an organic holding in Pluckley, Kent, certified with the Soil Association. The farm has a long history of traditional, non-intensive management and was acquired by the current owners in 1995. The farm specialises in rearing traditional English breeds & produces organically reared free-range chicken and Devon Dimple turkeys for Christmas, organic beef, lamb and pork. Our meat is for sale direct from the farm or by mail order.

LUDDESDOWN ORGANIC FARMS LTD

Court Lodge, Luddesdown, Nr. Cobham, DA13 0XE

Tel: 01474 813376 Fax: 01474 815044

organic@luddesdown.u-net.com www.luddesdownorganicfarms.co.uk

Soil Association S38S. 950 acres producing cereals, beans, red clover for seed, forage, beef and vegetables. All grown to Soil Association standards. Wholesaler and retailer, including vegetable box scheme, delivery scheme and home produced beef. Member of the Soil Association Organic Farms Network.

MOLLYCODDLES OF ROCHESTER

44 High St., Rochester, ME1 1LD

Tel: 01634 848895 www.mollycoddlesofrochester.co.uk

Natural and organic body and skin care for you and the ones you love. Visit us in our 16th century shop or on our 21st century website, from where all items will be despatched to be delivered next day where possible.

NASH NURSERY LTD

Nash, Nr. Ash, Canterbury, CT3 2JU

Tel: 01304 812250 paul@nashnursery.co.uk www.nashnursery.co.uk

Soil Association G2528. Organic farm producing chicken, turkey, ducks and geese, fruit and vegetables. Abattoir and processing room on-site.

NEAL'S YARD REMEDIES

8 East St., Bromley, BR1 1QX

Tel: 020 8313 9898 Fax: 020 8313 9898 mail@nealsyardremedies.com www.nealsyardremedies.com

Retail store specialising in natural remedies and cosmetics, including herbs, homeopathy, aromatherapy, nutrition and flower remedies.

THE OLD DAIRY

Rectory Farm, Sutton Road, Maidstone, ME17 3LY

Tel: 01622 861113 enquiry@marofoods.co.uk www.theolddairy-online.co.uk

We sell organic products through our box scheme and shop.

THE ORGANIC HEALTH SHOP

10 High St., Tunbridge Wells, TN1 1UX

Tel: 01892 538155 Fax: 01892 538155

A wide range of organic food and drink including vegetable and fruit boxes, vitamins, minerals, supplements, skin and hair care products, cosmetics, books, cleaning products, natural paint and organic pet food.

REGENT HEALTH

12 Albert Road, Belvedere, DA17 5LJ

Tel: 01322 446244

Large range of organic, gluten-free, dairy-free, diabetic, chilled and frozen foods available. Local deliveries (minimum order). Friendly advice, mail service. If we haven't got it, we will get it!

RIPPLE FARM ORGANICS

Crundale, Canterbury, CT4 7EB

Tel: 01227 730898 martin@ripplefarmorganics.co.uk www.ripplefarmorganics.co.uk

Soil Association G737. Growers of organic vegetables, salad and soft fruit to supply own local, year-round, box scheme, farmers' markets and London organic shops.

RIVERFORD ORGANIC VEGETABLES – HOME DELIVERY (KENT)

63 Oaklands, South Godstone, RH9 8HX

Tel: 0845 009 3564 Fax: 0845 009 3564 andrewg@riverfordhomedelivery.co.uk www.riverford.co.uk

Award-winning (BBC Radio 4 Farmer of the Year 2005) organic vegetable box scheme operating in various parts of West Kent. Various box sizes to suit all households, from a single occupant to a large family. A selection of fruit, dairy products, wine, fruit juices etc. also available. Order weekly, fortnightly or whenever you like. Can order online at www.riverford.co.uk or by telephone on 0845 600 2311.

RIVERFORD ORGANIC VEGETABLES – NORTH-WEST KENT

67 Byron Drive, Erith, DA8 1YD

Tel: 0845 600 2311 Fax: 01322 434 286 pat@riverfordhomedelivery.co.uk www.riverford.co.uk

Award-winning (BBC Radio 4 Farmer of the Year 2005) organic vegetable box scheme operating in Bexley, Dartford, Orpington and surrounding areas. Box sizes to suit all households, from a single person to a large family. A selection of fruit, dairy products, wine, juices and chocolate are also available. Order weekly, fortnightly or whenever you like. Can order and pay online at www.riverford.co.uk or by phone: 0845 600 2311.

ROMSHED FARM

Underriver, Sevenoaks, TN15 0SD

Tel: 01732 463372 Fax: 01732 454136 romshed@weald.co.uk

Organic eggs, chicken meat, duck, lamb and beef. Monthly deliveries and local sales outlets including farm gate.

SIMPLY WILD FOOD COMPANY

 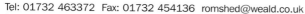 

Pullens Farm, Lamberhurst Rd., Horsmonden, TN12 8ED

Tel: 08456 586142 Fax: 08456 586148 enquiries@simplywildorganics.co.uk www.simplywild.biz

Simply Wild is a family-run business which offers a range of home delivery boxes, each containing fresh locally produced organic vegetables, fruit, eggs, bread and meat to your doorstep.

WILLOW FARM B&B

Stone Cross, Bilsington, Ashford, TN25 7JJ

Tel: 01233 721700 Fax: 01233 720484

renee@willow-farm.freeserve.co.uk www.willowfarmenterprises.co.uk

B&B on an organic smallholding in peaceful rural area. Close to Yalding Gardens. Easy access M20, Channel ports and Tunnel. From £25 per person per night.

WINGHAM COUNTRY MARKET

Shatterling, Canterbury, CT3 1JW

Tel: 01227 720567 Fax: 01227 720567

We sell an extensive range of organic produce at our farm shop, including fresh vegetables grown on our Soil Association registered (G977) farm.

LONDON-EAST

CLEAN BEAN

170 Brick Lane, London E1 6RU

Tel: 020 7247 1639 Fax: 020 7247 1639 cleanbean@ssba.info

Soil Association P2200. Clean Bean manufactures fresh organic tofu which is supplied to restaurants and wholefood stores in the London area, and sold from our stalls at Borough Market every Saturday and Spitalfields Organic Market every Sunday.

THE CLERKENWELL KITCHEN

31 Clerkenwell Close, London, EC1R 0AT

Tel: 020 7101 9959 Fax: 020 7014 3614

info@theclerkenwellkitchen.co.uk www.theclerkenwellkitchen.co.uk

The Clerkenwell Kitchen is a café and catering company committed to sourcing organic, local, seasonal and fairly traded produce, ethically reared meats and sustainable fish. British produce is favoured wherever possible, and we don't fly any apples in from New Zealand when we can get organic ones from Kent! In fact we are growing our very own apples in our kitchen garden as well as herbs and vegetables. Open Monday to Friday 8–5, evenings and weekends by arrangement.

EOSTRE ORGANICS LTD

Unit 2, North Side Hangars, Old Buckenham Airfield, Attleborough, Norfolk, NR17 1PU

Tel: 01953 456294 Fax: 01953 456145 dot.bane@eostreorganics.co.uk www.eostreorganics.co.uk

An organic grower co-operative, mainly wholesaling but we also attend markets and have stands at Norwich Provisions Market (6 days) and Old Spitalfields (Sun), Acre Lane, Brixton (Sat), Sunnyside Community Gardens, Islington (Sat), Calthorpe Communty Gardens, Gravesend Rd (Fri), Archway (Sat), Hildreth St., Balham (Sun), Hoe St., Walthamstow (Sat), Sloane Square / Duke of York Square off Kings Rd., Chelsea, Borough Market (Fri & Sat), Bellenden Rd., Peckham (Sat). We also pack boxes for distribution by others.

FRESH & WILD

194 Old Street, The City, London EC1V 9FR

Tel: 020 7250 1708

Fresh & Wild are the leading specialist retailer of organic foods and natural remedies.

OLD SPITALFIELDS ORGANIC MARKET

65 Brushfield St., London E1 6AA

Tel: 01243 779716

Every Sunday, covered market from 10am–5pm. Established 1993. The alternative to supermarkets and cheaper. Largest range certified organic fresh fruit, veg, breads, dairy, meat, wine etc. from producers and traders.

THE ORGANIC DELIVERY COMPANY

68 Rivington St., London, EC2A 3AY

Tel: 020 7739 8181 Fax: 020 7613 5656 info@organicdelivery.co.uk www.organicdelivery.co.uk

Large range of organic vegetarian and vegan groceries of the highest quality delivered to you, throughout London and nationwide. Affordable and convenient. Order by telephone or securely online. Highly commended in the Soil Association awards, and registered with them. Licence number P8888.

FOR DETAILS OF SYMBOLS USED IN THE ENTRIES, SEE PAGE 17

SECOND NATURE
78 Wood St., Walthamstow, London E17 3HX
Tel: 020 8520 7995 Fax: 020 8520 7995 mail@econat.co.uk www.econat.co.uk
Second Nature is an organic and wholefood shop in east london. We deliver fruit and veg locally – all of our stock is GMO-free.

LONDON-NORTH

ALTERNATIVES HEALTH CENTRE
1369 High St., Whetstone, London N20 9LN
Tel: 020 8445 2675 www.naturesalternative.co.uk
Health food shop with clinic. Organic, tinned, packets, frozen and chilled products, supplements, homeo-pathic and herbal remedies, tinctures, cosmetics, books and magazines.

BLISS ORGANICS LTD
102B Belgravia Workshops, 157-163 Marlborough Rd., London N19 4NF
Tel: 020 7281 7995 Fax: 020 7281 7995
Soil Association P7529. Organic cakes and patisserie made to order. Specialities include cakes without wheat, sugar, dairy etc.

BORN
168 Stoke Newington Church St., Stoke Newington,
London N16 0JL
Tel: 020 7249 5069 Fax: 020 7249 7225 info@borndirect.com www.borndirect.com
Retail and internet shop specialising in organic, natural and practical products for parents and their babies. We're the experts on washable cotton nappies! Organic range includes organic cotton and wool babywear (underwear, nightwear, outerwear and bedding), organic herbal teas for pregnancy and after-wards, toiletries made with organic ingredients (Weleda, Green People, Urtekram), organic massage oils.

BUMBLEBEE
30-33 Brecknock Rd., London N7 0DD
Tel: 020 7607 1936 info@bumblebee.co.uk www.bumblebee.co.uk
A huge range of organic and vegetarian foods, specialising in organic fruit and vegetables, cheeses, olive oils and mediterranean foods, organic wines and beers, gluten- and wheat-free products, as well as fair traded and macrobiotic ranges. Deliveries in London, Oxford and Greater London. Local box scheme. Carrier deliveries cost £10 to anywhere in the UK mainland.

THE CELTIC BAKERS
42B Waterloo Rd., Cricklewood, London NW2 7UH
Tel: 020 8452 4390 Fax: 020 8452 8235 info@thecelticbakers.co.uk www.thecelticbakers.co.uk
A dedicated organic vegetarian bakery specialising in most aspects of hand-made bread production (including 100% ryes and sourdough methods), cakes, pastries and savouries.

DUKE OF CAMBRIDGE
30 St. Peters St., Islington, London N1 8JT
Tel: 020 7359 3066 duke@dukeorganic.co.uk www.dukeorganic.co.uk
Soil Association certified. Organic gastro pub serving high quality organic food and drink, twice daily changing menu, choice of 40 wines, real ales. No-smoking restaurant area where bookings can be made in advance. Won TimeOut Gastro Pub of the Year 2000. Organic Food Awards 2004 Restaurant of the Year Highly Commended. Observer Food Monthly Awards 2004/5/6.

ECO-CUISINE.CO.UK

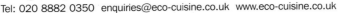

4 Hedge Lane, Palmers Green, London N13 5SH

Tel: 020 8882 0350 enquiries@eco-cuisine.co.uk www.eco-cuisine.co.uk

Catering business. We use organic, free range products in our catering, using the freshest produce available and supporting British farmers/producers.

EOSTRE ORGANICS LTD

Unit 2, North Side Hangars, Old Buckenham Airfield,
Attleborough, Norfolk, NR17 1PU

Tel: 01953 456294 Fax: 01953 456145 dot.bane@eostreorganics.co.uk www.eostreorganics.co.uk

An organic grower co-operative, mainly wholesaling but we also attend markets and have stands at Norwich Provisions Market (6 days) and Old Spitalfields (Sundays), Acre Lane, Brixton (Saturdays), Sunnyside Community Gardens, Islington (Saturdays), Calthorpe Communty Gardens, Gravesend Rd (Fridays), Archway (Saturdays), Hildreth St., Balham (Sundays), Hoe St., Walthamstow (Saturdays), Sloane Square / Duke of York Square off Kings Rd., Chelsea, Borough Market (Fridays and Saturdays), Bellenden Rd., Peckham (Saturdays). We also pack boxes for distribution by others.

FINCHLEY ROAD FARMERS' MARKET

02 Centre Car Park, Finchley Rd., Finchley, London NW6 1RZ

Tel: 020 7833 0338 info@lfm.org.uk www.lfm.org.uk

Near Homebase, Wednesdays 10am–3pm. Buses: 13, 82 and 113. Buses 268 and 187 go into car park. A For further details, see London Farmers' Markets on page 37.

FRESH & WILD

49 Parkway, Camden, London, NW1 7PN

Tel: 020 7428 7575

Fresh & Wild are the leading specialist retailer of organic foods and natural remedies.

FRESH & WILD

32-40 Stoke Newington Church Street, Stoke Newington, London, N16 0LU

Fresh & Wild are the leading specialist retailer of organic foods and natural remedies.

GREEN BABY CO LTD

345 Upper Street, Islington, London N1 0PD

Tel: 020 7359 7037 info@greenbaby.co.uk www.greenbaby.co.uk

Alongside our core ranges of supersoft organic cotton clothing and nappies, we now offer wooden toys, toiletries, maternity wear and baby equipment – all produced in an environmentally sound, sustainable way.

GROWING COMMUNITIES

The Old Fire Station, 61 Leswin Road, London, N16 7NX

Tel: 020 7502 7588 Fax: 020 7502 0021

grow.communities@btinternet.com www.growingcommunities.org

Growing Communities runs a weekly organic box scheme in Hackney, North London, a weekly Farmers' Market in Stoke Newington where all the producers sell organic, biodynamic or wild produce, and which promotes organic food growing in the city from its three sites in Hackney. See our website for more details and join our box scheme online.

HAELAN CENTRE

41 The Broadway, Crouch End, London N8 8DT

Tel: 020 8340 4258 Fax: 020 8292 2232 info@haelan.co.uk www.haelan.co.uk

One of Britain's original wholefood and herbal stores, offering a complete range of vegetarian and vegan organic food, organic skin care, also eco cleaning products, an on-site complementary health clinic, herbal dispensary and homeopathic pharmacy.

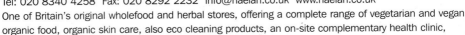

HUGO'S CAFÉ
23-25 Lonsdale Road, London NW6 6RA
Tel: 020 7372 1232 Fax: 020 7328 8097
We serve organic vegetarian and meat dishes.

HUMAN NATURE
13 Malvern Rd., London NW6 5PS
Tel: 020 7328 5452 Fax: 020 7328 5452
Shop with extensive vegetarian products, eco products. Manufacturers of much written about 'Energy Bomb and Massage', described in the press as 'the best in the world'.

ISLINGTON FARMERS' MARKET
William Tyndale School, behind Town Hall, Upper Street, Islington, London N1 2AQ
Tel: 020 7833 0338 info@lfm.org.uk www.lfm.org.uk
Sundays 10am–2pm. Tube to Angel or Highbury. See London Farmers' Markets on page 37.

JUST ORGANIC
113 Wilberforce Rd., London N4 2SP
Tel: 020 7704 2566 Fax: 020 7704 2566
Soil Association P2042. Fresh organic fruit and vegetables, delivered to your door. £11.50 or £17 mixed boxes, free delivery.

MOTHER EARTH HEALTH FOODS
282-284 St. Pauls Rd., Islington, London N1 2LH
Tel: 020 7354 9897 Fax: 020 7249 5965
shop@motherearth-health.com www.motherearth-health.com
We've been here promoting healthy and organic food in the heart of our north London Community for more than 15 years.

MOTHER EARTH HEALTH FOODS
5 Albion Parade, Albion Rd., Stoke Newington, London N16 9LD
Tel: 020 7275 9099 Fax: 020 7249 5965
shop@motherearth-health.com www.motherearth-health.com
We've been here promoting healthy and organic food in the heart of our north London Community for more than 15 years.

NATURAL HEALTH
339 Ballards Lane, N. Finchley, London N12 8LJ
Tel: 020 8445 4397 Fax: 020 8445 4397 www.naturesalternative.co.uk
Health food store with clinic for alternative therapies. Organic foods, supplements, tinctures, homeopathic and herbal remedies, cosmetics, books, tapes and CDs.

NEAL'S YARD REMEDIES
68 Chalk Farm Rd., Camden, London NW1 8AN
Tel: 020 7284 2039 Fax: 020 7428 0390 mail@nealsyardremedies.com www.nealsyardremedies.com
Natural remedies: medicinal herbs and tinctures, homeopathic remedies, flower essences, essential oils, books.

PITFIELD BEER SHOP & BREWERY
14 Pitfield St., London N1 6EY
Tel: 020 7739 3701 Fax: 020 7729 9636 sales@pitfieldbeershop.co.uk www.pitfieldbeershop.co.uk
Organic Farmers & Growers registered. Award-winning organic brewery and shop offering over 600 beers and ciders, many organic. Self-brew wine and beer supplies. Wholesale and mail order across UK.

      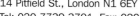

QUEENS PARK FARMERS' MARKET

Salusbury Road Primary School, Salusbury Rd., London NW6 6RG

Tel: 020 7833 0388 info@lfm.org.uk www.lfm.org.uk

Sundays 10am–2pm. Tube to Queens Park. At these producer-only farmers' markets, the farmers sell foods they have grown or raised on their own farms directly to the public. No produce is bought in. All the produce is grown within 100 miles of the M25, wherever possible within 50 miles of the M25. Markets are open every week, rain or shine, apart from Christmas. Operated by London Farmers' Markets, 11 O'Donnell Court, Brunswick Centre, London WC1N 1NY.

REVITAL HEALTHSHOP

35 High Rd, Willesden Green, London NW10 2TE

Tel: 020 8459 3382 Fax: 020 8459 3722 enquire@revital.com www.revital.com

Health shop.

RIVERFORD HOME DELIVERY

2 Stephanie Court, Conewood Street, London, N5 1DD

Tel: 020 7359 5702 Fax: 020 7359 5702 paulj@riverfordhomedelivery.co.uk www.riverford.co.uk

Award-winning organic vegetable box scheme operating in Camden & Islington. A good variety of box sizes to suit all households, from a single person to a large family. A selection of fruit, dairy products, wine, juices and chocolate are also available. Order weekly, fortnightly or whenever you like. Can order and pay online at www.riverford.co.uk or by phone: 0845 600 2311. BBC Radio 4 Farmer of the Year 2005.

TEMPLE HEALTH FOODS

17 Temple Fortune Parade, London NW11 0QS

Tel: 020 8458 6087 Fax: 020 8905 0800

Complete range of wholefoods with many organic alternatives, books and information leaflets. Delivery service, free newsletter and samples.

TEXTURE

84 Stoke Newington Church Street, London N16 0AP

Tel: 020 7241 0990 Fax: 020 7241 1991 jag@textilesfromnature.com www.textilesfromnature.com

Eco textiles by mail order, retail, wholesale and manufacturer of pillows, cushions, bed linen, curtains and fabric by the metre.

LONDON-SOUTH

ABEL & COLE

16 Waterside Way, Wimbledon, London SW17 0HB

Tel: 08452 626262 Fax: 020 8947 6662 organics@abel-cole.co.uk www.abel-cole.co.uk

Delivering organic food and drink across southern England including organic fruit and vegetables, British organic meats, sustainably caught fish, dairy goods, freshly baked bread and much more. Working with a network of over 50 British producers to bring delicious, local, seasonal and organic food fresh from the grower. With free home delivery and online ordering you can do your weekly shop in under 10 minutes! (Awarded Organic Retailer 2004 and Best Home Delivery Service 2004 by the Soil Association.) Organic Food Awards 2004 Local Food Initiative Highly Commended. Alternative telephone number: 020 8944 3780.

AS NATURE INTENDED

186-188 Balham High Rd, Balham, London SW12 9BP
Tel: 020 8675 2923 Fax: 020 8675 2853
enquiries@asnatureintended.uk.com www.asnatureintended.uk.com
An independent organic food retailer stocking a wide range of organic and special dietary foods, baby foods, beers, wines, spirits, toiletries, cosmetics, ecological cleaning products. Also stocks a large range of natural remedies, seasonal foods and gifts.

G. BALDWIN & CO

171-173 Walworth Rd, London, SE17 1RW
Tel: 020 7703 5550 Fax: 020 7252 6264 Contact: Stephen Dagnell
sales@baldwins.co.uk www.baldwins.co.uk
Herbalist and essential oils. Complementary and alternative product supplier.

BALHAM WHOLEFOOD & HEALTH STORE

8 Bedford Hill, Balham, London SW12 9RG
Tel: 020 8673 4842
Wholefood shop selling a range of organic products, supplements and cleaning products. Open Monday, Wednesday, Friday and Saturday 9.30am–1.30pm and 2.30pm–6.00pm. Tuesday and Thursday 9.30am–1.30pm and 2.30pm–6.00pm.

BLACKHEATH FARMERS' MARKET

Blackheath Rail Station Car Park, 2 Blackheath Village, London SE3 0TX
Tel: 020 7833 0338 info@lfm.org.uk www.lfm.org.uk
Sundays 10am–2pm. For further details, see London Farmers' Markets on page 37.

CAPRICORN ORGANICS

Brockley, London SE24 2NL
Tel: 020 8306 2786 alison@capricornorganics.co.uk www.capricornorganics.co.uk
A local service offering a wide range of fully certified fresh organic produce delivered to your door. Place your own order or have a box from just £10.

DANDELION

120 Northcott Road, London SW11 6QU
Tel: 020 7350 0902
Wide range of organic fresh and dried foods including take-away foods, vitamins, supplements, etc.

DARBY & MEAKIN

162 Effra Road, Wimbledon, London SW19 8PR
Tel: 020 8767 5858 info@darbyandmeakin.co.uk www.darbyandmeakin.co.uk
We sell boxes of fresh delicious organic fruit and vegetables, sourced ethically and as locally as possible, with boxes starting at just £10 & free home delivery on all orders.

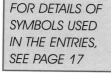
FOR DETAILS OF SYMBOLS USED IN THE ENTRIES, SEE PAGE 17

EOSTRE ORGANICS LTD

Unit 2, North Side Hangars, Old Buckenham Airfield, Attleborough, Norfolk, NR17 1PU
Tel: 01953 456294 Fax: 01953 456145
dot.bane@eostreorganics.co.uk www.eostreorganics.co.uk

An organic grower co-operative, mainly wholesaling but we also attend markets and have stands at Norwich Provisions Market (6 days) and Old Spitalfields (Sundays), Acre Lane, Brixton (Saturdays), Sunnyside Community Gardens, Islington (Saturdays), Calthorpe Communty Gardens, Gravesend Rd (Fridays), Archway (Saturdays), Hildreth St., Balham (Sundays), Hoe St., Walthamstow (Saturdays), Sloane Square / Duke of York Square off Kings Rd., Chelsea, Borough Market (Fridays and Saturdays), Bellenden Rd., Peckham (Saturdays). We also pack boxes for distribution by others.

FARMAROUND

Offices B143, New Covent Garden Market, Nine Elms Lane, London SW8 5PA
Tel: 020 7627 8066 Fax: 01748 822007 info@farmaround.co.uk www.farmaround.co.uk

Home delivery service of assorted bags of fresh organic produce. Prices from £4 for a mini fruit box, also organic grocery range. Delivery charge: £1 throughout Greater London and Berkshire.

FRESH & WILD

305-311 Lavender Hill, Clapham Junction, London, SW11 1LN

Fresh & Wild are the leading specialist retailer of organic foods and natural remedies.

HERE

Chelsea Farmers' Market, 125 Sydney St., Chelsea, London SW3 6NR
Tel: 020 7351 4321 Fax: 020 7351 2211 shop@here.uk.com

The most comprehensive supermarket in the UK, stocking only 100% organic foods and drinks. Natural supplements and body care. Café area/take-out. Deliveries in London. Mail Order.

HONOR OAK MEDITERRANEAN DELI

72 Honor Oak Park, London, London SE23 1DY
Tel: 020 8699 3113 deli@twist.demon.co.uk

Organic bread, fruit & veg for sale. Open 7 days a week. Local delivery service available within 2 mile radius (£25 min order). Also available: fresh meat counter, cooked meats, cheese, antipasti. Home cooked dishes such as lasagne available, organic and veggie cooked dishes available on request. Open Mon–Fri 10am–8pm, Sat 10am–7pm, Sun 11am–5pm.

MONMOUTH COFFEE COMPANY

2 Park St, London SE1 9AB
Tel: 020 7645 3585 Fax: 020 7645 3565
beans@monmouthcoffee.co.uk www.monmouthcoffee.co.uk

Coffee roasters, wholesalers and retailers.

NEAL'S YARD REMEDIES (HEAD OFFICE)

8-10 Ingate Place, Battersea, London SW8 3NS
Tel: 020 7498 1686 Fax: 020 7498 2505 mail@nealsyardremedies.com www.nealsyardremedies.com

Neal's Yard Remedies manufactures and retails natural cosmetics in addition to stocking an extensive range of herbs, essential oils, homeopathic remedies and reference material. Customer Services: 020 7627 1949, cservices@nealsyardremedies.com. Are you interested in complementary medicine? Neal's Yard Remedies runs courses on Natural Medicine, Organic Nutrition, Aromatherapy, Herbalism, Flower Remedies and homeopathy. Contact Emma Thomson on 020 7574 0031 for further information.

NEAL'S YARD REMEDIES

32 Blackheath Village, Blackheath, London SE3 9SY
Tel: 020 8318 6655 mail@nealsyardremedies.com www.nealsyardremedies.com
Retail shop selling Neal's Yard Remedies products.

NEAL'S YARD REMEDIES

12-14 Chelsea Farmers' Market, Sydney St., London SW3 6NR
Tel: 020 7351 6380 mail@nealsyardremedies.com www.nealsyardremedies.com
Neal's Yard Remedies manufactures and retails natural cosmetics in addition to stocking an extensive
range of herbs, essential oils, homeopathic remedies and reference material.

NEAL'S YARD REMEDIES

6 Northcote Road, Clapham Junction, London SW11 1NT
Tel: 020 7223 7141 Fax: 020 7223 7174 mail@nealsyardremedies.com www.nealsyardremedies.com
Natural health shop with a therapy centre attached.

THE OLD POST OFFICE BAKERY

76 Landor Rd., Clapham, London SW9 9PH
Tel: 020 7326 4408 Fax: 020 7326 4408 www.oldpostofficebakery.co.uk
Organic craft bakery, hand-made yeasted and sourdough bread including 100% rye sourdough. Soil
Association Licence no. P5506.

PASSION ORGANIC

17 Ansdell Rd, London, SE15 2DT
Tel: 020 7277 6147 maria@passionorganic.com www.passionorganic.com
Passion Organic – Delicious Food, Passionate Values is an organic and ethical events catering company.
We have created events with a difference for some of the UK's leading businesses and social change
organisations. We'd love to hear from you!

PECKHAM FARMERS' MARKET

Peckham Square, Peckham High Street, London SE15 5QN
Tel: 020 7833 0338 info@lfm.org.uk www.lfm.org.uk
Sundays 9.30am–1.30pm. Buses 12, 36, 171, 345. Rail to Peckham Rye or Queens Road. See next
entry for further details.

PIMLICO ROAD FARMERS' MARKET

Orange Square, corner of Pimlico Rd., and Ebury St., London SW1W 0NZ
Tel: 020 7833 0388 info@lfm.org.uk www.lfm.org.uk
Saturdays 9am–1pm. Tube to Sloane Square, buses 11, 211 and 239. At these producer-only farmers'
markets, the farmers sell foods they have grown or raised on their own farms directly to the public. No
produce is bought in. All the produce is grown within 100 miles of the M25, wherever possible within 50
miles of the M25. Markets are open every week, rain or shine, apart from Christmas. Operated by London
Farmers' Markets, 11 O'Donnell Court, Brunswick Centre, London WC1N 1NY.

PIZZA ORGANIC LTD

75 Gloucester Rd., London SW7 4SS
Tel: 020 7370 6575 info@pizzapiazza.co.uk www.pizza-organic.co.uk
A great menu packed full of organic options, featuring stonebaked pizza, sautéed pasta, gourmet burg-
ers, grilled fish and fabulous desserts. Pizza Organic is certified by the Soil Association and was Highly
Commended in the 2003 Organic Food Awards. All restaurants open 7 days a week but opening times
may vary, call 020 8397 3330 for further details.

PIZZA ORGANIC LTD

20 Old Brompton Rd., London SW7 3DL

Tel: 020 7589 9613 info@pizzapiazza.co.uk www.pizzaorganic.co.uk

A great menu packed full of organic options, featuring stonebaked pizza, sautéed pasta, gourmet burgers, grilled fish and fabulous desserts. Pizza Organic is certified by the Soil Association and was Highly Commended in the 2003 Organic Food Awards. All restaurants open 7 days a week but opening times may vary, call 020 8397 3330 for further details.

PLANET ORGANIC

25 Effie Rd, Fulham, London SW6

Tel: 020 7731 7222 deliveries@planetorganic.com www.planetorganic.com

Planet Organic is about good food. We are the original one-stop organic and natural food supermarket with an in-house juice bar and freshly cooked organic food to go. We are the modern mecca for those seeking everything for a healthy lifestyle.

PROVENDER

103 Dartmouth Road, Forest Hill, London SE23 3HT

Tel: 020 8699 4046 Fax: 020 8699 4046

Wholefoods, organic bakers, café, healthy food, organic croissants and pastries, quiches, organic meals.

REVITAL HEALTHPLACE

3a The Colonades, 123-151 Buckingham Palace Rd, London SW1W 9SH

Tel: 020 7976 6615 enqire@revital.com www.revital.com

Health shop, over 80% organic foods and cosmetics.

RIVERFORD HOME DELIVERY – BROMLEY & CROYDON

20 Deepdene Rd., London SE5 8EG

Tel: 020 7738 5076 kevin@riverfordhomedelivery.co.uk www.riverford.co.uk

Box scheme.

RIVERFORD ORGANIC VEGETABLES – SOUTHWARK

6 Portal Close, West Norwood, London SE27 0BN

Tel: 01803 762720 Fax: 01803 762718 ged@riverfordhomedelivery.co.uk www.riverford

Veg box delivery scheme.

SPARKES, G G

24 Old Dover Rd., Blackheath, London SE3 7BT

Tel: 020 8355 8597 Fax: 020 8355 8597

We are a family business established in 1952 and we have been selling organic meat and cheeses for over 16 years. We deliver to London and the South-East. Home deliveries, not a box scheme.

SPARKES, G G

Mobile Shop Unit, New Cross Road Market, East Dulwich, London SE22

Tel: 020 8355 8597

Mobile shop unit. We are a family business established in 1952 and we have been selling organic meat and cheeses for over 16 years. We deliver to London and the South-East. Home deliveries, not a box scheme.

TODAY'S LIVING

92 Clapham High Street, London SW4 7UL

Tel: 020 7622 1772 Fax: 020 7720 2851 info@todaysliving.co.uk

Health food shop selling a wide range of supplements, foods, frozen goods and organic spices.

WELL BEAN

9 Old Dover Road, Blackheath, London SE3 7BT
Tel: 020 8858 6854

Large range of organic foods, wholefoods, gluten-free, diabetic, dairy-free. Nutritional advice, mail order, local deliveries. If we haven't got it, we'll get it!

WELL BEING

19 Sydenham Rd., London SE26 5EX
Tel: 020 8659 2003
Health food shop.

WIMBLEDON PARK FARMERS' MARKET

Wimbledon Park Junior School, Havana Road, Wimbledon, London SW19 8EJ
Tel: 020 7833 0388 info@lfm.org.uk www.lfm.org.uk
Saturdays 9am–1pm. Tube to wimbledon Park. At these producer-only farmers' markets, the farmers sell foods they have grown or raised on their own farms directly to the public. No produce is bought in. All the produce is grown within 100 miles of the M25, wherever possible within 50 miles of the M25. Markets are open every week, rain or shine, apart from Christmas. Operated by London Farmers' Markets, 11 O'Donnell Court, Brunswick Centre, London WC1N 1NY.

LONDON–WEST

AINSWORTHS HOMEOPATHIC PHARMACY

36 New Cavendish St., London W1G 8UF
Tel: 020 7935 5330 Fax: 020 7486 4313 ainsworth01@btconnect.com www.ainsworths.com
Homeopathic remedies for prevention and treatment of all your livestock. Books and courses on homeopathy. All animals can be treated without residues. Help and advice in implementing homeopathic regimes on the farm. Lectures and seminars by arrangement.

ALARA

58-60 Marchmont St., London WC1N 1AB
Tel: 020 7837 1172 Fax: 020 7833 8089
All organic products. Vitamins, beauty, fresh veg, fruit and dairy.

AS NATURE INTENDED

201 Chiswick High Rd., Chiswick, London W4 2DA
Tel: 020 8742 8838 Fax: 020 8742 3131
enquiries@asnatureintended.uk.com www.asnatureintended.uk.com
An independent organic food retailer stocking a wide range of organic and special dietary foods, baby foods, beers, wines, spirits, toiletries, cosmetics, ecological cleaning products. Also stocks a large range of natural remedies, seasonal foods and gifts.

AS NATURE INTENDED

17-21 High St., Ealing, London W5 5DB
Tel: 020 8840 1404 Fax: 020 8840 8278
enquiries@asnatureintended.uk.com www.asnatureintended.uk.com
An independent organic food retailer stocking a wide range of organic and special dietary foods, baby foods, beers, wines, spirits, toiletries, cosmetics, ecological cleaning products. Also stocks a large range of natural remedies, seasonal foods and gifts.

BUSHWACKER WHOLEFOODS

132 King Street, Hammersmith, London W6 0QU
Tel: 020 8748 2061 Fax: 020 8748 2061
Everything you would expect in a good wholefood shop, with the emphasis on organically grown products including fresh fruit and vegetables, free range eggs and baby foods. Lots of vegetarian takeaways, macrobiotic specialities, gluten-free foods, natural remedies and body care. We veto genetically modified foods.

EALING FARMERS' MARKET

Leeland Rd, West Ealing, London W13 9HH
Tel: 020 7833 0338 info@lfm.org.uk www.lfm.org.uk
Saturdays 9am–1pm. At these producer-only farmers' markets, the farmers sell foods they have grown or raised on their own farms directly to the public. No produce is bought in. All the produce is grown within 100 miles of the M25, wherever possible within 50 miles of the M25. Markets are open every week, rain or shine, apart from Christmas. Operated by London Farmers' Markets, 11 O'Donnell Court, Brunswick Centre, London WC1N 1NY.

EOSTRE ORGANICS LTD

Unit 2, North Side Hangars, Old Buckenham Airfield,
Attleborough, Norfolk, NR17 1PU
Tel: 01953 456294 Fax: 01953 456145 dot.bane@eostreorganics.co.uk www.eostreorganics.co.uk
An organic grower co-operative, mainly wholesaling but we also attend markets and have stands at Norwich Provisions Market (6 days) and Old Spitalfields (Sundays), Acre Lane, Brixton (Saturdays), Sunnyside Community Gardens, Islington (Saturdays), Calthorpe Communty Gardens, Gravesend Rd (Fridays), Archway (Saturdays), Hildreth St., Balham (Sundays), Hoe St., Walthamstow (Saturdays), Sloane Square / Duke of York Square off Kings Rd., Chelsea, Borough Market (Fridays and Saturdays), Bellenden Rd., Peckham (Saturdays). We also pack boxes for distribution by others.

FARM W5

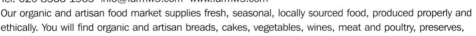

19 The Green, Ealing, London W5 5DA
Tel: 020 8566 1965 info@farmw5.com www.farmw5.com
Our organic and artisan food market supplies fresh, seasonal, locally sourced food, produced properly and ethically. You will find organic and artisan breads, cakes, vegetables, wines, meat and poultry, preserves, British cheeses, hand-made chocolates and much more.

FRESH & WILD

210 Westbourne Grove, Notting Hill, London, W11 2RH
Tel: 020 7229 1063
Fresh & Wild are the leading specialist retailer of organic foods and natural remedies.

FRESH & WILD

69-75 Brewer Street, Soho, London W1F 9US
Tel: 020 7434 3179
Fresh & Wild are the leading specialist retailer of organic foods and natural remedies.

LIDGATE, C

110 Holland Park Avenue, London W11 4UA
Tel: 020 7727 8243 Fax: 020 7229 7160
Organic beef and lamb from Highgrove, home of HRH Prince Charles. Deliveries to City and West London daily. Eros award for Top Twenty London food shops, National Pie Championships in 1993 & 1996, Utrecht European Championship Gold Medal awards 1998, Tatler magazine Best UK Butchers 1998/99.

LONDON FARMERS' MARKETS

11 O'Donnell Court, Brunswick Centre, London WC1N 1NY

Tel: 020 7833 0388 Fax: 020 7812 1061 info@lfm.org.uk www.lfm.org.uk

12 certified farmers' markets in London. No farmers' market is entirely organic but each market has a range of organic farmers and producers. Saturday markets 9am–1pm at Ealing, Notting Hill, Twickenham, Pimlico & Wimbledon Park. Sunday markets 10am–2pm at Blackheath, Islington, Marylebone, Peckham, Pinner and Queens Park. Wednesdays 10am–3pm at Finchley Road. At these producer-only farmers' markets, the farmers sell foods they have grown or raised on their own farms directly to the public. No produce is bought in. All the produce is grown within 100 miles of the M25, wherever possible within 50 miles of the M25. Markets are open every week, rain or shine, apart from Christmas. Operated by London Farmers' Markets, 11 O'Donnell Court, Brunswick Centre, London WC1N 1NY.

MARYLEBONE FARMERS' MARKET

Cramer St. Car Park, corner Moxton St., off Marylebone High St., London W1U 4EA

Tel: 020 7833 0338 info@lfm.org.uk www.lfm.org.uk

Sundays 10am–2pm. Tube to Bond Street or Baker Street. At these producer-only farmers' markets, the farmers sell foods they have grown or raised on their own farms directly to the public. No produce is bought in. All the produce is grown within 100 miles of the M25, wherever possible within 50 miles of the M25. Markets are open every week, rain or shine, apart from Christmas. Operated by London Farmers' Markets, 11 O'Donnell Court, Brunswick Centre, London WC1N 1NY.

MILLER OF KENSINGTON

14 Stratford Road, Kensington, London W8 6QD

Tel: 020 7937 1777

Soil Association organic meat specialist; catering service up to 100 people. Delicatessen and traiteur.

MONMOUTH COFFEE COMPANY

27 Monmouth St, London WC2H 9EU

Tel: 020 7379 3516

beans@monmouthcoffee.co.uk www.monmouthcoffee.co.uk

Coffee roasters, wholesalers and retailers.

NEAL'S YARD REMEDIES

15 Neal's Yard, Covent Garden, London WC2H 9DP

Tel: 020 7379 7222 mail@nealsyardremedies.com www.nealsyardremedies.com

Soil Association certified products. Toiletries, herbs, aromatherapy products.

NEAL'S YARD REMEDIES

9 Elgin Crescent, London W11 2JA

Tel: 020 7727 3998 mail@nealsyardremedies.com www.nealsyardremedies.com

Neal's Yard Remedies manufactures and retails natural cosmetics in addition to stocking an extensive range of herbs, essential oils, homeopathic remedies and reference material.

NOTTING HILL FARMERS' MARKET

Car Park behind Waterstones access via Kensington Place London W8

Tel: 020 7833 0338 info@lfm.org.uk www.lfm.org.uk

Saturdays 9am–1pm. Tube to Notting Hill Gate. At these producer-only farmers' markets, the farmers sell foods they have grown or raised on their own farms directly to the public. No produce is bought in. All the produce is grown within 100 miles of the M25, wherever possible within 50 miles of the M25. Markets are open every week, rain or shine, apart from Christmas. Operated by London Farmers' Markets, 11 O'Donnell Court, Brunswick Centre, London WC1N 1NY.

So Organic *is all about choice: about the life you want to live.*

The idea for *So Organic* came from my own frustrations in trying to go organic!

About 4 years ago I became committed to organic, after discovering my local farmers' market and becoming hooked on real food that tasted great, and that made me feel good.

I then started to read much more about the other reasons why organic is so important, such as health, environmental considerations, and the impact of the chemicals used to produce cosmetics and textiles.

When I read that 60% of what is applied to the skin may be absorbed, and that many mainstream toiletries are made from a potentially toxic chemical cocktail, I became very concerned and started to look for alternatives. If I was concerned about pesticide residues and chemicals in the food that I ate, I obviously had to care about what I put onto my skin, because that could end up inside me too.

Organic skin care products were available but were difficult to find; I would have to visit several stores to find what I needed, and even when I was able to find organic health and beauty products, there was never anyone available to give me good advice.

For me, as an ordinary consumer without a degree in chemistry, it was difficult to distinguish between products that were genuinely natural and a lot of marketing hype.

I knew that I wasn't alone in having these difficulties finding the products that I wanted, so I decided to do research and create a place where people like me could find all of the organic lifestyle products they want to use. *So Organic* was created to offer choice.

But why do people choose an organic lifestyle? There are all sorts of reasons for all sorts of people: The traditional stereotype of organic being for eco-warriors or hippies is over. Organic consumers are very diverse; many have allergies, or suffer from conditions that make them want to avoid chemicals in all aspects of their life; some do choose organic as the most environmentally friendly option, and organic products also appeal to vegan and vegetarian consumers and those who are concerned about animal welfare. Often people choose to go organic when pregnant, as the best start for their baby.

Male or female, young or old, organic consumers are everywhere these days!

At *So Organic* we are finding that more and more people are choosing organic as a complete lifestyle choice: they might start with a deodorant, but quickly want to convert everything from toothpaste to T-shirts.

The mainstream press are running features on organic products very regularly now, and consumers are much more aware of the benefits. Ingredients which have been shown to have negative health implications such as parabens, sodium lauryl sulphate and synthetic fragrance, are frequently coming under the media spotlight. When you hear the statistics, and learn more about what is in the conventional products, it is no wonder that people are turning to organic alternatives in their droves.

But in my experience customers are typically very confused, and they don't know who to trust. Many have bought products from conventional brands which claim to be 'natural', and are then horrified to find that these products contain ingredients such as parabens or synthetic fragrance, which they have been desperate to avoid.

I see it as my job, and that of other responsible organic retailers, to help customers make sense of the confusion and give enough advice for them to be able to make an informed choice.

A lot of confusion exists about what constitutes a genuinely organic product. For me, it depends on the type of product.

There is huge debate about many ingredients that are traditionally used in cosmetics and it is important to give a balanced view. There are certain ingredients that I always avoid: parabens (type of preservative), sodium lauryl sulphate (foaming agent), synthetic fragrance, mineral oil and propylene glycol (for texture and stability). There are lots of companies working very hard to produce safe and effective cosmetic products without the use of these ingredients. When it is possible to make safe everyday skin care without them, why continue to use products that contain them?

Organic certification agencies such as the Soil Association do a great job, and have very high standards: when you buy a product carrying their symbol, you know you really are getting the highest percentage of organic ingredients possible. However, the list of products that has been certified by them is still quite limited.

The situation is difficult as there are only so many permissible ingredients, and to be certified a product must contain a minimum 70% organic ingredients. It's currently just not possible to make many products such as toothpaste, sun tan lotion, hair conditioner, and cosmetics in a Soil Association-certified organic version.

As a consumer, it's frustrating that not everything that you need in your daily routine is available in a certified organic form, as having a symbol makes the decision making process much easier. However, with a little research it is possible to find almost everything you need, with none of the undesirable chemicals you have read about and with a large proportion of organic ingredients.

At *So Organic* our philosophy is to be a trusted friend to our customers. If we would recommend a product to our friends, then we stock it; if we wouldn't, then we don't! My advice would be to decide which ingredients you wish to avoid, and understand why you should be avoiding them. Try to keep a balanced view – just as there are unscrupulous manufacturers making organic or natural claims about products that don't deserve them, there are also unfounded scare stories about ingredients too. Ask questions! Anyone who is honestly trying to do the right thing and offer genuinely natural products won't mind you asking questions, and if they don't know the answer they should go away and find out for you.

Samantha Burlton

PIZZA ORGANIC LTD

100 Pitshanger Lane, London W5 1QX

Tel: 020 8998 6878 info@pizzapiazza.co.uk www.pizza-organic.co.uk

A great menu packed full of organic options, featuring stonebaked pizza, sautéed pasta, gourmet burgers, grilled fish and fabulous desserts. Pizza Organic is certified by the Soil Association and was Highly Commended in the 2003 Organic Food Awards. All restaurants open 7 days a week but opening times may vary, call 020 8397 3330 for further details.

PLANET ORGANIC

22 Torrington Place, London WC1E 7HJ

Tel: 020 7436 1929 Fax: 020 7436 1992 deliveries@planetorganic.com www.planetorganic.com

Planet Organic is the original one-stop organic and natural food supermarket with Juice Bar, Food to Go and café. We have 9,000 products in grocery, fruit & veg, meat & fish, and health & body care. We are the modern mecca for those seeking everything for a healthy lifestyle.

PLANET ORGANIC

42 Westbourne Grove, London W2 5SH

Tel: 020 7727 2227 Fax: 020 7221 1923 deliveries@planetorganic.com www.planetorganic.com

Planet Organic is about good food. We are the original one-stop organic and natural food supermarket with an in-house juice bar and freshly cooked organic food to go. We are the modern mecca for those seeking everything for a healthy lifestyle.

PORTOBELLO WHOLEFOODS

266 Portobello Rd., London W14 0EP

Tel: 020 8968 9133 Fax: 020 8960 1840

Portobello Wholefoods stocks an ever-increasing range of healthfood products, including natural remedies, vitamins and minerals, organic produce and gluten-free. Regular special offers and friendly service provides everything you need in a healthfood shop – and more. . . . Open 7 days a week.

THE RITZ

150 Piccadilly, London W1J 9BR

Tel: 020 7493 8181 Fax: 020 7493 2687 tburke@theritzlondon.com

Restaurant.

SHEEPDROVE ORGANIC FARM FAMILY BUTCHER

5 Clifton Rd., Maida Vale, London W9

Tel: 020 7266 3838 sales@sheepdrove.com www.sheepdrove.com

Family butcher selling the Sheepdrove Farm range of meats including beef, lamb, mutton, pork, bacon, gammon, sausages, burgers and poultry.

THE TEA & COFFEE PLANT

180 Portobello Rd., London W11 2EB

Tel: 020 7221 8137 coffee@pro-net.co.uk www.coffee.uk.com

Coffee roaster; supplies coffee, cocoa, tea, herb tea for retail, retail mail order, caterers and own label packs for retailers. Coffee can be beans or ground, 100g packs upwards. Certified by the Fair Trade Foundation.

THOROGOODS OF EALING

113 Northfields Ave, Ealing, London W13 9QR

Tel: 020 8567 0339 Fax: 020 8566 3033

Beef, lamb, pork, chicken, turkeys, bacon, cooked ham. Local delivery.

THE TROUBADOUR DELI

267 Old Brompton Road, London, London SW5 9JA

Tel: 020 7341 6341 Fax: 020 7341 6329 Christopher@troubadour.co.uk www.troubadour.co.uk

A delicatessen that sells organic, free range eggs from Chapell Farm amongst other organic produce.

URBAN KITCHEN

63-65 Goldney Road, London, London W9 2AR

Tel: 020 7286 1700 Fax: 020 7286 1709

events@urban-productions.co.uk www.urban-productions.co.uk

Urban is a bespoke event-making company with full event production services and a luscious kitchen in-house. We are accredited by the Soil Association to provide organic menus for every occasion. Clients include BBC, MTV, Deutsche Bank, Sony, M&C Saatchi, Armani and Marks & Spencer, along with a large number of private clients.

SURREY

BODY AND SOUL ORGANICS

Unit 20, Burrows Lea Farm, Hook Lane, Shere, GU5 9QQ

Tel: 01483 202918 Fax: 08717 143340

bodyandsoul@organic-gmfree.co.uk www.organic-gmfree.co.uk

Collection and delivery service, wide range of fruit and veg, wholefoods, dairy, wines, beers, meat, poultry, etc., gluten-free, dairy-free, special diets, over 2,000 organic lines. Home delivery in Surrey, phone for details.

BROADWAY HEALTH CENTRE

60 The Broadway, Cheam, Sutton, SM3 8BD

Tel: 020 8643 5132

Stockists of organic cereals, nuts and dried fruits, drinks, teas, chocolate, etc. No fresh fruit or vegetables.

CHAPMAN'S ORGANIC PRODUCTS

20 St. George's Walk, Croydon, CR0 1YG

Tel: 020 8681 1995 Fax: 020 8681 1995 info@chapmansorganic.co.uk www.chapmansorganic.co.uk

We sell a wide range of organic dry products, gluten- and wheat-free products, dietary products, vegetarian products, organic fruit & vegetables, organic dairy products and a wide range of natural supplements and beauty products.

CRANLEIGH ORGANIC FARM SHOP

Lower Barrihurst Farm, Dunsford Road, Cranleigh, GU6 8LG

Tel: 01483 272896 Fax: 01483 273486 organicfarmshop@btopenworld.com

Mixed farm producing vegetables, herbs, meat and poultry. Our farm shop also sells produce from other local organic farms.

DRYDOWN FARM

Hound House Rd., Shere, GU5 9JG

Tel: 01483 203821 Fax: 01483 205419 profound-pursuits@yahoo.co.uk

Local deliveries of organic and free range meat. Lamb, beef and pork from traditional and rare breeds, reared for outstanding flavour and texture. Turkeys and hams at Christmas.

SURREY

FIVE RIVERS DELI

40 The High Street, Thames Ditton, KT7 0SA

Tel: 020 8972 9287

Five Rivers is a delicatessen, fine food store and café stocking a large range of organic and fair trade food and drink. From everyday provisions through to luxury food and gift items such as hampers, Five Rivers sources high quality organic products wherever possible.

HORTI HALCYON

Heath Mill House, Heath Mill Lane, Fox Corner, Worplesdon, GU3 3PR

Tel: 01483 232095 enquiries@hortihalcyon-organic.co.uk www.hortihalcyon-organic.co.uk

Over 50 varieties of organic vegetables and herbs are grown by us. Boxes range from £9.50 upwards and contents can be varied to suit customer needs. Delivery within 15-mile radius. Farmers' markets in Wimbledon and Chiswick. Shop open Thursdays and Fridays 9.30am–4pm (longer during the summer).

LEE HOUSE FARM

Lee House Farm, Plaistow, RH14 0PB

Tel: 07973 826189 Fax: 01403 753311 info@leehousefarm.co.uk www.leehousefarm.co.uk

We do everything here, from rare breed pork to rare breed carrots and spinach! Bacon, sausages, lamb, boiling fowl, free range eggs, turkeys and beautiful Sussex beef, all butchered to your specification.

NEAL'S YARD REMEDIES

Neal's Yard Remedies, 15 King Street, Richmond, TW9 1ND

Tel: 020 8948 9248 mail@nealsyardremedies.com www.nealsyardremedies.com

Natural health and beauty shop with two therapy rooms.

NEAL'S YARD REMEDIES

2 Market St., Guildford, GU1 4LB

Tel: 01483 450434 mail@nealsyardremedies.com www.nealsyardremedies.com

Neal's Yard Remedies manufactures and retails natural cosmetics in addition to stocking an extensive range of herbs, essential oils, homeopathic remedies and reference material.

OLIVERS WHOLEFOOD STORE

5 Station Approach, Kew Gardens, Richmond, TW9 3QB

Tel: 020 8948 3990 Fax: 020 8948 3991 sara@oliverswholefoods.co.uk

"This shop is an inspiration. Effortless, curved displays are plumped with Rococco chocolate, Richmond Park Honey, organic cooking oils and alcohol. The fridges have a wide selection of tofu and tempeh and there's river trout and organic meat in the freezers. At Christmas organic poultry and hams, and free range game are available. Many things make this store stand out from the crowd, notably regular bakery deliveries from Cranks and the Authentic Bakery and the fact that the entire Dr Hauschka range is stocked including the make-up. Education is the key theme – as well as selling books galore, Oliver's runs weekly lectures from health experts like John Briffa."– Time Out Shopping Guide 2004.

PIZZA ORGANIC LTD

(Head Office) 1 Linkfield St., Redhill, RH1 1HQ

Tel: 01737 770200 Fax: 01737 767888 3 Linkfield St., Redhill, Surrey, RH1 1HQ

Tel: 01737 766154 info@pizza-organic.co.uk www.pizza-organic.co.uk

A great menu packed full of organic options, featuring stonebaked pizza, sautéed pasta, gourmet burgers, grilled fish and fabulous desserts. Pizza Organic is certified by the Soil Association and was Highly Commended in the 2003 Organic Food Awards. All restaurants open 7 days a week but opening times may vary, call 020 8397 3330 for further details.

THE PUMPKIN PATCH

10 High Street, Banstead, SM7 2LJ
Tel: 01737 371007
Natural health shop and vegetarian deli, organic foods, toiletries, therapy centre.

RIVERFORD HOME DELIVERY – BROMLEY & CROYDON

20 Deepdene Rd., London, SE5 8EG
Tel: 020 7738 5076 Fax: 020 7738 5076 kevin@riverfordhomedelivery.co.uk www.riverford.co.uk
Independent franchise of Riverford Organic Vegetables.

RIVERFORD HOME DELIVERY – GUILDFORD

Holly Heights, Farnham Lane, Haslemere, GU27 1HE
Tel: 0845 600 2311 annie@riverfordhomedelivery.co.uk www.riverford.co.uk
Home delivery of organic vegetable boxes.

ROUNDHURST FARM LTD

Tennysons Lane, Haslemere, GU27 3BN
Tel: 01428 656445 Fax: 01428 656380 enquiries@roundhurstfarm.com www.roundhurstfarm.com
Producing organic beef from pedigree pure bred Sussex herd. Beef is well hung and sold at farmers' markets or at the farm or mail order.

SUNSHINE ORGANICS
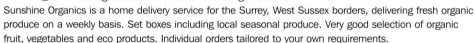
Tel: 01483 268014
amanda@sunshine-organics.co.uk www.sunshine-organics.co.uk
Sunshine Organics is a home delivery service for the Surrey, West Sussex borders, delivering fresh organic produce on a weekly basis. Set boxes including local seasonal produce. Very good selection of organic fruit, vegetables and eco products. Individual orders tailored to your own requirements.

EAST SUSSEX

AGRIPAL ENTERPRISES, 'WICKHAM MANOR FARM'

Wickham Manor Farm, Pannel Lane, Winchelsea, TN36 4AG
Tel: 01797 226216 info@wickhammanor.co.uk www.wickhammanor.co.uk
B&B and equine B&B. Specialists in quality organic beef, lamb and mutton. Suckler herd of Simmental x cows producing prime finished cattle from extensive grazing marshes. Berkshire pigs producing quality pork. Hampshire Down x Lleyn lambs producing top quality meat with characteristic tender juicy texture and unique flavour. Breeders of pedigree Lleyn stock. Also growers and retailers of organic cereals, and pulses.

ASHURST ORGANICS

The Orchard, Ashurst Farm, Ashurst Lane, Plumpton, Lewes, BN7 3AP
Tel: 01273 891219 Fax: 01273 891943 ashurstveg@tiscali.co.uk
Soil Association G1796; P1796. Local organic vegetable box scheme supplying fresh vegetables to Brighton, Lewes, Haywards Heath, Eastbourne and Worthing.

BARCOMBE NURSERIES

Mill Lane, Barcombe, Lewes, BN8 5TH
Tel: 01273 400011 barcombenurseries@tiscali.co.uk
Vegetable growers throughout the year with our own local box scheme delivered to your door, weekly or fortnightly. We grow a wide range of vegetable varieties and offer some choice.

BATTLE HEALTH STORE

83 High St., Battle, TN33 0AQ

Tel: 01424 772435 sussexhealth@hotmail.com

A family-run, local health store selling wholefoods, vegetarian and special diet foods, herbal remedies and supplements. We aim to provide as many organic lines as possible.

BOATHOUSE ORGANIC FARM SHOP

The Orchard Uckfield Rd., Ringmer, Lewes, BN8 5RX

Tel: 01273 814188 Fax: 01273 814188

info@boathouseorganicfarmshop.co.uk www.boathouseorganicfarmshop.co.uk

Shop providing full range of organic meats, veg, groceries and dairy, some sourced from our own farm. Prize-winning sausages, home cured and smoked bacon. Organic Food Awards 2006 Gold for Charcuterie – bacon – green through cut. Meat cut to order. Farm address: Boathouse Organic Farm, Isfield, Uckfield TN22 5TY. Tel: 01825 750641.

CORIANDER RESTAURANT & DELI

5 Hove Manor, Hove Street, Hove, BN3 2DF

Tel: 01273 730850 Fax: 01273 774555 info@corianderbrighton.com www.corianderbrighton.com

Innovative restaurant serving simple yet exotic food from around the world – absolutely delicious and 90% organic. We promote sustainable living in all aspects of our business. Delicatessen selling prepared foods, cooked meats, dried goods etc.

DEAN, K & E

Court Lodge Farm, Udimore, Rye, TN31 6BB

Tel: 01424 882206 Fax: 01424 882206 clfarm@onetel.com

Soil Association G5591. Romney sheep and pedigree Sussex cattle breeding stock for sale. Organic beef and lamb in packs or cuts from the farm and from local farm shops. Organic wheat, barley and peas available.

ECO CARPET CARE LTD

31 Fourth Avenue, Hove, BN3 2PN

Tel: 01273 771111 info@ecocarpetcare.co.uk www.ecocarpetcare.co.uk

Eco Carpet Care Ltd and its network of responsible carpet cleaners is setting a new standard around the UK for what is acceptable when having your carpets, upholstery or mattresses cleaned. We are passion-ate about promoting excellent health, superior hygiene and the sustainability of the environment by clean-ing carpets without the use of toxic chemicals and harmful solvents. Thanks to state-of-the-art equipment and new natural products you no longer have to use harsh chemicals in your home or business to get your carpets clean, which means you no longer have to sacrifice your health and the health of those around you for a clean carpet.

FOOD FORE THOUGHT

Wickham Manor Farm,

Pannel Lane, Winchelsea, TN36 4AG

Tel: 01797 225575 info@foodforethought.co.uk www.wickhammanor.co.uk

Grower and processor of all our own livestock: lamb, beef and pork catering for local farmers' markets, London, and wholesale to both London and local restaurants.

FRANCHISE MANOR FARM

Spring Lane, Burwash,

Tel: 01435 883151 Fax: 01435 883151 simon@thenetherfieldcentre.co.uk

Organic mixed farm: arable, beef, sheep, pigs, laying hens. Has on-site meat chiller store and butchery room with Soil Association licence.

FULL OF BEANS

96 High St., Lewes, BN7 1XH

Tel: 01273 472627 Fax: 01273 472627 tempeh@globalnet.co.uk

We manufacture organic tofu, tempeh, wholegrain mustard, miso. Shop has home-made vegetarian and vegan snacks, cakes, pulses, dried fruit, nuts, herbs, spices and many more delights.

GOSSYPIUM

19 High Street, Lewes, BN7 2QA.

Tel: 01273 472211 info@gossypium.co.uk www.gossypium.co.uk

Gossypium is about understanding the real value of clothing. All Gossypium products are made with organic and fairly traded cotton. The collection includes yogawear, casual wear, nightwear, underwear and baby-wear. Head Office, Gossypium House, Abinger Place, Lewes, East Sussex, BN7 2QA. Tel: 01273 409372.

HANKAM ORGANICS

Hankham Hall Rd., Hankham, Pevensey, BN24 5BE

Tel: 01323 741000 Fax: 01323 741000

One and a half acres of organic crops under glass, lots of leafy crops including spinach, lettuce and herbs. Local box scheme with doorstep deliveries. Also supply wholesale.

HARVEST SUPPLIES

Harvest Home, Chuck Hatch, Hartfield, TN7 4EN

Tel: 01342 823392 Fax: 01342 825594

Distribute for local growers. Retail business at home, door to door deliveries, wholesale deliveries to shops, restaurants etc. Full selection of veg, fruit, herbs and wholefoods in Sussex and Kent.

HEN ON THE GATE
FARM SHOP

Clayton Farm, Newick Lane, Mayfield, TN20 6RE

Tel: 01435 874852 Fax: 01435 873930 claytonfarm@btinternet.com

Organic farm shop selling home produced beef, lamb, pork, chicken, vegetables and ready meals as well as a wide selection of groceries. Art gallery, café and farm walks.

HIDDEN SPRING VINEYARD
& ORGANIC ORCHARDS

Vines Cross Road, Horam, TN21 0HF

Tel: 01435 812640 Fax: 01435 813542 info@hiddenspring.co.uk www.hiddenspring.co.uk

Soil Association G1459. Hidden Spring Vineyard and Organic Orchards set in gentle Sussex countryside. Visitors can sample the wine and seasonal fruit, 10 apple varieties and 3 pear varieties. Phone first. Caravan Club approved site.

HODSON, J H W & S E

Higham Farm, Bells Yew Green, Tunbridge Wells, TN3 9AU

Tel: 01892 750363 Fax: 01892 752179

Soil Association G4555. Organic beef from our pedigree Sussex herd and organic lamb from our pedigree Poll Dorset flock. Self-catering granary accommodation in High Weald area of outstanding natural beauty.

HOLLYPARK ORGANICS

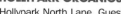

Hollypark North Lane, Guestling, TN35 4LX

Tel: 01424 812229 Fax: 01424 812025

Certified Biodynamic farm (BDAA 303 UK6). Home produced goat's meat, unpasteurised goat's milk, cheeses and yoghurts a speciality. Vegetables and salads all year round. Culinary/medicinal herbs.

EAST SUSSEX

IEKO NATURAL PAINTS

1 The Jackdaws, Highgate Works, Tomtits Lane, Forest Row, RH18 5AT

Tel: 01342 824466 info@ieko.co.uk www.ieko.co.uk

We stock an outstanding selection of the best non-toxic, eco friendly paints and finishes available. From Earthborn Claypaint to Osmo Hardwax Oil, the products we supply are based on sustainable natural ingredients enabling you to create a beautiful home without risking your health or the environment. Our products have also been used on organic farms.

INFINITY FOODS CO-OPERATIVE LTD

25 North Rd., Brighton, BN1 2AA

Tel: 01273 603563 Fax: 01273 675384 www.infinityfoods.co.uk

Organic and wholefoods, cruelty-free cosmetics, fresh fruit and vegetables, organic bread baked on the premises.

IZZARD, MRS MARGARET

Gifford Farm Cottage, Battle Rd., Dallington, TN21 9LH

Tel: 01424 838210 Fax: 01424 838210

I have poultry, eggs, single cows and calves, do B&B, plus gardening.

LADYWELL ORGANIC

Court Lodge Farm, Udimore, Rye, TN31 6BB

Tel: 01424 882206 Fax: 01424 882206 ladywell@clfarm.co.uk

Packs of fresh or frozen farm born and reared pedigree Sussex beef and Romney lamb. Packs from 4 to 11 kg, ready cut or cut to your requirements. Other packs available to order. Local delivery available. Produce also available at local farmers' markets.

LANSDOWN HEALTH FOODS

44 Cliffe High St., Lewes, BN7 2AN

Tel: 01273 474681

Retail health food shop selling a wide range of organic goods, takeaway, bread, dairy, body care, herbal remedies, household and baby products.

MIDDLE FARM

West Firle, Lewes, BN8 6LJ

Tel: 01323 811411 Fax: 01323 811622 info@middlefarm.com www.middlefarm.com

Soil Association P6214 (shop), G5831 (beef). Open family farm with own butchery, bakery, specialist food and cheese sections, restaurant and The National Collection of Cider and Perry, producing and selling raw milk from pedigree Jersey herd and organic beef.

MONTEZUMA'S CHOCOLATES

15 Duke St., Brighton, BN1 1AH

Tel: 01273 324979 Fax: 0845 450 6305 www.montezumas.co.uk

Soil Association P6067. Manufacturer and retailer of award-winning British organic chocolate. Highly acclaimed innovative and exciting products.

THE NATURAL STORE

2 Rochester Gardens, Hove, BN3 3AW

Tel: 01273 746781 customerservices@thenaturalstore.co.uk www.thenaturalstore.co.uk

Natural and organic luxury internet department store. Organic cotton clothes, bedlinen and towels. Organic food and drink. natural and organic toiletries. Products for babies, little ones, pets, travel and the garden.

NEAL'S YARD REMEDIES

2A Kensington Gardens, Brighton, BN1 4AL

Tel: 01273 601464 mail@nealsyardremedies.com www.nealsyardremedies.com

Neal's Yard Remedies manufactures and retails natural cosmetics in addition to stocking an extensive range of herbs, essential oils, homeopathic remedies and reference material.

OAKWOOD FARM

Poppinghole Lane, Robertsbridge, TN32 5BL

Tel: 01580 830893 Fax: 01580 830201

Soil Association G2575 & P6079. Top fruit, soft fruit, single variety apple juice, pear juice, apple & blackberry, pear & raspberry, cider and perry. Also attend Lewes Farmers' market. Supply box schemes and wholesale markets.

OLIVER, E M & R J H

Blacklands, Crowhurst, Battle, TN33 9AB

Tel: 01424 830360 Fax: 01424 830360 architects@mnroliver.fsbusiness.co.uk

HDRA 55251, Soil Association (personal membership) 8718. An organic smallholding producing vegetables and goats milk for family, any surplus for sale to B&B, campers and holiday guests. Architects (RIBA) to environment-conscious designs. Camping.

THE ORGANIC CAKE COMPANY

The Clocktower, Highgate Works,

Tomtits Lane, Forest Row, RH18 5AT

Tel: 01342 823564 sales@theorganiccakecompany.co.uk www.theorganiccakecompany.co.uk

Delicious organic cakes, freshly baked with local and fair trade ingredients. Supremely tangy lemon sponge, very chocolatey chocolate sponge, luscious carrot cake with local cheese topping, a rare fruit cake made with porter that tastes like fruit cake should and lasts 3 months. Available at farmers' markets, retailers and online. Gluten-free, dairy-free available. Delivery across South-East and national courier service.

PASKINS HOTEL

18/19 Charlotte St., Brighton, BN2 1AG

Tel: 01273 601203 Fax: 01273 621973 welcome@paskins.co.uk www.paskins.co.uk

Most of our food is organic and we are justly proud of our varied vegetarian breakfasts. Our tasteful rooms are individually designed and we have a welcoming bar.

REAL FOOD DIRECT

Unit 4, Level 3, New England House, New England Street,
Brighton, BN1 4GH

Tel: 01273 621222 Fax: 01273 626226 info@realfood-direct.com www.realfood-direct.com

Organic food home delivery for Brighton and Hove: fruit and vegetables, fresh bread, meat and fish, dairy, wholefoods, baby food, green cleaning products and lots more.

RYE HEALTH STORE

90 High St, Rye, TN31 7JN

Tel: 01797 223495 sussexhealth@hotmail.com

A busy local shop selling a full range of wholefoods, special diet foods, supplements and natural remedies. Many organic wines are stocked.

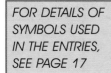

FOR DETAILS OF SYMBOLS USED IN THE ENTRIES, SEE PAGE 17

SCHMIDT NATURAL CLOTHING

Corbiere, Nursery Lane, Nutley, TN22 3NS

Tel: 0845 345 0498 Fax: 01825 714676 catalogue@naturalclothing.co.uk www.naturalclothing.co.uk

Catalogue of organic clothing, nappies, bedsheets, duvets, toys and toiletries for babies, children and adults by mail order. Eczema, sensitive skin, chemical allergy specialists. Excellent range of underwear, socks, slippers, nightwear, including specialised sleepsuit for eczema and biodynamic lambskins. Emphasis is placed on hygiene and comfort of products, fair trade practice, and attentive personal service. Products certified by International Natural Textile Association, BDAA and Real Nappy Association.

SEASONS FOREST ROW LTD

10-11 Hartfield Rd., Forest Row, RH18 5DN

Tel: 01342 824673 Fax: 01342 826119

sales@seasons-forest-row.co.uk www.seasons-forest-row.co.uk

Two shops. Large range of wholefoods and fresh produce, most organic, many biodynamic. Also natural cosmetics, wooden toys, large range of books on biodynamics and anthroposophy. Separate shop for organic fruit and vegetables. Wholesale to shops, restaurants and institutions in Sussex. Business owned by charitable trust.

SEASONS OF LEWES

199 High Street, Lewes, BN7 2NS

Tel: 01273 473968

Vegetarian/Vegan restaurant 75% ingredients organic. GMO-free. Outside catering available. Weddings, buffets etc. Food from the freezer (vegetarian meals, soups, pies). Family business. Open Tues–Sat 10am–5pm.

SEDLESCOMBE ORGANIC VINEYARD

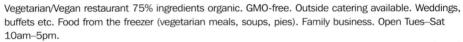

Hawkhurst Rd., Cripp's Corner, Nr. Robertsbridge, TN32 5SA

Tel: 0800 980 2884 Fax: 01580 830122

sales@englishorganicwine.co.uk www.englishorganicwine.co.uk

England's oldest organic vineyard (Est 1979) producing a range of award-winning English red, white and sparkling wines, as well as fruit juices, fruit wines, liqueurs and cider – all to Soil Association organic standards. Member of the Soil Association Organic Farms Network.

ST. MARY'S RETREAT HOUSE

Church St., Hartfield, TN7 4AG

Tel: 01892 770305

Restore body, soul and spirit in a peaceful setting near the Ashdown Forest. Vegetarian home cooking with organic produce. Not a B&B!

TABLEHURST FARM

London Rd., Forest Row, RH18 5BJ

Tel: 01342 823173 Fax: 01324 824873 tablehurst_farm@talk21.com

Mixed biodynamic community farm producing and selling excellent award-winning home grown biodynamic and organic meat, some seasonal fruit, vegetables and eggs. Shop open Thursday–Saturday only, 9–5. Organic Food Awards 2004, 2006.

TRINITY WHOLEFOODS CO-OPERATIVE LTD

3 Trinity Street, Hastings, TN34 1HG

Tel: 01424 430473

Soil Association R1595. Trinity Wholefoods is a co-operative founded in 1985 by local residents. We sell a range of products including fresh bread, bagged nuts, seeds, pulses, grains, frozen goods, chilled products and fresh organic veg, and we have a takeaway counter. All welcome. Mon–Sat 9am–5.30pm.

WEALDEN WHOLEFOODS

Pilgrims, High St., Wadhurst, TN5 6AA
Tel: 01892 783065 Fax: 01892 783351
barbara@wealdenwholefoods.co.uk www.wealdenwholefoods.co.uk
Wholefood shop and café selling mostly organic products. We also stock fair traded and environmentally friendly products. In the process of expanding both the shop and café, and the range of goods carried.

WEST SUSSEX

THE ACORN CENTRE

Todhurst Site, North Heath, Pulborough, RH20 1DL
Tel: 01798 873533 Fax: 01798 873533 michellewykes@aldingbournetrust.co.uk
Training centre for adults with learning disabilities, we grow our own organic vegetables which are sold through our farm shop. Other organic produce also available. Coffee shop. Soil Association G2586, P5118.

ALDINGBOURNE COUNTRY CENTRE

Blackmill Lane, Norton, Chichester, PO18 0JP
Tel: 01243 542075 Fax: 01243 544807 acc@aldingbournetrust.co.uk www.aldingbournetrust.co.uk
Aldingbourne Country Centre is a sheltered training centre for adults with learning difficulties. A wide range of organic products are produced on the 1.7 hectare site and these are available on the menu in the café, from the site shop and at local farmers' markets. The centre has conference facilities for hire, a woodland walk and conservation area and also specialises in horticulture (bedding/herbaceous plants, hanging baskets), furniture restoration and hand-made art and craft products. For further details contact Linda Thompson or Matt Swanson.

BERRY, N

Great Water Farm, Ashurstwood, RH9 3PQ
Tel: 01342 826752
Organic lamb in freezer-ready packs available all year round. Free local delivery, whole lamb £85, half lamb £45, also delicious garlic-flavoured lamb burgers, the healthy alternative for children.

CORNERWEIGHS

Elm Lodge, Caudle Street, Henfield, BN5 9DQ
Tel: 01273 492794 cornerweighs@aol.com
One of the best natural and organic food shops in West Sussex. A touch-screen library is available to all visitors and a close association with Natural Solutions Healing Centre complementary health practice is a great and unique asset. Henfield is easy to find and has free parking. Come and find your one-stop health solution right here in the country.

DOWN TO EARTH

2-3 Goldrings, West Street, Midhurst, GU29 9NQ
Tel: 01730 815133 Fax: 01730 815133 down_to_earth@btinternet.com
Local organic foods including dairy, greengrocery, meat and gourmet prepared foods. Wholefoods and special dietary needs. Veg boxes for delivery or collection, refill service for eco detergents, organic toiletries and food supplements, real nappies.

LAINES ORGANIC FARM

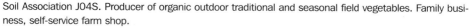

47 Newbury Lane, Cuckfield, RH17 5AA
Tel: 01444 452480 Fax: 01444 452480
Soil Association J04S. Producer of organic outdoor traditional and seasonal field vegetables. Family business, self-service farm shop.

LANGMEADS OF FLANSHAM LTD – ROOKERY FARM EGGS

Rookery Farm, Flansham, Bognor Regis, PO22 8NN
Tel: 01243 583583 Fax: 01243 585354
Soil Association G7241, OF&G 11UK F02075. Our organic eggs are available wholesale from the farm or via our delivery rounds, and retail from the farm or via farmers' markets.

MONTEZUMA'S CHOCOLATES

29 East St., Chichester, PO19 1HS
Tel: 01243 537385 Fax: 0845 450 6305 www.montezumas.co.uk
Soil Association P6067. Manufacturer and retailer of award-winning British organic chocolate. Highly acclaimed innovative and exciting products.

NATURAL WAY

33A Carfax, Horsham, RH12 1EE
Tel: 01403 262228 Fax: 01403 262228
Offer wide range of pre-packed wholefoods and produce sold by well known names in the wholefood industry. Not vegetables or eggs.

OLD CHAPEL FORGE

Old Chapel Forge, Lagness, Chichester, PO20 1LR
Tel: 01243 264380 info@oldchapelforge.co.uk www.oldchapelforge.co.uk
We are Gold Award holders for the Green Tourism Business scheme and purchase where possible from organic local suppliers such as veg from Veg Out and Rother Valley organics in Rogate, Hampshire, milks and other everyday organic produce from supermarkets.

OLD PLAW HATCH FARM LTD

Sharpthorne, East Grinstead, RH19 4UL
Tel: 01342 810652/810201 Fax: 01342 811478 info@plawhatchfarm.co.uk
200-acre biodynamic farm producing upasteurised milk, cream, cheese, eggs, beef, pork sausages and smoked bacon, soft fruit, vegetables and salads. All available through its own farm shop which opens seven days a week.

RIVERFORD HOME DELIVERY – BRIGHTON

3 The Daisycroft, Henfield, BN5 9LH
Tel: 01273 492915 www.riverford.co.uk
Box scheme.

RIVERFORD HOME DELIVERY – WORTHING

Tel: 0845 600 8311 www.riverford.co.uk
Local licensed distributor for Riverford Organic Vegetables.

ST. MARTIN'S TEA ROOMS

3 St. Martin's St., Chichester, PO19 1NP
Tel: 01243 786715 Fax: 01243 786715 info@organictearooms.co.uk www.organictearooms.co.uk
Medieval tea room in centre of Chichester, sensitively restored in 1979 by Keith Nelson (present proprietor). No smoking throughout. No convenience or tinned foods. Three cosy log fires and walled garden.

TUPPENNY BARN LTD

Tuppenny Barn, Tuppenny Lane, Southborne, PO10 8HG
Tel: 079775 336684 Fax: 01243 574107 maggie@tuppennybarn.com www.tuppennybarn.com
Recently established smallholding growing organic veg, herbs, cut flowers, soft fruit & top fruit. School visits welcomed. Also retail recycled stationery goods & bags with profits going back into smallholding.

VEG OUT

Coombers Barn Farm, 72 Orchardside, Hunston, Chichester, PO20 6PQ
Tel: 01243 781438 Fax: 01243 511461
Veg box scheme.

WAYSIDE ORGANICS

Wayside, Woodhorn Corner, Oving, Chichester, PO20 2BT
Tel: 01243 779716 Fax: 01243 779716 bart.ives@talk21.com
Soil Association G1510; P5555. Local deliveries, farm gate sales, stall at old Spitalfields market,
Sundays. Growers of salads, vegetables, herbs and top and soft fruits to Soil Association standards.

WILLOW NURSERY
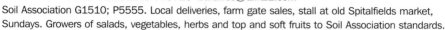
44 Hill Lane, Barnham, PO22 0BL
Tel: 01243 552852 Fax: 01243 552852 willownursery@ntlworld.com
Soil Association G9512. Grow a wide range of vegetables and salad crops sold through a year-round box
scheme. Also supply fruit boxes. Deliveries within West Sussex and East Hampshire.

THE SOUTH

BERKSHIRE

BROCKHILL FARM ORGANIC SHOP

Brockhill Farm, Brock Hill, Warfield, Bracknell, RG42 6JU
Tel: 01344 882643 Fax: 01344 882643
A complete range of organic food under one roof: fresh fruit and vegetables, meat, poultry, fish, dairy pro-
duce, groceries, wine, beer, spirits, confectionery, eco products, etc.

CHURCH FARM

Beale Park, Lower Basildon, Reading, RG8 9NH
Tel: 0118 984 5172 farmnet@soilassociation.org
The farm has chosen rare breeds of sheep and cattle (such as Portland sheep and British White cows) –
their grazing habits create the right conditions in the meadows to sustain the wild flowers. Farmer Clive Hill
manages the livestock according to organic standards, and care is taken that they do not overgraze the
pastures and upset its delicate ecology. Farm trail open to visitors all year round. Please always contact the
farm to check opening times before you set off. Member of the Soil Association Organic Farms Network.

EAT ORGANIC

15 Marlborough Avenue, RG1 5JB
Tel: 0118 987 1854 Fax: 0871 994 1330 enquiries@eatorganic.co.uk www.eatorganic.co.uk
We are have a small market garden near Henley where we grow salad and brassicas. We also source fruit
and veg from other local and UK suppliers. We source some fruit and veg from Europe where not available in the UK. We stock pantry, bread, household cleaning and dairy items. We also run a box scheme,
delivering to South Oxfordshire, Henley, Reading, Wokingham, Bracknell and Maidenhead.

GARLANDS ORGANIC

6 Reading Road, Pangbourne, RG8 7RS
Tel: 0118 984 4770 Fax: 0118 984 4220
Soil Association G1619. A fantastic organic emporium, home-grown vegetables, groceries, fine cheeses,
local and British meat, supplements, etc. Special diets, regional breads, consulting room, lovely shop,
great staff. Parking behind.

THE KINDERSLEY CENTRE AT SHEEPDROVE ORGANIC FARM
The Kindersley Centre, Sheepdrove Organic Farm, Warren Farm, Lambourn, RG17 7UU
Tel: 01488 674737 Fax: 01488 72285
pippa.regan@thekindersleycentre.com www.thekindersleycentre.com
Sustainable, organic and environmentally sound, The Kindersley Centre combines exceptional surround-ings with the most advanced technology and attentive service. Set at the heart of award-winning Sheepdrove Organic Farm, the centre is housed within a beautiful, eco-friendly building, surrounded by fields and woodlands. A range of meeting places and adaptable seating for up to 200 people.

MONTEZUMA'S CHOCOLATES
12 Peascod St., Windsor, SL4 1DU
Tel: 0845 450 6304 Fax: 0845 450 6305 claire.beech@montezumas.co.uk www.montezumas.co.uk
Soil Association P6067. Manufacturer and retailer of award-winning British organic chocolate. Highly acclaimed innovative and exciting products.

THE ORGANIC BEEF COMPANY
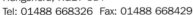
The Old Craven Arms, Inkpen,
Hungerford, RG17 9DY
Tel: 01488 668326 Fax: 01488 668429
enquiries@theswaninn-organics.co.uk www.theswaninn-organics.co.uk
Organic beef farm and butchery managed with The Swan Inn – organic restaurant, bar food and organic farm shop specialising in all organic meats and ready meals. An integrated organic business.

Waltham Place Organic Farm & Gardens

Waltham Place is a unique organic estate which offers a wonderful experience. We welcome visitors to our beautiful estate to see and learn more about our work here.
Enquiries to The Estate Office, Church Hill White Waltham, Berkshire, SL6 3JH
Tel: 01628 825517 estateoffice@walthamplace.com
www.walthamplace.com
For more information see our entry in the directory

ORGANIC BUFFET
2 Collis St., Reading, RG2 0AE
Tel: 0118 987 3740 vincecharles@onetel.com www.organicbuffet.co.uk
We specialise in buffets served at corporate events, meetings, training-days, networking lunches, private parties, weddings . . . any occasion, any numbers, where good food is required. Based in Berkshire, we cover the Thames Valley area. Alternative tel no: 07876 236412.

RANGER ORGANICS LTD
Holmes Oak Farm, Collins End, Goring Heath, Reading, RG8 7RJ
Tel: 01491 682568 Fax: 01491 681694 ranger.organics@virgin.net
Soil Association R07M. Traditional range of English and Continental cuts of home produced organic beef sold at local and London Farmers' Markets. Beef Highly Commended at the Organic Food Awards 2002; poultry winner 1999 and highly commended 2000. Rare breed poultry and laying geese.

RIVERFORD HOME DELIVERY

28 Matthews Green Rd., Wokingham, RG41 1JU
Tel: 0118 989 0053 ruth@riverfordhomedelivery.co.uk www.riverford.co.uk
Organic vegetable box scheme operating in Berkshire, varied box sizes to suit different households. Can order online at www.riverford.co.uk.

RUSHALL FARM

Scratchface Lane, Bradfield, RG7 6DL
Tel: 0118 974 4547 jst@rushallfarm.org.uk www.rushallfarm.org.uk
Rushall Farm is a mixed organic farm situated in the heart of the beautiful Pang valley. It has cattle, sheep, and woodland, and grows a range of cereal crops. It is also home to the John Simonds Trust, an educational charity that promotes a love and understanding of farming and the countryside.

SHEEPDROVE ORGANIC FARM

Warren Farm, Sheepdrove, Lambourn,
Hungerford, RG17 7UU
Tel: 01488 674721 Fax: 01488 73335 manager@sheepdrove.com www.sheepdrove.com
Driven by a passionate concern for animal welfare, wildlife preservation and a sustainable rural economy, we produce our own organic beef, lamb, mutton, chicken and pork. We hang and cut all our meat on the farm, and offer a bespoke service with nationwide delivery. Organic and environmentally sound, The Kindersley Centre combines exceptional surroundings with state of the art technology for meetings, conferences and events for between 8 and 200 delegates. Member of the Soil Association Organic Farms Network. Organic Food Awards 2004, 2006.

THE SWAN INN ORGANIC FARM SHOP

Craven Rd., Inkpen, Hungerford, RG17 9DX
Tel: 01488 668326 Fax: 01488 668306
enquiries@theswaninn-organics.co.uk www.theswaninn-organics.co.uk
Organic beef, lamb, pork, chicken and turkey all matured and butchered on premises. Bacon, gammons, sausages, burgers, ready to eat organic meals all manufactured on premises, and sliced cold roast beef and ham. Special orders available. Over 1,000 items of veg, dairy, dry goods in stock. 10 luxurious bedrooms and gourmet restaurant. Public House, organic bar meals.

TRUE FOOD CO-OP

Unit D6, Acre Road Business Park, Acre Road, Reading, RG2 0SA
Tel: 0845 330 8272 organics@truefood.coop www.truefood.coop
The True Food Co-op holds markets selling affordable organic foods and eco-household products in community venues around Reading. Check out our website for the dates and times of your nearest market.

WALTHAM PLACE
ORGANIC FARM & GARDENS

Waltham Place Farm, Church Hill, White Waltham, Maidenhead, SL6 3JH
Tel: 01628 825517 Fax: 01628 825045 estateoffice@walthamplace.com www.walthamplace.com
Certified by the Soil Association no. G557 since 1989, Waltham Place is dedicated to organic husbandry working alongside the natural ecosystem and to the principles of self-sufficiency. We welcome visitors and customers to visit us and learn about all aspects of life at Waltham Place. We are open to the public Wednesdays in aid of the NGS; Fridays 11am–2pm for walks; by appointment for groups Tuesdays and Thursdays, May to September. Our produce is available from our farm shop and Tea Rooms Tuesday–Friday 10am–4pm and includes seasonal vegetables, preserves, home reared meat, home-made bread and dairy products and from local farmers' markets. Tea room serves light organic lunches, beverages and home-made cakes. We can arrange educational tours and biodynamic growing courses throughout the year; contact the office for more details.

WILTON HOUSE

33 High Street, Hungerford, RG17 0NF

Tel: 01488 684228 Fax: 01488 685037 welfares@hotmail.com www.wiltonhouse.freeserve.co.uk

Although not totally organic, Wilton House offers mainly organic or locally produced wholesome food in its classic English town house. Elegant, high standard accommodation with 2 beautiful en-suite bedrooms from £30pp per night.

DORSET

AUBERGINE

31 Easton St., Portland, DT5 1BS

Tel: 01305 860484 jane@aubergines.plus.com www.auberginehealthyliving.com

Shop selling local organic produce such as milk, bread, eggs, meat & ready meals as well as offering a local veg box scheme and organic wholefoods and the full Ecover range – including refills.

BECKLANDS FARM

Becklands Farm,

Whitchurch Canonicorum, Bridport, DT6 6RG

Tel: 01297 560298 becklandsorganicfarm@btopenworld.com www.becklandsorganicfarm.com

Small farm shop with farm produce, organic groceries and Ecover cleaning products, eco-environmental information and crafts. Sells own Red Ruby Devon x beef, geese, eggs, cheese and vegetables in season. Home-made preserves using farm fruit. Logs, planked poplar, comfrey root cuttings and plant fertiliser. Seasoned ash for refectory table available – grown on the farm, which has been organic since 1962. Becklands is one of Rick Stein's Food Heroes and recommended by Delia Smith's website. Sometimes en suite B&B with full organic breakfast. During 14th July–8th September, organic lunches and teas (optional) outside from 12.30 on Thursdays plus guided farm walks at 2pm (Adults £3.50, children £2, or family ticket £10). Groups any time by arrangement. Two hour guided walk includes introduction to organic farming, badger sett, wildlife ponds and egg collection. Member of the Soil Association Organic Farms Network.

BOTHEN HILL PRODUCE

7 Green Lane, Bothenhampton,

Bridport, DT6 4ED

Tel: 01308 424271 Fax: 01308 424271 sales@bothenhillproduce.co.uk www.bothenhillproduce.co.uk

Family-run smallholding producing wide range of quality vegetables throughout the year, also lamb from our closed flock of pedigree Hampshire Down sheep. Local box delivery scheme. Wholesale available.

CANNINGS COURT ORGANIC FARM SHOP
AND BOX SCHEME

Cannings Court, Pulham, Nr. Sturminster Newton, DT2 7EA

Tel: 01258 818035 john.cannings-court@care4free.net

We have a farm shop and local delivery box scheme, supplying fresh vegetables, eggs and salads from our own fields and polytunnels. We also sell local organic bread, milk, cream, cheese and yoghurt and a range of organic fruit from near and far. Our produce is better, fresher and on average cheaper than anything supermarkets sell. Visit us and find out.

COWDEN HOUSE

Frys Lane, Godmanstone, Dorchester, DT2 7AG

Tel: 01300 341377 www.cowdenhouse.co.uk

Vegetarian bed and breakfast located in beautiful downland. Wonderful views and walking/cycling country. Warm hospitality, peace and quiet, local organic produce used to create delicious breakfasts and optional dinners.

DOWN TO EARTH

18 Princes St., Dorchester, DT1 1TW
Tel: 01305 268325
Retailers of a wide range of organic produce including butter, cheese, eggs, fruits and vegetables, bread, dried foods, frozen and chilled produce. Specialists in British cheeses.

EWELEAZE FARM

The Cartshed, Church Lane,
Osmington, Weymouth, DT3 6EW
Tel: 01305 833690 peter@eweleaze.co.uk www.eweleaze.co.uk
Soil Association G6652. Small organic farm producing Aberdeen Angus beef, lamb and eggs. Farm shop open Monday–Saturday 8am–6pm, Sundays 10–2. Camping is available during August, with access to a private beach. A holiday cottage in nearby Osmington village is available for weekly lets (see website).

FORD FARM, ASHLEY CHASE ESTATES

Parks Farm, Litton Cheney, Dorchester, DT2 9AZ
Tel: 01308 482580 Fax: 01308 482608 cheese@fordfarm.com www.fordfarm.com
Soil Association P4414. Traditional West Country farmhouse cheese producers. Organic, kosher and flavoured cheeses are our speciality, including traditional cloth-wrapped cheddar.

FRUITS OF THE EARTH

2a Victoria Grove, Bridport, DT6 3AA
Tel: 01308 425827
Organic vegetables, milk, cereals, wine, teas, rice, coffees, pulses, bread, chocolate, yoghurts, dried fruit, herbs, spices, and lots more.

GOLD HILL ORGANIC FARM

Child Okeford, Nr. Blandford Forum, DT11 8HB
Tel: 01258 861413 Fax: 01258 861413 vegetables4@hotmail.com www.goldhillorganicfarm.co.uk
From May until March we sell up to 35 varieties of vegetables, fruit, organic beef, milk and bread through our farm shop, Wed & Thurs 2–6, Fri 9–6, Sat 9–4 & Sun 10–2. Also at Castle Cary Market (Tuesdays 8.30–11.30). For home delivery ring 01258 863716.

GREEN & PLEASANT

Sydling Brook, Upsydling, Dorchester, DT2 9PQ
Tel: 01300 341262 greenandpleasant@googlemail.com
We grow a wide variety of vegetables on a 15-acre site in Upsydling and market them through our box scheme. Doorstep service in Weymouth and Portland and a 'drop' scheme in Sherborne, Yeovil and Leigh.

GREEN VALLEY FARM SHOP

Longmeadow, Godmanstone, Dorchester, DT2 7AE
Tel: 01300 342164 Fax: 01300 342164
We are a farm shop selling principally organic products including organic vegetables, local organic meat, eggs, milk, bread, cheese, wines, wholefoods, groceries, Ecover products and refill systems.

THE HEALTH MINISTRY
16 High St., Christchurch, BH23 1AY
Tel: 01202 471152 Fax: 01202 471152
Wide range of organic dried goods e.g. nuts, pulses, flour, drinks, ice cream, spreads, etc.

JUICE CAFÉ LTD

9 Burlington Arcade, Old Christchurch Rd., Bournemouth, BH1 2HZ
Tel: 01202 314143
Café using some organic ingredients.

DORSET

THE KINGCOMBE CENTRE

Lower Kingcombe, Toller Porcorum, Dorchester, DT2 0EQ

Tel: 01300 320684 Fax: 01300 321409

nspring@kingcombe-centre.demon.co.uk www.kingcombe-centre.demon.co.uk

Residential study centre in converted farm buildings beside the river Hooke, offering courses and holidays in a wide range of subjects for adults and children, fit and disabled. Day visits for schools and guided walks. Organically reared pork and lamb.

LEAKERS BAKERY

29 East St, Bridport, DT6 3JX

Tel: 01308 423296

Organic bread made from Stoates Flour, Cann Mills, Shaftesbury, Dorset. Most of our produce is made from local ingredients.

LONG CRICHEL BAKERY

Long Crichel, Wimborne, BH21 5JU

Tel: 01258 830852 Fax: 01258 830855 sales@longcrichelbakery.co.uk www.longcrichelbakery.co.uk

Soil Association P6534. Organic bakery including handcrafted bread and cakes baked in a wood fired brick oven. Open Tuesday–Saturday 9–5, Sunday 10–2. If travelling, phone first. Fresh organic vegetables in season from walled garden.

LONG CRICHEL ORGANIC GARDEN

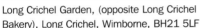

Long Crichel Garden, (opposite Long Crichel Bakery), Long Crichel, Wimborne, BH21 5LF

Tel: 01258 830295 longcrichelgarden@cooptel.net

Soil Association G7461. We grow organic vegetables and fruit in 2.5 acres including a delightful walled garden using permaculture/forest gardening methods. Our speciality is oriental salad and herb production. Local veg box scheme. Registered for WWOOFers.

LONGMEADOW ORGANIC VEGETABLES

Godmanstone, Dorchester, DT2 7AE

Tel: 01300 341779 Fax: 01300 341779 chapmans.longmeadow@virgin.com

Soil Association C60W. We are an organic market garden, established 1987, growing a variety of vegetables and some fruit, available through our own box scheme and Green Valley Farm Shop.

MANOR FARM

Godmanstone, Dorchester, DT2 7AH

Tel: 01300 341415 Fax: 01300 341170 will@manor-farm-organic.co.uk www.manor-farm-organic.co.uk

Mixed farm, organic since 1986. Pasteurised whole and semi-skimmed milk and cream. Lamb and mince prepared for the freezer. Also wheat, combed wheat reed and rearing calves. Day visits for schools, etc. Accommodation (self-catering or partially catered) is economical. Occasional open days.

MANOR FARM ORGANIC MILK LTD

Manor Farm, Godmanstone, Dorchester, DT2 7AH

Tel: 01300 341415 Fax: 01300 341170 pam@manor-farm-organic.co.uk

www.manor-farm-organic.co.uk

Producers of organic cartonned, pasteurised whole milk, semi-skimmed milk and cream. Distribution over the south of England. Member of the Soil Association Organic Farms Network. Organic Food Awards 2004 Fresh Meat Commended.

MODBURY FARM

Burton Bradstock, Bridport, DT6 4NE
Tel: 01308 897193 Fax: 01308 897193 timgarry@btinternet.com
Soil Association P7552, G7551. Organic Jersey herd with farm shop selling our own milk, cream and summer vegetables. Also locally sourced organic and non-organic produce (meat, eggs, cheese, ice cream, preserves, etc).

NEAL'S YARD (NATURAL) REMEDIES LTD

Peacemarsh, Gillingham, SP8 4EU
Tel: 01747 834634 Fax: 01747 834601 cservice@nealsyardremedies.com www.nealsyardremedies.com
Manufacturer and seller of natural skincare products, herbal remedies, homeopathic remedies and aromatherapy products.

REAL MEALS

64 Arnewood Rd., Bournemouth, BH6 5DL
Tel: 01202 418381
Caterer, delivery of hot organic lunches. Nice, friendly people, will do gluten-free, dairy-free, wheat-free.

RECTORY FARM

East Chaldon Road, Winfrith Newburgh, Nr. Dorchester, DT2 8DJ
Tel: 01305 852835
Organic eggs. Soil Association G2057. The farm lies approx 2.5 miles from Lulworth Cove. Open free of charge to visitors.

SLEPE FARM LTD

Slepe Farm, Slepe, Nr. Poole, BH16 6HS
Tel: 01202 622737 Fax: 01202 620844 j.selbybennett@virgin.net
Soil Association G7085. Beef and corn farm with wild heath grazed beef and wild game, wildlife and large barn available for exhibitions and craftsmen's workshops (furniture design and restoration).

SPETCH, LEONARD

Thorncombe Farm, Higher Bockhampton, Dorchester, DT2 8QH
Tel: 01305 251695
Small family farm specialising in high quality beef reared on well managed grassland. Some cereals also grown.

STOATE, NR AND SONS

Cann Mills, Shaftesbury, SP7 0BL
Tel: 01747 852475 Fax: 01747 851936 michael@stoatesflour.co.uk www.stoatesflour.co.uk
Traditional stoneground flour millers since 1832 producing a full range of organic flour for all your baking requirements.

STURTS FARM COMMUNITY

Sheiling Trust, Three Cross Road, West Moors, Ferndown, BH22 0NF
Tel: 01202 870572 (farm) Fax: 01202 854763 office@sturtsfarm.com www.sturtsfarm.com
Fully biodynamic certified large market garden, farm includes dairy, beef, poultry, pigs, 90 acres. Farm shop includes full range of fruit and veg, dry goods, health products. Shop tel: 01202 894292. Garden tel: 01202 875275.

SUNNYSIDE ORGANIC FARM

Sunnyside Farm, Lower Kingcombe, Toller Porcorum, Dorchester, DT2 0EQ
Tel: 01300 321537 Fax: 01300 321537
mandiefletcher@sunnyside95.fsnet.co.uk www.sunnysideorganicfarm.co.uk
Soil Association G875, P7913. Mixed organic farm with luxury holiday cottage, farm shop for seasonal vegetables, lamb, beef and eggs, and local artist exhibiting in the middle of the Dorset Wildlife Trust Reserve.

SYDLING BROOK ORGANIC FARM SHOP

Sydling Estate, Up Sydling, Dorchester, DT2 9PQ
Tel: 01300 341992 Fax: 01300 341166 info@sydling.co.uk www.sydling.co.uk
Home reared traditional and rare breed meats and poultry – direct from Sydling Estate. Award-winning hand-made cheese. We also stock a wide range of organic produce including chocolate, milk, coffee, cereals, bread and eggs. Open Mon–Sat 10–5pm.

TAMARISK FARM

West Bexington, Dorchester, DT2 9DF
Tel: 01308 897781/897784 farm@tamariskfarm.co.uk www.tamariskfarm.co.uk
All home grown on family farm by the sea. Order direct from the farm: beef, lamb, mutton, sausages, wholemeal wheat and rye flours, and vegetables all year round (Soil Association no. P07W). Farm shop open every Tuesday afternoon 4–6.30pm and every Friday morning between 8.30 and 11.00am for meat and flour, or at any other time by arrangement.

WEST DORSET COMMUNITY TRADING CO. LTD

56 Redlands Lane, Broadwindsor, Beaminster, DT8 3ST
Tel: 01308 867538 tanya.harley@btopenworld.com
Organic fruit and vegetable local delivery scheme, using local farms and also imports for a wide range of produce all year round.

HAMPSHIRE & ISLE OF WIGHT

BROUGHTON ORGANICS

The Anchorage, Salisbury Rd., Broughton, Nr. Stockbridge, SO20 8BX
Tel: 01794 301234
Soil Association T07S and ECEAT (European Centre for Eco-Agro Tourism). Broughton Organics grow and supply organic produce (specialising in vegetables, eggs and poultry meat). We aim to provide an alternative to globalisation by supplying local food to local people. Camping available.

COLLINS, MJ&LK

Park Farm, Heckfield, Hook, RG27 0LD
Tel: 0118 932 6535 Fax: 0870 167 4860 martin@parkfarm.fsnet.co.uk
Organic beef, pork and lamb produced with traditional breeds, also fresh fruit and veg and dairy products. Visitors to the shop are welcome to walk around the farm – bring your wellies. Open Tuesday, Wednesday a.m., Thursday, Friday & Saturday. Shop tel: 0118 932 6650.

CROCKSHOP AND RALPH'S HEALTH FOODS

71–72 St. James St., Newport, PO30 1ET
Tel: 01983 522353 Fax: 01983 522353 elliam@aol.com
We stock over 4,000 items including organic grains, nuts, seeds and flour. A large stock of gluten-free, egg-free, wheat-free, dairy-free, yeast-free and sugar-free products. Vegan and vegetarian products. Soya and rice milks and cheeses, carob chocolates etc.

GODSHILL ORGANICS

Newport Rd., Godshill, Isle Of Wight, PO38 3LY

Tel: 01983 840723 Fax: 01983 840723 godshill.organics@btconnect.com www.godshillorganics.com

Soil Association G1724, P5015. Wide range of fresh produce grown on-site. Weekly deliveries and seasonal box scheme. On-site shop selling very wide range of groceries and fresh veg. Local farmers' market each Friday.

HARROWAY ORGANIC GARDENS

Kingsclere Rd., Whitchurch, RG28 7QB

Tel: 01256 895346 Fax: 01256 895346 hogveg@hotmail.com

Soil Association G971, P971. Organic farm and farm shop, selling organic vegetables, fruit, eggs and cheese.

LANTERN FOODS

59 Middle Mead, Hook, RG27 9TE

Tel: 01256 766855 Fax: 01256 766855 djbarber@btinternet.com www.lanternfoods.co.uk

Local family business in north Hampshire supplying organic and dietary foods, natural toiletries and ethical household products. Home delivery service. See website for presence at local markets.

LAVERSTOKE PARK ORGANIC FARM

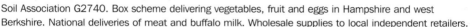

Laverstoke Park Farm, Overton, RG28 3DR

Tel: 01256 772800 info@laverstokepark.co.uk

Soil Association G2740. Box scheme delivering vegetables, fruit and eggs in Hampshire and west Berkshire. National deliveries of meat and buffalo milk. Wholesale supplies to local independent retailers.

MILL FARM ORGANIC SHOP

Mill Farm, Isington, Nr. Alton, GU34 4PN

Tel: 01420 22331 Fax: 01420 22331 info@millfarmorganic.co.uk www.millfarmorganic.co.uk

Soil Association G6840. Fully organic farm. Status achieved Dec 2002. Producer of pedigree beef and lamb. Farm Open Days at certain times of the year. Shop open Thursday, Friday & Saturday 9am–5pm. Shop stocks own as well as other organic and local produce. Farm trails open all year with maps available in the shop. Member of the Soil Association Organic Farms Network.

NATURALLY HEALTH FOODS

5 Waterloo Court, Andover, SP10 1QJ

Tel: 01264 332375 naturally.andover@btopenworld.com www.naturallyhealthfoods.co.uk

Independent health store supplying a wide selection of organic foods, an extensive range of VMS, herbal and homeopathic remedies, local veg box scheme, eco household products and much more.

NATURALLY ORGANIC

Elm Cottage, Pond Lane, Clanfield, PO8 0RG

Tel: 023 9236 0196 Fax: 023 9236 0196

Wholesale distribution of certified organic fruit and vegetables. Also organic fruit and vegetable box home delivery service.

NORTHDOWN ORCHARD

South Litchfield, Basingstoke, RG25 3BP

Tel: 01256 771168 nothdownorchard@ukonline.co.uk

Organic growers established for 15 years, marketing produce through our local box scheme delivering to Overton and Basingstoke. We also sell seasonal produce at Basingstoke farmers' market.

ORGANICALLY SPEAKING

2 Hartley Mews, High Street, Hartley Wintney, RG27 8NX

Tel: 01252 845577 info@organically-speaking.com www.organically-speaking.co.uk

Our shop in Hartley Wintney sells a large range of organic products including fruit, veg, bread, groceries, meat, fish, dairy, household products and skincare and hampers. Our delivery service operates in Surrey, Hampshire and Berkshire.

ORGANIC BOX DELIVERIES

5 Fathoms Reach, Hayling Island, PO11 0RA

Tel: 023 9235 9933 info@organicboxdeliveries.com www.organicboxdeliveries.com

A retail outlet utilising Soil Association accredited supplier Sunnyfields Organics box scheme for all of my produce. I serve all of Portsmouth, Havant and Hayling Island areas.

ORGANICK

Wylds Farm, Warren Rd., Liss, GU33 7DF

Tel: 01730 891490 Fax: 01730 891490 nick@organick.org.uk www.organick.org.uk

North-east Hampshire-based organic farm which grows a range of produce direct from our farm and sells through our farm shop, local farmers' markets and our box delivery scheme.

PARK FARM ORGANICS

Heckfield, Hook, RG27 0LD

Tel: 0118 932 6650 mandy@parkfarmorganics.co.uk www.parkfarmorganics.co.uk

Organic beef, pork and lamb produced with traditional breeds, also fresh fruit and veg and dairy products. Open Tuesday to Saturday. Local box scheme.

RIVERFORD HOME DELIVERY

208 Gainsborough Rd, Basingstoke, RG21 3EQ

Tel: 0845 600 2311 Fax: 01803 762718 boxscheme@riverford.co.uk www.riverford.co.uk

Independent local licensed distributor of Riverford Organic Vegetables, delivering vegetable boxes to parts of Hampshire, Surrey and Berkshire.

RIVERFORD HOME DELIVERY – PORTSMOUTH AND CHICHESTER

5 The Vale, Locks Heath, Fareham, SO31 6NL

Tel: 0800 600 2311 paulandsue@riverfordhomedelivery.co.uk www.riverford.co.uk

Award-winning Riverford organic vegetable box scheme. A range of different boxes to suit most households' needs. Visit the web site www.riverford.co.uk or telephone 0800 600 2311 to see if we deliver in your area, to check predicted box contents, and to place orders. Alternative tel no. 01489 557208.

SCOLTOCKS HEALTH FOODS

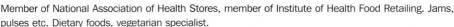

1 Market Place, Ringwood, BH24 1AN

Tel: 01425 473787

Member of National Association of Health Stores, member of Institute of Health Food Retailing. Jams, pulses etc. Dietary foods, vegetarian specialist.

SUNNYFIELDS ORGANIC

Jacobs Gutter Lane, Totton, Southampton, SO40 9FX

Tel: 023 8087 1408 Fax: 023 8087 1146 info@sunnyfields.co.uk www.sunnyfields.co.uk

Sunnyfields grows a large range of organic vegetables and sells a full range of organic products through our shop (open 7 days) and home delivery service to Hampshire and London.

TIMBER!

5 Star Lane, Ringwood, BH24 1AL

Tel: 01425 483505 sanastephens@yahoo.co.uk www.loveorganic.com

Organic clothing from well established organic companies such as People Tree, Bishopston Trading and many more. All the companies we use have their own certified cotton. We also sell Green Baby clothing and other organic products such as bedding.

UPTON HOUSE FARM

Upton House Farm, Wonston, Winchester, SO21 3LR

Tel: 01962 760219 Fax: 01962 761419

Producing British chickens that taste like those that granny produced before chemicals intruded. Supplier of organic poultry compost.

WARBORNE ORGANIC FARM

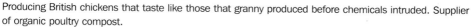

Warborne Farm, Warborne Lane, Boldre, Lymington, Hampshire & Isle of Wight, SO41 5QD

Tel: 01590 688488   Fax: 01590 688096

boxscheme@warborne.fsnet.co.uk www.warbornefarm.co.uk

Warborne Organic Farm, situated in Boldre, near Lymington, grows over 400 varieties of organic fruit, vegetables, herbs and flowers throughout the year. Livestock includes sheep (new season lamb, hogget and mutton), chickens, duck, guinea fowl and geese. All produce is sold direct from the farm, either through the award-winning farm shop and butchery or vegetable box scheme.

WEEK FARM/AVON ORGANICS

Wattons Lane, Matcham, Ringwood, BH24 2DG

Tel: 01202 484628 csnow-weekfarm@btinternet.com

Organic beef/sheep farmer/producer, together with vegetable box scheme, supplying Bournemouth to Ringwood and surrounding areas.

THE WINCHESTER BAKERY

51 Hatherley Rd., Winchester, SO22 6RR

Tel: 01962 861477

Soil Association P5584. Organic home-made bread, available through local shops and farmers' markets.

MIDDLESEX

CAPEL MANOR COLLEGE

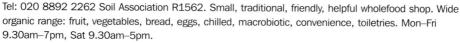

Bullsmore Lane, Enfield, EN1 4RQ

Tel: 020 8366 4442 enquiries@capel.ac.uk www.capel.ac.uk

Soil Association G7651. An organic sheep flock with Lincoln Longwoods and Suffolks. Sell organic hay, lamb and breeding stock. The farm is managed by Capel Manor College which specialises in horticulture and associated land-based industry courses.

GAIA WHOLEFOODS

123 St. Margaret's Rd., Twickenham, TW1 2LH

Tel: 020 8892 2262 Soil Association R1562. Small, traditional, friendly, helpful wholefood shop. Wide organic range: fruit, vegetables, bread, eggs, chilled, macrobiotic, convenience, toiletries. Mon–Fri 9.30am–7pm, Sat 9.30am–5pm.

MIDDLESEX / WILTSHIRE

PINNER FARMERS' MARKET

Queens Head car park, Pinner High Street, Pinner, HA5 5PJ

Tel: 020 7833 0388 info@lfm.org.uk www.lfm.org.uk

Sundays 10am–2pm. Tube to Pinner. At these producer-only farmers' markets, the farmers sell foods they have grown or raised on their own farms directly to the public. No produce is bought in. All the produce is grown within 100 miles of the M25, wherever possible within 50 miles of the M25. Markets are open every week, rain or shine, apart from Christmas. Operated by London Farmers' Markets, 11 O'Donnell Court, Brunswick Centre, London WC1N 1NY.

PIZZA ORGANIC LTD
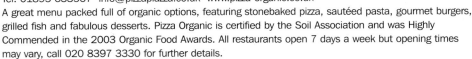

3-5 High St., Ruislip, HA4 7AU

Tel: 01895 633567 info@pizzapiazza.co.uk www.pizza-organic.co.uk

A great menu packed full of organic options, featuring stonebaked pizza, sautéed pasta, gourmet burgers, grilled fish and fabulous desserts. Pizza Organic is certified by the Soil Association and was Highly Commended in the 2003 Organic Food Awards. All restaurants open 7 days a week but opening times may vary, call 020 8397 3330 for further details.

REVITAL HEALTH CENTRE (HEAD OFFICE)

78 High St, Ruislip, HA4 7AA

Tel: 01895 629950 Fax: 01895 630869 enquire@revital.com www.revital.com

Revital has everything you need for optimum nutrition and health care. We are the largest independent health food retailer in the UK and offer a quick, efficient mail order service.

RIVERFORD HOME DELIVERY

Flat 7, 4 Waldegrave Park, Twickenham, TW1 4TE

Tel: 020 8892 2204 Fax: 020 8892 2204 simone@riverfordhomedelivery.co.uk www.riverford.co.uk

Organic vegetable box scheme operating in Richmond, Twickenham & West London. Various box sizes to suit different households. Can order online at www.riverford.co.uk.

TWICKENHAM FARMERS' MARKET

Holly Road Car Park, Holly Road, off King Street, Twickenham, TW1 4EA

Tel: 020 7833 0388 info@lfm.org.uk www.lfm.org.uk

Saturdays 9am–1pm. At these producer-only farmers' markets, the farmers sell foods they have grown or raised on their own farms directly to the public. No produce is bought in. All the produce is grown within 100 miles of the M25, wherever possible within 50 miles of the M25. Markets are open every week, rain or shine, apart from Christmas. Operated by London Farmers' Markets (see Pinner entry above).

WILTSHIRE

CLARE'S ORGANICS

Barneys Barn, Berrycroft, Ashbury, Swindon, SN6 8LX

Tel: 01793 710810 info@claresorganics.co.uk www.claresorganics.co.uk

Soil Association accredited monthly and ad-hoc meat box delivery scheme. Set box and bespoke box options. Free delivery within a 20-mile radius.

COLESHILL ORGANICS

The Garden Cottage, Coleshill, Swindon, SN6 7PT

Tel: 01793 861070 Fax: 01793 861070 info@coleshillorganics.co.uk www.coleshillorganics.co.uk

Totally organic vegetables, regularly inspected by the Soil Association and using no GMOs, delivered to your door. Organic farming supports much more wildlife than industrial farming. We also use minimal packaging and recycle all our boxes.

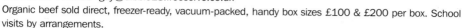

DIBBLE, G & E

Eastrop Farm, Highworth, SN6 7PP

Tel: 01793 762196 guy@dibble18.freeserve.co.uk

Organic beef sold direct, freezer-ready, vacuum-packed, handy box sizes £100 & £200 per box. School visits by arrangements.

EASTBROOK FARMS
ORGANIC MEAT

Eastbrook Farm, The Calf House, Cues Lane, Bishopstone, Swindon, SN6 8PL

Tel: 01793 790460 Fax: 01793 791239

orders@helenbrowningorganics.co.uk www.helenbrowningorganics.co.uk

Soil Association PH53S. Nationwide home delivery service of organic meat. Supplier to the major super-markets. The Helen Browning's range of organic products is sold through Sainsbury's and the Co-op. Helen Browning's Flying Pig will answer your catering needs, be it major outside event or private party. Member of the Soil Association Organic Farms Network. Organic Food Awards 2004 Charcuterie Highly Commended; Fresh Meat Winner.

THE GREEN HOUSE

120 Fisherton St., Salisbury, SP2 7QT

Tel: 01722 325515 sanastephens@yahoo.co.uk www.loveorganic.com

Organic clothing from well established organic companies such as People Tree, Bishopston Trading and many more. All the companies we use have their own certified cotton. We also sell Green Baby clothing and other organic products such as bedding.

HARVEY, M & A

Goulters Mill, Nettleton, Nr. Chippenham, SN14 7LL

Tel: 01249 782555 Fax: 01249 782555

We produce Lleyn sheep for breeding and for meat. Eggs for sale from the farm gate. Light Sussex chicks also available from farm gate. We also have paying guests to stay. Soil Association no. G2641. Deliveries made all over UK.

HAZELBURY PARTNERS

Hazelbury Manor, Box, Corsham, SN13 8HX

Tel: 01225 812088 Fax: 01225 810875

Soil Association G1825. Delicious organic lamb, pork, and beef, hens and duck eggs, produced on family-run farm using rare breed lambs and pigs.

LOWER SHAW FARM

Old Shaw Lane, Shaw, Swindon, SN5 9PJ

Tel: 01793 771080 enquiries@lowershawfarm.co.uk www.lowershawfarm.co.uk

Courses and gatherings. Permaculture, fungus forays, crafts, yoga, circus skills, singing, cooking, herbs, families. Friendly atmosphere, home grown and local food. Organic gardens and animals. Ask us for a programme.

NEAL'S YARD REMEDIES

27 Market Place, Salisbury, SP1 1TL

Tel: 01722 340736 mail@nealsyardremedies.com www.nealsyardremedies.com

Neal's Yard Remedies manufactures and retails natural cosmetics in addition to stocking an extensive range of herbs, essential oils, homeopathic remedies and reference material.

WILTSHIRE

THE ORGANIC EXPERIENCE

7 The Bridge, Chippenham, SN15 1HA
Tel: 01249 720274

We sell an extensive range of food, drink, ecological cleaning and body care products including our own and others fresh fruit and vegetables, fresh meat, dairy, frozen, ice cream, and a full range of groceries including cereals, pulses etc. Home delivery available.

PURELY ORGANIC

Deverill Trout Farm, Longbridge Deverill, Warminster, BA12 7DZ
Tel: 01985 841093 Fax: 01985 841268 trout@purelyorganic.fsnet.co.uk www.purelyorganic.co.uk
Trout farm and shop selling a full range or organic produce, smoked trout, paté, watercress, etc.

PURTON HOUSE

Purton House, Church End, Purton, Swindon, SN5 4EB
Tel: 01793 772287 Fax: 01793 772750 rowie@purton-house.co.uk www.purton-house.co.uk
Organic vegetable, fruit, eggs & meat box scheme. Local door deliveries or collection points. Farmers' markets. We grow over 90 types of vegetables and fruit and many different varieties of each. Our boxes are excellent value for money and always have a good variety of fresh produce.

PYTHOUSE FARM ORGANIC PRODUCE

Pythouse Walled Garden, West Hatch, Tisbury, Salisbury, SP3 6PA
Tel: 01747 870444 info@pythouse-organics.com www.pythouse-organics.co.uk
We supply our own farm-reared organic beef and lamb from our shop near Tisbury. For directions to the shop please visit the 'Contact Us' page on our website. We also do courier delivery to mainland UK. You can order online, by email, by post or by telephone.

RIVERFORD HOME DELIVERY – SWINDON
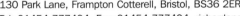  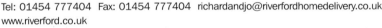

130 Park Lane, Frampton Cotterell, Bristol, BS36 2ER
Tel: 01454 777404 Fax: 01454 777404 richardandjo@riverfordhomedelivery.co.uk
www.riverford.co.uk
Home and workplace delivery of Riverford Organic Vegetables via box scheme for Swindon and Wiltshire. Products delivered include vegetables, fruit, eggs, milk, wine and other organic foods. See www.riverford.co.uk for full details.

SWINDON PULSE WHOLEFOOD CO-OP
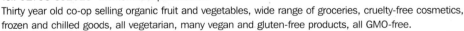

27 Curtis St., Swindon, SN1 5JU
Tel: 01793 692016 www.swindonpulse.co.uk
Thirty year old co-op selling organic fruit and vegetables, wide range of groceries, cruelty-free cosmetics, frozen and chilled goods, all vegetarian, many vegan and gluten-free products, all GMO-free.

TALLYWACKER FARM

50 The Ridings, Kington St. Michael,
Chippenham, SN14 6JG
Tel: 01249 750035 sales@tallywackerfarm.co.uk www.tallywackerfarm.co.uk
Soil Association registered producer/processor. Producers of organic fruit and veg. Home delivery box scheme to Corsham, Chippenham, Devizes, Malmesbury, Tetbury, Wooton Bassett, west Swindon, Calne, Melksham, Neston, Somerfords, Trowbridge surrounding villages and all areas in between. Commended for veg in Organic Food Awards 2004.

THOMAS FAMILY BUTCHERS, MICHAEL

51 The Triangle, Malmesbury, SN16 0AH
Tel: 01666 823981 Fax: 01666 823981 m.thomas51@tiscali.co.uk
www.michaelthomasbutcher.co.uk
Fruit/veg, organic nuts, pulses, dried fruit, dairy products, whole foods, eco cleaning products, vitamins, minerals.

WESTWOOD FARM

Rode Hill, Colerne, Nr. Chippenham, SN14 8AR
Tel: 01225 742854
Organic farm growing delicious seasonal vegetables, fruit and herbs. The fruit is used for the hand-crafted preserves (jams, jellies, marmalades, chutneys). Hand-made Dundee and rich celebration cakes are another speciality available by order and direct sales.

WHO CARES

Unit F1, Avonside Enterprise Park, New Broughton Road,
Melksham, SN12 8BT
Tel: 01225 791886 Fax: 01225 705740 www.whocares.gb.com
A caring, ethical and fair trade supermarket selling a large range of organic products: Pertwood Farm meat, Yeo Valley dairy and lots of other foods; also organic cotton clothes, cotton wool and more.

YATESBURY ORGANICS

GR Gantlett & Son, Yatesbury House Farm, Yatesbury,
Calne, SN11 8YF
Tel: 01672 539191 Fax: 01672 539039 boxes@yatesbury.net www.yatesbury.net
Soil Association G2931. Vegetables, pedigree Aberdeen Angus beef. All home-grown. Box deliveries. Please come and see us.

THE SOUTH-WEST

BRISTOL COUNTY BOROUGH

ALVIS BROS LTD

Lye Cross Farm, Redhill, Bristol, BS40 5RH
Tel: 01934 864600 Fax: 01934 862213 enquiries@lyecrosscheese.co.uk www.lyecrosscheese.co.uk
Organic farmhouse cheesemaker and packer of the renowned Lye Cross Farm brand. Full range of organic cheddars, UK territorials and cheese powder. All suitable for vegetarians. Nationwide distribution and farm shop.

THE BETTER FOOD COMPANY

The Bristol Proving House, Servier St., St. Werburghs, Bristol, BS2 9QS
Tel: 0117 935 1725 Fax: 0117 941 4520 admin@betterfood.co.uk www.betterfood.co.uk
Organic grocery store, based in the Centre for Ethical Trade and Creative Play, specialising in fresh vegetables, salads and fruit from their Walled Garden in Wrington, near Bristol. The huge range of other produce includes a delicatessen counter and butcher's counter, dairy, all basics such as rice, pasta and cereals, chocolate, wine & spirits and cleaning materials. Opening times are Monday–Wednesday 9am–6pm, Thursday & Friday 9am–7pm, and Saturday 9am–5pm. Organic Food Awards 2004: Local Food Initiative Joint Winner.

BORDEAUX QUAY

V-Shed, Canons Way, Bristol, BS1 5UH

Tel: 0117 906 5550 Fax: 0117 906 5567 kath.cockshaw@bordeaux-quay.co.uk

www.bordeaux-quay.co.uk

Restaurant, brasserie, bar, deli, bakery and cookery school in a converted warehouse on Bristol's harbourside. European cooking using local and regionally sourced organic ingredients.

BORN

64 Gloucester Rd., Bristol, BS7 8BH

Tel: 0117 924 5080 Fax: 0117 924 9040 info@borndirect.com www.borndirect.com

Retail and internet shop specialising in organic, natural and practical products for parents and their
babies. We're the experts on washable cotton nappies! Organic range includes organic cotton and wool
babywear (underwear, nightwear, outerwear and bedding), organic herbal teas for pregnancy and after-
wards, toiletries made with organic ingredients (Weleda, Green People, Urtekram), organic massage oils.
We are open Monday–Saturday 9.30–5.30.

CAFÉ MAITREYA

89 St Mark's Road, Easton, Bristol, BS5 6HY

Tel: 0117 951 0100 Fax: 0117 951 0200 thesnug@cafémaitreya.co.uk www.cafémaitreya.co.uk

The UK's top gourmet vegetarian restaurant (Vegetarian Society Awards 2004). Café Maitreya is a café-
restaurant serving modern vegetarian food prepared with love and care and using quality seasonal ingredients, many of which are organic. Daytimes Friday–Sunday, evenings Tuesday–Saturday.

EARTHBOUND

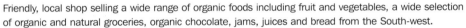

8 Abbotsford Rd., Cotham, Bristol, BS6 6HB

Tel: 0117 904 2260

Friendly, local shop selling a wide range of organic foods including fruit and vegetables, a wide selection
of organic and natural groceries, organic chocolate, jams, juices and bread from the South-west.

THE FOLK HOUSE CAFÉ

40A Park Street, Bristol, BS1 5JG

Tel: 0117 926 2987 info@bristolfolkhouse.co.uk www.bristolfolkhouse.co.uk

Visit Bristol Folk House Café for good food, good coffee and good company. Park Street's best kept secret
is coming out into the open! We use organic produce, as local as possible, and cook from scratch to give
you the best dishes around. Come and see for yourself – relaxed and comfortable café area with a beautiful courtyard for when the sun has put his hat on. Open Monday–Thursday 9.30–4.00pm, Friday–Saturday
9.30am–4.30pm. (Times may vary according to term/holiday, music festivals etc.). For more information on
the café, sample menus and party bookings please call 0117 926 2987 during café hours or see our
website. All our food is made from scratch using organic produce (at least 90% of our menu is from certified organic ingredients).

FRESH & WILD

85 Queens Road, Clifton, Bristol, BS8 1QS

Tel: 0117 910 5930

Fresh & Wild are the leading specialist retailer of organic foods and natural remedies.

HARVEST NATURAL FOODS

11 Gloucester Rd., Bristol, BS7 8AA

Tel: 0117 942 5997 Fax: 0117 924 9073 info@harvest-bristol.coop www.harvest-bristol.coop

We are a wholefood retailer specialising in organic and fair traded goods, including fresh fruit and chocolate, ice cream, tea, coffee, wine, beer. Body care and eco cleaning products.

LEIGH COURT FARM

Abbots Leigh, Bristol, BS8 3RA
Tel: 01275 375756 Fax: 01275 375756 mail@leighcourtfarm.org.uk www.leighcourtfarm.org.uk
Vegetable box scheme, Bristol Farmers' market (June–December), volunteers, practical training, working with communities, not for profit, promoting local food economy, part fully certified, S. A. Licence no. G3034. Delivery to S'ville, Hotwells, Easton, Cotham, and to offices with more than 20 customers.

MURRAY, T & P A

153 Gloucester Rd., Bishopston, Bristol, BS7 8BA
Tel: 0117 942 4025
Butcher and delicatessen. Purveyors of organic meats and delicatessen foods.

THE NATURAL NURSERY

185 North St., Southville, Bristol, BS3 1JQ
Tel: 0117 966 8483 info@naturalnursery.co.uk www.naturalnursery.co.uk
Organic and fairly traded products for families including organic clothes for newborns to 7 years, cloth nappies, natural toiletries, slings, fair toys. Secure online ordering or visit our Bristol shop.

NEAL'S YARD REMEDIES

126 Whiteladies Rd., Clifton, Bristol, BS8 2RP
Tel: 0117 946 6034 Fax: 0117 946 6034 mail@nealsyardremedies.com www.nealsyardremedies.com
Stockists of a wide variety of natural remedies and cosmetics. Many certified organic, including herbs and tinctures, homeopathic and flower remedies, e.g., essential oils, bath and body products, massage oils and books.

ONE PLANET

39-41 Picton St., Bristol, BS6 5PZ
Tel: 0117 942 6644 roger@oneplanetwholefoods.co.uk
Vegetarian and vegan community wholefoods store selling organic, Fair traded and local produce, fruit and veg, dairy, breads, with 100% organic juice bar.

PRIMROSE CAFÉ ICE CREAM

Boyces Avenue, Clifton, Bristol, BS8 4AA
Tel: 0117 946 6577 primrosecafé@talk21.com
Soil Association P7528. Producer of small quantities of pure natural ice creams, sorbets and frozen yoghurts. All handmade on our own premises. Organic Food Awards 2004 Ice Cream Highly Commended.

QUARTIER VERT

85 Whiteladies Rd., Bristol, BS8 2NT
Tel: 0117 973 4482 Fax: 0117 974 3913 info@quartiervert.co.uk www.quartiervert.co.uk
Restaurant, cookery school, bakery, catering. Simple European traditional cooking using local organic ingredients.

RIVERFORD – BRISTOL

Riverford, Buckfastleigh, Devon, TQ11 0LD
Tel: 01803 762720 Fax: 01803 762718 sales@riverford.co.uk riverford.co.uk
Independent local licensed distributor from Riverford Organic Vegetables Limited.

SHEEPDROVE ORGANIC FARM FAMILY BUTCHER

3 Lower Redland Rd., Bristol, BS6 6T
Tel: 0117 973 4643 Fax: 0117 946 7957 graham.symes@sheepdrove.com www.sheepdrove.com
Family butcher selling the Sheepdrove Farm range of meats including beef, lamb, mutton, pork, bacon, gammon, sausages, burgers and poultry. Alternative tel no. 0117 973 1153.

Delfland Nurseries: who they are, why they started, how they've evolved...

Left to right: Eleanor, John, Jill, Lois.

Delfland Nurseries is the leading commercial organic propagator: 2007 is their tenth consecutive year of registration with the Soil Association. Situated near March in Cambridgeshire, just outside the village of Doddington, the nursery is less than 10m above sea level on the edge of a fen 'island' with fertile black fields to the west. The site is 15 acres, of which 7 acres (3 hectares) is glasshouses. You can find a good image of the nursery if you type the postcode into Google Earth.

The nursery is owned and run by husband and wife team John Overvoorde and Jill Vaughan. John's father's family were market gardeners for several generations, and lived near Delft in Holland (hence Delfland Nurseries). John was born in the East Riding of Yorkshire and was interested in growing from a very early age. He studied horticultural production at Sutton Bonington (Nottingham University). After four years in the family business near Hull growing greenhouse crops, he moved to start Delfland a week before his twenty-fifth birthday in 1979.

Jill was born in Devizes, a market town in Wiltshire. Many of her forebears were keen vegetable gardeners through choice or necessity, and she developed a love of freshly picked fruit and vegetables from childhood. Her father had an allotment where he grew the traditional range of vegetables, including some outdoor cucumbers which won the 'Naggers & Braggers' cup (held at his local, the Nag's Head). Her grandfather had most of his garden down to vegetables, and kept bantams. One of her grandmothers was famous for growing peas, and always had some ready to take on family holidays in June. As a teenager Jill worked on a local family farm, and decided to combine her interests in agriculture and geography by becoming a soil scientist. At eighteen she left home to study physical geography and geology at London University followed by an MSc in Soil Science at Aberdeen. For sixteen years she was employed as a consultant soil scientist by ADAS (Agricultural Development and Advisory Service), leaving to work with John in 1996.

John began by growing lettuce for supermarkets, but after five years he wanted more of a challenge and started plant raising. Beginning with brassicas, he soon progressed to lettuce, celery and tomatoes and now grows 'anything from seed'.

The move to organic plants began in 1998, and now accounts for over one third of production. Customers range from very large enterprises to small family units supplying box schemes, farmers' markets and farm shops, including many of the businesses listed in this guide. Although many of their customers are in East Anglia, they supply all over the UK, excluding Northern Ireland.

John always sold spare trays of vegetable plants to local gardeners and small-holders on Saturday mornings, plus pansies in the autumn. Eventually trade grew to the point where part of a greenhouse was converted into a shop. It now sells a wide range of ornamental plants for bedding, baskets and tubs. A full range of vegetable plants is stocked, of the same quality and varieties supplied to commercial growers, but sold individually on a 'pick & mix' basis. In 2001 a mail order service was launched. "Many people these days don't have the time, space or expertise to grow everything from seed. With monthly deliveries of plants from March to October, they can have fresh organic vegetables all year round." A simple website was added in 2002, followed by online ordering and payment in 2004. Delfland were one of the finalists in the East of England e-commerce awards in 2005.

John and Jill are both keen gardeners who test all of the website varieties in their vegetable plot. They also have a mini-orchard, and soft fruit which is shared with the local wildlife. John grows tomatoes, cucumbers, peppers and aubergines in a corner of a greenhouse. He also grows melons which he inherited from one of his Dutch grandfathers, saving the seed from the best-tasting fruit each year. Other hobbies include going to the gym and Arabic dancing (Jill) and squash (John).

They have two teenage daughters: Lois and Eleanor, whose birthday falls on Christmas Eve ("one sowing date we didn't get right, though she was 10 days early!"). The girls aren't keen on gardening, but love the cooking and eating part. They do propagate and sell cacti in the nursery shop, and are good at getting bargains from cacti specialists at shows. Eleanor wants to be an actor; Lois wants to be a green engineer, and is currently building a wind turbine for the house.

About thirty people are employed, with some working parent-friendly hours in school term-time only. The work is seasonal, with peaks November to January (tomato plants) and March to July (everything else). Up to thirty extra staff are taken on, most of whom are from eastern Europe, including Poland, Latvia, Lithuania and Slovakia.

"The great thing about running a family business is that you can put your own values into practice," says Jill. "We believe that people are our most valuable business asset, and we have achieved the Investors in People standard. We get to know our customers personally, and make a point of helping new businesses by selling them single trays of plants, and giving advice on what to grow – and sometimes how to grow it! The recent growth in demand for local fresh food has helped many smallholders to survive, and some are even employing some part-time staff."

Using their scientific backgrounds, they both get involved in many new and novel crops including herbs for medicinal and cosmetic uses. They also try to put something back into the industry: John serves on the HDC Protected Crops Panel, which decides how to allocate funds for research and Jill is a member of the Soil Association Horticulture Standards Committee and treasurer of the British Tomato Growers' Association. Jill and her two daughters were closely involved in the development of the Tomato Zone, an educational website for children aged 5 to 16.

For the future, they see the organic side of the business developing as the market expands. "It feels good to be involved in both the supply of fresh, organic vegetables and in helping people to grow their own."

SOUTHVILLE DELI

262 North St, Southville, Bristol, BS3 1JA

Tel: 0117 966 4507 pgw-awe@dircon.co.uk

We are a retail store selling organic wholefoods including bread, dairy products & eggs. In addition we have a small delicatessen carrying as wide a range of organic luxury goods as possible, including fresh olives, cheeses & chocolates. We also grind organic & fair trade coffees to order.

STONEGROUND

5 The Mall, Clifton, Bristol, BS8 4DP

Tel: 0117 974 1260

Veggie, GMO-free shop stuffed with pulses, cereals and soya plus 200 organic delights and award-winning fresh bread. Excellent organic, veggie wines and beers. Also vits/supplements and herbal remedies. Local where possible.

WILD OATS WHOLEFOODS

9-11 Lower Redland Road, Redland, Bristol, BS6 6TB

Tel: 0117 973 1967 Fax: 0117 923 7871 info@woats.co.uk www.woats.co.uk

Organic natural foods grocery specialising in chilled, frozen and ambient foods, wines, beers, toiletries, natural medicines, household products, organic and natural paints, books. Mail order service available.

WINDMILL HILL CITY FARM SHOP

Philip Street, Bedminster, Bristol, BS3 4EA

Tel: 0117 963 3233 Fax: 0117 963 3252 Info@windmillhillcityfarm.org.uk

www.windmillhillcityfarm.org.uk

We sell locally produced food including organic meat, free-range eggs, goats milk and vegetables grown by organic methods on our inner-city farm. Open Tuesday–Saturday, 10am–5pm.

CHANNEL ISLANDS

FARM FRESH ORGANICS

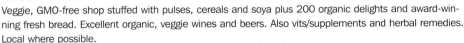

La Bienvenue Farm, La Grande
Route de St. Laurent, St. Lawrence, Jersey, JE3 1GZ

Tel: 01534 861773 Fax: 01534 861772 Contact: Steven & Linda Carter

We grow a wide range of organic vegetables and import fruit which we supply island-wide through our box scheme. We supply pre-packed produce to supermarkets.

GUERNSEY ORGANIC GROWERS

La Marcherie, Ruette Rabey, St Martin's, Guernsey, GY4 6DU

Tel: 01481 237547 Fax: 01481 233045 guernseyorganics@cwgsy.net

www.cwgsy.net/business/guernseyorganics

We operate a box delivery scheme in Guernsey, using as much of our own produce as possible, supplemented with vegetables from Jersey organic farmers and occasionally topped up from the UK. We also offer organic fruit and Jersey organic eggs.

HANSA WHOLEFOOD

Southside, St. Sampsons, Guernsey, GY2 4AE

Tel: 01481 249135 hansa@cwgsy.net

Established 27 years; over 5,000 lines of quality vitamins, minerals, herbal products (Solgar, FSC, etc.). Natural toiletries, sports nutrition, wholefoods, organic products. Mail order specialists. VAT-free. Friendly reliable service.

HANSA WHOLEFOOD

20 Fountain St., St. Peter Port, Guernsey, GY1 1DA
Tel: 01481 723412 Fax: 01481 716388 hansa@cwgsy.net
Established 27 years; over 5,000 lines of quality vitamins, minerals, herbal products (Solgar, FSC, etc.). Natural toiletries, sports nutrition, wholefoods, organic products. Mail order specialists. VAT-free. Friendly reliable service.

THE ORGANIC SHOP

68 Stopford Rd., St. Helier, Jersey, JE2 4LZ
Tel: 01534 789322
Fresh fruit, vegetables, dairy, meat and poultry, wine and beer. Full range of household cleaning materials and toiletries. Comprehensive delivery service including box scheme.

VERMONT FARM

Route Du Coin, St. Brelade, Jersey, JE3 8BT
Tel: 01534 742383 Fax: 01534 498500
We produce a large range of fresh seasonal organic vegetables, home grown strawberries and organic eggs. Organic pork, home-made sausages, organic whole chickens, chicken joints and Christmas turkeys are all prepared in our butchery room on the farm. In our farm shop we also sell a wide range of imported organic fruit.

VERS LES MONTS ORGANIC FARM

La Rue De La Presse, St. Peter, Jersey, JE2 3FE
Tel: 01534 481573
Soil Association G2465 P5325. A small mixed farm producing a wide range of mixed vegetables, potatoes and eggs, sold from the farm stall and box scheme.

CORNWALL & THE ISLES OF SCILLY

A & N HEALTH FOODS

62 Fore St., Saltash, PL12 6JW
Tel: 01752 844926
Health food shop, selling a range of organic and eco-friendly produce and products, vitamins etc.

ALDERMAN, C G

Menaburle Farm, Boconnoc, Lostwithiel, PL22 0RT
Tel: 01208 873703 inquiry@cornishcottageholidays.co.uk www.cornishcottageholidays.co.uk
A mixed farm of cereals, vegetables, sheep and beef, which also offers self-catering accommodation.

ARCHIE BROWNS HEALTHFOODS

Old Brewery Yard, Bread St., Penzance, TR18 2EQ
Tel: 01736 362828
Retail shop and vegetarian/vegan restaurant selling organic and/or vegan dairy, goats milk, cheeses, yoghurts, soya products, jams, chocolates, pasta, flour, cereals, nuts, grains, fruits, pulses, biscuits, artisan bread, preserves, honey, drinks, gluten-free products, natural beauty products and natural cleaning products. Deli counter and oriental section.

BARWICK FARM

Tregony, Truro, TR2 5SG
Tel: 01872 530208 barwickfarmorganics@tiscali.co.uk
Soil Association G7204. Producing Cornish Jersey dairy products: milk, butter, clotted cream and liquid creams from our own cows. Good healthy natural products.

BODINNICK FARM

St Stephens, St Austell, TR2 4EH

Tel: 01726 882421 rose.barnecut@virgin.net

Cornish family-run farm producing prime organic beef and lamb for top local and London outlets. Box scheme direct from farm for local customers.

BOSAVERN FARM

St. Just, Penzance, TR19 7RD

Tel: 01736 786739 Fax: 01736 786739 joandguy@bosavern.demon.co.uk

Farm gate shop, open Saturdays 10am until 2pm, selling freshly picked organic vegetables, organic beef, naturally reared pork and free-range eggs, all produced at Bosavern Farm.

BOSWEDNACK MANOR

Zennor, St Ives, TR26 3DD

Tel: 01736 794183 boswednack@ravenfield.co.uk

Peaceful vegetarian B&B on 3-acre wildlife reserve and smallholding. Five rooms and self-catering cottage. Sea, sunsets, superb walks, non-smoking. St. Ives, Tate Gallery and beaches 5 miles.

BROWDA FARM

Linkinhorne, Callington, PL17 7NB

Tel: 01579 362235

Soil Association G4671. East Cornwall: Bed and breakfast accommodation in our large comfortable 17th century farmhouse on lovely 250-acre organic farm near Bodmin Moor. Informal and friendly. Wonderfully peaceful and gloriously unspoilt. B &B £32p.p.p.n. No smoking, no pets.

BUTTERVILLA

Buttervilla Farm, Polbathic, St Germans, Torpoint, PL11 3EY

Tel: 01503 230315 info@buttervilla.com www.buttervilla.com

Situated in fifteen acres of exceptionally beautiful rolling countryside, Buttervilla is a recently refurbished, eco-friendly Cornish farmhouse fully equipped with modern conveniences. We care for our land in a sustainable, natural way and are rewarded with an abundance of wildlife around our grounds and trails to really help you get close to nature. Currently in conversion with the Soil Association.

CARLEYS OF CORNWALL LTD

The Parade, Truro, TR1 1UJ

Tel: 01872 270091 Fax: 01872 270092 info@carleys.co.uk www.carleys.co.uk

Soil Association P1584. We are an organic supermarket specialising in locally produced fresh fruit and vegetables, meat and dairy foods. We also import fruit and veg directly from suppliers, manufacture our own 'Carleys' brand products and have a rapidly expanding home delivery service.

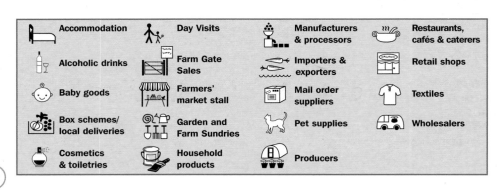

Accommodation	Day Visits	Manufacturers & processors	Restaurants, cafés & caterers
Alcoholic drinks	Farm Gate Sales	Importers & exporters	Retail shops
Baby goods	Farmers' market stall	Mail order suppliers	Textiles
Box schemes/ local deliveries	Garden and Farm Sundries	Pet supplies	Wholesalers
Cosmetics & toiletries	Household products	Producers	

THE CHEESE SHOP

29 Ferris Town, Truro, TR1 3JH
Tel: 01872 270742
Farmhouse cheeses: handmade and unpasteurised, including organic cheeses, from Cornwall and across the UK.

CHURCHTOWN FARM

Churchtown Farm, Lanteglos By Fowey, PL23 1NH
Tel: 01726 870375 Fax: 01726 870376
National Trust coastal farm selling organic beef and lamb. Extensive range available in any quantity including delicious barbecue products. Phone first. Soil Association no. G 1784. Organic Food Awards 2004 Fresh Meat Highly Commended.

COOMBE MILL FARM

Pillaton Mill, Nr. Saltash, PL12 5AN
Tel: 01579 350315
Organic lamb and eggs.

CORNISH ORGANICS

Four Lanes, Redruth, TR16 6LZ
Tel: 01209 215789 Fax: 01209 202579 cornishorganics@hotmail.com
Totally organic farm shop. Our own Aberdeen Angus beef, Large Black pork and bacon, eggs, veg and fruit. Bread baked daily in the farmhouse kitchen, milk and cream from our own cows, ice cream, fish and lots more.

COSWINASAWSIN

The Duchy College, Rosewarne, Cambourne, TR14 0AB
Tel: 01209 722100 Fax: 01209 722159
Coswinsawsin grows a variety of crops including field vegetables, sugar beet, potatoes, and cereals. Farm trail, educational visits, open days and farm walks are all available by arrangement with the office. Coswinsawsin Farm is an important resource for the newly created Organic Studies Centre at the Duchy College, Rosewarne, and is the most westerly of the Elm Farm Research Centre demonstration farms network. Member of the Soil Association Organic Farms Network.

COUNTRYSTORE HEALTHFOODS

3-5 Bond Street, Redruth, TR15 2QA
Tel: 01209 215012
Two shops selling a whole range of organic foods, eco products, body care, babycare, toiletries, etc.

CUSGARNE ORGANIC FARM

Cusgarne Wollas, Cusgarne, Nr. Truro, TR4 8RL
Tel: 01872 865922 organicbox@btconnect.com
Box scheme serving from Helston to Fowey and in between. Grow more than 70 varieties of organic vegetables and fruit, organic free range eggs, organic Angus x suckler herd for beef.

GEAR FARM SHOP

St. Martin, Helston,
TR12 6DE
Tel: 01326 221150 Fax: 01326 221150 pathosking@btinternet.com
Farm shop selling organic vegetables, fruit, bakery, wholefoods, dairy, fish.

GOONGILLINGS FARM

Goongillings Farm, Constantine, Falmouth, TR11 5RP

Tel: 01326 340630 enquiries@goongillings.co.uk www.goongillings.co.uk

Soil Association G4621. Four attractive holiday cottages and a restored antique gypsy caravan on a beautiful waterside organic farm, on the renowned Helford River in West Cornwall. Quay, boats, tennis court. Pets welcome.

GREAT GARGUS FARM

Tregony, Truro, TR2 5SQ

Tel: 01872 530274 Fax: 01872 530274 gargonauts@farming.co.uk

Lamb, grown on Cornish grass, from our long-standing Dorset x Texel flock. Whole or half, jointed and packed to choice, ready for freezer or oven, available to order. Simply delicious.

THE GREENHOUSE

6 High St., St Keverne, Helston, TR12 6NN

Tel: 01326 280800 t.g.o.r@hotmail.co.uk www.thegreenhouse-stkeverne.co.uk

Restaurant in the lovely village of St. Keverne, seating 26 plus 8 outside in the summer. Making bread & ice cream & smoking fish at the restaurant for our weekly menu, also a specials board. No farmed fish, game when in season. Alcohol is all organic. Modern rustic cooking.

HENDRA FARM ORGANICS

 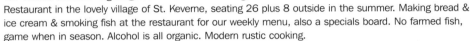

Hendra Farm, Rose, Truro, TR4 9PS

Tel: 01872 572301 Fax: 01872 572301 josymons@bushinternet.com

A wide range of vegetables grown for box scheme. Salads and leafy greens usually picked the morning of delivery. Beef available to order.

KEIGWIN FARMHOUSE

Nr. Morvah, Penzance, TR19 7TS

Tel: 01736 786425 Fax: 01736 786425 g.wyatt-smith@virgin.net www.yewtreegallery.com

Member of the Soil Association, registered with the Wholesome Food Association. Vegetarian B&B in a 300 year old farmhouse on Penwith peninsula. Organic and home grown and home-made produce; extensive gardens and beach nearby. Packs of herbs and saladings for sale.

KEVERAL FARMERS LTD

Keveral Farm, Nr. Seaton, Looe, PL13 1PA

Tel: 01503 250135 info@keveral.org www.keveral.org

Soil Association PK02W. Workers co-op run, organic veg and fruit, sold through local box scheme. Also available: apple juice and cider, preserves, Shiitake/oyster mushrooms and fruiting logs, wild magic liquid feed, organic herb plants, willow cuttings, camping.

LANSALLOS BARTON FARM

Lansallos, Looe, PL13 2PU

Tel: 01503 272293

Soil Association demonstration Farm. Cream teas and organic meat for sale in tea room. Open at Easter and June to September. Member of the Soil Association Organic Farms Network.

LESQUITE FARM

Lansallos, Looe, PL13 2QE

Tel: 01503 220315 Fax: 01503 220137 tolputt@lesquite-polperro.fsnet.co.uk

www.lesquite-polperro.fsnet.co.uk

Bed and breakfast, self-catering, organic potatoes, Aberdeen Angus vacuum-packed beef, all found on delightful secluded farm, easily accessible to all parts of Cornwall, 3 miles to the coast, between Fowey and Polperro.

LITTLE CALLESTOCK FARM

Zelah, Truro, TR4 9HB

Tel: 01872 540445 Fax: 01872 540445 liznick@littlecallestockfarm.co.uk
www.littlecallestockfarm.co.uk

Organic Farmers & Growers UKF090940. Delightful spacious barn conversions, ETC 4 and 5 stars, luxuriously equipped. Whirlpool baths, four poster beds, woodburners, on organic dairy farm with Jersey herd. Peaceful location, countryside, coastal walks. Centrally positioned. Brochure available. Organic eggs from farm gate.

MAKING WAVES VEGAN GUEST HOUSE

3 Richmond Place, St Ives, TR26 1JN

Tel: 01736 793895 simon@making-waves.co.uk www.making-waves.co.uk

Beautiful eco-renovated 19th Century house. Ocean views, peaceful, minutes from shop, beaches and harbour. Delicious food using organic ingredients. Special diets catered for. Children welcome. Voted 'Best Vegan Guest House' by *Vegan* magazine.

MEWTON, P G

Nancarrow Farm, Maranzanvose, Truro, TR4 9DQ

Tel: 01872 540343 pgmewton@talk21.com

Great beef and great lamb, organic, wholesome and delicious. Meat as it should be! Tastes just right.

THE NATURAL STORE

16 High St., Falmouth, TR11 2AB

Tel: 01326 311507 Fax: 01326 311507

A comprehensive range of organic foods, wholefoods and natural remedies including organic fruit and vegetables, organic meat. Natural foods and products of all sorts. Eco-friendly babycare and cleaning products.

THE NATURAL STORE

Trengrouse Way, Helston, TR13 8RT

Tel: 01326 564226 Fax: 01326 564226

A comprehensive range of organic foods, wholefoods and natural remedies including organic fruit and vegetables, organic meat. Natural foods and products of all sorts, including babycare and eco friendly cleaning products in our newly extended premises.

OLDS, VIVIAN LTD

2 Chapel Road, St. Just, Penzance, TR19 7HS

Tel: 01736 788520 Fax: 01736 788520 mail@vivianolds.co.uk www.vivianolds.co.uk

Soil Association P2997. Butchers with own slaughterhouse offering local and nationwide delivery of locally reared and purchased organic beef, pork and lamb including meat boxes. Why not try our special sausages?

OUGHS UNICORN GROCERS

10 Market St., Liskeard, PL14 3JJ

Tel: 01579 343253 www.oughs.co.uk

Delicatessen stocking some organic goods.

THE PAVILION

The Pavilion, Seaton, Torpoint, PL11 3JD

Tel: 01503 250732 bookings@seatonpavilion.co.uk

We are a beach bar and café offering stunning views across the bay to Looe and the Looe valley. Recently opened, we are striving to source the best Cornish organic produce and with our upstairs restaurant we are aiming for full Soil Association certification and to encourage local producers to move into organic ranges with our support.

PENHEALE ORGANICS LTD

1 Rundle Court, Station Road, Liskeard, PL14 4DA

Tel: 01579 345777 Fax: 01579 346886 rayboyd@btconnect.com www.cornishlegend.co.uk

Manufacturers of the Cornish Legend range of luxury organic ice creams: a wide and interesting range of Cornish products, all made at our creamery in Liskeard, using milk from our own organic dairy farm. Winners of the 2004 Soil Association Organic Food Awards Ice Cream section, plus Highly Commended in the same category.

PLANTS FOR A FUTURE

The Field, Higher Penpol, St. Veep, Lostwithiel, PL22 0NG

Tel: 01208 873554 www.pfaf.org

Day visits and tours, courses on woodland gardening, permaculture, nutrition, research, information, demonstration and supply of edible and otherwise useful plants. Plants for a Future is a registered charity researching and demonstrating ecologically sustainable vegan organic horticulture in the form of woodland gardening and other permacultural practices.

RIDER, J & J

East Penrest, Lezant, Launceston, PL15 9NR

Tel: 01579 370186 Fax: 01579 370477 jrider@lineone.net www.eastpenrest.freeserve.co.uk

Soil Association G1897. Organic beef and sheep farm of 120 acres with 5 star self-catering accommodation in converted barn. Children especially welcome. Beautiful countryside. Home cooked meals available. Lamb sold from the farm gate as available – please telephone first.

RIVERFORD HOME DELIVERY

6 Camelot View, Camelford, PL32 9TU

Tel: 01840 211470 sharon@riverfordhomedelivery.co.uk www.riverford.co.uk

Licensed distributor for Riverford Organic Vegetables. Organic vegetable box scheme operating in north & mid-Cornwall, varied box sizes delivered to your door. Can order online at www.riverford.co.uk.

RIVERFORD HOME DELIVERY – WEST CORNWALL

Veyn Barn, Benoak, St.Keyne, Liskeard, PL14 4RR

Tel: 01579 346134 Fax: 01579 346134 tonyandjoyce@riverfordhomedelivery.co.uk

West Cornwall's independent local licensed distributor from Riverford Organic Vegetables award-winning vegetable box scheme. Weekly home delivery to most areas of west Cornwall.

ROSEVINNICK ORGANIC FARM

Bofarnel, Lostwithiel, PL22 0LP

Tel: 01208 871122

Organic beef, pork, ham, bacon, pork sausages and hogs pudding from traditional Large Black pigs, chives, parsley and sage. Telephone first.

ROSKILLYS OF CORNWALL

Tregellast Barton Farm, St Keverne, Helston, TR12 6NX

Tel: 01326 280479 Fax: 01326 280320 Admin@roskillys.co.uk www.roskillys.co.uk

We produce organic ice creams, sorbets, yoghurt ices and fudge. All the ice creams and fudges are made on the farm using 100% natural ingredients with organic milk and cream from our own Jersey herd on our family-run organic Jersey farm on the Lizard Peninsula in Cornwall. We have three cottages available for self-catering holidays and breaks. We also have tea rooms, an ice cream parlour and shop.

ROSUICK ORGANIC FARM & CORNISH CAMELS

Rosuick Organic Farm, St. Martin, Helston, TR12 6DZ

Tel: 01326 231302 Fax: 01326 231302 oates@rosuick.co.uk www.oatesorganic.co.uk

Family-run organic farm and shop specialising in home produced beef, lamb, pork, sausages, burgers, eggs, veg and organic wool along with other local gifts. Great for a day visit to see the camels, farm and shop. Beautiful farmhouses (sleep 10/11) and cottages (sleep 6) available for holidays, all with modern facilities and access to tennis court. Also available: camel trekking with 'Cornish Camels' operating from the farm. Most of the self-catering cottages are less than 20 metres from the camel pen and are surrounded by a multitude of free range barnyard animals. See our website, and also www.cornishcamels.co.uk.

SEAWITCH COTTAGE B & B

Seawitch Cottage, Chapel Rd., Leedstown, Hayle, TR27 6BA

Tel: 01736 850917 seawitch.hearts@btinternet.com www.seawitchcottage.com

Organic B&B in West Cornwall. Close to St Ives Bay. Five miles from north and south coasts. Offers luxury guest suite for two with organic breakfasts, packed lunches and evening meals.

SOUTH PENQUITE FARM

South Penquite, Blisland, Bodmin, PL30 4LH

Tel: 01208 850491 Fax: 0870 136 7926 thefarm@bodminmoor.co.uk www.southpenquite.co.uk

Soil Association G4771. Camping and field studies on a working organic hill farm high on Bodmin Moor. Interesting farm walk including diverse wildlife habitats, a bronze age hut settlement, a mile of beautiful riverbank and an imposing standing stone. Mongolian Yurt available for that 'back to nature' holiday! Member of the Soil Association Organic Farms Network.

SOUTH TORFREY FARM LTD/ ORGANIC FARM HOLIDAYS

Gollant, Fowey, PL23 1LA

Tel: 01726 833126 Fax: 01726 832625 www.southtorfreyfarm.com

Soil Association G2019. A small family farm growing poultry for meat, Longhorn cattle and mixed arable crops. We offer peaceful breaks in our award-winning barn conversions – children and pets very welcome.

STAMPAS FARM

Treamble, Rose, Truro, TR4 9PR

Tel: 01872 572837

Soil Association GCS081/G2322. Organic market garden growing vegetables and soft fruits for sale at local country markets (Truro and Perranporth). Some produce sold through local box schemes and direct from the farm.

STEPHEN GELLY FARM

Lanivet, Bodmin, PL30 5AX

Tel: 01208 831213/832557 mhcollinge@aol.com

Organic poultry, lamb and beef.

ST. KEW HARVEST

St. Kew Services, St. Kew Highway, Bodmin, PL30 3EF

Tel: 01208 841818

Sells fruit and vegetables and home baked bread. Also stocking a range of organic produce including Carley's pickles and preserves, Helsett dairy produce, Barwick dairy produce, Origin coffee, Kittows meat (including their organic range) and organic cookies.

CORNWALL & SCILLY

SUNFLOWER WHOLEFOODS

16A Cross St., Camborne, TR14 8EX
Tel: 01209 715970
Organic wholefoods.

TREE OF LIFE ORGANICS

Scala Nij, Mithian, St Agnes, Truro, TR5 0QE
Tel: 01872 552661   treeoflife@eurobell.co.uk
Soil Association registered nos. P2068, G2068. We are a small company that is committed to the sustainable organic way of life. We can supply top quality fresh fruit and vegetables and eggs produced locally. Delivery area: Perranporth, St. Agnes, Redruth, Truro and St. Austell.

TRENBERTH, W D & B D

Trevallard Farm, Mount Hawke, Truro, TR4 8DL
Tel: 01209 890253
Soil Association G2763. Producing beef and grain.

TRETHINNICK FARM

St. Cleer, Liskeard, PL14 6RR
Tel: 01579 346868
Organic lamb and beef supplied to own local client base.

TREVALON ORGANIC VEGETABLES

Trevalon, Herodsfoot, Liskeard, PL14 4RS
Tel: 0845 3305034   marksimon@i12.com
Vegetable box delivery, farm gate sales every Saturday 10am–1pm, wholesale, group and school visits, community supported agriculture, courses and working horses.

TREVARNO ORGANIC SKINCARE

Trevarno Manor, Helston, TR13 0AB
Tel: 01326 555977   Fax: 01326 574282   enquiry@trevarno.co.uk   www.trevarno.co.uk
We produce a wide range of natural skin care products including facial cleansing, toning and moisturising. Hand care, body care and a dedicated baby care range. A full range of natural organic soaps is also available.

TREVAYLOR ORGANIC EGGS

Trevaylor, Killiow, Rea, Truro, TR3 6AG
Tel: 01872 864 949
Organic eggs.

TREVELYAN FARM

Rosudgeon, Penzance, TR20 9PP
Tel: 01736 710410
Organic seasonal vegetables, meat and other local produce.

WETHERDEN, BEN & CATHY

Downacarey Bridge, St Giles on the Heath, Launceston, PL15 9RT
Tel: 01566 775732   info@organicpullets.co.uk   www.organicpullets.co.uk
Organic pullets available all year, Black Rock, Speckeldy, Utility Light Sussex, Lohmann Tradition, Silver Link, Bluebell and Magpie, any age, any quantity. Delivery possible. Others reared to order.

WIDDICOMBE FARE

4 West St., Millbrook, Torpoint, PL10 1AA
Tel: 01752 822335 jowidd@beeb.net
Retail fruit and vegetables, wholefoods etc. including large range of organic produce.

WOODA FARM

Crackington Haven, EX23 0LF
Tel: 01840 230140 max@woodafarm.co.uk www.woodafarm.co.uk
Producer of organic lamb, eggs, apples, juice and vegetables. Self-catering cottage or catered accommodation with large barn workspace.

DEVON

ACLAND ORGANIC MEATS

East Acland Farm, Landkey, Barnstaple, EX32 0LD
Tel: 01271 830216
Soil Association M12W. Beef and lamb.

ALAN'S APPLE

26 Fore St. Kingsbridge, TQ7 1NY
Tel: 01548 852308
Traditional greengrocer stocking organic vegetables, organic dairy produce, organic ice cream.

THE ARK WHOLEFOODS SHOP

38 East St., Ashburton, TQ13 7AX
Tel: 01364 653020 the-ark@clara.co.uk
Small is beautiful: this shop is crammed full of a huge variety of lines including many organic ones. Vegetables are sourced from Heart of Devon and Woodlands Organics. Baked goods are home-made or come from a local vegetarian bakery. Organic lines are represented in most dry goods and dairy sectors too.

THE BARTON

The Barton, Poughill, Crediton, EX17 4LE
Tel: 01363 866349 a.wander@btinternet.com
Luxury on farm self-catering holiday accommodation with indoor pool.

BEE ORGANIC

56 Highweek Village, Newton Abbot, TQ12 1QQ
Tel: 07817 467936
Soil Association G6389. A small-scale operation growing a huge range of vegetables and herbs and fruit. We particularly specialise in heritage varieties to conserve genetic diversity, and grow for flavour. Alternative telephone: 07789 741339.

B NATURAL

14 The Strand, Exmouth, EX8 1AD
Tel: 01395 279144 sue.try@virgin.net
A healthfood shop in the centre of Exmouth with a strong commitment to organically grown and local produce, and environmentally friendly and ethically traded products. We stock fresh organic vegetables and fruit from Rod and Ben's farm in Kenn, mouth-watering organic breads and cakes from Otterton Mill's renowned bakery, organic cheeses, yoghurts, juices and smoothies, wholesome convenience foods such as frozen organic vegetables and delicious Devon-made ice creams, and natural body care products.

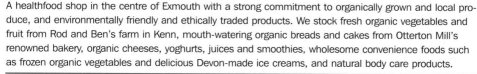

BLACKLAKE FARM

East Hill, Ottery St. Mary, EX11 1QA

Tel: 01404 812122 catherine@blacklakefarm.com www.blacklakefarm.com

The ruby red Devon cattle and Dorset sheep thrive on the old pasture of Blacklake Farm. The Gloucester old spot pigs are free-range. We sell fine quality meats from traditional breeds of cattle, sheep and pigs – all born, bred, reared and finished on the farm. The meat is butchered locally and hung for the correct times to give optimum flavour and tenderness. Shepherds Flock wool throws and scarves are made from the wool of our pedigree flock of Dorset Down sheep. The Hay House is a beautifully restored and furnished self-catering holiday house. Educational visits. Member of the Soil Association Organic Farms Network.

BOWDEN FARM

Bowden Farm, Muddiford, Barnstaple, EX31 4HR

Tel: 01271 850502 stay@bowdenfarm.com www.bowdenfarm.com

Traditional 17th century farm with sea views offering superb Bed & Breakfast. Shetland sheep and beef Shorthorn cattle, for lamb, mutton and beef with outstanding flavour. Beautiful naturally coloured woollen products and sheepskins.

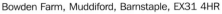

BRAMLEY WOOD & BUCKLAND FILLEIGH ORGANIC

Bramley Wood, Buckland Filleigh, Beaworthy, EX21 5JD

Tel: 01409 281693

Sustainable woodland organic enterprise deriving main income from local delivery (not a box scheme) of organic free range eggs, mushrooms, horticulture, plant raising and forest fruits. Forestry products include charcoal, logs, timber; we have a new log cabin built from our own timber. Sustainable planning permission advice, alternative energy.

CERIDWEN HERBS

Ceridwen, Old Rectory Lane, Pyworthy, EX22 6SW

Tel: 01409 254450 cdt-dlee@supanet.com

Soil Association G2255/P7995. Organic veg, fruit, herbs, plants, jams, chutneys, eggs. Part of Holsworthy Organics veg box scheme. Farmers' markets and Tavistock pannier market (Fridays).

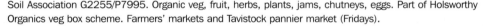

THE COURTYARD CAFÉ AND SHOP

The Square, Chagford, TQ13 8AE

Tel: 01647 432571 Fax: 01647 432985 compost@properjob.eclipse.co.uk www.properjob.ik.com

Café, wholefood and greengrocery shop. All goods are either organic, fair traded, local or all three.

DARTMOOR DIRECT CO-OPERATIVE LTD

Mitchelcombe Farm, Holne, Newton Abbot, TQ13 7SP

Tel: 01364 631528

Home delivery service: bottled water, local produce and organic foods.

DITTISHAM FARM

Capton, Dartmouth, TQ6 0JE

Tel: 01803 712452 sue@self-cater.co.uk www.self-cater.co.uk/dff

Organic beef – 'Red Ruby Devon' breed. Organic rare-breed pork 'Berkshire' breed. See our pigs at the Devon, Cornwall, Bath & West & Royal Shows – ring for confirmation. Organic hen & duck eggs. Self-catering accommodation in rural bungalow for 2 adults (+ cot).

DROUGHTWELL FARM

Sheldon, Honiton, EX14 4QW

Tel: 01404 841349 droughtwellfarm@aol.com

Organic sheep and beef. Self-catering for 2 plus a cot in one end of the farmhouse, dog welcome.

EARTHSTAR

Little East Lake Farm, East Chilla,
Beaworthy, EX21 5XF
Tel: 01409 221417 morobley549@hotmail.com
We are producers and sellers, direct to the consumer, of Soil Association symbol standard eggs, vegetables, preserves and soft fruit. Produce delivered locally. Members of Holsworthy Organics veg box scheme.

ELDER, D

Lower Chitterley Farm, Silverton, Exeter, EX5 4BP
Tel: 01392 860856 Fax: 01392 860856 darren1963landie@aol.com
Direct sales to the public of beef, lamb, poultry and eggs produced to Soil Association standards.

ENDACOTT, W A LTD

21 East St., Okehampton, EX20 1AT
Tel: 01837 52888 Fax: 01837 54381
Soil Association P4830. Wholesale and retail bakers and confectioners – organic bread and rolls.

EVERSFIELD ORGANIC

Ellacott Barton, Bratton Clovelly, Okehampton,
EX20 4LB
Tel: 01837 871400 Fax: 01837 871114 info@eversfieldmanor.co.uk www.eversfieldorganic.co.uk
Taste the Eversfield difference. Well hung, traceable organic beef, lamb and pork raised on our 850-acre estate and delivered to your door. Also wild pheasant, venison, Christmas hampers, chicken. Fully accredited butchery, hanging & packing facilities. Find us at the Tavistock Farmers' market, website or telephone 0845 6038004 or email us.

FISHLEIGH ESTATE

Fishleigh House, Okehampton, EX20 3QA
Tel: 01837 810124 Fax: 01837 810124 enquiries@fishleighestate.com www.fishleighestate.com
We sell fully traceable, well hung organic beef and lamb, and have won many prestigious conservation awards including the Bronze Otter Award. We are members of CLA, NFU and the Soil Association. Member of the Soil Association Organic Farms Network.

FORD BARTON LTD

Ford Barton, Stoodleigh, Tiverton, EX16 9PP
Tel: 01398 351139 Fax: 01398 351157 sales@fordbarton.co.uk www.fordbarton.co.uk
Soil Association G5659. Naturally dyed, organic Wensleydale wool from our own sheep, using mainly dyes from the farm. Producing an exclusive range of knitted and woven household goods and garments.

GREAT CUMMINS FARM

Tedburn St. Mary, Exeter, EX6 6BJ
Tel: 01647 61278 Fax: 01647 61278 davidgaraway@yahoo.co.uk
Soil Association G5570. Production and sale of organic vegetables, soft fruit, lamb and eggs.

GREENFIBRES

99 High St., Totnes, TQ9 5PF
Tel: 01803 868001 Fax: 01803 868002 mail@greenfibres.com www.greenfibres.com
Organic clothing, bedding, fabrics, household linen and mattresses made from organic raw materials (organic cotton, organic linen, organic wool) under fair and safe working conditions. Feel and look good while supporting organic agriculture and ethical work practices. We also stock organic cleaning products.

DEVON

THE GREEN HOUSE

2A Lower Pannier Market, Crediton, EX17 2BL

Tel: 01363 775580

Comprehensively stocked, mostly organic, wholefood shop including dried, chilled, frozen goods, fresh local fruit and veg, environmentally friendly cleaning products, Ecover refills, cosmetics, natural remedies, fair trade, gifts and cards. Friendly helpful staff.

GREENLIFE SHOP

11–13 Fore St., Totnes, TQ9 5DA

Tel: 01803 866738 Fax: 01803 866538 shop@greenlife.co.uk www.greenlife.co.uk

Although Greenlife is not entirely organic, all fresh fruit and vegetables are certified organic, plus we have a huge selection of organic foods and other products including personal care products.

GRIFFIN'S YARD

North Rd., South Molton, EX36 3AZ

Tel: 01769 572372 Fax: 01769 572372 jenny@craftsgallerygriffinsyard.co.uk

Natural and organic foods retailer, plus café and crafts gallery. Local and organic fresh produce wherever possible. Car parking.

GROWERS ORGANIC PLANT CENTRE

Milizac Close, Yealmpton, PL8 2JS

Tel: 01752 881180 joa@growersorganics.com www.growersorganics.com

Soil Association approved vegetable, herb, fruit and ornamental plants suitable for outside or inside production. Retail plant centre and mail order. Stalls at local Devon markets. Wholesale available in south Devon area. Mail order catalogue and directions available at www.growersorganics.com.

THE HEALTH FOOD STORE

Gammon Walk, Barnstaple, EX31 1DJ

Tel: 01271 345624

Organic spreads, oats, flakes, oils and much more, with a friendly information service.

HEALTHWISE

81 Fore Street, Kingsbridge, TQ7 1AB

Tel: 01548 857707

Health shop stocking organic nuts, seeds, breakfast cereals, pies, Beany burgers, dairy products, juices, soya milk and yoghurts, teas, coffee, artisan bread, body care products and Ecover household products.

HERBIE'S WHOLEFOOD VEGETARIAN RESTAURANT

15 North St., Exeter, EX4 6Q

Tel: 01392 258473

Vegetarian restaurant using organic ingredients where available and local produce in season.

HERON VALLEY CIDER AND ORGANIC JUICE

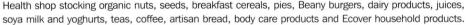

Crannacombe Farm, Hazelwood, Loddiswell, Kingsbridge, TQ7 4DX

Tel: 01548 550256 Fax: 01548 550256

National award-winning producers of organic apple based fruit juices and sparkling and traditional still organic ciders, pressed from hand-selected fruit at our farm based in stunning river Avon valley. Organic Food Awards 2004 Non Alcoholic Drinks Highly Commended.

HIGHDOWN ORGANIC FARM

Highdown Farm, Bradninch, Exeter, EX5 4LJ

Tel: 01392 881028 Fax: 01392 881272 svallis@highdownfarm.co.uk www.highdownfarm.co.uk

Soil Association G2121. We offer quality self-catering accommodation on our organic dairy farm. Peacefully situated in the heart of Devon, with breathtaking views of the surrounding countryside.

HIGHER CROP
'Pynes', Bridford, Nr. Exeter, EX6 7JA
Tel: 01647 252470

Soil Association G6688. We grow products that are unavailable in supermarkets, and maintain the availability of rare and old vegetable forms from around the world. We have started a seed bank for ourselves.

HIGHER FINGLE FARM
Higher Fingle Farm, Crockernwell, Exeter, EX6 6NP
Tel: 01647 281281 intray@higherfingle.co.uk www.higherfingle.co.uk

Organic free range ducks, chickens, geese and turkeys direct from the farm. Processed in our high welfare licensed abattoir to our unique dry plucked & hung methods. Suppliers direct to public and wholesale to a range of nationwide outlets.

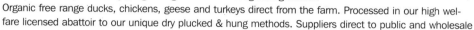

HIGHER HACKNELL
ORGANIC MEAT

 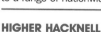

Higher Hacknell Farm, Burrington, Umberleigh, EX37 9LX
Tel: 01769 560909 Fax: 01769 560909 enquiries@higherhacknell.co.uk www.higherhacknell.co.uk
Producer and retailer of quality tasty organic meat. Our 350-acre family farm in Devon has been organic since 1988 and won numerous awards for conservation and for our produce. Nationwide weekly deliveries and local delivery, also at Exeter and Exmouth farmers' markets. Member of the Soil Association Organic Farms Network. Organic Food Awards 2004, 2006.

HIGHER SHARPHAM BARTON FARM
Coachyard Cottage, Sharpham, Ashprington, TQ9 7UT
Tel: 01803 732324

Annual on farm family camp, 1st week in August.

HIGHFIELD HARVEST
Highfield Farm, Clyst Rd., Topsham, EX3 0BY
Tel: 01392 876388 Fax: 01392 876388

Highfield Harvest organic farm shop, award-winning organic vegetables from our 118-acre family farm plus organic meat, dairy, wines, groceries. Open Tues–Sat 9–6, Sun 10–1, closed Mondays. Soil Association certified (no. S41M). Member of the Soil Association Organic Farms Network.

HILL COTTAGE & SOUTH BEER
Beer Mill Farm, Clawton, Nr. Holsworthy, EX22 6PF
Tel: 01409 253093 lgsg@supanet.com www.selfcateringcottagesdevon.co.uk

Self-catering cottages; we grow our own organic veg and eggs (not certified) and supply guests from local certified sources (veg box scheme and Providence Farm). Soil Association members as individuals.

HILLHEAD FARM
Ugborough, Ivybridge, PL21 0HQ
Tel: 01752 892674 Fax: 01752 690111 info@hillhead-farm.co.uk www.hillhead-farm.co.uk
Accommodation in comfortably appointed Victorian farmhouse with lovely views over the rolling south Devon countryside. Delicious breakfasts with organic, home baked bread and home-made preserves, local bacon and sausages.

HORWOOD ORGANICS
Horwood House, Horwood, Bideford, EX39 4PD

Tel: 01271 858231 Fax: 01271 858413 gill@horwoodhouse.co.uk www.horwoodhouse.co.uk
Beautiful Grade 2 listed Georgian house surrounded by own organic farmland with far reaching views across landscaped gardens and rolling Devon countryside. Two large bedrooms, en suite, south facing, from £35pp pn.

HURFORD, T & J

Wixon Farm, Chulmleigh, EX18 7DS
Tel: 01769 580438
Soil Association G1747. Organic Aberdeen Angus beef and chicken produced to Soil Association standards, sold from farm or from Bristol Farmers' market every Wednesday 9am–2pm, Corn Street, Bristol.

JOSHUA'S HARVEST STORE

Joshua's Harvest Store, Gosford Road, Ottery St Mary, EX11 1NU
Tel: 01404 815473 nikki@joshuasharveststore.co.uk www.joshuasharveststore.co.uk
One of England's leading specialist food stores. Voted Best Speciality Food Store in Devon in the Devon Life Awards 2004 and voted one of the Top Organic Retailers in the UK in the Vision in Organic Retailing Awards 2004. Selling fresh, premium organic and local produce as well as foods for various dietary needs, a popular range of own-made ready meals and freshly baked goods, as well as fruit & veg, general groceries, cooking ingredients, gifts and greetings cards. Also has an excellent café selling 'tasting platters' and allowing customers to sample some of the produce sold in-store.

KILWORTHY KAPERS

11 King St., Tavistock, PL19 0DS
Tel: 01822 615039
We stock a wide range of organically grown foods including dried fruit, sugar, sausage mix, tea, coffee, soya milk, soups, tinned beans, jams and spreads, oils, vinegar, stock cubes, flours, cereals, nuts, and eggs. Also supplements, herbal remedies, toiletries, cleaning products, etc.

KINGDOM, RUTH

Gibbett Moor Farm, Rackenford, Tiverton, EX16 8DJ
Tel: 01884 881457
Soil Association G2438. Small suckler herd of Devon cattle on rare Culm grassland. Their meat is well hung, of excellent flavour.

KITTOW, J D & S E

Elbury Farm, Broadclyst, Exeter, EX5 3BH
Tel: 01392 462817 Fax: 01392 462817
Soil Association G7302. Traditional Devon mixed farm farm trail and the opportunity to see how the dairy, beef, sheep and arable enterprises integrate into a sustainable farming system. Visitors by appointment, occasional open days.

LAWN ROOMS – LOWER COOMBE ROYAL

Lower Coombe Royal, Kingsbridge, TQ7 4AD
Tel: 01548 852880 paul@lowercoomberoyal.co.uk www.lowercoomberoyal.co.uk
Set in its own private valley in the heart of the South Hams, the one bedroom five star self-catering accommodation opens straight out onto the gardens and its own Italianate terrace. It has been as organically prepared as possible with the bed made from sustainable wood, a mattress made of entirely organic fibres, organic towels, linens and toiletries. An organic welcome pack is also supplied, including Paul's home-made bread. We have eight acres of organic gardens and a growing organic vegetable patch. We use non-harmful cleaning products. Plans for the near future include a fresh water swimming pool, solar and hydro power and bees to make our own honey. Silver Green Tourism Business Scheme award.

LEAFCYCLE

Coombe Farm, Cove, Tiverton, EX16 7RU
Tel: 01398 331808 Fax: 01398 331808 www.leafcycle.co.uk
Soil Association C37W. Leafu a highly nutritious vegan organic food ingredient made from leaves.
Leafcycle camps – a green space for green camps. The Occasional Café, an outdoor organic experience.

LINSCOMBE FARM ORGANIC VEGETABLES

Newbuildings, Sandford, Crediton, EX17 4PS

Tel: 01363 84291 Fax: 01363 85481 info@linscombe.co.uk www.linscombe.co.uk

Linscombe Farm run an award-winning organic vegetable box scheme and attend selected Devon farmers' markets. We aim to provide the best possible seasonal produce to local people who care about what they eat and where it comes from. All the vegetables that we supply are grown by ourselves, nothing is bought in or imported. We grow over 300 varieties of vegetables, 98% of which are grown from seed here on the farm. Conservation and wildlife are at the heart of our farm. We have been planting trees and hedges since we came here in 1996 and we have areas of rough grassland to provide habitat for small (and not so small) mammals, plants, insects and fungi. Linscombe Farm was selected by the Soil Association to be its first National Demonstration Farm for Composting and Soil Management, demonstrating best practice for the productive and safe re-use of farm wastes.

LITTLE COMFORT FARM

Little Comfort Farm, Braunton, EX33 2NJ

Tel: 01271 812414 Fax: 01271 817975 jackie.milsom@btclick.com www.littlecomfortfarm.co.uk

Soil Association G7089. Organic mixed farm of 70 acres producing Devon cattle, Lleyn x Texel sheep, poultry and pigs, farm gate and mail order sales. Self-catering holidays in four barn conversions. School visits for farm and wildlife. Coarse fishing.

LOWER TURLEY FARM

Lower Turley Farm, Cullompton, EX15 1NA

Tel: 01884 32234

Soil Association registered no. W32/W. Small farm with occasional sale of lamb. Organic fleece, carded wool and hand-made felted products (mainly hats) for sale. Traditional woodcrafts, chairs, yew longbows and trugs made to order.

LUGG SMALLHOLDING, SUE

Orswell Cottage Organic Garden, Stoke Rivers, Barnstaple, EX32 7LW

Tel: 01598 710558

Soil Association G7413; Henry Doubleday Organic Research Association. Small organic holding: sheep, goats and poultry are part of the eco system of vegetable production. Eggs from free range roaming hens and ducks. Guinea fowl, lamb, vegetables and herb plants. Barnstaple Pannier market on Fridays.

MARSHFORD ORGANIC PRODUCE

Churchill Way, Northam, Nr. Bideford, EX39 1NG

Tel: 01237 477160 enquiries@marshford.co.uk www.marshford.co.uk

Soil Association E19W, PE19W. Award-winning growers and retailers, 100% organic. Our own vegetables, salads and herbs. Other local Devon meat, poultry, eggs, dairy etc. Selection of groceries. Visit our website for the extensive list of produce available.

THE MEAT JOINT

Hillsborough House, Loxhore, Barnstaple, EX31 4SU

Tel: 01271 850335 Fax: 01271 850335 themeat.joint@care4free.net

Soil Association G4331. From our small farm in Loxhore, North Devon, we supply beef, pork, lamb, chicken, bacon, sausages and Christmas turkeys. Contact Kim Seggons for price list and delivery arrangements.

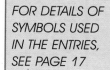

FOR DETAILS OF SYMBOLS USED IN THE ENTRIES, SEE PAGE 17

DEVON

MIDDLE CAMPSCOTT FARM

Middle Campscott Farm, Lee, Ilfracombe, EX34 8LS
Tel: 01271 864621 farm@middlecampscott.co.uk www.middlecampscott.co.uk
Soil Association G1923, P1923. We produce hard pressed ewes and goats milk cheeses using milk from
our own farm to make the cheese; wool and woollen products from our naturally coloured Shetland sheep
and the ewes of our milking flock. These include organic sheepskins, knitting wool in natural colours,
jumpers knitted to order, baby blankets, throws, craftwork cushions, and textiles for soft furnishings. We
also produce lamb, mutton and Ruby Devon beef.

MIDDLE WHITECLEAVE

Middle Whitecleave, Burrington, Umberleigh, EX37 9JN
Tel: 01769 520506 john_burns_@hotmail.com www.organicgeese.com
Farmgate and mail order sales of organic goose / geese produced from our own organic breeding flock.
Also breed and rear beef cattle and sheep.

MOORLANDS FARM SHOP

Whiddon Down, Okehampton, EX20 2QL
Tel: 01647 231666 enquiries@moorlandsfarmshop.co.uk www.moorlandsfarmshop.co.uk
Farm shop selling meat produce from the Fishleigh Estate and open Tuesday–Friday 8am–5.30pm,
Saturday 9.30am–5.30pm. National delivery.

NATURAL WAY

28 Hyde Rd., Paignton, TQ4 5BY
Tel: 01803 665529 Fax: 01803 665529 info@naturalwayhealth.co.uk www.naturalwayhealth.co.uk
Organic drinks, fruits, nuts, pulses and cereals. Range of organic herbal supplements and body care prod-
ucts. Mail order service available.

NATURE'S PLATE – ORGANIC VEGETARIAN CATERERS

8 Taddiford Rd., Exeter, EX4 4AY
Tel: 01392 413578 naturesplate@yahoo.com www.naturesplate.co.uk
Nature's Plate – organic vegetarian wholefood experience. Event and private function caterers. Locally
sourced, freshly prepared, delicious and nutritious cuisine. Soil Association, Vegetarian and Vegan Society
certified and also carbon-balanced.

NATURE'S ROUND

Dart Mills, Old Totnes Rd., Buckfastleigh, TQ11 0NF
Tel: 07810 127376 naturesround@beeb.net
Bulk fruit and vegetable enquiries. Year round home delivery; vegetables, fruit, eggs, Dartmoor water (still
& sparkling), fruit juices, tofu, wholefoods. Three sizes of vegetable boxes: can modify, or you choose from
a weekly price list. Wholesome Food Association.

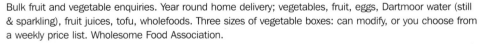

NICHOLSONS WHOLEFOOD & HEALTH SHOP LTD

12 Fore St., Kingsbridge, TQ7 1DQ
Tel: 01548 854347 Fax: 01548 854335
An Aladdin's cave packed with a vast selection of wholefoods including gluten-free and eco friendly prod-
ucts, wide choice of supplements and toiletries.

NORWEGIAN WOOD ORGANIC BED & BREAKFAST

Norwegian Wood, Berry Pomeroy, Totnes, TQ9 6LE
Tel: 01803 867462 heather@norwegianwood.eclipse.co.uk www.organicbedandbreakfast.info
Generous organic breakfasts. In-house nutritional therapist/iridologist. No microwaves, no smoking.
Ecologically sensitive household. Meat eaters, vegan, lacto-vegetarian, wheat-free or raw food catered for
with confidence. One mile from Totnes.

ORCHARD WHOLEFOODS

16 High St., Budleigh Salterton, EX9 6LQ

Tel: 01395 442508 janelong@gmx.net

We are a well-stocked health shop with an ever-growing organic section. It includes almost all vegetarian foods, except for fresh fruit and vegetables, body care, eco products.

OTTERY WHOLEFOODS

5A Mill St., Ottery St. Mary, EX11 1AB

Tel: 01404 812109 Fax: 01404 815020 ottery.wholefoods@virgin.net

We sell an extensive selection of fresh, local, organic produce: dried fruit, cereals, grains, pasta, flour, wines, beers, and ecological cleaning and sanitary products.

PALMER, MS KATE

West Yeo Farm, Witheridge, Tiverton, EX16 8PY

Tel: 01884 861269

Soil Association G7284. Historic farm with Red Devon beef, rare breed coloured sheep and arable production. Culm grassland borders the Little Dart River, featuring otters and kingfishers. Old orchard restoration.

THE PANTRY

13 Station Rd, South Brent, TQ10 9BE

Tel: 01364 73308 thepantry@btinternet.com

Local sausages & bacon (some organic), organic vegetables, bread, milk, yoghurt.

PERCY'S COUNTRY HOTEL & RESTAURANT

Coombeshead Estate, Virginstow, Nr. Okehampton, EX21 5EA

Tel: 01409 211236 Fax: 01409 211460 info@percys.co.uk www.percys.co.uk

The 2003 Organic Restaurant of the Year, and a showcase for the Westcountry's expansive larder of superlative organic produce. A tremendous amount of the menu, including a bespoke breed of lamb, vegetables, herbs and dazzling eggs, is home grown. Exmoor duck and chicken, too, set on a stunning 130-acre estate. Eight deluxe bedrooms with jacuzzis and king size beds, relaxation and rejuvenation.

PROVIDENCE FARM ORGANIC MEATS

Providence Farm, Crosspark Cross, Holsworthy, EX22 6JW

Tel: 01409 254421 Fax: 01409 254421 info@providencefarm.co.uk www.providencefarm.co.uk

Winners of Organic Food Awards 2000, 2001, 2002 and 2003. Producing quality chicken, duck, guinea fowl, goose, pork, bacon, sausages, lamb, beef and eggs. Farm shop selling whole range of local organic fare.

REAL FOOD DELI

22 Duke St., Dartmouth, TQ6 9TZ

Tel: 01803 833200

We stock organic nuts, seeds, honey, rice, bread and savouries, etc.

REAPERS

18 Bampton St., Tiverton, EX16 6AA

Tel: 01884 255310

Reapers is a wholefood health food store, featuring a wide range of organic goods, including fresh fruit and vegetables.

RICHARD'S
64 Fore St., Topsham, Exeter, EX3 0HL
Tel: 01392 873116 Fax: 01392 873116 r4richard@aol.com
Fruit and vegetables, eggs and fruit juices.

RIVERFORD FARM SHOP
Riverford, Staverton, Totnes, TQ9 6AF
Tel: 01803 762523 Fax: 01803 762571 office@riverfordfarmshop.co.uk www.riverfordfarmshop.co.uk
Organic and locally produced beef, lamb, chicken, pork, free range eggs, cheese, wine, bread and pies,
dry goods and Riverford Organic Milk.

RIVERFORD FARM SHOP AT KITLEY
Kitley, Yealmpton, Plymouth, PL8 2LT
Tel: 01752 880925 Fax: 01752 880263 office@riverfordfarmshop.co.uk www.riverford.co.uk
Soil Association registered farm shop and café offering a wide range of organic food (vegetables, meat,
dairy, wine, dry goods and plant seeds etc.). Emphasis on quality food from local producers.

RIVERFORD FARM SHOP TOTNES
High St., Totnes, TQ9 5RY
Tel: 01803 863959 Fax: 01803 868380 office@riverford.co.uk www.riverfordfarmshop.co.uk
Carrying an excellent selection of meat, poultry, dairy, fruit, vegetables and delicatessen you can be
always sure of finding something for supper (and the perfect bottle of wine to go with it)! If the shop
doesn't have something you want, we can order it for you.

RIVERFORD HOME DELIVERY – EXETER & EAST DEVON
Tel: 01803 865015 jonripley@riverfordhomedelivery.co.uk www.riverford.co.uk
Independent local licensed distributor from Riverford Organic Vegetables.

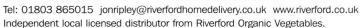

RIVERFORD ORGANIC VEGETABLES
Wash Barn, Buckfastleigh, TQ11 0LD
Tel: 01803 762720 boxscheme@riverford.co.uk www.riverford.co.uk
Soil Association W24W. Award-winning organic vegetable box scheme, delivering to houses from the tip of
Cornwall right up to Kent, throughout London and south Wales. One of the founding members of the
South Devon Organic Producers, a producer group of 13 family-run farms who grow 85 different varieties
for the box scheme, making Riverford one of the largest producers of organic vegetables in the UK.
Member of the Soil Association Organic Farms Network. Organic Food Awards 2004 Commended Box
Scheme; Fresh Fruit and Veg Highly Commended.

ROBERT OWEN COMMUNITIES
Lower Sharpham Barton Farm, Ashprington, Totnes, TQ9 7DX
Tel: 01803 732502 Fax: 01803 732502 sharphamfarm@roc-uk.org
Day centre for people with learning disabilities. Dairy, beef, sheep, laying birds and vegetables. Produce
milk, meats, eggs and veg.

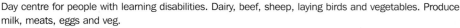

ROBERTSON'S ORGANIC CAFÉ
8 Pepper St., Tavistock, PL19 0BD
Tel: 01822 612117 robertsonshumblepie@yahoo.co.uk
We have just opened and are in the process of applying for Soil Association certification. Everything we
serve is organic, right down to the salt and pepper. We serve organic and vegetarian sandwiches, salads,
juices and smoothies, all made fresh to order. Our spicy mexican wrap is the talk of the town, or try a
Godminster cheddar and caramelised onion tart, salads, ciabattas filled with roasted vegetables and of
course a huge range of delicious cakes from Izzy's organic bakery. Organic and fair trade teas and coffees,
amazing fresh juices and smoothies, a real paradise for people who just like good food. Set in the beautiful
town of Tavistock, on the western edge of Dartmoor. Open Mon–Sat, 8.30 am–5.00 pm.

RODANDBENS

Bickham Farm, Kenn,
Exeter, EX6 7XL

Tel: 01392 833833 Fax: 01392 833832 rod@rodandbens.com www.rodandbens.com

Mixed farm supplying vegetables locally and nationwide using mail order. Highly commended Organic Food Awards 2002 and 2003. Rick Stein's food superheroes. Organic Food Awards 2004, 2006.

ROSE COTTAGE ORGANICS

Rumleigh, Bere Alston, PL20 7HN

Tel: 01822 840297 pmayston@fish.co.uk

Soil Association G5300. Seasonal vegetables, apples, soft fruit and herbs, grown in Tamar Valley. Produce sold via local farmers' markets.

SACKS

80 High St., Totnes, TQ9 5SN

Tel: 01803 863263

Soil Association R1907. We sell a comprehensive range of organic vegetarian food. A wide range of fresh organic fruit and vegetables always in stock.

SEASONS

8 Well St., Exeter, EX4 6QR

Tel: 01392 201282

Organic vegetables, grains, beans, pulses, dried fruit and natural groceries.

SEEDS BAKERY & HEALTH STORE

35 High St., Totnes, TQ9 5NP

Tel: 01803 862526

Bakery baking organic bread and non-organic cakes and savouries.

SEEDS BAKERY & HEALTH STORE

19 High St., Exmouth, EX8

Tel: 01395 265741 Fax: Contact: Sue & John Aylwin

Bakery baking organic bread and non-organic cakes and savouries.

SHARPHAM PARTNERSHIP LTD

Sharpham Estate, Ashprington,
Totnes, TQ9 7UT

Tel: 01803 732203 Fax: 01803 732122 info@sharpham.com www.sharpham.com

Soil Association G2483. A 200-acre tenancy on a 500-acre estate that is almost all organic (and biody-namic). Producing organic milk, organic cheeses. Non-organic estate grown and bottled wines. Visit our website for details of tours and of opening times.

SHILLINGFORD ORGANICS

The Barns, Barton Lane, Shillingford Abbot, Exeter, EX2 9QQ

Tel: 01392 832729 Fax: 01392 832729 info@shillingfordorganics.co.uk
www.shillingfordorganics.co.uk

Family-run farm producing fresh organic vegetables, herbs and eggs for box deliveries to Teign Valley and Exeter area. We have developed fresh salad products and ready made meals. We pride ourselves on pro-ducing top quality boxes with plenty of variety and unbeatable freshness.

SMALE, P M & M E

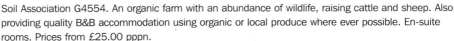

The Barton, Burrington, Umberleigh, EX37 9JQ

Tel: 01769 520216 bartonfarm@yahoo.com www.burrington-barton.co.uk

Soil Association G4554. An organic farm with an abundance of wildlife, raising cattle and sheep. Also providing quality B&B accommodation using organic or local produce where ever possible. En-suite rooms. Prices from £25.00 pppn.

TAMAR ORGANICS

Woodlands Estate, Gulworthy, Tavistock, PL19 8DE

Tel: 01822 834887 Fax: 01822 834284 sales@tamarorganics.co.uk www.tamarorganics.co.uk

Soil Association G1823, P1823. Seed and organic mail order company specialising in organic seeds for gardeners and growers. Organic garden centre, seeds, plants and soft fruit, open Monday–Friday 9.30am–5pm, Saturday 10.30am–3pm; Closed Sundays and Bank Holidays.

TOMS, R & M

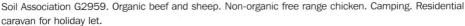

Parkhill Farm, Shirwell, Barnstaple, EX31 4JN

Tel: 01271 850323 Fax: 01271 850323

Soil Association G2959. Organic beef and sheep. Non-organic free range chicken. Camping. Residential caravan for holiday let.

EDWIN TUCKER & SONS LTD

Brewery Meadow, Stonepark, Ashburton, Newton Abbot, TQ13 7DG

Tel: 01364 652233 Fax: 01364 654211 seeds@edwintucker.com www.edwintuckers.com

Mail order and retail shop selling seeds, organic seeds and potatoes. We have retail outlets which carry stocks of feed, saddlery, gardening equipment and agricultural fertilisers. Our mail order department sells seeds, organic seeds and potatoes, including some unusual varieties.

URSELL, D J & S J

Aller Farm, Dolton, Winkleigh, EX19 8PP

Tel: 01805 804414 Fax: 01805 804737 ursell@farmersweekly.net

Soil Association G791. We supply traditional beef which has hung for four weeks. Also supply lupins and cereals, all organic.

WARD, G R & R J

Parsonage Farm, Iddesleigh, Winkleigh, EX19 8SN

Tel: 01837 810318

Soil Association G6241. Organic dairy.

WELL HUNG MEAT CO

Tordean Farm, Dean Prior, Buckfastleigh, TQ11 0LY

Tel: 0845 230 3131 sales@wellhungmeat.com www.wellhungmeat.com

Soil Association Organic Food Awards Winners (2001, 2002, 2004, 2006) and Rick Stein 'Food Hero', We deliver the very best organic meat to your door. Our range includes organic lamb, beef, poultry and pork, and turkeys for Christmas. All of our meat is hung in the traditional manner; this makes it taste 'how meat used to taste'. The meat has a succulence and tenderness that is second to none – something for you, your family and friends to enjoy. Orders can be placed via the website or by email or phone. We will be very happy to help.

FOR DETAILS OF SYMBOLS USED IN THE ENTRIES, SEE PAGE 17

WEST CHILLA FARM

West Chilla, Beaworthy, EX21 5XQ

Tel: 01409 221256 ramsay@westchilla.fsnet.co.uk www.westchillafarm.co.uk

Soil Association G5225. We are a small beef and sheep enterprise with Devon cattle and Poll Dorset sheep. We run a self-catering holiday cottage that sleeps 5. The farm is abundant with wildlife.

WEST FORDE ORGANICS

The Barton, Poughill, Crediton, EX17 4LE

Tel: 01363 866349 westfordeorganics@btopenworld.com

Direct sales of top quality home produced organic lamb.

WEST HILL FARM

West Hill Farm, West Down, Ilfracombe, EX34 8NF

Tel: 01271 815477 Fax: 01271 813316 info@westhillfarm.org www.westhillfarm.org

Our dairy herd graze organic pastures in sight of the sea and have views for 50 miles. Their milk is processed in our modern dairy into a wide range of products, and distributed within 25 mile radius in our chiller vans. We welcome school visits and are a demonstration farm for the Soil Association. Our farm shop is open 24 hours, 7 days a week. Member of the Soil Association Organic Farms Network.

WEST ILKERTON FARM

West Ilkerton Farm, Lynton, EX35 6QA

Tel: 01598 752310 Fax: 01598 752310 eveleigh@westilkerton.co.uk www.westilkerton.co.uk

Hill livestock farm: store and breeding stock for sale at certain times of the year. Organic Devon cattle and Exmoor Horn and Exmoor Horn x sheep (breeding stock and young stock) will be for sale in autumn. See www.westilkerton.co.uk. Self-catering holiday cottage, ETC 4 star, to let. Horse drawn tours over Exmoor using Shire horses.

WEST LAKE FARM

Chilla, Beaworthy, EX21 5XF

Tel: 01409 221991 Fax: 01409 221991 westlakefarm@lineone.net

We press and produce a range of award-winning organic single variety and blended apple juices, slowly fermented ciders, cider vinegar and organic fruit vinegars. Hand crafted from west country apples.

WILLOW VEGETARIAN GARDEN RESTAURANT

87 High St., Totnes, TQ9 5PB

Tel: 01803 862605

Tasty vegetarian and vegan meals hand-prepared using masses of organic ingredients. Drinks are all organic. Prices are very reasonable. Sunny secluded walled garden. Special nights every week. Children welcome.

WOODLAND ORGANICS

Moorfoot Cross, Woodland, Nr. Denbury, Newton Abbot, TQ12 6EQ

Tel: 01803 813760

Wholesome Food Association member. 7-acre holding ethically producing over 80 varieties of fruit and vegetables plus free range eggs. Operating direct delivery veg boxes plus supplying trade locally.

YARNER

Bovey Tracey, TQ13 9LN

Tel: 01364 661503 Fax: 01364 661504 mail@yarner.com

Soil Association G7555. Organic farm and function venue. High quality bulk spring water supplied to Yeo Valley as an ingredient for Rocombe Farm and Marks & Spencer organic sorbet product ranges.

SOMERSET

ALHAM WOOD CHEESES

Higher Alham Farm, West Cranmore, Shepton Mallet, BA4 6DD
Tel: 01749 880221 www.buffalo-organics.co.uk
Organic cheeses and dairy produce from our own herds of organic buffalo and cow. A variety of soft and hard buffalo cheese made with buffalo milk from our own organic herd, also buffalo meat and beef from same organic herds and buffalo yoghurt in glass jars (so not by mail order).

ALVIS BROS LTD

Lye Cross Farm, Redhill, Bristol, BS40 5RH
Tel: 01934 864600 Fax: 01934 862213 enquiries@lyecrosscheese.co.uk www.lyecrosscheese.co.uk
Soil Association P1542. Organic farmhouse cheesemaker/packer of the renowned Lye Cross Farm brand. Full range of organic cheddars, UK territorials and cheese powder. All suitable for vegetarians. Nationwide distribution and farm shop.

ARCADIA ORGANICS

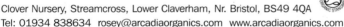

Clover Nursery, Streamcross, Lower Claverham, Nr. Bristol, BS49 4QA
Tel: 01934 838634 rosey@arcadiaorganics.com www.arcadiaorganics.com
Soil Association Symbol holder nos. G1866 and P1866. 20-acre organic market garden producing vegetables for our local box scheme delivering in north Somerset.

AVALON VINEYARD

The Drove, East Pennard,
Shepton Mallet, BA4 6UA
Tel: 01749 860393 pennardorganicwines@mail.com www.pennardorganicwines.co.uk
Soil Association P/T15W. With our organically grown grapes and other fruits we make table wine and a range of different fruit wines and liqueurs. We make mead from organic honey, also traditional Somerset cider and our own apple juice.

BARLEY WOOD WALLED GARDEN

Long Lane, Wrington, BS40 5SA
Tel: 0117 935 1725 Fax: 0117 941 4520 admin@betterfood.co.uk www.walledgarden.co.uk
Restored Victorian kitchen garden open to the public, weekly box scheme using seasonal produce from the garden. The produce is sold in the Better Food Company in Bristol, and also direct to the public, other shops and restaurants. A wonderful piece of our heritage for all to enjoy, set on a gentle southern slope overlooking the Mendips. Ideal for a family visit – learn about the garden's history, buy the plants and produce and visit the tearooms and craft workshops.

BATH ORGANIC COMMUNITY GARDEN

c/o 28 Ashley Avenue, Bath, BA1 3DS
Tel: 01225 312116 tim@bathorganicgroup.org.uk
Community garden on inner city allotment site providing training, employment and volunteering opportunities for the local community. Courses and workshops. Open days. Plant sales. Open every Saturday 10am–1pm.

BATH ORGANIC FARMS

6 Brookside House, Weston, Bath, BA
Tel: 01225 421507 www.bathorganicfarms.co.uk
Soil Association R7796. Supply from our own farms. Beef, lamb, pork, poultry and milk, cheese, eggs, fresh vegetables from local organic producers. Restaurant/café. Organic Food Awards 2004 Fresh Meat Highly Commended.

BATH SOFT CHEESE/PARK FARM B&B

Park Farm, Kelston, Bath, BA1 9AG

Tel: 01225 331601 Fax: 01225 331906 bathsoftcheese@hotmail.com www.parkfarm.co.uk

Soil Association G6169. Handmade soft and blue cheese made from our own milk, also Wyfe of Bath hard cheese. Mail order available, B&B in charming farmhouse.

BORN

134 Walcot St., St. Swithins Yard, Bath, BA1 5BG

Tel: 01225 311212 Fax: 01225 334434 info@borndirect.com www.borndirect.com

Retail and internet shop specialising in organic, natural and practical products for parents and their babies. We're the experts on washable cotton nappies! Organic range includes organic cotton and wool babywear (underwear, nightwear, outerwear and bedding), organic herbal teas for pregnancy and afterwards, toiletries made with organic ingredients (Weleda, Green People, Urtekram), organic massage oils. We are open Monday–Saturday 9.30–5.30.

BRIDIE'S HEALTHY LIVING CENTRE
AND ORGANIC FOOD CO-OP

Unit 1A, Northover Buildings, Beckery Old Rd, Glastonbury, BA6 9NU

Tel: 01458 830577 simonganz@hotmail.com

We are practising and promoting all forms of healthy sustainable living, recognising raw organic food as being vital to sustain ourselves and our environment.

BROWN COW ORGANICS

Perridge Farm, Pilton, Shepton Mallet, BA4 4EW

Tel: 01749 890298 enquiries@browncoworganics.co.uk www.browncoworganics.co.uk

Soil Association G2130, P6108. Award-winning beef (Organic Food Awards 2001, 2002, 2003) pork, poultry vegetables, ready prepared meals and dairy products delivered to your door. As featured on Rick Stein's Food Heroes and BBC Radio 4's The Food Programme. Member of the Soil Association Organic Farms Network. Organic Food Awards 2004, 2006.

BRYMORE SCHOOL FARM TRUST

Brymore School, Cannington, Bridgwater, TA5 2NB

Tel: 01278 652428 Fax: 01278 653244

We are a secondary school of agriculture, horticulture and engineering with a mixed farm enterprise. We sell beef and table birds through farmers' markets and pork, lamb and free range eggs privately.

BURDGE, J C

Fenswood Farm, Says Lane, Langford, Nr. Bristol, BS40 5DZ

Tel: 01934 852639

Soil Association G4489. We are producers of organic beef and lamb using traditional breeds, i.e. Devon x cattle, Hampshire Down sheep. Organic meat delivered locally at reasonable prices.

CASTLE FARM

Midford, Bath, BA2 7BU

Tel: 01225 344420 Fax: 01225 344420 markvedwards@blueyonder.co.uk

Established organic growers and producers. Organic beef, herbs, fruit and vegetables. Farm gate sales and local box delivery service.

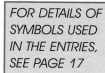
FOR DETAILS OF SYMBOLS USED IN THE ENTRIES, SEE PAGE 17

SOMERSET

CERES NATURAL FOODS LTD

9-11 Princes Street, Yeovil, BA20 1EN
Tel: 01935 428791 Fax: 01935 426862 info@ceresfoods.com www.ceresfoods.com

Trading since 1977; now operating from a large, dynamic, modern, light & airy shop with a retail floor area approaching 1500 sq ft. We are lacto-vegetarians and so do not sell meat or fish products but are happy to supply foods from vegan through to those containing eggs, honey and dairy products. We are an organic shop with expanding own label organic and natural food ranges packed fresh in-house. Our food ranges include organic, gluten-free, dairy-free, sugar-free, ethnic, local produce and special diet needs. Non-food ranges include supplements, herbals, homeopathics, aromatherapy, magnatherapy, flower remedies, ecological cleaning products, books: self-help, cookery, natural medicine, diet and fitness, hardware and more. We operate a recycling policy, our own-label supplements bottles attract a refund on their return, cardboard is separated and collected for recycling on a weekly basis; supplier filler packaging is kept and re-used for fulfilling mail and internet orders.

COBBS WHOLEFOODS

No. 7, Brunel Precinct, Somerton, TA11 7PY
Tel: 01458 274066

Cobbs specialise in stocking locally sourced organic produce including fruit, veg and local organic free range eggs; organic specialist breads and gluten-free foods available daily. We also stock all organic wholefoods.

COUNTRY HARVEST

8 St. James Courtyard, Taunton, TA1 1JR
Tel: 01823 252843

Wholefoods, organic and gluten-free foods. Supplements, herbal and homoepathic remedies, pick-up point for box schemes, qualified staff. Local deliveries to post code areas TA1, TA2, TA3, TA4, TA6.

COURT FARM

14 Chapel Lane, Winford, Bristol, BS18 8EU
Tel: 01275 472335

Biodynamic farm for 30 years – products from our own milk production. Natural and fruit yoghurt, unpasteurised milk, double cream, free range pork and beef. Local deliveries into Bristol. Organic Food Awards 2004 Yoghurt Commended.

DAISY AND CO

Tree Tops Farm, North
Brewham, Bruton, BA10 0JS
Tel: 01749 850254 Fax: 01749 850815 sales@daisyandco.co.uk www.daisyandco.co.uk

Dairy farm (Jersey cows). Cheese makers – wholesale/retail via internet/farmers' markets/farm gate. Soft 'Camembert'-style cheese: plain, covered in crushed peppercorns, or oak smoked. Hard cheese.

DEMUTHS VEGETARIAN RESTAURANT

2 North Parade Passage, Bath, BA1 1NX
Tel: 01225 446059 us@demuths.co.uk www.demuths.co.uk

Demuths' food is exciting 'world' food with lots of choice for vegans and those on wheat-free diets. We source as many local vegetables as possible and all our wines, beers, coffees are 100% organic. Our Green world cookbook is available to buy from the restaurant.

EDCOMBE FARM

Rodney Stoke, Cheddar, BS27 3UP
Tel: 01749 870073

Grow a variety of mixed vegetables sold mainly through Bristol Farmers' Market. Organic lamb in season, September to May, please phone for details.

THE FINE CHEESE CO

29 & 31 Walcot St., Bath, BA1 5BN

Tel: 01225 483407 am@finecheese.co.uk www.finecheese.co.uk

The Fine Cheese Co are artisan cheese selectors and maturers based in Bath. We list around 100 British cheeses, many from our SW region. We have both a retail and an internet shop and we also supply hotels, restaurants and other shops. Our dedicated range of crackers for cheese and cheese accompaniments are best sellers in 650 delicatessens in this country and throughout the world.

FLAXDRAYTON FARM

2 Broomhill Lane, Lopen, South Petherton, TA13 5LA

Tel: 01460 241427 Fax: 01460 241427 peter@flaxdrayton.fsnet.co.uk www.somersetorganiclink.co.uk

Organic vegetable grower marketing all produce through Somerset Organic Link, a co-operative formed by organic growers in south Somerset.

GALINGALE

3 Victoria Gardens, Henstridge, BA8 0RE

Tel: 01963 362702 galingaleorganic@tiscali.co.uk

Soil Association G4112. Vegetables, fruit, herbs: 2 acres with polytunnels, raised beds and small orchard. On-farm stall for sales of produce; please ring for availability.

THE GOOD EARTH

4 Priory Rd., Wells, BA5 1SY

Tel: 01749 678600

We have a wholefood shop and restaurant established over 25 years ago. Organic products account for a substantial amount of our business today. We have over 1,000 natural and organic products on sale from a combination of local suppliers and wholesalers.

GREENS OF GLASTONBURY

Newton Farm, Redlake Dairy, Page Lane, West Pennard, Nr. Glastonbury, BA6 8NN

Tel: 01458 834414 Fax: 01458 835072 greensofglastonbury@ukonline.co.uk

Soil Association P5176, Organic Farmers & Growers UKF040548. Family business since 1920 making hand-made cylindrical cloth bound farmhouse Cheddar and Double Gloucester cheese, available as whole round or in quarters.

HARDWICK BROTHERS

Cobbs Cross Farm, Goathurst, Bridgwater, TA5 2DN

Tel: 01278 671359 Fax: 01278 671359

We produce organic beef, lamb, poultry, potatoes and run a mountain board centre and we run a three-bedroom holiday cottage. Day visits – educational and activity.

HARVEST NATURAL FOODS

37 Walcot St., Bath, BA1 5BN

Tel: 01225 465519 Fax: 01225 401143 shop@harvest-bath.co.uk www.harvest-bath.co.uk

We are a GMO-free store selling a wide range of organic produce: wine and champagne, grains and mueslis, veg (all kinds), dried fruits (all kinds), yoghurt, milk, soya milk, tofu, tea, gluten-free, herbs, cleaning products, toiletries, supplements, etc. We also have a delicatessen selling fresh vegetarian and vegan produce.

SOMERSET

HIGHER RISCOMBE FARM

Higher Riscombe Farm, Exford, Nr. Minehead, TA24 7JY

Tel: 01643 831184

Soil Association G4852. Organic farm bed and breakfast in the heart of Exmoor National Park. Spacious rooms, home cooking, panoramic views. Specialist producers of organic Christmas geese, ducks and lamb. Mail order available.

HIGH STREET ORGANICS

57A High St., Bruton, BA10 0AW

Tel: 01749 813191 Fax: 01749 813191

Small friendly shop offers full range of organic foods including fresh fruit and vegetables, frozen, chilled and dry goods, also eco cleaning products and toiletries.

HINDON ORGANIC FARM

Hindon Organic Farm, Nr Minehead, Exmoor, TA24 8SH

Tel: 01643 705244 Fax: 01643 705244 info@hindonfarm.co.uk www.hindonfarm.co.uk

Soil Association G2707, P6655. Winners of The Organic Producer of the Year Award 2003/4. Organic Exmoor hill farm meat produce, accommodation and farm shop. Only off own farm: quality traditionally hung Aberdeen Angus beef, hill lamb, Gloucester Old Spot pork, dry cured bacon, home cured ham and real sausages. B&B – s/c cottage (English Tourism Council 4 star); luxury organic breakfasts. Member of the Soil Association Organic Farms Network. Organic Food Awards 2004 Fresh Meat Commended.

HUNTSTILE ORGANIC FARM

Goathurst, Bridgwater, TA5 2DQ

Tel: 01278 662358 Fax: 01278 662358

lizzie@huntstileorganicfarm.co.uk www.huntstileorganicfarm.co.uk

A warm welcome awaits you at Huntstile, our working organic vegetable farm set in the foothills of the Quantocks between Bridgwater and Taunton, offering B&B, camping and self-catering accommodation for holidays, workshops, farm shop, organic catering. Mobile: 07725 278280.

THE LARDER

22 West Street, Wiveliscombe, Taunton, TA4 2JP

Tel: 01984 623236 Fax: 01984 623287 larderltd@tiscali.co.uk

We are a special food shop selling a range of organic products including vegetables, dairy products, beans, pulses, grains, jams, marmalades, pastas, beverages, pet food, Ecover range and more.

LONDON ROAD FOOD CO-OP

Riverside Community Centre, York Place, London Road, Bath, BA1 6AE

Tel: 07837 784715

We provide our members with foods from local organic and fair trade sources at the lowest possible prices, including wholefoods, locally produced veg boxes and bread. Annual membership costs £1–£10 on a sliding scale.

LYNG COURT ORGANIC MEAT
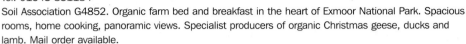

Lyng Court, West Lyng, Taunton, TA3 5AP

Tel: 01823 490510

Quality beef and lamb grazed on the Somerset Levels. Farm gate sales and local delivery. Beef in 10kg mixed packs of joints, steaks etc., lamb jointed and packed to order.

MAGDALEN FARM

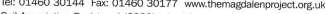

Magdalen Farm, Winsham, Chard, TA20 4PA
Tel: 01460 30144 Fax: 01460 30177 www.themagdalenproject.org.uk
Soil Association Registered (G932) mixed farm, beef sucklers, pigs, field veg, polytunnels, and cereals, selling vegetables and meat via box scheme and farm gate sales. Residential education centre. Member of the Soil Association Organic Farms Network.

MERRICKS ORGANIC FARM

Park Lane, Langport, TA10 0NF
Tel: 01458 252901 Fax: 01458 252901
simon@merricksorganicfarm.co.uk www.merricksorganicfarm.co.uk
22-acre market garden supplying farm-run box scheme with vegetables and fruit. Also organic pork, poultry and eggs. Two holiday cottages on farm.

NEAL'S YARD REMEDIES

7 Northumberland Place, Bath, BA1 5AR
Tel: 01225 466944 mail@nealsyardremedies.com www.nealsyardremedies.com
Neal's Yard Remedies manufactures and retails natural cosmetics in addition to stocking an extensive range of herbs, essential oils, homeopathic remedies and reference material.

NORWOOD FARM

Bath Road, Norton St
Philip, Nr. Bath, BA2 7LP
Tel: 01373 834856 Fax: 01373 834765 catemack.norwood@tiscali.co.uk www.norwoodfarm.co.uk
Soil Association G814. Organic mixed farm, with rare and native breeds. Open to visitors mid-March to mid-September. Every day. Farm shop with organic meat and local produce open all year. Fair Trade groceries. Member of the Soil Association Organic Farms Network.

ORGANICA

Tweentown Corner, Cheddar, BS27 3JF
Tel: 01934 741644 cheddarorganica@aol.com www.cheddarorganica.com
Organica is a retail outlet for huge range of organic foods, fruit and vegetables from mainly local suppliers. A range of supplements, boxes and gifts are also available. Specialist wholefoods available to order.

THE ORGANIC SHOP

20 Market St., Crewkerne, TA18 7LA
Tel: 01460 74447 Fax: 01460 74447
We only sell organic produce: everything from fresh veg, meat, groceries, toiletries, baby products, dairy, yoghurt, eggs, Ecover cleaning products, body care, baby clothes, nappies, frozen and chilled foods, tofu, pesto, a complete range of organic foods and environmentally friendly products. The shop has been completely refitted with environmentally friendly fittings including organic paints, FSC timber, and a porcelain tiled floor, and we only use environmentally friendly products in the shop including recycled paper till rolls and bags from the Soil Association. If we haven't got it in stock, we will do our best to obtain it for you.

PITNEY FARM SHOP

Glebe Farm, Pitney, Langport, TA
Tel: 01458 253002 Fax: 01458 253002 info@pitneyfarmshop.co.uk www.pitneyfarmshop.co.uk
Soil Association G4130. Mixed organic farm producing organic eggs, lamb, beef, pork, bacon and a range of organic sausages, also interesting seasonal vegetables. Mostly direct sales through our farm shop or local outlets.

SOMERSET

PLOWRIGHT ORGANIC PRODUCE

Stowey Rocks Farm, Over Stowey, Bridgwater, TA5 1JB
Tel: 01278 734580 rplowright@tinyonline.co.uk www.plowrightorganicproduce.co.uk
Plowright Organic Produce is a small farm business near Bridgwater in Somerset. POP grows a wide range of organic vegetables, soft fruit and herbs. POP has a local organic veg box scheme of home grown, seasonal produce and also supplies wholesale vegetables and soft fruit. The box scheme was runner-up in the Organic Food Awards 2004.

PROCKTERS FARM SHOP

Prockters Farm, West Monkton,
Taunton, TA2 8QN
Tel: 01823 413427 Fax: 01823 413390
Farm shop in old stone buildings on working mixed organic farm. Full range of own organic beef, lamb and veg. Wide range of local cheeses, wine, bread, etc.

PROVENDER DELICATESSEN

3 Market Square, South Petherton, TA13 5BT
Tel: 01460 240681 Fax: 08701 694835 www.provender.net
Licensed delicatessen with large organic selection of groceries, cheeses, dairy, ice cream and juices.

RIVERFORD HOME DELIVERY – SOMERSET EAST

12 Millers Way, Taunton, TA4 3NP
Tel: 01823 433883 Fax: 01823 431783 patrick@riverfordhomedelivery.co.uk www.riverford.co.uk
Award-winning organic vegetable box scheme operating in east Somerset. Box sizes to suit all households from a single person to a large family. A selection of fruit, dairy products, wine, juices and chocolate are also available. Order weekly, fortnightly or whenever you like. Can order and pay online at www.riverford.co.uk or by phone: 0845 600 2311. BBC Radio 4 Farmer of the Year 2005.

RIVERFORD ORGANIC VEGETABLES – NORTH SOMERSET & BATH

46 Wimblestone Road, Winscombe, BS25 1JP
Tel: 01934 844918 Fax: 01934 844918 gilbertandliz@riverfordhomedelivery.co.uk www.riverford.co.uk
Award-winning organic vegetable box scheme operating in north Somerset, Bath, Chippenham, Warminster and surrounding areas. Box sizes to suit all households from a single person to a large family. A selection of fruit, dairy products, wine, juices and chocolate are also available. Order weekly, fortnightly or whenever you like. Can order and pay online at www.riverford.co.uk or by phone: 0845 600 2311. BBC Radio 4 Farmer of the Year 2005.

ROOTS FABULOUS WEST COUNTRY FOOD

7a Bath Place, Taunton, TA1 4ER
Tel: 01823 337233 tauntonroots@aol.com
A deli food shop sourcing only from the west country (Somerset, Dorset, Devon and Cornwall). Stocking organic products where possible ranging from preserves, cheese, pastry, soft drinks, coffee and tea. Also stocking only local organic vegetables.

SEASONS WHOLEFOODS

10 George Street, Bath, BA1 2EH
Tel: 01225 469730
Take-away salads, savouries, soups etc. A large range of organic products available in the shop.

SHINER'S HERBS

The Walled Garden, Newton-St-Loe, Bath, BA2 9BU
Tel: 01225 874794 sue_shiner@yahoo.co.uk
Set in a beautiful walled garden and orchard, Shiner's is a new nursery on the edge of Bath, growing a large range of potted organic herbs and flowers; fresh-cut culinary herbs; herbal products & gifts from our shop. Visitors are welcome to enjoy the garden & orchard. Open Wed–Sun 1–5pm. Office: 01225 874794. Garden: 07968 019204.

SOMERSET LOCAL FOOD DIRECT

Unit 1, Thomas Way, Glastonbury, BA6 9LU
Tel: 01458 830801 Fax: 01458 830811 orders@sfmdirect.co.uk www.localfooddirect.co.uk
A delivery service for much of Somerset, Bristol and Bath delivering local farmers' market produce. We endeavour always to have an organic option.

SOMERSET ORGANIC LINK

The Cider Press Room, Flaxdrayton Farm, Drayton,
South Petherton, TA13 5LR
Tel: 01460 241427 Fax: 01460 241427
christina@somersetorganiclink.co.uk www.somersetorganiclink.co.uk
Fruit and vegetable boxes, *à la carte* supply to your home via Somerset Local Food Direct. A co-operative of organic farmers in Somerset, SOL supplies fresh organic produce to outlets in Somerset and beyond. SOL buys produce from outside the county and from European partners, when necessary, to meet demand. Sales and marketing service for organic vegetable producers in Somerset, forum for crop planning, opportunities to share labour and equipment. Mobile: 07881 865709.

SOMERSET ORGANICS

Gilcombe Farm Shop, Gilcombe Farm, Bruton, BA10 0QE
Tel: 01749 813710 info@somersetorganics.co.uk www.somersetorganics.co.uk
Mail order organic meat, farm shop, local and London farmers' markets, farmhouse accommodation, e-commerce business of the year 2000. 300-acre organic farm.

SPENCERS GROCERY STORE

4 Tucker Street, Wells, BA5 2DZ
Tel: 01749 672357 shop@spencersofwells.co.uk www.spencersofwells.co.uk
Traditional family grocery store. Free local delivery. Personal counter service. Local baked organic bread, cakes. Organic fruit juices, organic sugar. Local: cheeses, cooked hams, honey, pickles. Brand name goods.

SPRING GROVE MARKET GARDEN

Spring Grove, Milverton, TA4 1NW
Tel: 07956 429531
Box scheme delivering in Milverton, Wiveliscombe and Wellington.

STONEAGE ORGANICS

Stoneage Farm, Cothelstone, Taunton, TA4 3ED
Tel: 01823 432488 Fax: 01823 432488
keith@stoneage-organics.co.uk www.stoneage-organics.co.uk
Soil Association M49W. Organic vegetables, box scheme deliveries from Taunton to Bristol to Shepton Mallet and en route. Organic lamb also available.

SUNSEED

12 South Street, Wellington, TA21 8NS

Tel: 01823 662313 info@sunseed.co.uk www.sunseed.co.uk

Health and wholefood retailer specialising in all things as natural as possible. Wide variety of usual things and unusual things: organic vegetables, fruit, food, drinks, chilled, frozen etc. Complementary therapies.

TOUCAN WHOLEFOODS

3 The Parade, Minehead, TA24 5NL

Tel: 01643 706101 Fax: 01643 708624 mail@toucanwholefoods.co.uk

Independent wholefood shop with a wide range of organic produce, including fresh fruit and veg, specialist breads, dairy and organic wines and beers. Range of organic baby care, body care and Ecover products also available. Quality vitamin supplements with free information.

THE TRADING POST
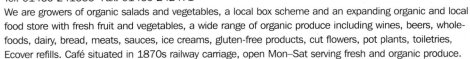

The Old Filling Station, Lopen Head,
South Petherton, TA13 5JH

Tel: 01460 241666 Fax: 01460 242471

We are growers of organic salads and vegetables, a local box scheme and an expanding organic and local food store with fresh fruit and vegetables, a wide range of organic produce including wines, beers, wholefoods, dairy, bread, meats, sauces, ice creams, gluten-free products, cut flowers, pot plants, toiletries, Ecover refills. Café situated in 1870s railway carriage, open Mon–Sat serving fresh and organic produce.

THE WHOLEFOOD STORE

29 High Street, Glastonbury, BA6 9DR

Tel: 01458 831004

One of Somerset's biggest and best organic, natural food stores. Our comprehensive range includes fresh bread from five different bakeries, a vibrant fresh fruit and vegetable section, and chilled and frozen products. We also stock bulk medicinal herbs, herbal and homeopathic remedies plus nutritional supplements. You can refill your bottles at the eco-refill station – 10 different shampoos, conditioners and liquid soap as well as Ecover cleaning products.

EAST ANGLIA

NORFOLK

ABBEY FARM ORGANICS
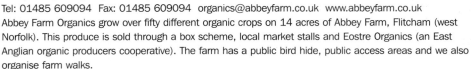

Abbey Farm, Abbey Rd, Flitcham, Kings Lynn, PE31 6BT

Tel: 01485 609094 Fax: 01485 609094 organics@abbeyfarm.co.uk www.abbeyfarm.co.uk

Abbey Farm Organics grow over fifty different organic crops on 14 acres of Abbey Farm, Flitcham (west Norfolk). This produce is sold through a box scheme, local market stalls and Eostre Organics (an East Anglian organic producers cooperative). The farm has a public bird hide, public access areas and we also organise farm walks.

ARTHUR'S ORGANIC DELIVERIES

Postal Farm, Lopham Rd., Kenninghall, NR16 2DT

Tel: 01953 887582 arthurs@limpets.freeserve.co.uk www.eostreorganics.co.uk

A local box scheme for south central Norfolk in an area bounded by Watton, Dereham, Hethersett, Diss, Thetford and including Wymondham and Attleborough. Produce from local organic co-operative used wherever possible. Organic fruit and veg, organic free range eggs, organic local apple juice, organic bread, monthly wholefood delivery. Ecover refill service. 20 years experience selling organic goods.

ASH FARM ORGANICS

Ash Farm, Stone Lane, Bintree, Dereham, NR20 5NA

Tel: 01362 683228 Fax: 01362 683228 info@ashfarmorganics.co.uk www.ashfarmorganics.co.uk

In our farm shop we sell pork, beef, poultry and vegetables (when available), all organically produced on our 370-acre family farm. We also sell lamb and free range eggs, organically produced within Norfolk. We make our own pork sausages, including a gluten-free variety, and cure and oak-smoke bacon and gammon. Our farm shop is open Fridays 10.30am–3.00pm and Saturdays 9.30am–12.00noon; any other time by appointment (The first two weekends after Christmas we'll be closed). You can also find us each 2nd Saturday of the month on Dereham farmers' market. We organise occasional farm tours.

AU NATUREL

Grove Farm, Holt Rd., Aylmerton, Norwich, NR11 8QA

Tel: 01263 837255 nicksherryamis@yahoo.co.uk

PYO or delivered strawberries, raspberries, blackberries, eating/cooking apples and plums.

BARKER ORGANICS

The Walled Garden, Wolterton Hall, Norwich, NR11 7LY

Tel: 01263 768966

Biodynamic Agricultural Association 370. Historic walled garden, a real live working kitchen garden growing vegetables and fruit using biodynamic methods. Selling all produce direct to the local community via a box scheme.

CATTERMOLE, SIMON – QUALITY BUTCHERS

King St., New Buckenham, Nr. Norwich, NR16 2AF

Tel: 01953 860264 simon@scatty.co.uk www.scatty.co.uk

Soil Association P6154. Butcher selling a large range of fresh organic meat and poultry products. Beef, pork, lamb, chicken, own sausages and bacon from our own smoke house.

COURTYARD FARM

Ringstead, Hunstanton, PE36 5LQ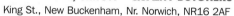

Tel: 01485 525251 Fax: 01485 525211 coutyard.organic@virgin.net

Organic cattle, sheep and pigs. Meat is sold direct from the farm, either pre-ordered or through the farm shop that is open every Wednesday from 3pm–5.30pm. Member of the Soil Association Organic Farms Network.

CRONE'S

Fairview, Fersfield Rd., Kenninghall, NR16 2DP

Tel: 01379 687687 Fax: 01379 688323 info@crones.co.uk www.crones.co.uk

Soil Association P1587. Makers of a range of award-winning apple juices and ciders. Also organic cider vinegar, apple cherry, pear and apple. Contact us for our full range. Sales ex-gate by prior appointment.

DIANE'S PANTRY

8 Market Place, Reepham, Norwich, NR10 4JJ

Tel: 01603 871075

Wholefood, healthfoods, supplements and small bakery with coffee shop attached. Organic bread baked to order.

FOR DETAILS OF SYMBOLS USED IN THE ENTRIES, SEE PAGE 17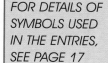

DOMINI QUALITY FOODS

Village Farm, The Street, Market Weston, Diss, IP22 2NZ
Tel: 01359 221333 Fax: 01359 221835 jcapon@dominifoods.fnset.co.uk
Small traditional farm selling top quality untreated milk, cream and butter from the Domini Jerseys.
Available from Wyken farmers' market, Stanton every Saturday, or telephone/email to order direct from
the farm.

EOSTRE ORGANICS LTD

Unit 2, North Side Hangars, Old Buckenham Airfield,
Attleborough, NR17 1PU
Tel: 01953 456294 Fax: 01953 456145 dot.bane@eostreorganics.co.uk www.eostreorganics.co.uk
An organic grower co-operative, mainly wholesaling but we also attend markets and have stands at
Norwich Provisions Market (6 days) and Old Spitalfields (Sundays), Acre Lane, Brixton (Saturdays),
Sunnyside Community Gardens, Islington (Saturdays), Calthorpe Communty Gardens, Gravesend Rd
(Fridays), Archway (Saturdays), Hildreth St., Balham (Sundays), Hoe St., Walthamstow (Saturdays),
Sloane Square / Duke of York Square off Kings Rd., Chelsea, Borough Market (Fridays and Saturdays),
Bellenden Rd., Peckham (Saturdays). We also pack boxes for distribution by others.

GARBOLDISHAM WINDMILL

Diss, IP22 2RJ
Tel: 01953 681593

Soil Association P4546. Bread flours, oat products, gluten-free flours available from mill or through shops
in Norfolk and Suffolk. Please telephone for details (may get answering machine).

THE GREEN GROCERS

2 Earlham House, Earlham Road, Norwich, NR2 3PD
Tel: 01603 250000 eat@thegreengrocers.co.uk www.thegreengrocers.co.uk
Organic supermarket offering local, organic and environmentally friendly groceries. The Green Grocers
offers a new way of shopping: fruit and veg, meats, frozen pizzas, dried produce, milk etc., eco products.
70% of fresh produce is locally sourced.

THE GREENHOUSE

42-46 Bethel St., Norwich, NR2 1NR
Tel: 01603 631007 www.greenhousetrust.co.uk
Environment centre. The Greenhouse is an educational charity providing solutions to environmental problems. The building houses an organic, vegetarian/vegan licensed café and shop (open for Sunday lunch
12–3.30) plus meeting rooms and herb garden. The shop acts as a contact point for a local veg box
scheme and is stockist of a wide range of organic and GMO-free foods. Also a resource centre offering
meeting space, offices and other facilities to local and regional voluntary groups.

HARVEYS PUREMEAT

63 Grove Rd., Norwich, NR1 3RL
Tel: 01603 621908 info@puremeat.org.uk www.puremeat.org.uk
Established 1924, Harveys is Norwich's only certified (Organic Food Federation) organic butcher and
game dealer. Retail shop, wholesale supplies to restaurants, hotels, etc. by arrangement. Local game
including venison. See website.

THE HERBARY

Church Farm, Middle Rd., Shouldham Thorpe, Kings Lynn, PE32 1TF
Tel: 01366 348175 Fax: 01366 348176 theherbary@btconnect.com
Soil Association G6463. Salads, growers of organic leafy herb and speciality salad crops.

HOUGHTON ORGANIC FARM

The Estate Office, Houghton, Kings Lynn, PE31 6UE
Tel: 01485 528569 Fax: 01485 528167 carwyn@houghtonhall.com www.houghtonhall.com
Soil Association G5603. Producers of organic beef and lamb from our herd of Longhorn cattle and flocks of Southdown and Norfolk Horn sheep, supplying local restaurants, box schemes and Fakenham farmers' market.

KENT, J R

Church Barn Farm, Arminghall, NR14 8SG
Tel: 01508 495574
Soil Association G1819. Farm gate sales of top fruit roots and squash. PYO blackcurrants, broad beans, other – rabbits and pigeons permitting.

LETHERINGSETT WATER MILL

 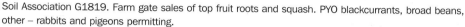

Riverside Rd., Letheringsett, Holt, NR25 7YD
Tel: Tel: 01263 713153
Water Mill (1798) restored to working order producing organic 100% wholewheat flour. Demeter BDAA member (no. 262). Working demonstrations when we make flour (varies between winter and summer). Mail order sales; deliveries to NR25 & all Norfolk.

MANGREEN TRUST

Mangreen Hall, Swardeston, Norwich, NR14 8DD
Tel: 01508 570444 Fax: 01508 578899 trust@mangreen.co.uk www.mangreen.co.uk
We farm one and a half acres of vegetables and fruit to Soil Association standards (cert. no. D10E). Retail outlet supplies fresh produce, both local and imported, complemented by general grocery items.

THE NATURAL FOODSTORE

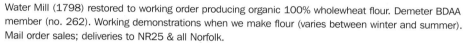

Norfolk House Yard, St Nicholas Street, Diss, IP22 3LB
Tel: 01379 651832
Our aim is to provide good quality wholefoods at affordable prices. We are entirely vegetarian with plenty of choice for vegans and those on special diets. We provide an increasing range of organically grown produce and use minimal packaging in recyclable materials.

NATURAL SURROUNDINGS

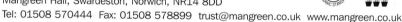

Bayfield Estate, Holt, NR25 7JN
Tel: 01263 711091 Fax: 01263 711091 loosley@farmersweekly.net www.naturalsurroundings.org.uk
Wildflower and countryside centre specialising in plants for the wildlife garden. Wildflower and herb nursery growing in peat-free, organic composts.

NEAL'S YARD REMEDIES

26 Lower Goat Lane, Norwich, NR2 1EL
Tel: 01603 766681 mail@nealsyardremedies.com www.nealsyardremedies.com
Neal's Yard Remedies manufactures and retails natural cosmetics in addition to stocking an extensive range of herbs, essential oils, homeopathic remedies and reference material.

PARADISE ORGANICS

123 Dereham Rd., New Costessey, Norwich, NR5 0SX
Tel: 01603 731049 tracey@paradiseorganics.co.uk www.paradiseorganics.co.uk
Member of Soil Association. Home delivery service of local (as much as possible) organic vegetables, fruit, wholefoods and cleaning products.

RAINBOW WHOLEFOODS

White Lodge Estate, Hall Rd., Norwich, NR4 6DG
Tel: 01603 630484 Fax: 01603 664066
info@rainbowwholefoods.co.uk www.rainbowwholefoods.co.uk
A sensational traditional wholefood shop with fresh organic vegetables, fresh organic bread daily and 14 types of seaweed. All our goods are guaranteed GMO-free.

SALLE MOOR HALL FARM

Salle Moor Hall Farm, Salle, Reepham, Norwich, NR10 4SB
Tel: 01603 879046 Fax: 01603 879047 sales@salleorganics.com www.salleorganics.com
Soil Association registered organic farm selling lamb, beef, eggs and vegetables direct to the door, through vegetable box scheme and wholesale. Also self-catering cottage.

SAVORY EGGS, J

Highfield Farm, Great Ryburgh, Fakenham, NR21 7AL
Tel: 01328 829249 Fax: 01328 829422 elizabethsavory@waitrose.com www.broadland.com/highfield
J. Savory Eggs laying flock. Soil Association No G2947. Speciality egg production. Mrs E. Savory, farmhouse B&B, member FHB, Four Diamonds ETB.

ST. BENEDICTS FOOD STORE

‹43 St. Benedicts Street, Norwich, NR2 4PG
Tel: 01603 623309
Retailer and wholesaler of some organic produce to the public and the catering trade.

THE TREEHOUSE

14-16 Dove St., Norwich, NR2 1DE
Tel: 01603 763258
The Treehouse sells freshly made meals, salads and home-made cakes at lunchtimes and Thurs–Sat evenings. We use a wide range of ingredients from local suppliers where possible.

WATTON EARTH

80A High Street, Watton, IP25 6AH
Tel: 01953 883883
We are a family-run shop selling fairtrade and organic food and drink, toiletries and gifts. We also sell food for special dietary requirements. We are a stockist of Essential Care skincare products.

YETMAN'S

37 Norwich Rd., Holt, NR25 6SA
Tel: 01263 713320
Restaurant using in-season local organic produce.

SUFFOLK

BUSHY LEY FARM SHOP

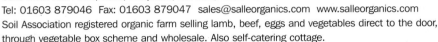

Elmsett, Ipswich, IP7 6PQ
Tel: 01473 658671
Soil Association T12E. Wide range of vegetables and fruit when in season. Open July to October, 8am–8pm seven days a week. All produce sold is grown on this farm.

CARLEY AND WEBB

29 Market Hill, Framlingham, IP13 9AN

Tel: 01728 723503 framlingham@carleyandwebb.com www.carleyandwebb.com

Specialist delicatessen and natural food store specialising in organic vegetables, bread and macrobiotic products. Free delivery service within 10 miles.

CARLEY AND WEBB

52 Thoroughfare, Woodbridge, IP12 1AL

Tel: 01394 385650 Fax: 01394 388984 www.carleyandwebb.com

We are a natural food store specialising in organic vegetables, bread and macrobiotic products. Large delicatessen, fresh fish.

CLARKES LANE ORCHARD

Clarkes Lane, Ilketshall St. Andrew, Beccles, NR34 8HR

Tel: 07786 663351

One and a half acre orchard/smallholding with old fruit tree varieties plus 400 dwarf trees, mostly apple, with pear, plum and cherry. Some fruit and vegetables available from the gate.

THE CHOCOLATE BOX

13 The Thoroughfare, Ipswich, IP1 1BX

Telephone: 01473 255135 info@chocolatsbelges.com www.chocolatsbelges.com

Boutique shop and online store selling organic chocolate from Booja Booja and Montezuma's along with fine Belgian chocolates, fair trade and no-sugar-added (diabetic friendly) chocolates and treats. Secure online payment and delivery included.

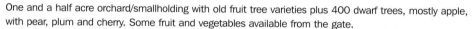

DAGANYA FARM

Nuttery Vale, Hoxne, Eye, IP21 5BB

Tel: 01379 668060

Soil Association G2108. Organic fruit and vegetables in season. Founder member of Eostre organics.

DESMOND DUNCAN'S ORGANIC VEGETABLE BOX SCHEME

37 Ensign Way, Diss, Norfolk, IP22 4GP

Tel: 01379 652101 Fax: 01379 652101 daduncan1962@aol.com www.organicsforall.co.uk

Organic vegetable box scheme operating in Ipswich, Colchester, Bury St Edmunds, Diss and Norwich. As well as local organic vegetables we also sell organic fruit, bread, eggs and apple juice. We encourage customer feedback and suggestions and we allow customers to stipulate which vegetables they don't want to receive. Mobile: 07771 863230.

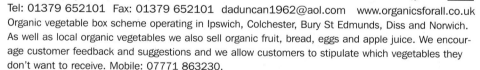

DJ PRODUCE LTD

Unit 1, Griffiths Yard, Gazeley Rd., Moulton, Newmarket, CB8 8SR

Tel: 01638 552709 Fax: 01638 552709 djproduce2005@yahoo.co.uk www.djproduce.co.uk

Organic Farmers & Growers 11UKP110089. Wide range of fruit and vegetable boxes delivered weekly to Cambridge, Newmarket, Ely and the surrounding area. Personal orders welcomed. Long established reputation for personal service, quality and value for money.

EDEN ORGANICS AND WHOLEFOODS

Southview, 165, Yarmouth Road, Broome, Bungay, NR35 2NZ

Tel: 07789 965904 Fax: 01986 896378 david.hirst@edenorganics.co.uk www.edenorganics.co.uk

We provide an organic fruit and vegetable box scheme together with a range of wholefoods and eco friendly products. We deliver on a Thursday and Friday to Bungay, Beccles, Lowestoft, Halesworth and surrounding villages.

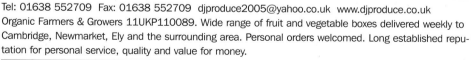

SUFFOLK

FOCUS ORGANIC LTD
14 The Thoroughfare, Halesworth, IP19 8AH

Tel: 01986 872899 Fax: 01986 872995 info@focusorganic.co.uk www.focusorganic.co.uk
Our wholefood shop sells as much organic produce as possible including cereals, nuts, fruits, flour, seeds, jams, sauces, spreads, juices, pasta and vegetables. Organic clothes and bed linen, Ecover products, aromatherapy candles, essential oils, recycled jewellery.

FOCUS ORGANIC LTD
76 High St., Souhwold, IP18 6DN

Tel: 01986 872899 Fax: 01986 872995 info@focusorganic.co.uk www.focusorganic.co.uk
Our wholefood shop sells as much organic produce as possible including cereals, nuts, fruits, flour, seeds, jams, sauces, spreads, juices, pasta and vegetables. Organic clothes and bed linen, Ecover products, aromatherapy candles, essential oils, recycled jewellery.

HILLSIDE NURSERIES
Hintlesham, Ipswich, IP8 3NJ

Tel: 01473 652682 Fax: 01473 652624
Soil Association G594. Box scheme (vegetables, fruit, eggs) using local and own produce wherever possible. Delivery Ipswich, Woodbridge, Felixstowe and surrounding areas.

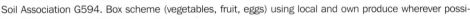

HUNGATE HEALTH STORE
4 Hungate, Beccles, NR34 9TL

Tel: 01502 715009
Retailers of a wide range of organic foods including fresh bread, biscuits, dried fruit and nuts, beans and lentils, chocolate, drinks. Also essential oils, bath and hair products.

LES CHOCOLATS BELGES
45 The Thoroughfare, Woodbridge, IP12 1AH

Tel: 01394 386302 Fax: 01394 385590 info@chocolatsbelges.com www.chocolatsbelges.com
Boutique shop and online store selling organic chocolate from Booja Booja and Montezuma's along with fine Belgian chocolates, fair trade and no-sugar-added (diabetic friendly) chocolates and treats. Secure online payment and delivery included.

LONGWOOD FARM
Tuddenham St. Mary, Bury St. Edmunds, IP28 6TB

Tel: 01638 717120 Fax: 01638 717120
Soil Association no. G669. Specialist organic meat producers, retailers of fine organic foods – meat, dairy, cheese and provisions. Huge range of over 2,000 items. Delivery nationwide plus local deliveries to postcode areas IP, NR, CB.

MAPLE FARM
By The Crossways, Kelsale, Saxmundham, Suffolk, IP17 2PL
Tel: 01728 652000 Fax: 01728 652001
info@maplefarmkelsale.co.uk www.maplefarmkelsale.co.uk
Small organic farm and market garden which produces and sells a wide range of vegetables, home milled flour, eggs and honey.

OREGANO
169/171 London Road North, Lowestoft, NR32 1HG

Tel: 01502 582907

Health foods, vitamins, supplements. Organic foods are featured in a large section in the store.

QUEEN'S HEAD
The Street, Bramfield, Halesworth, IP19 9HT
Tel: 01986 784214 Fax: 01986 784797
enquiries@queensheadbramfield.co.uk www.queensheadbramfield.co.uk
Award-winning dining pub, serving food daily. Many ingredients collected direct from small local organic farms. Close to Southwold and the rest of Suffolk's Heritage Coast.

SWALLOW ORGANICS
High March, Darsham, Saxmundham, IP17 3RN
Tel: 01728 668201 Fax: 01728 668201
Naturally grown fruit and vegetables, herbs and pot plants. Farm gate sales and vegetable boxes supplied to order, for collection only. Self-catering holiday accommodation available.

WAKELYNS AGROFORESTRY
Metfield Lane, Fressingfield, IP21 5SD
wolfe@wakelyns.demon.co.uk
Soil Association G2249. Organic arable and agroforestry research undertaken largely as part of the Elm Farm Research Centre programme. Vegetables, potatoes and other produce are sold locally, principally through the Eostre organic co-operative.

THE EAST MIDLANDS

CAMBRIDGESHIRE

CAMBRIDGE ORGANIC FOOD CO
Penn Farm Studios, Harston Rd., Haslingfield, Cambridge, Cambridgeshire, CB23 1JZ
Tel: 01223 873300   Fax: 01223 873300 info@cofco.co.uk www.cofco.co.uk
The Cambridge Organic Food Co. represents most of the organic farms in the Cambridge area. As well as boxes of organic fruit and vegetables we supply locally baked bread, eggs, flour and a range of other organic food products.

COTTO
183 East Rd., Cambridge, CB1 1BG
Tel: 01223 302010 gemma@cottocambridge.co.uk www.cottocambridge.co.uk
Cotto is a restaurant/café/bakery that uses mostly Soil Association certified organic ingredients, sourced locally where possible. Our menu is cooked freshly to order and changes weekly according to what is in season. We bake our own organic bread in a wood-fired oven.

DAILY BREAD CO-OPERATIVE (CAMBRIDGE) LIMITED
Unit 3, Kilmaine Close, Cambridge, CB4 2PH
Tel: 01223 423177 Fax: 01223 425858 cambridge@dailybread.co.uk www.dailybread.co.uk
Soil Association P4448. We retail and wholesale wholefoods with a good and increasing range of organic flours, grains, cereals, pulses, fruit and vegetables.

DELFLAND NURSERIES LTD
Benwick Road, Doddington, March, PE15 0TU
Tel: 01354 740553 Fax: 01354 741200 jill@delfland.co.uk www.organicplants.co.uk
Vegetable, salad, herb, strawberries and ornamental plants for outdoor and greenhouse/polytunnel production. Wholesale deliveries made all over the UK. Retail shop and mail order for gardeners and allotment holders – online catalogue at www.organicplants.co.uk.

CAMBRIDGESHIRE

EDGEBANK ORGANICS
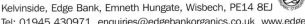

Kelvinside, Edge Bank, Emneth Hungate, Wisbech, PE14 8EJ

Tel: 01945 430971 enquiries@edgebankorganics.co.uk www.edgebankorganics.co.uk

Edgebank Organics produces and sells soft and top fruit including strawberries, raspberries, gooseberries, blackcurrants, blackberries, rhubarb, apples, pears, cherries, plums from May through to October. Fresh fruit and home-made jam are available at the farm gate and local farmers' markets. Mobile: 07798 641202.

GUILDEN GATE SMALLHOLDING

86 North End, Bassingbourn, Royston, SG8 5PD

Tel: 01763 243960 simon.saggers@btinternet.com www.guildengate.co.uk

Soil Association G5970. Mixed organic smallholding offering local veg box scheme and guided tours. Wildflower meadow, veg & herb fields, woodland, pond and orchards. Interesting on-site water and energy resource cycles. A practical design for living and working in a more ecologically sound and sustainable way. Member of the Soil Association Organic Farms Network.

NATURALLY YOURS
 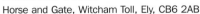 

Horse and Gate, Witcham Toll, Ely, CB6 2AB

Tel: 01353 778723 orders@naturally-yours.demon.co.uk www.naturally-yours.co.uk

Suppliers of organic and additive-free foods including meat, fish, fruit and vegetables and groceries. Full traditional butchery service. Fruit and vegetable box scheme. Free delivery within defined area.

NEAL'S YARD REMEDIES

1 Rose Crescent, Cambridge, CB2 3LL

Tel: 01223 321074 cambridge@nealsyardremedies.com www.nealsyardremedies.com

Neal's Yard Remedies manufactures and retails natural cosmetics in addition to stocking an extensive range of herbs, essential oils, homeopathic remedies and reference material.

ORGANIC CONNECTIONS INTERNATIONAL LTD

Riverdale, Town St., Upwell, Wisbech, PE14 9AF

Tel: 01945 773374 Fax: 01945 773033

sales@organic-connections.co.uk www.organic-connections.co.uk

Soil Association IP1653 & G1885. Fruit and vegetable suppliers to all aspects of the organic market. We grow, market and pre-pack, and make nationwide deliveries of our award-winning box scheme. Suppliers to pre-packers.

ORGANIC HEALTH (CAMBRIDGE)

87 Church Rd., Hauxton, Cambridge, CB2 5HS

Tel: 01223 870101

Specialist retailer of organic, biodynamic and special diet foods. Thousands of lines including organic fruit and veg, meat and fish, breads, dairy, vegetarian and vegan foods and lots more. Phone for details. Opening times Thurs 9–6.30, Fri 9–5, Sat 9–5.

PETERBOROUGH HEALTH FOOD CENTRE

25 The Arcade, Westgate, Peterborough, PE1 1PZ

Tel: 01733 566807 Fax: 01733 566807

We stock organic beans and pulses, dried fruit, teas, honey, cooking oils, juices, cereals, flour, chocolate and soya milk.

RIVER NENE HOME DELIVERY

36 Landcliffe Close, St Ives, Cambs, PE27 3JF

Tel: 01480 498989 lizede@rivernene.co.uk www.rivernene.co.uk

A regional organic box scheme that delivers to homes across the Midlands and Eastern Countries. River Nene organic farm is situated near Yaxley, Peterborough where we grow over 60 organic vegetables which are packed on the farm one day and delivered the next.

RIVER NENE HOME DELIVERY CAMBRIDGE

20 Meadow Road, Great Gransden, Sandy, Bedfordshire, SG19 3BD

Tel: 01767 677852 Fax: 01767 677852 martinandjulie@rivernene.co.uk www.rivernene.co.uk

Box scheme delivery service.

RIVER NENE ORGANIC VEGETABLES

Stan's Farm, Yaxley, PE7 3TW

Tel: 0845 078 6868 boxscheme@rivernene.co.uk www.rivernene.co.uk

Home delivery of fresh organic vegetable boxes, direct to the door. Growing over 60 varieties throughout the seasons, with five vegetables boxes. Prices start at £7 including delivery.

WATERLAND ORGANICS

Willow Farm, Lode, Cambridge, CB5 9HF

Tel: 01223 812912 Fax: 01223 812912 www.waterlandorganics.co.uk

Soil Association G1709. Run local box scheme around Cambridge. Supply local shops and restaurants with fruit and vegetables. Mail order strawberry and soft fruit bushes.

WILD COUNTRY ORGANICS

11 Chalky Rd., Great Abington, Cambridge, CB1 6AT

Tel: 07787 560038 adrian@wildcountryorganics.co.uk www.wildcountryorganics.co.uk

We grow a wide variety of organic vegetables and salads all year round to supply box schemes, wholesalers and our own box scheme delivering in and around Cambridge.

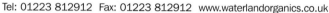

DERBYSHIRE

ABERDEEN ANGUS BEEF
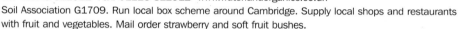

Ball Beard Farm, Laneside Rd., New Mills, High Peak, SK22 4QN

Tel: 01663 747795

Livestock farm breeding, rearing and selling its own organic Aberdeen Angus beef at the farm or delivered to your door within a sixty mile radius of New Mills.

BEANO'S WHOLEFOODS

Holme Road, Matlock Bath, DE4 3NU

Tel: 01629 57130 Fax: 01629 57143 john@beanos.go-plus.net

Box scheme delivering selection of organic fruit & vegetables.

DERBYSHIRE DALES ORGANICS

Common End Farm, Bradley, Nr. Ashbourne, DE6 3BQ

Tel: 01335370356 Fax: 01355370356 jwhowson@wildmail.com

Small family-run mixed organic farm nestled in the Derbyshire dales specialising in poultry, lamb, pork and related products.

ECO ECO LTD

The Courtyard, Hope, S33 6RD

Tel: 01433 623113 info@eco-eco.co.uk www.eco-eco.co.uk

Our store in Hope, in the north of Derbyshire, carries a full range of eco-clothing for men, women and young children alongside accessories, organic body care and an exciting range of fair trade and recycled jewellery. We are easy to find, and are open Wednesday to Sunday from 10.00–4.30.

THE GREEN BOX COMPANY

Hague St., Glossop, SK13 8NR

Tel: 01457 856843 info@greenboxcompany.co.uk www.thegreenboxcompany.co.uk

Fruit and vegetable box scheme delivering in Glossop, Derbyshire and surrounding area. Also eggs, cheese, jams and marmalades. Mobile number 07906 494065.

HEARTHSTONE FARM

Riber, Matlock, DE4 5JW

Tel: 01629 534304 Fax: 01629 534372

enquiries@hearthstonefarm.co.uk www.hearthstonefarm.co.uk

B&B in the farmhouse three en suite double rooms. We produce beef, pork, and lamb and make our own sausages, bacon and burgers. We grow and sell organic potatoes and buy in organic chicken all for sale in the farm shop. Open all day Monday, Tuesday, Thursday, Friday, Saturdays 9–2, Sundays 10–12, closed Wednesday.

JEFFERY, H & SON

Aston House Farm, Sudbury, Nr. Ashbourne, DE6 5AG

Tel: 01283 585410 r.jeffery@btconnect.com www.newlandowner.co.uk

Beef from longhorn cattle born and reared on this organic farm is available fresh or frozen by appointment from the farmhouse, mobile: 07971 566907. The farm is conveniently situated just off the A50 on Lichfield Rd, Sudbury.

LOWER HURST FARM

Lower Hurst Farm, Hartington,
Nr. Buxton, SK17 0HJ

Tel: 01298 84900 Fax: 01298 84732 sales@lowerhurstfarm.co.uk www.lowerhurstfarm.co.uk

Soil Association G7616, P7654. A small farm in Derbyshire producing exclusive organic beef from its own herd of pure bred Hereford cattle. Full range of products are available including award-winning Steak & Cider Pies. Available through mail order or secure online shop. A 'Monthly' shop is held at the farm on the 1st Friday and Saturday 10–4 in every month, and the farm also holds Open Days where visitors can walk the farm trail, take a tractor tour around the Herefords or simply relax in the stunning surroundings whilst enjoying a delicious steak and a glass of wine. Member of the Soil Association Organic Farms Network. Organic Food Awards 2004 Highly Commended; Fresh Meat Commended. Green Directory Taste Awards 2006 best roasting joints and best ready meal, steak & kidney pie.

MEYNELL LANGLEY ORGANIC FARM SHOP

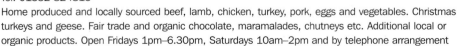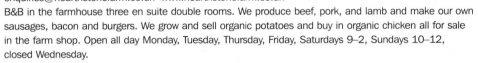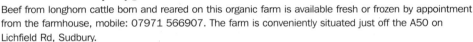

Meynell Langley, Kirk Langley, Ashborne, DE6 4NT

Tel: 01332 824815

Home produced and locally sourced beef, lamb, chicken, turkey, pork, eggs and vegetables. Christmas turkeys and geese. Fair trade and organic chocolate, maramalades, chutneys etc. Additional local or organic products. Open Fridays 1pm–6.30pm, Saturdays 10am–2pm and by telephone arrangement Monday–Thursday.

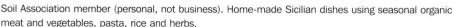

MIMMO'S

1 St. Mary's Gate, Wirksworth, Matlock, DE4 4DQ

Tel: 01629 826724

Soil Association member (personal, not business). Home-made Sicilian dishes using seasonal organic meat and vegetables, pasta, rice and herbs.

NATURAL CHOICE

24 St. John St., Ashbourne, DE6 1GH

Tel: 01335 346096 Fax: 01335 346096 naturalchoice@tiscali.co.uk www.naturalchoicehealth.co.uk

Health foods, wholefoods, natural supplements. Natural therapy centre.

NEW HOUSE ORGANIC FARM

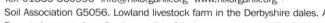

Kniveton, Ashbourne, DE6 1JL

Tel: 01335 342429 bob@newhousefarm.co.uk www.newhousefarm.co.uk

OF&G 11UK F030109. Hill farm producing beef, lamb, eggs, veg and fruit. Farm shop. School visits. Waymarked archaeological farm trail. Accommodation in converted barn with solar panel and wind turbine. Also large organised camping.

NIXORGANIX

Crystal Springs Farm, Brailsford, Ashbourne, DE6 3BG

Tel: 01335 360996 info@nixorganix.org www.nixorganix.org

Soil Association G5056. Lowland livestock farm in the Derbyshire dales. Aberdeen Angus cattle and Polled Dorset sheep are kept for the quality of their meat and suitability for natural methods. Beef and lamb always available. Educational visits and informal circular walks to view farm and conservation activities.

NORTHERN TEA MERCHANTS

Crown House, 193 Chatsworth Rd.,

Chesterfield, S40 2BA

Tel: 01246 232600 Fax: 01246 555991 enquiries@northern-tea.com www.northern-tea.com

We are organic coffee roasters and packers of organic cocoas. We can also offer organic tea packing and organic tea bag manufacture. Retail shop and café, online shop.

ORGANIC HEAVEN

4 Theatre Yard, Chesterfield, S40 1PF

Tel: 08452 235453 info@organicheaven.org.uk www.organicheaven.org.uk/

A retail shop for the Chesterfield & north-east Derbyshire area, selling a wide variety of products. We have a delicatessen in the shop, with a focus on local produce and special diets. We run an 'ethical points' store-card scheme as well as providing a local hub for ethically-minded people. From Easter we 2007 we shall be supplying toiletries and household cleaning products, and will have refill facilities in our expanded shop.

ORGANIC PUMPKIN

Kingfisher Cottage, King St., Duffield, Derby, DE56 4EU

Tel: 01332 370254 Fax: 01332 370254 www.organicpumpkin.co.uk

Organic Food Federation No. 00461. Fresh seasonal organic vegetables picked and delivered the same day. Evening delivery Wednesday and Thursday.

THE ORGANIC SHOP

44 Market St, New Mills, SK22 4AA

Tel: 01663 747550 Fax: 01663 747550 theorganicshop@aol.com

Complete range of organic produce (excluding meat), Ecover refill, cosmetics, deli counter.

SOUND BITES

11 Morledge, Derby, DE1 2AW

Tel: 01332 291369 Fax: 01332 291369 info@soundbitesderby.org.uk www.soundbitesderby.org.uk

We are an organic ethical shop in the heart of Derby offering a large range of veggie food, takeaway food, baby products, magazines, alcohol, household cleaning, organic scoop and weigh, ethical body care products and much more. We endeavour to support local organic producers where ever we can. Come in and look around, our range of stock is fantastic!

SUNFLOWER HEALTH STORE

20 Market Place, Ilkeston, DE7 5QA

Tel: 0115 930 4750

We sell a wide range of groceries, supplements and cosmetics, stocking as many organic and ethically produced goods as possible. We are pleased to order items not stocked if available.

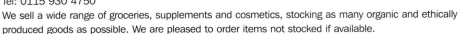

UNSTONE GRANGE ORGANIC GARDENING FOR HEALTH

Crow Lane, Unstone, Nr. Chesterfield, Derbyshire, S18 4AL

Tel: 01246 411666 Fax: 01246 412344 garden@unstonegrange.co.uk www.unstonegrange.co.uk

We provide gardening opportunities for volunteers from all over Derbyshire: people with learning disabilities, mental health issues, single parents, retired, people changing careers or downshifting. Others are well and want to stay well, or want to learn about organic horticulture.

WILD CARROT

5 Bridge St., Buxton, SK17 6BS

Tel: 01298 22843 shop@wildcarrot.freeserve.co.uk www.wildcarrot.freeserve.co.uk

Soil Association GC5018, R7228. We are a wholefood workers co-op specialising in organic foods and alcohol, fair traded goods and environmentally friendly products. We support local and UK growers and prepare organic veg boxes. We are a member of Organic 2000.

LEICESTERSHIRE

BAMBURY ORGANIC FARM

Bambury Farm, Bambury Lane, Peatling Magna, LE8 5UE

Tel: 0116 247 8907 Fax: 0116 247 8907 bamburyfarm@btinternet.com

Soil Association G1104. Bambury Organic Farm is a small family-run farm providing fresh organic vegetables to the local community. There are a range of box sizes, plus a wide selection of fruit and free range eggs. Free delivery is included in the service.

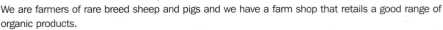

BROCKLEBY FARM SHOP

Asfordby Hill, Melton Mowbray, LE14 3QU

Tel: 01664 813200 www.brocklebys.co.uk

We are farmers of rare breed sheep and pigs and we have a farm shop that retails a good range of organic products.

CHEVELSWARDE
ORGANIC GROWERS

The Belt, South Kilworth, Lutterworth, LE17 6DX

Tel: 01858 575309 organics@chevelswardeorganics.co.uk www.chevelswardeorganics.co.uk

Soil Association DO3M, organic status awarded 1975; HDRA. Off licence. Growers to Soil Association standards: vines for white and red wine, vegetables for local box scheme and farm shop supplies. Shop open daily for veg, fruit, wines and organic groceries.

CURRANT AFFAIRS
9A Loseby Lane, Leicester, LE1 5DR
Tel: 0116 251 0887 shop@currantaffairs.co.uk www.currantaffairs.co.uk
Currant Affairs is a natural food store selling a wide range of organic produce. We also have an on-site bakery producing freshly prepared takeaway.

EDEN

2 Adam & Eve St., Market Harborough, LE16 7LT
We are a retailer of organic, fair trade and natural foods in the centre of Market Harborough. We offer a great selection of rolls, savouries and cakes, all freshly made.

GNC

18 Silver St., Leicester, LE1 5ET
Tel: 0116 262 4859 www.gnc.co.uk
Nationwide health supplement stores, including some organic products.

GREEN AND PLEASANT WHOLEFOODS
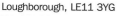
59A Queens Rd., Clarendon Park, Leicester, LE2 1TT
Tel: 0116 270 2974 jill@rowleyrats.fsnet.co.uk www.greenandpleasant.net
Wholefoods, organic products, non-toxic body care and household goods, natural health care, fair trade and local products.

GROWING CONCERN

Home Farm, Woodhouse Lane, Nanpantan,
Loughborough, LE11 3YG
Tel: 01509 239228 Fax: 01509 239228
goodfood@homefarmorganics.co.uk www.growingconcern.co.uk
Redevelopment since winning Organic Food Award includes visitors' rare breed centre, on-farm bakery-restaurant, ready made meals. Mail order.

MANOR FARM

Long Whatton, Loughborough, LE12 5DF
Tel: 01509 646413 Fax: 01509 843344
shop@manororganicfarm.co.uk www.manororganicfarm.co.uk
Soil Association G1778, Shop Licence P4948, Elm Farm Research Centre Demonstration Farm. Award-winning mixed organic family farm producing cereals, vegetables, potatoes, meat and eggs. All sold through our farm shop and at local farmers' markets, including home-made sausages and burgers. Farm trail open. Farm shop open Thursday, Friday & Saturday. Member of the Soil Association Organic Farms Network.

THE NATURALLY GOOD FOOD DELIVERY SERVICE
 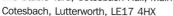   
The Stable Yard, Cotesbach Hall, Main Street,
Cotesbach, Lutterworth, LE17 4HX
Tel: 01455 556878 Fax: 01455 550855 orders@goodfooddelivery.co.uk www.goodfooddelivery.co.uk
Shop, home delivery and mail order for huge range of organic wholefoods, fruit & veg, plus gluten-free and dairy-free foods, toiletries and household cleaners. Hard to find foods found! Also the Keeper, an alternative to tampons.

FOR DETAILS OF SYMBOLS USED IN THE ENTRIES, SEE PAGE 17

LEICESTERSHIRE

NEWCOMBE, P C & K J

Lubcloud Farm, Oaks In Charnwood, Loughborough, LE12 9YA
Tel: 01509 503204 Fax: 01509 651267
Soil Association G2934. Organic dairy farm with 120 milking cows. Bed and breakfast accommodation in the beautiful Charnwood Forest within the National Forest area.

PICKS ORGANIC FARM SHOP

The Cottage, Hamilton Grounds, King St.,
Barkby Thorpe, LE4 3QF
Tel: 0116 269 3548 Fax: 0116 269 3548
Home produced organic pork, beef, lamb, chicken, turkey, guinea fowl, duck and eggs. Seasonal fruit and vegetables, free local delivery, and box scheme available. Farm shop selling organic meats, vegetables, wines, beers, ales, breads, ice creams, dairy produce, jams, chutneys, etc.

POLEBROOK HAYES ORGANIC FARM

3 Markfield Lane, Botcheston, Leicester, LE9 9FH
Tel: 07764 814008 suejohno@btinternet.com
Organic box scheme and mail order fruit and veg delivery to Markfield and surrounding villages.

QUENBY HALL ORGANIC FOODS

Quenby Hall, Hungarton, LE7 9JF
Tel: 0116 259 5224 Fax: 0116 259 5224 enquiries@quenbyhall.co.uk www.quenbybeef.co.uk
Soil Association G2914. Organic English Longhorn beef, born and raised on the ancient natural grassland, sold to order, free local delivery; mail order throughout UK mainland.

RAW N PURE

3 Markfield Lane, Botcheston, Leicester, LE9 9FH
Tel: 01509 502108 rawnpure@btinternet.com www.rawnpure.org
Fruit, veg and salad mail order and box scheme delivering to addresses in Loughborough, Leicester and surrounding areas. Alternative telephone: 07812 990603.

RIVER NENE ORGANIC HOME DELIVERY

47 Carter Close, Enderby, Leicester, LE19 4BZ
Tel: 0116 286 9713 gev@rivernene.co.uk www.rivernene.co.uk
Independent local licensed distributor for River Nene organic vegetables. Award-winning organic vegetable box scheme delivering in west Leicestershire, Nuneaton, Hinckley and the surrounding area. Offering differing box sizes to suit all households from a single occupant to a large family. A selection of fruit & vegetables, dairy products, wine and juices are also available. Order weekly, fortnightly or whenever you like. Can order online at www.rivernene.co.uk or by telephone on 0845 078 6868.

RIVER NENE ORGANIC HOME DELIVERY

32 Heathgate Close, Birstall, LE4 3GU
Tel: 0116 267 2222 jitparek@rivernene.co.uk www.rivernene.co.uk
Award-winning organic vegetable box scheme delivering in central and north Leicestershire. Offering differing box sizes to suit all households from a single occupant to a large family. A selection of fruit & vegetables, dairy products, wine and juices are also available. Order weekly, fortnightly or whenever you like. Free home or work delivery. Can order online at www.rivernene.co.uk or by telephone on 0845 078 6868.

WATTS, D A

The Bungalow, Springfield Farm, Sapcote, LE9 4LD
Tel: 01455 272840 watts.donkeylane@btinternet.com
Soil Association G1251 P5631. Organic vegetable producer/own box scheme around Hinckley and surrounding area (50% own or local). Also fruit, eggs and bread. Small beef herd.

WINDMILL ORGANIC STORES

Wymondham Windmill, Butt Lane,
Wymondham, Melton Mowbray, LE14 2BU
Tel: 01572 787700 Fax: 01572 787700
sales@windmillorganicstores.co.uk www.windmillorganicstores.co.uk
Organic shop and delivery scheme of food and non-food items. Online shop and free delivery on all orders over £15 to one address. Veg box scheme.

WOOD – FAMILY BUTCHER, MICHAEL F

51 Hartopp Rd., Leicester, LE2 1WG
Tel: 0116 270 5194 Fax: 0116 270 5194 www.mfwood.co.uk
Soil Association R1979. Retailing of beef, lamb, pork, chicken, turkey, cheese, eggs and butter from a traditional butcher's shop established in 1968.

LINCOLNSHIRE

ALFORD FIVE SAILED WINDMILL

East Street, Alford, LN13 9EQ
Tel: 01507 462136 enquiries@fivesailed.co.uk www.fivesailed.co.uk
Working windmill producing stoneground flours from certified organic grain and cereals of high nutritional value and flavour. Mill, shop and tea room open all year. Open as follows: Jan-Mar: Tues, Sat & Sun; Apr, May, June: Tues, Fri, Sat & Sun; July, Aug, Sep: Daily; Oct: Tues, Fri, Sat & Sun; Nov & Dec: Tues, Sat & Sun. Opening times 10am–5pm (Sun 11am–4pm) Winter closing 4pm. Additional opening for school and bank holidays.

BRIDGE FARM ORGANIC FOODS

Bridge Farm, Snitterby Carr, Gainsborough, DN21 4UU
Tel: 01673 818272 Fax: 01673 818272 patty.bridgefarmconservat@virgin.net
Produce organic goats milk and cheese, organic vegetables. Education resource centre. Rural skills workshops. Members join farm conservation group, receive newsletters, attend open days, undertake conservation tasks.

BROXHOLME FARM SHOP

Grange Farm, Broxholme, Nr. Saxilby, LN1 2NG
Tel: 01522 704212
Lincolnshire Organic Producers, Soil Association G4752. Soil Association eggs, potatoes and Christmas turkeys. Turkeys available by mail order or collected from our farm shop.

CLODDYGATE FARM ORGANIC BED & BREAKFAST

Cloddygate Farm, Owes Lane, Skidbrooke, Louth, LN11 7DE
Tel: 01507 358679 cloddygatefarm@tiscali.co.uk http://myweb.tiscali.co.uk/cloddygatefarm
Good quality organic bed & breakfast in a warm, relaxing, nineteenth century farmhouse set in open farm land on the Lincolnshire coast near Louth. We use organic, fairtrade & additive-free local food. We make all our own preserves using home grown & organic ingredients and keep a few hens in the garden – you won't get fresher eggs anywhere. National nature reserves run along the coast north and south of us, full of wild birds, flowers, and visited by Atlantic grey seals to give birth to their pups in winter. Great for walking, cycling, photography or just relaxing in the garden or by the fire with a book.

LINCOLNSHIRE

ECOLODGE

Rose Cottage, Station Rd., Old Leake, Boston, PE22 9RF
Tel: 01205 871396 gclarke@internationalbusinessschool.net
www.internationalbusinessschool.net/ecolodge
Ecolodge built from Lincolnshire wood, powered by wood and wind. Filtered rainwater for washing. Self-catering. Sleeps 4. Spacious, secluded in 8 acres of wood/meadowland. Walking, cycling and birding. £150 short breaks £300 per week. 10% discount for bookings 3 months or more in advance.

EDEN FARMS

Old Bolingbroke, Spilsby, PE23 4EY
Tel: 01790 763582 Fax: 01790 763582 info@edenfarms.co.uk www.edenfarms.co.uk
Soil Association S31M. Organic salads and vegetables. Eden Farms has been growing organic vegetables for 23 years, and delivers to homes and shops in Lincolnshire, Nottinghamshire and the East Midlands. Also farmers' markets in these areas. Organic Food Awards 2004 Highly Commended Box Scheme.

FENELLA'S GARDEN

Fenella's Garden, Bridge Farm, Snitterby Carr, DN21 4UU
Tel: 01673 818491 hello@fenellasgarden.co.uk www.fenellasgarden.co.uk
Fenella's Garden is an organic market garden based in North Lincolnshire growing fruit, veg, herbs and flowers. We also have small flock of chickens producing organic eggs. We sell through our own box scheme and to local shops.

HOLBEACH WHOLEFOODS

32 High St., Holbeach, Spalding, PE12 7DY
Tel: 01406 422149 springsunshine@aol.com
Natural food store – loose wholefoods, vegetarian and vegan foods, natural healthcare, organic bread, fruit and veg to order. Bulk discounts. Owners vegan, ethical business. Not a box scheme.

KEEP YOURSELF RIGHT

4 Ravendale St., Scunthorpe, DN15 6NE
Tel: 01724 854236
Health food shop selling a wide range of pre-packed organic foods.

LOUTH WHOLEFOOD CO-OP

7-9 Eastgate, Louth, LN11 9NB
Tel: 01507 602411
Wholefood shop selling wide range of organic products including fresh fruit and vegetables, dried fruit, nuts, cereals, tea, coffee, wine, cheese, yoghurt, other chilled and frozen products, toiletries, essential oils, and much more.

MAUD FOSTER MILL

Willoughby Rd., Boston, PE21 9EG
Tel: 01205 352188
The tallest working windmill in Britain, producing stoneground organic flours to Organic Food Federation symbol standard for the wholesale and retail trade.

MOUNT PLEASANT WINDMILL & TRUE LOAF BAKERY
North Cliff Road, Kirton-In-Lindsey, DN21 4NH
Tel: 01652 640177 Fax: 01652 640177 trueloafbakery@aol.com
www.trueloafbakery.co.uk and www.mountpleasantwindmill.co.uk
Four-sailed windmill, restored 1991, producing a range of 10 Soil Association (No. P1497) organic stone-ground flours solely by windpower. Mill, flour sales, tea room, open Tuesday to Sunday all year. Organic bakery with traditional wood fired oven producing good selection of organic breads. Open all year. School & Group visits welcome. Evening tours also available. Coaches must book prior to visit.

NATURAL REMEDY WAREHOUSE
4 Broadgate House, Westlode St., Spalding, PE11 2AF
Tel: 01775 724994 Fax: 01775 761104 nrw@enzymepro.com www.spalding.org.uk/nrw
We stock a variety of organic foods, e.g. bread, flour, honey, yoghurts. Special requests taken. 10% discount on case orders.

THE PINK PIG ORGANIC FARM

Shop, Restaurant and Farm Trail
Holme Hall, Holme, Scunthorpe, DN16 3RE
Tel: 01724 844466 Fax: 01724 866493 enquiries@pinkpigorganics.co.uk www.pinkpigorganics.co.uk
Fantastic wooden beamed farm shop and 80-seater restaurant. Home grown pork, eggs, vegetables and chickens plus local beef and lamb. Home-made ready meals, quiches, cakes, pies and soups. Member of the Soil Association Organic Farms Network.

PRIORY FREE RANGE FOODS

Welton Farm, 51 Priory Rd., Ruskington, Sleaford, NG34 9DJ
Tel: 01526 832574 heather@prioryfreerangefoods.co.uk www.prioryfreerangefoods.co.uk
Priory Free Range Foods is a farm business based near Sleaford in Lincolnshire producing pig, poultry and sheep products and vegetables to Soil Association standards. Open all day Friday and Saturday mornings, local delivery within a ten mile radius of Ruskington for orders over £10, Monday–Thursday.

RIVER NENE HOME DELIVERY (KETTERING & EAST NORTHANTS)

18 High Street, Collyweston, Stamford, PE9 3PW
Tel: 01780 444223 Fax: 01780 444223 mandyandmel@rivernene.co.uk www.rivernene.co.uk
Independent local licensed distributor for River Nene organic vegetables. Award-winning organic vegetable box scheme delivering in Kettering, Desborough, Rothwell, Thrapston, Oundle and surrounding villages. Offering box sizes to suit all households, from a single occupant to a large family. A selection of fruit and vegetable products, wines, beers, dairy and juices are also available. Order weekly, fortnightly or whenever you like. Log on to www.rivernene.co.uk or by telephone on 0845 078 6868.

SADD, B M

Birchwood Farm, Drawdyke, Sutton St. James, Spalding, PE12 0HP
Tel: 01945 440388
Soil Association S34M. Field (potatoes, brassicas, etc.) and glasshouse salad crops. Not a box scheme, but boxes made up for collection.

SPICE OF LIFE
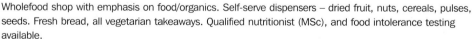

4 Burghley Centre, Bourne, PE10 9EG
Tel: 01778 394735 drwnutrition@aol.com
Wholefood shop with emphasis on food/organics. Self-serve dispensers – dried fruit, nuts, cereals, pulses, seeds. Fresh bread, all vegetarian takeaways. Qualified nutritionist (MSc), and food intolerance testing available.

STRAWBERRY FIELDS

Scarborough Bank, Stickford, Boston, PE22 8DR
Tel: 01205 480490 Fax: 01205 480490 pam@strawberryfields75.freeserve.co.uk
Soil Association B40M. Growing organically since 1975, we specialise in the higher value, more exotic end of the market, inspirational and glowing with health!. Our reputation is built on quality, continuity, reliability and personal service.

VINE HOUSE FARM

Deeping St. Nicholas, Spalding, PE11 3DG
Tel: 01775 630208 Fax: 01775 630244 birdseed@vinehousefarm.co.uk www.vinehousefarm.co.uk
Soil Association G2618. Organic farm that has won many conservation awards including Silver Lapwing award, NFU Farming Excellence award, Waitrose Leaf Marque award. Growing and selling potatoes, french beans, courgettes and sweetcorn and producing other seasonal veg for the farm shop, which also sells wild bird food.

WILSFORD ORGANICS

11 Main St., Wilsford, Grantham, NG32 3NS
Tel: 01400 230224
Soil Association licensed G1708. Organic vegetables and free range eggs to public and wholesale in village of Wilsford, between Sleaford and Grantham, Lincolnshire.

WOODLANDS

Kirton House, Kirton, Nr. Boston,
Lincolnshire, PE20 1JD
Tel: 01205 722491 Fax: 01205 722905 info@woodlandsfarm.co.uk www.woodlandsfarm.co.uk
Soil Association G2224, P5094. Mixed organic farm, producing vegetables, beef and lamb for local, regional and multiple outlets. Organic bronze turkeys available Christmas and Easter. Box scheme delivering to LN, PE, NN & LE postcodes. Member of the Soil Association Organic Farms Network. Organic Food Awards 2004 Producer of the Year; Fresh Fruit and Veg Winner.

NORTHAMPTONSHIRE

ARCADIA ORGANICS

Moorfield Courtyard, Warkton, Kettering, NN16 9XJ
Tel: 01536 525298 Fax: 01536 373609
information@arcadiaorganics.co.uk www.arcadiaorganics.co.uk
Retail farm shop: fresh fruit and veg, meats from Graig Farm Organics, dairy, bakery, box scheme delivery locally (10 miles). Also books. Opening times: Mon–Thurs 10am–5.30pm, Sat 9am–12 midday.

DAILY BREAD CO-OPERATIVE LTD
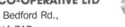   

The Old Laundry, Bedford Rd.,
Northampton, NN4 7AD
Tel: 01604 621531 Fax: 01604 603725 northampton@dailybread.co.uk www.dailybread.co.uk
Soil Association P1498. A drop-off point for Leafcycles organic box scheme, we retail wholefoods, with an increasing range of organic flours, grains, nuts, fruits, etc. Also organic soya milk, yoghurts and cheeses.

LEAFCYCLES

24 St. Michaels Ave, Northampton, NN1 4JQ
Tel: 01604 628956 leafcycles@hotmail.co.uk
We deliver organic fruit and vegetables from Eden Farms in Lincolnshire. Deliveries by bicycle in the Northampton area, by vehicle in Daventry can be made to your home or workplace. Collection from us possible up to 9pm. Evening deliveries also available in NN1.

ORGANIC TRAIL

18 Diswell Brookway, Deanshanger, Milton Keynes, MK19 6GB
Tel: 01908 568952 Fax: 01908 568952 contact@organictrail.co.uk www.organictrail.co.uk
Local delivery of English organic vegetables to your door (seasonal produce): wide delivery area including Milton Keynes, Towcester, Olney and surrounding villages – check the website for the list.

RIVER NENE HOME DELIVERY (KETTERING & EAST NORTHANTS)
18 High Street, Collyweston, Stamford, Lincolnshire, PE9 3PW
Tel: 01780 444223 Fax: 01780 444223 mandyandmel@rivernene.co.uk www.rivernene.co.uk
Independent local licensed distributor for River Nene organic vegetables. Award-winning organic vegetable box scheme delivering in Kettering, Desborough, Rothwell, Thrapston, Oundle and surrounding villages. Offering box sizes to suit all households from a single occupant to a large family. A selection of fruit and vegetable products, wines, beers, dairy and juices are also available. Order weekly, fortnightly or whenever you like. Log on to www.rivernene.co.uk or by telephone on 0845 078 6868.

RIVER NENE HOME DELIVERY (NORTHAMPTONSHIRE/OXON)
71 Byfield Rd., Woodford Halse, NN11 3QS
Tel: 01327 264400 Fax: 01295 760936 robandrachel@rivernene.co.uk www.rivernene.co.uk
Award-winning organic vegetable box scheme delivering in Northamptonshire and north Oxon. Offering differing box sizes to suit all households from single occupants to a large family. A selection of fruit, dairy products, wine, fruit juices etc. also available. Order weekly or whenever you like. Can order online at www.rivernene.co.uk or by telephone on 0845 078 6868.

RUSSELLS OF EVENLEY
23 The Green, Evenley, Brackley, NN13 5SQ
Tel: 01280 702452 Fax: 01280 840274 nicks40@v21.me.uk www.evenley.net
Village delicatessen offers some organic lines. Organic bread daily, organic produce occasionally. Other products available to order.

SAVE THE BACON
Castle Ashby Road, Yardley Hastings, NN7 1EL
Tel: 01604 696859 Fax: 01604 696859 doug@savethebacon.com www.savethebacon.com
We source British organic foods: meat, poultry, fish, cheese and farmhouse cooking. We take orders over the telephone and internet. Deliveries locally (Northants, Milton Keynes, Beds) and nationally.

SWADDLES ORGANIC
Royal Oak, Daventry, NN11 8QY
Tel: 0845 456 1768 Fax: 0870 871 1113 info@swaddles.co.uk www.swaddles.co.uk
Soil Association P1904. Producers of many award-winning meats, pies, bacon, hams, sausages, ready meals. Mail order service of own produce throughout UK, plus a range of organic dairy, grocery, fruit and veg.

NOTTINGHAMSHIRE

GREEN'S MILL & SCIENCE CENTRE
Windmill Lane, Sneinton, Nottingham, NG2 4QB
Tel: 0115 915 6878 Fax: 0115 915 6875 enquiries@greensmill.org.uk www.greensmill.org.uk
Soil Association P4518. Museum: a working tower windmill built in 1807, once operated by the mathematician George Green (1793-1841), now producing organic stoneground flours, including Organic Foods award-winning wholemeal and white spelt flour. Organic Food Awards 2004 Flour Highly Commended.

NATURAL FOOD COMPANY
11 Eaton Place, Bingham, NG13 8BD
Tel: 01949 876483 info@naturalfoodcompany.net
Health food shop and delicatessen, general groceries, fresh bread, chilled and frozen products, cleaning products, toiletries, cosmetics, supplements.

NATURAL FOOD COMPANY

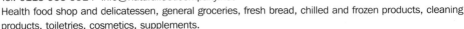

37A Mansfield Road, Nottingham, NG1 3FB

Tel: 0115 955 9914 info@naturalfoodcompany.net

Health food shop and delicatessen, general groceries, fresh bread, chilled and frozen products, cleaning products, toiletries, cosmetics, supplements.

NATURAL FOOD COMPANY

151 -153 Bramcote Lane, Wollaton, Nottingham, NG8 2QJ

Tel: 0115 928 3828 info@naturalfoodcompany.net

Health food shop and delicatessen, general groceries, fresh bread, artisan cheeses, chilled and frozen products, cleaning products, toiletries, cosmetics, supplements.

OUT OF THIS WORLD

Villa St., Beeston, Nottingham, NG9 2NY

Tel: 0115 943 1311 info@ootw.co.uk www.outofthisworld.coop

Small chain of ethical and organic supermarkets in Newcastle-upon-Tyne, Leeds, York and Nottingham. Selling over 5,000 products; most food products certified organic, plus fairly traded crafts, recycled paper and body care products etc. Consumer co-op with over 17,500 members.

RIVER NENE ORGANIC BOX SCHEME

5 Martindale Close, Gamston, Nottingham, NG2 6PN

Tel: 0115 981 0002 allan@rivernene.co.uk www.rivernene.co.uk

Box scheme.

ROOTS NATURAL FOODS

526 Mansfield Rd., Sherwood, Nottingham, NG5 2FR

Tel: 0115 960 9014

Pure vegetarian, organic retailer, box scheme and delivery service.

ROSEMARY'S HEALTH FOODS

6 Lincoln Street, Nottingham, NG1 3DJ

Tel: 0115 950 5072 Fax: 0115 950 5072

 enquiries@rosemaryshealthfoods.co.uk www.rosemaryshealthfoods.co.uk

We sell an extensive range of organic healthy, dried, fresh, chilled, frozen foods, toiletries and herbal remedies.

SHOULS, DI

Barn Farm Cottage, Kneeton Road, East Bridgford, NG13 8PH

Tel: 01949 20196

B&B £30 per person per night. A warm welcome awaits you here in this delightful cottage overlooking the Trent Valley. Three large bedrooms, two sitting rooms, 2 bathrooms, garden, good off-road parking. Self-catering flat available and self-catering barn in conversion. Soil Association supporter of long standing.

TRINITY FARM

Awsworth Lane, Cossall, NG16 2RZ

Tel: 0115 944 2545 Fax: 0115 932 0073 orders@trinityfarm.co.uk www.trinityfarm.co.uk

Meat, game, fish, veg, salad, fruit, cheese, milk, eggs, wholefoods, toiletries, household products. Farm shop with full range of dairy and dried goods including nursery stock.

SOUTH MIDLANDS

BEDFORDSHIRE

PRIORY ORGANIX

13 Wedgwood Rd., Bedford, MK41 7NW
Tel: 07854 393217 www.prioryorganix.co.uk
Fresh certified organically grown vegetables and fruit available in a range of pre-packed box sizes every Thursday. Ordering our organic produce is easy. Organically grown, our vegetables are packed on an organic farm in Lincolnshire. As many items as possible will have been picked early Thursday morning. Delicious and freshly harvested contents varying with the seasons. Our boxes contain a mixture of in-season vegetables, selected from a range of over 50 varieties.

RIVER NENE HOME DELIVERY CAMBRIDGE

20 Meadow Road, Great Gransden, Sandy, SG19 3BD
Tel: 01767 677852 Fax: 01767 677852 martinandjulie@rivernene.co.uk www.rivernene.co.uk
Box scheme delivery service.

RIVER NENE ORGANIC VEGETABLES – BEDFORDSHIRE

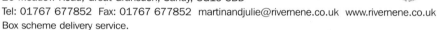

21 Langford Rd., Henlow, SG16 6AF
Tel: 0845 078 6868 Fax: 01462 811811 markandjackie@rivernene.co.uk www.rivernene.co.uk
River Nene Organic Vegetables – home delivery box scheme for Bedfordshire.

SHERRY'S HEALTH FOODS

58 High St., Biggleswade, SG18 0LJ
Tel: 01767 220020 Fax: 01767 782663 sheradbrit@aol.com
Health food shop with wide range of organic foods, vitamins and mineral supplements, herbs, homeopathy, aromatherapy.

WHOLEFOODS & HEALTH

1 Thurlow St., Bus Station Square, Bedford, MK40 1LR
Tel: 01234 219618 Fax: 01234 312929
Extensive range of natural food products, vitamins, minerals, herbal supplements special dietary and organic foods.

BUCKINGHAMSHIRE

CHURCH FARM

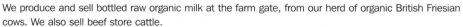

4 Winslow Rd, Swanbourne, Milton Keynes, MK17 0SW
Tel: 01296 720219
We produce and sell bottled raw organic milk at the farm gate, from our herd of organic British Friesian cows. We also sell beef store cattle.

FIELDFARE ORGANIC AND NATURAL LTD

The Barns, Nash Lee Lane, Wendover, HP22 6BG
Tel: 0845 601 3240 Fax: 01296 622245 office@fieldfare-organics.com www.fieldfare-organics.com
Soil Association P1870. Organic Retail Guild. Home delivery of all your organic requirements: fruit and vegetables, bakery and dairy, meat, poultry and fish, wholefoods, wines, beers, aromatherapy and baby care. Our deliveries cover most of London and Hertfordshire, and some of Bucks, Beds and Middlesex.

The Vintage Roots Story . . .

Wine is bottled history, flavours of a summer long gone. A few nights ago I opened a bottle of Botobolar Cabernet Sauvignon 1994 from Mudgee, Australia. Admittedly the cork had dried up, and disintegrated when I tried to pull it from the neck. I ended up pushing it into the bottle, then sieving the garnet nectar through my kitchen sieve into a jug. The fourteen year old wine was blood red, turning to amber at the edges, the nose lively, cedary with smoky black fruit aromas. In the mouth, rich prune and red cherry with layers of vanillary oak and a touch of eucalyptus. It was vibrant, alive and every sip was a joy!

The producer of that wine was Gil Walquist, a Swedish journalist who moved to Australia with his wife in the 1970s. An environmentalist, wine lover and committed organic pioneer who believed in a sustainable, non-chemical approach to viticulture and winemaking, you could tell Gil was committed: he had a sign up at the entrance to his farm saying 'Trepassers will be Composted'! You have to take your hat off to such folk, who in those early years followed their hearts, and often against the odds (and usually much ridicule from their neighbours) produce astoundingly good wines with real integrity.

It was nine years before the grapes for that 1994 Cabernet were grown that the seed of an idea for Vintage Roots was planted. Three friends Peter, Lance and myself, were in our mid-twenties, and had known each other from University and travelling days. In 1983 we set off for France in a friend's customised bus, with five other 'fruity' adventurers. We earned money and had a huge amount of fun picking grapes (*vendage*) in Bourgueil in the Loire valley, followed by a couple of pretty miserable weeks picking apples. On board the bus we had my reggae sound system called 'Surgery': we played several gigs in the Tours and Poitiers areas, as well as getting on a few local radio shows. Our bus, all painted up yellow and red with wood smoke puffing out the chimney on top and thumping dub reggae pumping out its windows, became quite a sight for the bemused French locals. It was during this trip that we enjoyed some great hospitality from some friends of Pete's parents (his mother is French). Pierre and Françoise lived in the suburbs of Tours, where we were able to park our bus up for some weeks, and enjoy the occasional good meal and possibly more importantly have use of their hot shower! They were quite alternative types and already into 'organic living', belonging to an organic cooperative – they even knew about some organic vineyards, which proved to be very useful later on.

Our reggae version of *Summer Holiday* ended in the run up to Christmas 1983, with one of our first and unsuccessful ventures into business. We saw money in the trees near one of our forest park ups outside the city, in the form of mistletoe – lots of huge bunches, there for the taking. We proceeded to harvest a LOT of it, practically filling the whole bus in the hope we could sell it around the markets in London in the run up to Christmas and make a killing. Sadly, Customs at Dover got us to take it all off, so they could send on the sniffer dogs to look for contraband (no kisses for them!). I'd like to think it was the fact that we lost lots of white berries rather than our poor selling techniques that we ended up giving most of it away. Well, hopefully we may have helped a few relationships blossom during the winter of 1993-4!

It was 1985, after plans to open up a wholefood restaurant in Reading failed that Peter called on that list of organic vineyards that Pierre and Françoise had given him. With Lance and I as willing business partners with £2,000 each to put into the pot, we travelled to France again with a bag full of reggae tapes and a tent, this time in my old Citroën to research and visit the organic wine producers. We were inspired by what we saw, whom we met and what we tasted: Vintage Roots was on its way, the name derived from a version of one of those reggae compilation tapes called *Roots in my Boots*.

So on 4th November 1986 Vintage Roots was officially born. We were not wine experts or businessmen, but had a yearning to create something for ourselves, and put our energy into something we really believed in. We started on Maggie Thatcher's Enterprise Allowance Scheme, which gave budding entrepreneurs £40 a week (equivalent to state benefit at the time) for a year to start a business.

Our first wine list was a single sheet of A4 with twelve wines. We hired a van and drove for three days round France to collect our first seventy cases. With newly printed business cards and an empty order book, we set up office in the front room of our terraced house in East Reading and got on the phone! First orders were for family and friends; week 1 – one case sold; week 2 – three cases; week 3 – no cases . . . We delivered orders in our own vehicles, taking the opportunity to cold call on any likely outlets that we saw.

In those early days, the whole concept of 'organic' was little understood. "Is it made from carrots?" and "Has it got any alcohol in?" were by far the two most commonly asked questions. We set out with almost evangelical zeal to convert the UK wine drinking public onto the benefits of drinking organic wine. It wasn't easy, and progress was slow. We stored a gradually increasing stock of wine in a network of (trusted) friends' houses and cellars across Reading, which helped keep our overheads low, and our thanks must go to those articulated lorry drivers that struggled round the back streets on our behalf. Profit was near non-exisitent for at least the first 4–5 years, and Peter left the business in 1991. From the mid 1990s onwards, sales started to flourish as the organic movement gathered pace and various major public health scares hit the headlines.

Fast forward to today (when we have Heinz organic baked beans and Tetley organic tea!): I am immensely proud of our business, which now employs fourteen people and turns over £4 million+ annually. We list over 350 organic wines, beers and spirits, many of which are well respected award winners, and service a diverse spectrum of customers across the whole UK, as well as export to seven countries. We're known as the organic wine specialists. I'm glad we stuck to our guns, and we celebrated our 20th anniversary in 2006. Of course the real respect must go to folk like Gil Walquist; I wonder how many trespassers he actually had?!

Neil Palmer
Co-director
Vintage Roots

FULLER'S ORGANIC FARM SHOP

Manor Farm, Beachampton, Milton Keynes, MK19 6DT

Tel: 01908 269868 Fax: 01908 262285 fullers.organics@farmline.com

Superb quality home produced rare breed organic meat and poultry. Resident Master Butcher, own cured ham and bacon, also eggs, vegetables, dairy and wide range of artisan products.

HEALTHRIGHT

27 High St., Chesham, HP5 1BG

Tel: 01494 771267

Health food store selling a full range of foods, supplements, herbal and homeopathic remedies, aromatherapy oils, filters, cleaning products, books, cassettes, CDs plus Bach care products.

HEALTHRIGHT

48c Friars Square, Aylesbury, HP20 2SP

Tel: 01296 397022 www.healthright.co.uk

We are a health store stocking a range of organic wholefoods and grocery products, also a growing range of body care products with organic ingredients.

ONLY NATURAL

41 St. Peters Court, Chalfont St. Peter, SL9 9QQ

Tel: 01753 889441 Fax: 01753 889441

Small volume of pre-packed organic products including frozen organic ready meals.

ONLY ORGANIC

Notley Farm, Long Crendon, Buckinghamshire, HP18 9ER

Tel: 01844 238064 talktous@onlyorganic.org www.onlyorganic.org

We are an organic produce home delivery company that is Soil Association certified. We cover Bucks, Berks, Oxon & Northants. We primarily deliver fresh fruit and veg, and deliver free to your home or office.

PIZZA ORGANIC LTD

54 London End, Old Beaconsfield, HP9 2JH

Tel: 01494 677758 info@pizzapiazza.co.uk www.pizza-organic.co.uk

A great menu packed full of organic options, featuring stonebaked pizza, sautéed pasta, gourmet burgers, grilled fish and fabulous desserts. Pizza Organic is certified by the Soil Association and was Highly Commended in the 2003 Organic Food Awards. All restaurants open 7 days a week but opening times may vary – call 020 8397 3330 for further details.

REDFIELD COMMUNITY

Buckingham Rd., Winslow, MK18 3LZ

Tel: 01296 713661 Fax: 01296 714983

info@redfieldcommunity.org.uk www.redfieldcommunity.org.uk

Redfield is an intentional community. We grow and raise our own organic produce as well as run courses and offer accommodation for groups.

REVITAL HEALTH AND BEAUTY

12 The Highway, Station Rd, Beaconsfield, HP9 1QQ

Tel: 01494 678787 www.revital.com

Health and beauty shop.

RIVERFORD HOME DELIVERY

24 Badgers Way, Marlow, SL7 3QU

Tel: 01628 440227 jillandsteve@riverfordhomedelivery.co.uk www.riverford.co.uk

Organic vegetable boxes delivered to your door in the Maidenhead, High Wycombe and Slough areas. Order online at www.riverford.co.uk.

RIVER NENE ORGANIC VEGETABLES – HOME DELIVERY (MILTON KEYNES)

14 Enterprise Lane, Campbell Park, Milton Keynes, MK9 4AP

Tel: 0845 078 6868 russell@rivernene.co.uk www.rivernene.co.uk

Award-winning organic vegetable box scheme delivering in Milton Keynes and Buckinghamshire. Offering differing box sizes to suit all households, from a single occupant to a large family. A selection of fruit, dairy products, wine, fruit juices etc. also available. Order weekly, fortnightly or whenever you like. Can order online at www.rivernene.co.uk or by telephone on 0845 078 6868.

THE SUSTAINABLE LIFESTYLES RESEARCH CO-OP LTD

The Office, Pond Cottage East, Cuddington Rd., Dinton, Aylesbury, HP18 0AD

Tel: 01296 747737 mikegeorge.lara@btinternet.com

Organic Food Federation 0071/01/981. Free range eggs, seasonal vegetables and fruit, especially Victoria Plums. Occasional lamb, mutton (Jacobs sheep). Selling at Tring Farmers' market and from farm stall. Full public access to 70 acres. Farm walks through woodland to the riverside. Run by volunteers.

GLOUCESTERSHIRE

ADEYS FARM ORGANIC MEATS

Adeys Farm, Breadstone, Berkeley, GL13 9HF

Tel: 01453 511218 Fax: 01453 511218

Organic beef, lamb, pork, bacon, burgers, speciality sausages, gammon, ham. Traditional breeds including Aberdeen Angus, Gloucester Old Spot, well hung and traditionally butchered.

BETTER FOR ORGANICS

Unit 3, Breadstone Business Centre, Breadstone, Berkeley, GL13 9HF

Tel: 01453 511711 enquiries@betterfororganics.co.uk www.betterfororganics.co.uk

High quality organic delivery service comprising fresh fruit and vegetables, fresh meat and poultry, eggs, milk, cheese, grains, freshly baked craft bread, household, body care and much more.

BOWLDOWN FARMS LTD

Bowldown Farms Ltd, Tetbury, GL8 8UD

Tel: 01666 890224 Fax: 01666 890433 admin@bowldownfarmsltd.co.uk

Soil Association G4157. We seek to retain the traditional Cotswold farm, specialising in organic North Devon beef, lamb and arable products. Conservation and amenity issues are uppermost in our priorities. Box scheme for lamb in autumn and developing box scheme for beef from March to May.

BUTTERCUP ORGANIC DAIRY AND FARM SHOP

Brookthorpe, Gloucester, GL4 0UN

Tel: 01452 812322

Fresh organic milk, yoghurt, cream and butter produced from the Buttercup herd. Organic fruit and vegetables grown on the farm and in the walled garden are sold in the farm shop, as well as home-produced beef and lamb. Shop also stocks organic bread, free range eggs, traditional cheeses, ice cream and a range of organic groceries. Ample parking. Open: Tues–Fri 11am–4.30pm, Sat 10am–1pm.

CAMPHILL OAKLANDS PARK

Horticulture, Oaklands Park, Newnham on Severn, GL14 1EF

Tel: 01594 516550 Fax: 01594 516550 kaigarden@onetel.com www.oaklandspark.org.uk

Biodynamic Agricultural Association 101. Working community with people with special needs. Involved with regional biodynamic land training (2 years), vegetables, herbs and fruit for wholesaling and box scheme. Some meat available for box scheme customers. Above contacts are for wholesale; box scheme contacts are: 01594 516344/510365, anna@bergamot.basil.freeuk.com and www.bergamot.basil.freeuk.com.

CROOKED END FARM ORGANICS

Ruardean, Forest of Dean, GL17 9XF

Tel: 01594 544482 crooked.end@talk21.com

Soil Association (G2393) and HDRA. Small mixed organic farm, close to forest and Wye Valley, producing free range eggs, fruit & vegetables in season, lamb, beef, pork, cider, perry. Self-catering holiday cottage. Stunning views to Welsh mountains.

DAYLESFORD ORGANIC FARMSHOP

Daylesford Organic Farmshop, Daylesford, Nr. Kingham, GL56 0YG

Tel: 01608 731700 Fax: 01608 658009

enquries@daylesfordfarmshop.com www.daylesfordorganic.com

At Daylesford we offer the freshest food in season, from our fully organic estates; we have a passionate commitment to quality. We practise compassionate farming and sustainability: organic beef, lamb, venison and poultry; heritage variety vegetables and fruits; award-winning handmade organic cheeses; organic breads, pastries, and much more. Discover the authentic taste of the best organic food from Daylesford – to take home or to enjoy in our café which was awarded Organic Restaurant of the Year in the Organic Food Awards 2004; Prepared Dishes Highly Commended; Soups and Sauces Winner; Sweet Preserves and Spreads Winner.

DUCHY HOME FARM

Duchy Home Farm, Tetbury, GL8 8SE

Tel: 01666 503507 Fax: 01666 503507 vegbox@duchyhomefarm.org.uk

Duchy Home Farm is located on the outskirts of the old market town of Tetbury and is the home farm to HRH The Prince of Wales. The farm runs a vegetable box scheme, delivering a wide variety of high quality, seasonal produce to customers in and around Tetbury, Cirencester and Stroud. (Deliveries within 10 mile radius of Tetbury only).

EASTLEACH DOWNS ORGANIC FARM

Tallet Barn, Eastleach Downs Farm, Eastleach, Cirencester, GL7 3PX

Tel: 01367 850315 Fax: 01367 850315 helen@eastleachdowns.co.uk www.eastleachdowns.co.uk

Home delivery of locally produced free range organic pork direct from the farmer.

GLOBAL ORGANIC MARKETS

Unit 5, Canal Ironworks, Hope Mill Lane, London Road, Brimscombe, Stroud, GL5 2SH

Tel: 01453 884123 Fax: 01453 884123 globalorganicmarkets@fsmail.net

Fresh fruit, vegetables and eggs: wholesale delivery and collection for box schemes, shops, restaurants and growers. Retail sales from our stalls in Stroud (Gloucestershire) Shambles Market (Friday 8.30–5pm) and Old Spitalfields, London (Sunday 9.30–6pm).

GOODNESS KNOWS

14 Francis St., Cheltenham, GL53 7NY

Tel: 01242 238762 Fax: 01242 525178 enquiries@goodnessknows.co.uk www.goodnessknows.co.uk

Freshly made organic fruit and vegetable baby purées for sale and delivery. Nine 'Mix and Match' pots to aid weaning for babies from 6 months. Free local home delivery, not a box scheme!

THE GREEN SHOP

Bisley, GL6 7BX

Tel: 01452 770629 Fax: 01452 770104 enquiries@greenshop.co.uk www.greenshop.co.uk

Fair traded tea and coffee, books, natural paints and finishes, organic body care, jams, preserves and chocolate, environmentally friendly cleaning products, plus hundreds of other environmental products.

HEALTH-WISE

27 North Walk, Yate, BS37 4AP

Tel: 01454 322168 Fax: 01454 322168

Open Mon–Sat 9am–5.30pm supplying organic cereals, nuts, seeds, jams, flour, vegetarian food, margarines, sheep and goats milk products.

HIGHLEADON HOLIDAY COTTAGES

 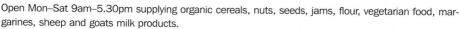

New House Farm, Highleadon, Newent, GL18 1HQ

Tel: 01452 790209 Fax: 01452 790209 cjojan@aol.com

Four star self-catering cottages, one cottage suitable for the disabled. Excellent tourist base for the Royal Forest of Dean; farm walk, no children, short breaks.

HOBBS HOUSE BAKERY

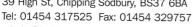

39 High St, Chipping Sodbury, BS37 6BA

Tel: 01454 317525 Fax: 01454 329757

admin@hobbshousebakery.co.uk www.hobbshousebakery.co.uk

We are licensed by the Soil Association (P1632), producing organic white and wholemeal bread for our own shops and wholesale outlets.

LA BODEGA

Taurus Crafts, The Old Park, Lydney, GL15 6BU

Tel: 01594 844841 Fax: 01594 845636 bodega@tauruscrafts.co.uk www.tauruscrafts.co.uk

La Bodega stocks local produce and organic foods, specialising in organic wines, chocolates, coffees and deli foods. We are part of the Taurus Crafts Centre, celebrating healthy living and creative design by bringing together wholesome food, fine arts and handmade crafts. The centre is open to the public from 10am–5.30pm every day.

LIVING EARTH PRODUCE

Ruskin Mill, Old Bristol Rd, Nailsworth, GL6 0LA

Tel: 01453 837510 Fax: 01453 835029

Organic and biodynamic food store. Vegetables, fruit, frozen meat, milk, cheese, yoghurts, herbs and spices, eggs and a wide range of groceries.

MAD HATTERS ORGANIC RESTAURANT

3 Cossack Square, Nailsworth, GL6 0DB

Tel: 01453 832615 Fax: 01453 832615 mafindlay@waitrose.com

Since there are GMOs in animal feeds, we use totally organic meat, milk, butter, cream and cheese. Non-smoking. Wheelchair access. Local seasonal organic produce cooked classically without additives or cheap substitutes by four enthusiastic and idealistic chefs. Organic wines, beers and soft drinks. Bright informal décor.

MOTHER NATURE

2 Bedford St., Stroud, GL5 1AY
Tel: 01453 758202 Fax: 01453 752595 mnstroud@aol.com
Food on three floors. Organic wine, meat, bread, dairy products, champagne and perry. Specialist in water filtration filters, purifiers and systems.

MULADULA

9 Union St., Stroud, GL5 2HE
Tel: 01453 768549 email@muladula.com www.muladula.com
Organic & ethical clothes for babies, children & adults, wooden toys, natural toiletries, latex mattresses etc.

THE NATURAL GROCERY STORE LTD

150–156, Bath Rd., Cheltenham, GL53 7NG
Tel: 01242 243737 Fax: 01242 238872 triple8.trading@virgin.net
Organic fresh fruit and vegetables, dairy, meat, poultry, fish, bread, cakes, wine, beer, spirits, cider, canned, dried and bottled groceries and provisions. All under one roof of 2,000 square feet. Open daily 8am–10pm.

NEAL'S YARD REMEDIES

9 Rotunda Terrace, Montpellier St., Cheltenham, GL50 1SW
Tel: 01242 522136 Fax: 01242 522136 nyr@chelt.net www.nealsyardremedies.com
Neal's Yard Remedies manufacture and sell natural skincare products, and stock an extensive range of herbs, essential oils, homeopathic remedies and books. We also have therapy rooms.

NEWARK FARM

Ozleworth, Wooton-under-Edge, GL12 7PZ
Tel: 01453 842144 Fax: 01453 521432
We produce beef, lamb, multicoloured free range hens' eggs, Ministry-approved seed potatoes, ware potatoes and vegetables.

NUTRITION CENTRE

133 Bath Rd., Cheltenham, GL53 7LT
Tel: 01242 514150 Fax: 01242 580509 sales@nutritioncentre.co.uk www.nutritioncentre.co.uk
Retail and mail order health food store with large range of organic foods and related products. Experienced and friendly trained staff. New website.

NUTRITION CENTRE

28 Winchcombe St., Cheltenham, GL52 1LX
Tel: 01242 529934 Fax: 01242 528700 sales@nutrition centre.co.uk www.nutritioncentre.co.uk
Retail and mail order health food store with large range of organic foods and related products. Experienced and friendly trained staff. New website.

NUTRITION CENTRE

98 High St., Tewkesbury, GL20 5JZ
Tel: 01684 299620 Fax: 01684 274462 sales@nutritioncentre.co.uk www.nutritioncentre.co.uk
Retail and mail order health food store with large range of organic foods and related products. Experienced, friendly, trained staff. New website.

THE ORANGE TREE

317 High Street, Cheltenham, GL50 3HW
Tel: 01242 234232
Vegetarian/vegan restaurant offering world cuisine in relaxed atmosphere. Special diets catered for. Small courtyard patio open in summer.

THE ORGANIC FARM SHOP

Abbey Home Farm, Burford Rd., Cirencester, GL7 5HF
Tel: 01285 640441 Fax: 01285 644827
info@theorganicfarmshop.co.uk www.theorganicfarmshop.co.uk
Soil Association G1715, R5253. 100% organic, award-winning farm, shop and vegetarian café with garden. Cookery courses, educational visits, woodland walk. Our own vegetables, meat, eggs and soft fruit, a vast range of organic food, textiles and environmentally friendly skin care, body care, books and magazines. Large meeting room, yurt and hut for hire, greenfield camping. Member of the Soil Association Organic Farms Network.

THE ORGANIC SHOP

The Square, Stow-on-the-Wold, GL54 1AB
Tel: 01451 831004
The first independently owned retail shop in the UK specialising in the sale of Soil Association symbol produce, including meat. Open 9.00am–5.30pm every day except Christmas and Boxing Day.

PIE AND MASH

10 Bennington Street, Cheltenham, GL50 4ED
Tel: 01242 702785 Fax: 07092 169006 kat@pienmash.com www.pienmash.com
Healthy home-cooked comfort food for meat eaters, vegans, vegetarians, coeliacs, diabetics. Low fat and low salt policy. All ingredients organic & locally sourced. Families & well behaved dogs welcome. Fully licensed. Now open: 3rd certified organic & non-smoking bar in the country!

PINETUM PRODUCTS

Pinetum Lodge, Churcham, GL2 8AD
Tel: 01452 750402 Fax: 01452 750402 www.pinetumlodge.ik.com
Associated with Good Gardeners Association. We run a B&B with excellent accommodation. Natural products and food used and a lecture on organics if required. Organic products for sale via mail order.

RAGMANS

Ragmans Lane Farm,
Lower Lydbrook, GL17 9PA
Tel: 01594 860244 Fax: 01594 860244 info@ragmans.co.uk www.ragmans.co.uk
Ragmans Lane Farm is a 60-acre farm in the Forest of Dean. Our juice and shiitake mushrooms are already certified organic. We produce 3 varieties of apple juice (sweet, medium and dry) and 3 juice blends: pear & apple juice; pear, raspberry & apple juice and raspberry & apple juice. We also produce logs that are pre-inoculated with organic shiitake spawn, available online. We have a comprehensive programme of permaculture and sustainable land use courses. We produce comfrey cuttings and roots for sale by mail order. We offer farm tours by appointment, a campsite, a bunkhouse available for hire for parties up to 16 people.

RIVERFORD HOME DELIVERY – NORTH GLOUCESTERSHIRE

2 Tannery Close, Leonard Stanley, Stonehouse, GL10 3PH
Tel: 01453 828488 Fax: 01453 828488 paul@riverfordhomedelivery.co.uk www.riverford.co.uk
Award-winning organic vegetable box scheme operating in north Gloucestershire. Please visit website www.riverford.co.uk or telephone 0845 600 2311 to see if we deliver in your area.

RIVERFORD HOME DELIVERY – SOUTH GLOUCESTERSHIRE & STROUD

18 Coleridge Gardens, Burnham on Sea, Somerset, TA8 2QA
Tel: 01278 786807 neal@riverfordhomedelivery.co.uk www.riverford.co.uk
Award-winning organic vegetable box scheme operating in Gloucestershire, Wiltshire and Monmouthshire. Please visit our website or telephone 0845 600 2311 to see if we deliver in your area.

RUSKIN MILL COLLEGE

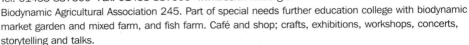

The Fisheries, Horsley, GL6 1PL
Tel: 01453 837500 Fax: 01453 837506 www.ruskin-mill.org.uk
Biodynamic Agricultural Association 245. Part of special needs further education college with biodynamic market garden and mixed farm, and fish farm. Café and shop; crafts, exhibitions, workshops, concerts, storytelling and talks.

SEVERN BANK ORGANICS

Camaroy Farm, Broadoak, Newnham-on-Severn, GL14 1JB
Tel: 01594 516367
We are an organic small-holding producing fresh seasonal vegetables and mixed salad bags all year round. We also produce organic eggs and limited amounts of pork. Our farm shop is open all year, Tuesday–Friday 2pm–6pm, Saturdays 9am–5pm and Sunday mornings. Please phone before visiting if you wish to check produce availability or place an order especially during winter.

SLIPSTREAM ORGANICS

34A Langdon Rd., Cheltenham, GL53 7NZ
Tel: 01242 227273 Fax: 01242 227798
info@slipstream-organics.co.uk www.slipstream-organics.co.uk
Soil Association R1732. Award-winning box scheme, established June 1994, supplying locally grown organic food to over 500 households in Cheltenham, Gloucester and Stroud. Good local supplier links.

ST. AUGUSTINES FARM

Arlingham, Gloucester, GL2 7JN
Tel: 01452 740277 Fax: 01452 740277 staugustines@btconnect.com
Visit a friendly family working organic dairy farm in the beautiful Severn Vale. Feed the many different farm animals, watch the milking, discover the wildlife and enjoy the real countryside. Member of the Soil Association Organic Farms Network.

STROUD COMMUNITY AGRICULTURE LTD

48c High St., Stroud, GL5 1AN
Tel: 0845 458 0814 info@stroudcommunityagriculture.org www.stroudcommunityagriculture.org
A community co-operative which runs a farm business. The farm grows vegetables and has pigs and cattle. Anyone can become a member and order a weekly veg bag with an option to buy meat also. Membership: 01453 840037.

SUNSHINE HEALTH SHOP & ORGANIC BAKERY

25 Church St., Stroud, GL5 1JL
Tel: 01453 763923
Over 3,000 organic and health food products including dietary supplements, herbal and homeopathic medicines, cosmetics and toiletries. Hand-crafted bread using nature's organic ingredients. Manufacturers of Thompson's Slippery Elm foods.

THORNBURY ORGANIC CO-OP

9 Crossways Rd., Thornbury, BS35 2YL
Tel: 01454 415345 judithdale@blueyonder.co.uk
Local buying co-op. We provide a wide range of organic groceries, fruit, vegetables, dairy, bread, wines, beers, fish and meat, which are locally sourced where possible. Local delivery only.

WHITFIELD FARM ORGANICS

Whitfield Farm Organics, Whitfield Farm, Falfield, Wotton under Edge, GL12 8DR

Tel: 01454 261010 jfb@whitfieldfarmorganics.co.uk www.whitfieldfarmorganics.co.uk

We produce beef that is grass-fed and organic beef, sold on farm and at local farmers' markets, plus organic soft fruit.

WYEDEAN WHOLEFOODS

13 Market Street, Cinderford, GL14 2RT

Tel: 01594 825455

Hundreds of organic lines. Wholefoods, gluten- and dairy-free, cruelty-free cosmetics; SLS-free toiletries. Excellent range of vitamins, minerals and herbals. Wide range of chilled and frozen products.

WYEDEAN WHOLEFOODS

15 Market Place, Coleford, GL16 8AW

Tel: 01594 810303

Hundreds of organic lines. Wholefoods, gluten- and dairy-free, cruelty-free cosmetics; SLS-free toiletries. Excellent range of vitamins, minerals and herbals. Wide range of chilled and frozen products.

WYEDEAN WHOLEFOODS

18 Newerne Street, Lydney, GL15 5RF

Tel: 01594 841907

Hundreds of organic lines. Wholefoods, gluten- and dairy-free, cruelty-free cosmetics; SLS-free toiletries. Excellent range of vitamins, minerals and herbals. Wide range of chilled and frozen products.

WYEDEAN WHOLEFOODS

Market Square, Newent, GL18 1PS

Tel: 01531 821922

Hundreds of organic lines. Wholefoods, gluten- and dairy-free, cruelty-free cosmetics; SLS-free toiletries. Excellent range of vitamins, minerals and herbals. Wide range of chilled and frozen products.

WYEDEAN WHOLEFOODS

2 Hare Lane, Gloucester, GL1 2BB

Tel: 01452 423577

Hundreds of organic lines. Wholefoods, gluten- and dairy-free, cruelty-free cosmetics; SLS-free toiletries. Excellent range of vitamins, minerals and herbals. Wide range of chilled and frozen products.

HERTFORDSHIRE

A2Z WHOLEFOODS

No. 69, Market Hall, Charter Place, Watford, WD12 2RN

Tel: 01923 243939 samsweiry@aol.com www.watfordmarket.co.uk

Natural & organic wholefoods. Open Tuesday, Friday and Saturday in Watford Indoor Market. Trade and individual bulk buyers always welcomed. Established since 1977. It is family business.

CLARE JAMES HEALTH FOODS

13A Hempstead Rd., Kings Langley, WD4 8BJ

Tel: 01923 263195

Health food shop selling an extensive range of organics: flour, dried fruit, nuts, pasta, grains, yoghurts, eggs, bread, sugar, honey, jams, cereals, juices, tea, toiletries and much more besides. Sorry, no fresh vegetables.

HERTFORDSHIRE

COOKS DELIGHT

360-364 High Street, Berkhamsted, HP4 1HU

Tel: 01442 863584 Fax: 01442 863702 rex@cooksdelight.co.uk www.organiccooksdelight.co.uk

Queens Award 2001/Business in the Community. National Training Award Champion. Certified organic and biodynamic shop buying ethically from UK where available, otherwise trading in an environmentally and socially responsible way, recycling. Fresh fruit and vegetables, grains, flours, 4,500 organic foods.

EASTWOODS OF BERKHAMSTED

15 Gravel Path, Berkhamsted, HP4 2EF

Tel: 01442 865012 Fax: 01442 877212

joe.collier@btinternet.com www.eastwoodsofberkhamsted.co.uk

Organic meat specialist, national winners of 8 Soil Association Awards. Order on line, mail order, fax, phone. 'Highgrove' meats, many products.

FAIRHAVEN WHOLEFOODS

27 Jubilee Trade Centre, off Jubilee Road, off Baldock Road, Letchworth, SG6 1SP

Tel: 01462 675300 Fax: 01462 483008 sales@fairhaven.co.uk www.fairhaven.co.uk

Large store, easy parking, personal service. Ring for directions. Deliveries throughout north Herts and south Beds. Huge range of organics, diet foods, supplements, body care and more.

GOOSE FAT AND GARLIC

52 Bell Street, Sawbridgeworth, CM21 9AN

Tel: 01279 722554 info@goosefatandgarlic www.goosefatandgarlic.co.uk

Located in the picturesque town of Sawbridgeworth, Goose Fat and Garlic is one of Hertfordshire's most popular restaurants, using only quality fresh ingredients. They have introduced a selection of dishes using organic meat from Soil Association certified Childhay Manor Farm to their new menus, and these are flying out of the kitchen. How do these sound? Slow roasted shoulder of pork with sauté potatoes, apple and red wine jus. Chicken breast stuffed with pesto butter and served with spaghetti. Leg of lamb steak simply chargrilled with rosemary and garlic served with buttered spinach and mash. As time goes on, they expect to increase the presence of organic ingredients on their menus.

HARMONY

53 High Street, Tring, HP23 5AG

Tel: 01442 822311

Dried goods, tinned goods and other foodstuffs. No fresh vegetables or meat produce. Environmentally friendly household cleaners, organic shampoos, body care ranges.

MILL GREEN MUSEUM & MILL

Mill Green, Hatfield, AL9 5PD

Tel: 01707 271362 Fax: 01707 272511 museum@welhat.gov.uk

Soil Association P1470. Working water mill producing organic stoneground wholemeal flour.

ORGANIC HARVEST

4 Middle Row, Old Stevenage, SG1 3AN

Tel: 01438 225222 Fax: 01438 225111

Family-run organic supermarket. Complete range of organic foods, eco products, allergy foods. Box scheme, range of fairly traded gifts and jewellery.

FOR DETAILS OF SYMBOLS USED IN THE ENTRIES, SEE PAGE 17

REDBOURNBURY WATERMILL

Redbournbury Lane,
Redbourn Road, St.Albans, AL3 6RS
Tel: 01582 792874 Fax: 01582 792874 redbrymill@aol.com www.redbournmill.co.uk
18th Century Working watermill producing a range of stoneground organic flours, including 100% wholemeal, unbleached white, brown, malted wheatflake, rye and spelt. Available in 500g to 32kg sizes. Mill open to public every Sunday afternoon from March to October – see website for more details.

OXFORDSHIRE

ARUJO ORGANICS

39a Rochester Way, Twyford, Adderbury,
Oxfordshire, OX17 3JU
Tel: 01295 811140 info@arujo-organics.com www.arujo-organics.com
Arujo Organics offer a large range of organic food, drink and natural household products. They run an organic vegetable box scheme in conjunction with a local organic farm. Arujo Organics are stockists of the Ecover eco-friendly household cleaning range and offer an in-store refill service.

BARRINGTON PARK ESTATE

Great Barrington, Burford, OX18 4US
Tel: 01451 843015 Fax: 01451 844705 adrian@barrington-park.co.uk
Situated in the Cotswold hills producing organic beef, lamb, eggs and arable crops.

BEANBAG NATURAL HEALTH

2 Wesley Walk, Witney, OX28 6ZJ
Tel: 01993 773922 Fax: 01993 708689 john@beanbag-health.co.uk www.beanbag-health.co.uk
Vegetarian health food shop, over 250 organic products. Meat-free, dairy-free, gluten-free, wheat-free.
Pick up point for Coleshill Organics box scheme.

CHILTERN ORGANICS

Tel: 01494 883868 info@chilternorganics.co.uk www.chilternorganics.co.uk
Free local delivery of organic vegetables, fruit eggs and cheeses based in Hambleden Valley near Henley-on-Thames delivering produce sourced locally wherever possible, to south Oxfordshire, south Bucks and east Berks.

CHIPPING NORTON ORGANICS

Unit 11, Elmsfield Industrial Estate, Chipping Norton, OX7 5XL
Tel: 01608 642973 Fax: 01608 642973
sales@chippingnortonorganics.co.uk www.chippingnortonorganics.co.uk
Soil Association registered no. R1816. Wide range of local, UK and imported veg and fruit. Boxes made up to suit individual requirements. Also bread, eggs, milk, all organic. Weekly deliveries within 15 mile radius of Chipping Norton.

EAT ORGANIC

Little Bottom Farm, Rotherfield Peppard,
Henley, RG9 5LT
Tel: 0118 987 1854 Fax: 0871 994 1330 enquiries@eatorganic.co.uk www.eatorganic.co.uk
We are have a small market garden near Henley where we grow salad and brassicas. We also source fruit and veg from other local and UK suppliers. We source some fruit and veg from Europe where not available in the UK. We stock pantry, bread, household cleaning and dairy items. We also run a box scheme, delivering to south Oxfordshire, Henley, Reading, Wokingham, Bracknell and Maidenhead.

FELLER, SON & DAUGHTER M.

54/55 Covered Market, Oxford, OX1 3DY

Tel: 01865 251164 Fax: 01865 200553

Soil Association P4455. Family organic butcher shop. Local delivery service available.

FRUGAL FOOD

17 West Saint Helen St., Abingdon, OX14 5BL

Tel: 01235 522239

Independent wholefood and organic grocery with friendly knowledgeable staff, selling a wide range of food, drink, supplements, remedies, cleaning products, body care and special diets.

GLUTTONS DELICATESSEN

110 Walton Street, Oxford, OX2 6AJ

Tel: 01865 553748

Friendly family-run delicatessen specialising in excellent home-cooked foods. Comprehensive range of local and organic produce, large selection of organic wines.

THE INNER BOOKSHOP

111 Magdalen Road, Oxford, OX4 1RQ

Tel: 01865 245301 Fax: 01865 245521 mail@innerbookshop.com www.innerbookshop.com

In the Green section there are books on organic farming, gardening. Also organic cookery in our nutrition and food section. There is also a section called Gaia, which carries books about living in harmony with the planet and the spiritual approach towards that. All stock is available online, new, bargain and secondhand and there is worldwide mail order.

IVY COTTAGE CAMPING

Sulgrave Road, Culworth, Banbury, OX17 2AP

Tel: 01295 768131

Seasonal organic fruit and veg, free range eggs, geese, ducks, chickens, cats. Many attractions nearby, easy distance to Oxford, Stratford and Warwick. Garden flat for minimum of 6 monthly let. Camping field available £6 per tent per night plus £1 per person.

MATTHEWS LTD, FWP –
THE COTSWOLD FLOUR MILLERS

Station Rd., Shipton under Wychwood, Chipping Norton, OX7 6JG

Tel: 01993 830342 Fax: 01993 831615 sales@fwpmatthews.co.uk www.fwpmatthews.co.uk

Soil Association P1521. Flour millers. An independent, family owned flour mill, producing high quality organic flours, supplying all markets from the home breadmaker to bakers' shops to large food production companies.

NEAL'S YARD REMEDIES

56 High St., Oxford, OX1 4AS

Tel: 01865 245436 Fax: 01865 245436 mark.higgins@lineone.net www.nealsyardremedies.com

Supplier of organic natural medicines and natural cosmetics.

NORTH ASTON ORGANICS

3 Somerton Rd., North Aston, OX25 6HP

Tel: 01869 347702 Fax: 01869 347702

We grow a wide range of vegetables and culinary herbs. We are committed to local delivery (20 miles radius) and freshness, with many items harvested on day of delivery.

RIVERFORD HOME DELIVERY – OXFORDSHIRE

1 Williamstrip Farm Cottages, Coln St. Aldwyns, Gloucestershire, GL7 5AU
Tel: 01285 750777 graham@riverfordhomedelivery.co.uk www.riverford.co.uk
Home delivery of organic food produce throughout Oxfordshire.

SARSDEN ORGANICS

Walled Garden, Sarsden Estate, Chipping Norton, OX7 6PW
Tel: 01608 659670 Fax: 01608 659670 sarsdenorganics@btopenworld.com
. 2-acre walled garden producing a variety of vegetables and fruit for sale locally on regular farmers' market
in Oxford. Veg box including fruit, herbs and flowers for collection from the walled garden one day a week
(Friday) by pre-arranged order form.

SAUNDERS, M

Step Farm, Lechlade Road, Faringdon, SN7 8BH
Tel: 01367 240558 Fax: 01367 244324 miles@stepfarm.fsnet.co.uk
Sell organic lamb, beef. Jointed and frozen. Opening times by arrangement. Member of the Soil
Association Organic Farms Network.

TOLHURST ORGANIC PRODUCE

West Lodge, Hardwick, Whitchurch-on-Thames, Pangbourne, Reading, RG8 7RA
Tel: 0118 984 3428 Fax: 0118 984 3428 tolhurstorganic@yahoo.co.uk
Organic growers since 1976. Box scheme deliveries to Reading and Oxford drop-off points. We produce
over 90% of the vegetables that we sell. Organic fruit also available. Alternative phone/fax: 01865
556151.

UHURU WHOLEFOODS

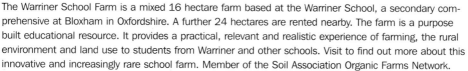

48 Cowley Rd., Oxford, OX4 1HZ
Tel: 01865 248249

Uhuru has 30+ years experience in the organic and natural wholefoods trade. Our stock ranges from
organic dairy produce to organic fruits and vegetables, wines and beers. Monthly local home deliveries.

WARRINER SCHOOL FARM

The Warriner School, Bloxham, Banbury, OX15 4LJ
Tel: 01295 720777 Fax: 01297 721676 www.atschool.eduweb.co.uk/warriner
The Warriner School Farm is a mixed 16 hectare farm based at the Warriner School, a secondary comprehensive at Bloxham in Oxfordshire. A further 24 hectares are rented nearby. The farm is a purpose
built educational resource. It provides a practical, relevant and realistic experience of farming, the rural
environment and land use to students from Warriner and other schools. Visit to find out more about this
innovative and increasingly rare school farm. Member of the Soil Association Organic Farms Network.

WILLOWBROOK FARM

Hampton Gay, OX5 2QQ
Tel: 01865 849957 Fax: 01865 849957 radwans@btinternet.com www.willow-brook-farm.co.uk
Family farm in Cherwell Valley ESA (Environmentally Sensitive Area) specialising in eggs, table birds, lamb
and goat.

*FOR DETAILS OF
SYMBOLS USED
IN THE ENTRIES,
SEE PAGE 17*

WEST MIDLANDS

HEREFORDSHIRE

ARKSTONE MILL PRODUCE

Arkstone Mill, Kingstone, Hereford, HR2 9HU
Tel: 01981 251135 paul@arkstonemill.co.uk
Organic vegetable box scheme serving Hereford and the Golden Valley area.

BUTFORD ORGANICS

Butford Farm, Bowley Lane, Bodenham, HR1 3LG
Tel: 01568 797195 Fax: 01568 797885 info@butfordorganics.co.uk www.butfordorganics.co.uk
Certified with the Soil Association (no. G5368). We are small-scale producers of award-winning cider and perry, organic pork, geese, eggs, seasonal vegetables, soft and top fruit.

DUNKERTONS CIDER CO LTD & SHOP

Luntley, Pembridge, Nr. Leominster, HR6 9ED
Tel: 01544 388653 Fax: 01544 388654 enquiries@dunkertons.co.uk www.dunkertons.co.uk
Ciders and perry, still and sparkling. Draught and bottled. Traditional local varieties of cider apples pressed, fermented and bottled at the mill. Retail shop open Monday–Saturday 10am–6pm (5pm in winter) for sales of ciders and perry. Organic Food Awards 2004 Cider Commended.

FIELD FAYRE

18-19 Broad Street, Ross-on-Wye, HR9 7EA
Tel: 01989 566683 Fax: 01989 566924 enquiries@field-fayre.co.uk www.field-fayre.co.uk
Friendly shop in the town centre specialising in organic produce including local fruit and vegetables, bread, dairy products, meat and fish, chocolate, wine, beer, local cider and much more! Ecover products also available.

FLIGHTS ORCHARD ORGANICS

Units 3 & 4, Lower Road Trading Estate, Ledbury, HR8 2DJ
Tel: 0845 658 9808 Fax: 0845 658 9809
info@flightsorchardorganics.co.uk www.flightsorchardorganics.co.uk
Marketing group of growers based in Herefordshire. Home delivery throughout the Midlands, wholesale delivery nationwide. Over 85 different sorts of fruit and vegetables grown throughout the year.

FLIGHTS ORCHARD ORGANICS HOME DELIVERY

Kendricks Cottage, Howlers Heath, Bromesberrow, Ledbury, HR8 1SE
Tel: 0845 658 9808 chris@flightsorchardorganics.co.uk www.flightsorchardorganics.co.uk
Fresh, tasty organic fruit and veg delivered direct to your door in a refrigerated van. Weekly or fortnightly deliveries to suit your needs. Boxes range from the single person's box to a large family box! Also available are organic eggs, apple juice, cider, nuts and seeds and mushrooms, plus seasonal promotions like Easter eggs and Christmas cheese platters.

FLIGHTS ORCHARD ORGANICS HOME DELIVERY

Sunflower Cottage, 6 Crescent Rd., Colwall, WR13 6QW
Tel: 07837 420 749 pete@flightsorchardorganics.co.uk www.flightsorchardorganics.co.uk
We distribute a range of organic veg and fruit boxes, mostly grown on our own farms in Herefordshire and Worcestershire. We believe in sustainability, access to fresh organic food for everyone, and a fair price for all. We deliver to homes in our distribution range, which covers Herefordshire, and includes Monmouth town and Ludlow too.

5-A-DAY
THE VEG BOX WAY!

FRESH, ORGANIC & LOCAL VEGETABLES
DELIVERED TO YOUR DOOR...

We deliver fresh-from-the-field, naturally grown, genuinely seasonal, organic produce direct to your door – so no heavy bags, long queues or fruitless searches for parking bays! Over the year, 85% of the box content comes from our farm or from a group of local producers, which means it is picked, packed and despatched within 24 hours.

LOCAL PRODUCE LOCAL PEOPLE direct to your door.

Kept chilled the flavour, freshness and importantly, the nutritional value is preserved from our field to your plate!

Choose a Veg Box to suit your needs.

Each week the contents will vary according to what is in season, but there will always be a balance of staples, exotics, roots and salads. The bigger boxes have a larger selection and greater quantity of vegetables; contents are listed on our website from Friday evening of the week before delivery.

STAPLES	The basic 'no nonsense' family sized mixed veg and fruit box.		£18.25
MULTI	A large 'just veg' box with a wide variety of seasonal produce.		£12.95
COMBI	A popular medium sized mixed box of seasonal veg and fruit.		£11.95
FRUIT SELECTION	Fruit, fruit and more fruit! A seasonal mix throughout the year.		£8.95
ESSENTIAL	A medium sized seasonal 'just veg' box.		£8.25
SOLO	A good variety of veg in smaller quantities.		£6.00
MINI FRUIT	Always apples, oranges and bananas.		£4.50
LARGE SALAD*	Not just lettuce and tomatoes! A lovely large box of summer season salad produce.		£12.00
MEDIUM SALAD*	Salad as you know it and more besides! Summer season produce at its best.		£9.00

† Summer season only. Prices correct at time of going to print.

FREE DELIVERY

Call 0845 658 9808

sales@flightsorchardorganics.co.uk
www.flightsorchardorganics.co.uk

Flights Orchard Organics

137

FODDER, THE HEALTH STORE

26-27 Church St., Hereford, HR1 2LR
Tel: 01432 358171 Fax: 01432 277861
The largest range of organic wholefoods, veg, bread, yoghurts, wines, cider in the area, plus herbal and homeopathic remedies. Also Ecover products, essential oils.

GREEN ACRES ORGANIC GROWERS

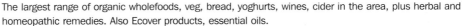

Green Acres Farm Shop, Dinmore,
Hereford, HR4 8ED
Tel: 01568 797045
Soil Association J14M. Organic market garden and farm shop established 1982. Sunday and Monday open by arrangement, Tuesday–Saturday 9am–5.30pm. Produce includes meat, vegetables, fruit, ice cream, cider, wine, preserves, bread etc. Local delivery service.

GREEN CUISINE LTD

Penrhos Court, Kington, HR5 3LH
Tel: 01544 230720 Fax: 01544 230754 daphne@greencuisine.org www.greencuisine.org
Soil Association E2051. Green Cuisine runs courses on food and health and offers consultations and natural therapies. The company also produce books and educational material. See also Penrhos Ltd and The Penrhos Trust.

GEORGE'S DELICATESSEN

25 High St., Kington, HR5 3AX
Tel: 01544 231400
A busy delicatessen selling a large range of cheeses, tea, coffee, loose spices, home-made cakes, wines and local ciders.

HAY WHOLEFOODS AND DELICATESSEN

41 Lion St., Hay-on-Wye, HR3 5AA
Tel: 01497 820708
Large and comprehensive wholefood shop with wide range of organic goods including wine, cheese, vegetables and groceries. Good delicatessen with organic choice where possible.

HELME, EBM AND SONS

Pool Hullock, Llandinabo, HR
Tel: 01989 730632 Fax: 01989 730632
Soil Association G613. General veg and Pool Hullock extra delicious organic chickens.

HENCLOSE ORGANIC FARM PRODUCE

Little Dewchurch, Hereford, HR2 6PP
Tel: 01432 840826
Demeter organic certification No. 394. Home-produced lamb, pork, kid, bacon, sausages and goats milk from old and semi-rare breeds. 25 years organic status. Phone for availability and collection. Self-catering converted barn for holidays or long lets. Gloucester Old Spot registered organic weaners for sale.

HOPES OF LONGTOWN

The Farmers Barn, Longtown, HR2 0LT
Tel: 01873 860444 info@hopesoflongtown.co.uk www.hopesoflongtown.co.uk
An independent village shop and post office retailing local products, fair trade teas and coffees, organic and vegan supplies, fresh fruit and veg and home-made cakes.

LEDBURY WHOLEFOODS

82 The Homend, Ledbury, HR8 1BX

Tel: 01531 632889 ledbury.wholefoods@virgin.net

Natural food and medicine store. Speciality and diet foods, gluten-free, organic and fair trade products. Vitamins and remedies, therapists, allergy testing, homeopathy, therapy rooms.

NATURE'S CHOICE RESTAURANT & GUESTHOUSE

Raglan House, 17 Broad Street, Ross-on-Wye, HR9 7EA

Tel: 01989 763454 Fax: 01989 763064 allanlyus@surfree.co.uk www.natures-choice.biz

Licensed organic restaurant and guesthouse specializing in varied dietary needs, gluten-free, vegan, vegetarian, meat, non-dairy etc. Delicious American and Mexican influenced foods in a smoke-free, eco-friendly environment. Centrally located in downtown Ross-on-Wye. All year round, Monday–Saturday 10am–5pm. Sundays 10am–2pm. Menus available on the website.

NITTY GRITTY WHOLEFOODS

24 West St., Leominster, HR6 8ES

Tel: 01568 611600

Traditional wholefood shop. Free range eggs and dairy produce, trees and herbaceous.

THE OLD DAIRY

Winnal Common Farm, Allensmore, Hereford, HR2 9BS

Tel: 01432 277283 winnal@aol.com www.winnal.com

Holiday cottage – a converted dairy – on a working organic farm.

OLD KING STREET FARM

Ewyas Harold, Hereford, HR2 0HB

Tel: 01981 240208 info@oldkingstreetfarm.co.uk www.oldkingstreetfarm.co.uk

Llama trekking and holiday cottages on our organic farm. Pomona cottage sleeps 4 and the Cider House sleeps 2. Day trekking with our gentle llamas, local organic picnic included.

PENRHOS

Penrhos Court, Kington, HR5 3LH

Tel: 01544 230720 Fax: 01544 230754 info@penrhos.co.uk www.penrhos.co.uk

700-year-old farmstead – now the most delightful hotel anywhere. Millennium Marque award for environmental excellence. Voted Best Organic Restaurant of the Year 2002. See also Green Cuisine Ltd and The Penrhos Trust.

STEVENSON, PEGGYANNE

Windle Park, Clifford, Hay0on-Wye, HR3 5HA

Tel: 01497 831666

Small organic farm in an idyllic setting with traditional Hereford cattle and a flock of Portland sheep. accommodation for riders and their horses, caravan site.

SURVIVAL WHOLEFOODS

Unit 1, Prince Of Wales Business Park, Bridge St., Leominster, HR6 8EA

Tel: 01568 614147 Fax: 01568 612678

A unique wholefoods experience. Shop with delivery service to the Midlands, Wales, Herefordshire, Shropshire, Worcestershire, Gloucestershire. Survival Wholefoods is run by Mark and Mary Hatt.

TY-MYNYDD MOUNTAIN FARM BED&BREAKFAST AND TIPI HOLIDAYS.

Ty-Mynydd, Llanigon, Hay-on-Wye, HR3 5RJ

Tel: 01497 821593 nikibarber@tiscali.co.uk www.tymynydd.co.uk

Organic bed and breakfast situated in the Black Mountains of Wales, offering stunning views, top quality comfort in a relaxed friendly home (see website). Breakfast using our own produce including home-made bread and sausages. We run our home on a chemical-free basis, recycling energy and waste. Members of the Tir Gofal environmental scheme.

WESTON'S CIDER

The Bounds, Much Marcle,

Ledbury, HR8 2NQ

Tel: 01531 660233 Fax: 01531 660619 marketing@westons-cider.co.uk www.westons-cider.co.uk

Soil Association P1776. Westons have been producing cider since 1880. The organic cider was winner at the Organic Food Awards in1998 and 2003. Producers of Organic Vintage Cider and Organize, the non-alcoholic nutrient drink. Organic Food Awards 2004 Cider Winners.

WYEDEAN WHOLEFOODS

4 Gloucester Road, Ross-on-Wye, HR9 5BU

Tel: 01989 562340

Hundreds of organic lines. Wholefoods, gluten- and dairy-free, cruelty-free cosmetics; SLS-free toiletries. Excellent range of vitamins, minerals and herbals. Wide range of chilled and frozen products.

SHROPSHIRE

BOXFRESH ORGANICS

Unit 5c, Rodenhurst Business Park, Rodington, SY4 4QU

Tel: 01952 770006 www.boxfreshorganics.co.uk

Delivery service of a wide range of organic fruit, veg, eggs, meat, dairy products and honey. We deliver in Shropshire, Staffordshire, West Midlands and Cheshire. Excellent, reliable customer service, easy online ordering, with the accent very much on locally grown produce. Alternative telephone 07786 918322.

BROAD BEAN

60 Broad St., Ludlow, SY8 1NH

Tel: 01584 874239

Retailers of organic wines, dairy produce, meat, wholefoods and fine foods, plus essential oils, vitamins, supplements, Brita water filters and cartridges.

CORVEDALE ORGANIC LAMB

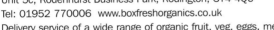

Corve House, Rowe Lane, Stanton Long, Much Wenlock, TF13 6LR

Tel: 01746 712539

Soil Association G4606. Organic lamb direct from farm to customer, traditional English breeds, traditional taste, no order too small, free delivery in south Shropshire area.

ELLESMERE ROAD ORGANIC NURSERY

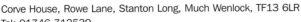

Ellesmere Road Organic Nursery, Cockshutt, Ellesmere, SY12 9AB

Tel: 01939 270270

Soil Association G1447. All produce grown on our nursery, vegetables, salads an fruit fresh picked, also PYO fruit.

FOOD FOR THOUGHT

Unit 3, Heath Hill Industrial Estate,
Dawley, Telford, TF4 2RH
Tel: 01952 630145 Fax: 01952 630145 info@ecoal.co.uk www.ecoal.co.uk
Soil Association R2086. We are an organic shop with regular local and national home delivery service. Wide range of organic, fair traded food, body care and eco-friendly products. Long established family business.

FORDHALL FARM

Tern Hill Rd., Market Drayton, TF9 3PS
Tel: 01630 638255 info@fordhallfarm.com www.fordhallfarm.com
We sell home reared, grass fed, beef and lamb. Our pastures have been organic for 60+ years and livestock are organically reared. Not currently registered but working with the Soil Association and other environmental organisations to secure the farm's future. Farm shop and nature trail open Friday to Sunday. Visit our website for the full story of Fordhall Farm.

GUNTON, JOHN & JACKIE

Green Gorse Wood, Whitchurch Rd, Prees, SY13 3JZ
Tel: 01948 841376
30 years on and we still grow organically and by hand a wide range of vegetables and some fruit, which we pick fresh and sell exclusively from our own stall on Whitchurch (Shropshire) traditional Friday Market throughout the year.

HAFREN ORGANICS
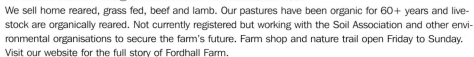

5 Greyfriars Bridge, Longden Coleham, Shrewsbury, SY3 7DS
Tel: 01743 231414 doctorfi38@hotmail.com www.hafrenorganics.co.uk
Fruit, vegetables, meat, poultry, fish, vegetarian products, bread, cakes, groceries, toiletries, Ecover refill service. Local produce a speciality. Box scheme delivery service.

HARVEST WHOLEFOODS

Lydham, Bishops Castle, SY9 5HB
Tel: 01588 638990 Fax: 01588 630298
We stock a wide range of wholefoods, organically grown fruit and vegetables, herbs and spices, natural remedies, environmental and biodegradable products, special dietary foods etc. Bulk discounts to order. Open Monday–Saturday 9am–5.30pm.

HONEYSUCKLE WHOLEFOOD CO-OPERATIVE LTD

53 Church St., Oswestry, SY11 2SZ
Tel: 01691 653125 info@honeysuckle-wholefoods.co.uk www.honeysuckle-wholefoods.co.uk
Soil Association P5639. Established in 1978, we sell a large range of organic fresh vegetables and fruit, locally grown when available. Also a wide selection of organic wholefoods and dairy products; also local bread, eggs and honey.

HOPE ORGANIC PRODUCE

Hope House, Sandy Lane, Stoke Heath, Market Drayton, TF9 2LG
Tel: 01630 638348 pete@hopeorganicproduce.co.uk www.hopeorganicproduce.co.uk
Soil Association B42M. Herb plants, seasonal vegetables sold in local shops/garden centres and farmers' markets.

HOPESAY GLEBE FARM

Hopesay, Craven Arms, SY7 8HD

Tel: 01588 660737 phil.moore@hopesay.freeserve.co.uk

Family-run organic smallholding selling at Birmingham and Moseley farmers' markets and Shrewsbury indoor market every Saturday. We also offer self-catering accommodation and B&B.

MASON, RUTH AND IAN

Five Acres, Ford, Shrewsbury, SY5 9LL

Tel: 07952 532719 iangmason@btinternet.com www.organicshropshire.co.uk

Over 50 varieties of apple: £15 per 30lb. box collected. 15 varieties of plum and gage. Graftwood at 50p per piece. Apple trees for sale.

MYRIAD ORGANICS BY ORDER

22 Corve Street, Ludlow, SY8 1DA

Tel: 01584 872665 Fax: 01584 879356 enquiries@organicbyorder.co.uk www.organicbyorder.co.uk

Soil Association R5414. One-stop organic food shop: all you need for a family shop plus seeds and books. Near Ludlow Station, customer parking. Friendly, well informed staff.

ORGANIC BY ORDER

22 Corve Street, Ludlow, SY8 1DA

Tel: 01584 874888 Fax: 01584 879356 enquiries@organicbyorder.co.uk www.organicbyorder.co.uk

Soil Association GCS012, G1915, P1916. Organic vegetables, fruit and all the produce stocked in Myriad Organics shop delivered throughout Shropshire, north Herefordshire and west Staffordshire.

PIMHILL FARM AND MILL

Lea Hall, Harmer Hill, Shrewsbury, SY4 3DY

Tel: 01939 290342 info@pimhillorganic.co.uk

Growers and millers of organic cereals supplying wholemeal flour, porridge oats and muesli.

RSPB LAKE VYRNWY

Bryn Awel, Llanwddyn, SY10 0LZ

Tel: 01691 870278 Fax: 01691 870313 jo.morris@rspb.org.uk www.rspb.org.uk

RSPB rears and producers organic lamb and beef. The lamb is sold locally through the RSPB shop at Lake Vyrnwy. The farm is part of a National Nature Reserve in the Berwyns. It is a farm that is business-viable and farmed to be wildlife-friendly.

WHEELER, S & SON

Brynmawr Newcastle,

Craven Arms, SY7 8QU

Tel: 01588 640298 Fax: 01588 640298 brynmawr@farmersweekly.net www.clunvalleyorganics.co.uk

Soil Association G6570. Mixed hill farm with eco-friendly self-catering cottage and caravan accommodation, specialising in potatoes, carrots and daffodil bulbs.

WILD THYME WHOLEFOODS

1/2 Castle Gates, Shrewsbury, SY1 2AQ

Tel: 01743 364559

A wide range of organic and natural products including fresh fruit and vegetables, nuts, pulses, snacks, beverages, body care, household, local crafts and complementary medicines.

STAFFORDSHIRE

BOOTS HERBAL STORES LTD

5 Castle Walk, Newcastle, ST5 1AN

Tel: 01782 617463 Fax: 01782 636098 bootsherbal@btconnect.com

Family business, established 1939. Stock organic and fair trade vegetarian foods wherever possible. Organic herbal tinctures, cosmetics toiletries and Ecover household products available.

FRUITS OF THE EARTH

44 Beggars Lane, Leek, ST13 8XE

Tel: 07751 760293 sales@fruitsoftheearth.info www.fruitsoftheearth.info

Box scheme delivery service to a 15-mile radius of Leek, Staffordshire. Market stall in Leek's Festival of Fine Foods every 3rd Saturday of the month.

THE REAL FOOD COMPANY

50 Sandbach Road South, Alsager, Stoke-on-Trent, ST7 2LP

Tel: 01270 873322 realfood.co@ntlworld.com

Organic wholefoods, vegetables and fruit, including box scheme, frozen and chilled organic meat and fish, cosmetics and toiletries, Ecover refills, herbal, homeopathic, supplements etc. Large choice to be found in helpful shop with knowledgeable staff. Local deliveries.

SAPORITO

Unit 4 Corn Exhange, Conduit Street, Lichfield, WS13 6JU

Tel: 01543 414155 Fax: 01543 414155 saporito@hotmail.co.uk www.shop-saporito.com

Mediterranean delicatessen: range includes organic herbs and spices, organic oils and speciality teas.

WARWICKSHIRE

BEANIE SERVICES

86 Nunts Park Avenue, Coventry, CV6 4GY

Tel: 07810 422136 steve@flightsorchardorganics.co.uk www.flightsorchardorganics.co.uk

We distribute a range of organic veg and fruit boxes, mostly grown on our own farms in Herefordshire and Worcestershire. We believe in sustainability, access to fresh organic food for everyone, and a fair price for all. We deliver to homes in our distribution range covering Coventry, Warwick, Leamington Spa, Kenilworth, Southam and all points in between.

CLEEN GREEN

43 Barons Croft, Sherbourne Grange, Nuneaton, CV10 9QQ

Tel: 0845 054 4757 Fax: 0845 054 4758 sales@cleengreen.co.uk www.cleengreen.co.uk

Biodegradable, hypoallergenic household cleaning products which are approved by the WWF, Naturewatch Trust & the Vegan Society. Our range includes washing powder, fabric conditioner, washing-up liquid, laundry liquid, nappy fresh, toilet cleaner, multi-surface cleaner, household polish & glass cleaner. The products have the following benefits: not tested on animals, natural (non-GM) ingredients, renewable resources, biodegradable, British-made, enzyme- & bleach-free, suitable for cesspits & septic tanks. We offer a free of charge home delivery service to the CV, B, LE & DE postcode areas within a 30 mile radius of Nuneaton (£10 minimum order value). Mail order also available.

FOR DETAILS OF SYMBOLS USED IN THE ENTRIES, SEE PAGE 17

ELMHURST ORGANIC FARM

Bow Lane, Withybrook, Coventry, CV7 9LQ

Tel: 01788 832233 Fax: 01788 832690

Soil Association G761. Organic meat producer and retailer. Beef, sheep, pigs and poultry and eggs. Shop retails only own produce, open Monday, Tuesday, Friday and Saturday, 9am–4pm. Member of the Soil Association Organic Farms Network. Mobile: 07754 697577.

FELDON FOREST FARM

Feldon Forest Farm, Frankton, Rugby, CV23 9PD

Tel: 01926 632246 contact.us@feldon-forest-farm.co.uk www.feldon-forest-farm.co.uk

Soil Association G2209. Organic mixed farm with rare breeds. Produce includes beef, eggs, flour, fruit, herbs, vegetables, lamb, wheat, wool, sheepskins and wood. Local delivery possible. We only sell our own produce. Educational visits by arrangement. Universities, colleges and groups all catered for.

FLIGHTS ORCHARD STRATFORD-ON-AVON

119 Evesham Road, Stratford-on-Avon, CV37 9BH

Tel: 07967 726184 paul@flightsorchardorganics.co.uk www.flightsorchardorganics.co.uk

We distribute a range of organic veg and fruit boxes, mostly grown on our own farms in Hereford and Worcester. We believe in sustainability, access to fresh organic food for everyone, and a fair price for all. We deliver to homes in our distribution range covering south Warwickshire and neighbouring post codes including parts of Worcestershire, Gloucestershire, Oxfordshire and the Solihull area.

GAIA

7 Regent Place, Leamington Spa, CV31 1EH

Tel: 01926 338805 shop@gaia.coop www.gaia.coop

Soil Association P5739. Vegetarian workers co-op selling organic vegetables and wholefoods, locally produced where possible, Fair Trade foods (mainly organic), and eco-friendly household products. Box scheme three days a week delivered by bicycle.

GARDEN ORGANIC, RYTON ORGANIC GARDENS

Ryton-on-Dunsmore, Coventry, CV8 3LG

Tel: 024 7630 3517 Fax: 024 7663 9229 enquiry@hdra.org.uk www.gardenorganic.org.uk

Soil Association T9217. Setting standards for organic products for amenity horticulture, HDRA is Europe's largest organic gardening organisation. It is dedicated to researching and promoting organic gardening, farming and food. Ryton Organic Gardens, ten acres displaying all aspects of organic horticulture for gardens, plus The Vegetable Kingdom, an interactive exhibition for all ages on the history and role of vegetables. Organic restaurant and shop open daily.

MYTHE FARM ORGANIC PRODUCE

Mythe Farm, Pinwall Lane, Sheepy Magna, Atherstone, CV9 3PF

Tel: 01827 722123 Fax: 01827 715738 info@garlandsleisure.co.uk www.garlandsleisure.co.uk

B&B in a beautiful farmhouse set on a working farm, £25-35 pppn.

NORTHLEIGH HOUSE

Northleigh House, Five Ways Road, Hatton, Warwick, CV35 7HZ

Tel: 01926 484203 Fax: 0121 707 4780 viv@northleigh.co.uk www.northleigh.co.uk

Northleigh House is a bed and breakfast and family evening meals with 9 rooms and we use almost entirely organic food. It is comfortable and quiet with gardens in the countryside and with a nice friendly atmosphere. It has 4 shields from The Tourist Board.

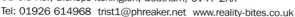

REALITY BITES ORGANIC MARKET GARDENS

38 Old Rd., Bishops Itchington, Southam, CV47 2RX
Tel: 01926 614968 trist1@phreaker.net www.reality-bites.co.uk
We are a small family business devoted to growing delicious organic produce, all of which we sell at local farmers' markets, through our box scheme and to certified local organic shops.

REVITAL HEALTHFOOD

Unit 1, Greenhill St, Stratford-upon-Avon, CV37 6LF
Tel: 01789 292353 www.revital.com
Health shop.

RIVER NENE ORGANIC VEGETABLES – HOME DELIVERY (WARWICK)

7 Villebon Way, Whitnash, Leamington Spa, CV31 2RD
Tel: 01926 338668 melanie@rivernene.co.uk www.rivernene.co.uk
Award-winning organic vegetable box scheme delivering in south Warwickshire. Offering differing box sizes to suit all households from a single occupant to a large family. A selection of fruit, dairy products, wine, fruit juices etc. also available. Order weekly, fortnightly or whenever you like. Can order online at www.rivernene.co.uk or by telephone on 0845 078 6868.

RYAN EVANS ORGANICS

Tel: 01902 762785
Organic meat and fish. Very competitive prices.

SHAKESPEARE BIRTHPLACE TRUST

Mary Arden's House & The Shakespear Countryside Museum,
Stratford-upon-Avon, CV37 9XL
Tel: 01789 204016 www.shakespeare.org.uk
Soil Association registered. We are an organic farm surrounding the childhood home of William Shakespeare's mother, displaying rare breeds and open throughout the year to visitors.

WARWICK HEALTH FOODS

40A Brook St, Warwick, CV34 4BL
Tel: 01926 494311
Family-run business, 25+ years, stockists of all kinds of organic foods, fresh fruit and vegetables always in stock, yeast-free bread and other speciality organic breads available.

THE WHOLEFOOD SHOP

c/o St Andrews Church House, Church Street, Rugby, CV21 3PT
Tel: 01788 567757 d.kerruish@ntlworld.co.uk
Retailing organic wholefoods, veg, fruit, bread, cakes, savouries – all organic; eco products, box scheme, local deliveries. Focal point for environmental groups. Open Thursday and Friday.

WILD & FREE

2 Central Buildings, Railway Terrace, Rugby, CV21 3EL
Tel: 01788 570400 info@wildandfree.net
Retail shop offering full range of organic fresh fruit and vegetables together with a box scheme, fresh breads, milk and dairy products, meat and poultry from local farms, wide range of organic packaged groceries, full range of Ecover cleaning products, natural hair and body care products, free deliveries to surrounding area.

WEST MIDLANDS COUNTY

BIRMINGHAM CITY CENTRE FARMERS' MARKET

New Street, near Victoria Square, Birmingham, B1

Tel: 0121 616 2644 citycentre@birmingham.gov.uk www.birmingham.gov.uk/farmers

Twice monthly, 1st and 3rd Wednesday of the month 10am–4pm; 3 times in December.

DOWN TO EARTH

96a Earlsdon Street, Earlsdon,
Coventry, CV5 6EJ

Tel: 024 7667 7500 downtoearthorganic@compuserve.com www.downtoearthorganic.co.uk

Soil Association P6189. Small, friendly retail shop and café packed top to bottom with fruit, vegetables (local wherever possible), groceries, dairy, eggs, meat and fish, wholefoods, nuts, seeds, rice and pulses, eco household products, skincare, body care. Home delivery and box scheme.

DROP IN THE OCEAN

17 City Arcade, Coventry, CV1 3HX

Tel: 024 7622 5273 info@naturalfoodcompany.net

Health food shop and delicatessen, general groceries, fresh bread, chilled and frozen products, cleaning products, toiletries, cosmetics, supplements.

FARM FRESH ORGANICS

40 Evenlode Rd., Solihull, B92 8EN

Tel: 0121 742 0764 Fax: 0121 742 5976

chris@farm-fresh-organics.co.uk www.farm-fresh-organics.co.uk

Offering free home delivery of a range of organic produce as well as dairy, bakery and pre-pack/eco products. You can choose your own produce. Also Internet shop from January 2007.

FLIGHTS ORCHARD ORGANICS (WALSALL)

20 Dilmore Lane, Fernhill Heath, Worcester, WR3 7TE

Tel: 0845 658 9808 Fax: 01531 633734

richard@flightsorchardorganics.co.uk www.flightsorchardorganics.co.uk

Fresh, tasty, organic fruit and veg delivered direct to your door in a refrigerated van. Weekly or fortnightly deliveries to suit you. Boxes range in size to suit the single person to the larger family. Personal service guaranteed! Additional items include eggs, apple juice, cider, nuts and seeds and mushrooms. Deliveries across the West Midlands including all of Birmingham, Walsall, Cannock and Lichfield (and all points in between).

FLIGHTS ORCHARD ORGANICS (WOLVERHAMPTON)

26 Alexander Rd., Codsall, Wolverhampton, WV8 1JQ

Tel: 0845 658 9808 linda@flightsorchardorganics.co.uk www.flightsorchardorganics.co.uk

Fresh, tasty organic fruit and veg delivered direct to your door in a refrigerated van. Weekly or fortnightly deliveries to suit your needs. Boxes range from the single person's box to a large family box! Also available are organic eggs, apple juice, cider, nuts and seeds and mushrooms, plus seasonal promotions like Easter eggs and Christmas cheese platters.

GREENSCENE

Unit 7, Gibb Terrace, The Custard Factory,
Birmingham, B9 4AA

Tel: 0121 224 7362 info@greensceneonline.co.uk www.greensceneonline.co.uk

A natural lifestyle shop with the lower floor retailing organic cotton children's and adults' yoga clothes, baby clothes and towels. We also have organic skincare and haircare for babies and adults, organic sanitary products, chemical-free cleaning, organic Auro paints.

GROUNDWORK BLACK COUNTRY

Dolton Way, DY4 9AL

Tel: 0121 530 5500 Fax: 0121 530 5501 bc@groundwork.org.uk www.groundwork-bc.org.uk

Building sustainable communities through joint environmental action, training, education and community links, open days.

HEALTH FOOD CENTRE

146-148 High St., Solihull, B91 3SX

Tel: 0121 705 0134 Fax: 0121 705 0134 barbara@healthfoodcentre.com www.healthfoodcentre.com

Dairy, meat, poultry, vegetables, bread, cakes, eggs, chocolates, dried fruit. Retail organic vegetables, pulses, etc; also bread and supplements.

HOPWOOD ORGANIC FARM

Bickenhill Lane, Catherine-de-Barnes,
Solihull, B92 0DE

Tel: 0121 711 7787 Fax: 0121 704 4033 sales@hopwoodorganic.co.uk www.hopwoodorganic.co.uk

Soil Association P5539 & G5540. Farm shop and home delivery of our own produce plus meat, poultry, cheeses, wholefoods, juices, jam and cereals.

KINGS HEATH FARMERS' MARKET

Junction of Vicarage Rd. and High St., Kings Heath, Birmingham, West Midlands, B14

Tel: 0121 444 4344 info@kingsheathfarmersmarket.org www.kingsheathfarmersmarket.org

1st Saturday of the month, 9am–3.30pm.

KINGS NORTON FARMERS' MARKET

The Green, Kings Norton, Birmingham, B38 8RU

Tel: 0121 451 3929 duncan@kingsnortonfarmersmarket.org.uk www.kingsnortonfarmersmarket.org.uk

Held once a month on the second Saturday from 9am–2pm on The Green in Kings Norton, Birmingham. We have 30 food stalls, some of which are certified organic.

KITCHEN GARDEN CAFÉ

17 York Rd., Kings Heath, Birmingham, B14 7SA
Tel: 0121 443 4725 Fax: 0121 443 4725

info@kitchengardencafé.co.uk www.kitchengardencafé.co.uk

Our garden shop sells unusual and edible plants, specialising in organic gardening. Our café serves organic breakfast, lunch and evening meals. Our delicatessen sells organic produce including fruit and vegetables, cheeses, wines and beers.

LEVERTON & HALLS

218 Mary Vale Rd., Bournville, Birmingham, B30 1PJ
Tel: 0121 451 1246 deniseleverton@aol.com

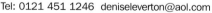  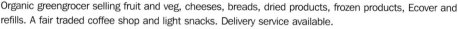

Organic greengrocer selling fruit and veg, cheeses, breads, dried products, frozen products, Ecover and refills. A fair traded coffee shop and light snacks. Delivery service available.

LOG HOME FARM

Oldwich Lane West, Chadwick End, Solihull, B93 0BJ
Tel: 01564 782244 loghomefarm@hotmail.co.uk

Organic free range eggs.

MOSELEY FARMERS' MARKET

Village Green, junction at Alcester Rd. traffic lights, Moseley, Birmingham, B13
Tel: 0121 449 3156 david@isgrove.co.uk
4th Saturday of the month except December, when it's the Saturday before Christmas. Organic produce includes, meat, ice cream, cheese, butter, yoghurt, smoked salmon, fruit, vegetables, nuts, seeds and soft fruit in season.

NATURAL WORLD

596 Bearwood Rd., Smethwick, B66 4BW
Tel: 0121 420 2145 naturalworld@healthfoodshop.co.uk www.healthfoodshop.co.uk
We have the largest range of organic food and drink products in the Midlands, plus body care products.

NATURAL WORLD

26 Great Western Arcade, Birmingham, B2 5HU
Tel: 0121 233 9931 naturalworld@healthfoodshop.co.uk www.healthfoodshop.co.uk
We have the largest range of organic food and drink products in the Midlands, plus body care products.

ONE EARTH SHOP

54 Allison Street, Digbeth, Birmingham, B5 5TH
Tel: 0121 632 6909
Vegan shop with large range of organic and fair trade products; wholefoods, chilled, confectionery etc. Local delivery (not a box scheme).

THE ORGANIC MUM BOX SCHEME
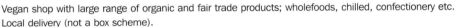

164 Coles Lane, Sutton Coldfield, B72 1NS
Tel: 07789 692549 thecolemans164@blueyonder.co.uk www.theorganicmum.co.uk
Family-run organic box scheme catering for the Sutton Coldfield area. Fruit, vegetables and sprouted seeds. Please call Becky for further information.

ORGANIC PLANET

210 Walsall Wood Road, Aldridge, Walsall, WS9 8HW
Tel: 01922 743983 Fax: 01922 743983 organic-planet@tiscali.co.uk
Small retail shop selling fresh organic fruit and vegetables, organic wholefoods and convenience foods plus a delivery service. We also carry a range of eco-friendly household products and toiletries.

ORGANIC ROOTS

Crabtree Farm, Dark Lane, Kings Norton, Birmingham, B38 0BS
Tel: 01564 822294 Fax: 01564 829212 info@organicroots.co.uk www.organicroots.co.uk
Soil Association G1880. Organic Roots is the only organic shop in the West Midlands wholly dedicated to supplying organic food of all types. Home delivery service based on our 500 lines of organic produce.

PEACEFUL MIND CAFÉ

46 Poplar Rd., Kings Heath, Birmingham, B14 7AG
Organic and local foods café with home baked cakes and fair trade coffees and teas.

RIVER NENE ORGANIC VEGETABLES HOME DELIVERY (SOLIHULL)

35 Ullenhall Rd, Knowle, Solihull, B93 9JD
Tel: 0845 078 6868 Fax: 0845 466 0060 colin@rivernene.co.uk www.rivernene.co.uk
Independent local licensed distributor from Riverford Organic Vegetables. Award-winning organic vegetable box scheme delivered to homes in Solihull and surrounding areas. Box sizes to suit single person up to large families. Wide range of other organic produce including fruit, dairy, alcohol and fruit juices. For more information or to place an order go to our website www.rivernene.co.uk or alternatively call 0845 078 6868.

ROSEMARY'S HEALTH FOODS

2/3 Mander Square, Mander Centre, Wolverhampton, WV1 3NN
Tel: 01902 427520 Fax: 01902 426147
enquiries@rosemaryshealthfoods.co.uk www.rosemaryshealthfoods.co.uk
We sell an extensive range of organic healthy, dried, fresh, chilled, frozen foods and herbal remedies.

ROSSITER, S & A – TRADITIONAL FAMILY BUTCHERS

247 Maryvale Road, Bournville, Birmingham, B30 1PN
Tel: 0121 458 1598 Fax: 0121 458 1598
Soil Association R2037, NFMT. Meat and poultry, bread, cheeses, eggs, cooked meats, pickles, preserves, trout and salmon. Small friendly family-run business with emphasis on customer satisfaction and confidence.

SAGE WHOLEFOODS

148 Alcester Rd., Moseley, Birmingham, B13 8HS
Tel: 0121 449 6909 Fax: 0121 449 6909 info@sagewholefoods.com www.sagewholefoods.com
A not-for-profit workers co-operative retailing a wide range of organic foods including fruit and vegetables, fair trade goods, specialist dietary food, supplements and remedies. Mon–Sat 9.30am–6.30pm.

SIBILA'S AT BODY AND BEING

Canal Square, Browning Street, Birmingham, B16 8EH
Tel: 0121 456 7634 delicious@sibilasrestaurant.co.uk www.sibilasrestaurant.co.uk
Organic vegetarian restaurant awaiting certification. The editor of this directory has eaten here (anonymously) and cannot praise the food highly enough. I would happily recommend it as being possibly the best vegetarian food I have ever eaten.

WORCESTERSHIRE

CAVES FOLLY NURSERIES

Evendine Lane, Colwall, Malvern, WR13 6DU
Tel: 01684 540631 bridget@cavesfolly.com www.cavesfolly.com

Specialist growers of perennials, grasses and alpines, all peat-free. Wonderful display gardens, wild flower meadow, etc. Garden design and advisory service specialising in organics and using environmentally sound products. Two bed holiday let available from Spring 2007. Set in beautiful location on our organic nursery. Reasonable rates. Please phone for details.

THE COTTAGE HERBERY

Mill House, Boraston, Nr. Tenbury Wells, WR15 8LZ
Tel: 01584 781575 Fax: 01584 781483 www.thecottageherbery.co.uk
Organic peat-free herbs, cottage garden plants and native plants. All plants grow in a permitted certified growing medium, Fertile Fibre. Talks given to groups. Catalogue: send 6 first class stamps. In 2006 we celebrate 30 years of organic and peat-free growing.

CRIDLAN & WALKER

23 Abbey Road, Malvern, WR14 3ES
Tel: 01684 573008 Fax: 01684 566017
Organic Farmers & Growers no. UKP100013. Organic meat, vegetables, milk, cheese and groceries.

THE DOMESTIC FOWL TRUST

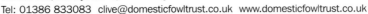

Station Rd., Honeybourne, WR11 7QZ

Tel: 01386 833083 clive@domesticfowltrust.co.uk www.domesticfowltrust.co.uk

Suppliers of high quality poultry housing and equipment. Traditional and hybrid poultry, ducks and geese. Mail order service. Full countrywide delivery. Open to the public.

FARM DIRECT PRODUCE

Merryvalls Farm, Bishops Wood Rd., Ombersley, WR9 0LD

Tel: 01905 356068 charlotte@farmdirectproduce.co.uk www.farmdirectproduce.com

Fresh, local organic produce delivered from the field to your home.

GREENLINK ORGANIC FOODS

11 Graham Rd., Great Malvern, WR14 2HR

Tel: 01684 576266 Fax: 01684 576266 greenlinkorganics@tiscali.co.uk www.greenlinkorganics.co.uk

Retail outlet specialising in organic foods, fresh fruit and veg, meat, fish, poultry, a wide range of whole-foods and body care products. Small café snack bar selling fresh daily prepared vegetarian food, teas and coffees.

HOMEFLIGHT DELIVERIES

Nordkapp, Suckley Road, Leigh, WR6 5LE

Tel: 07753 443852 neil@flightsorchardorganics.co.uk www.flightsorchardorganics.co.uk

We distribute a range of organic veg and fruit boxes, mostly grown on our own farms in Herefordshire and Worcestershire. We believe in sustainability, access to fresh organic food for everyone, and a fair price for all. We deliver to homes in our distribution range covering Worcester, Malvern, Kidderminster and neighbouring postcodes.

OXTON ORGANICS

Broadway Lane, Fladbury, Pershore, WR10 2QF

Tel: 01386 860477 Fax: 01386 860477 boxes@oxtonorganics.co.uk www.oxtonorganics.co.uk

Soil Association E17M. Fruit, vegetables and eggs delivered locally via our box scheme. Also online ordering via our website.

THE RETREAT

The Retreat, Stoke Bliss, Tenbury Wells, WR15 8RY

Tel: 01885 410431 mdk46@tiscali.co.uk

Space to be! Self-catering accommodation, sleeps 2-4 people. Hereford/Worcestershire borders, wildflower meadow, walks and peace. Pets and children welcome, local food available to order.

ROSEMARY'S HEALTH FOODS

10 The Shambles, Worcester, WR1 2RF

Tel: 01905 612190 Fax: 01905 612190

enquiries@rosemaryshealthfoods.co.uk www.rosemaryshealthfoods.co.uk

We sell an extensive range of organic healthy, dried, fresh, chilled, frozen foods and herbal remedies.

SKYLARK ORGANIC BOXES

Pullens Farm, Bromyard Road, Cradley, Malvern, WR13 5JN

Tel: 01886 881097 mail@skylarkboxes.co.uk www.skylarkboxes.co.uk

Box scheme.

STEELE, W O & SONS

Chapel Farm, Netherton, Nr. Pershore, WR10 3JG
Tel: 01386 710379 Fax: 01386 710379 adrian@wosteele.fsnet.co.uk
Soil Association S37M; Organic Arable Marketing Group; Organic Seed Producers Ltd, Graig Farm. Mixed lowland organic farm specialising in wheat, oats, beans, potatoes, beef and lamb since 1986. Farm gate sales and sales to mills, butchers and box schemes. Please phone first.

UPPER WICK FARM

Upper Wick Farm, Rushwick, Worcestershire, WR2 5SU
Tel: 01905 422243
Upper Wick Farm is a 100-hectare farm lying in the beautiful Teme valley in Worcestershire, minutes from Worcester city itself. The farm has beef cattle and sheep together with a farm shop, traditional orchards, cereals and potatoes. Visit the farm to discover more. A small self-contained holiday cottage is available with views across the orchard. Home grown prepared meals are available using organic ingredients. Member of the Soil Association Organic Farms Network.

WOODCOTE FARM

Dodford, Bromsgrove, B61 9EA
Tel: 01562 777795 Fax: 01562 777024 woodcotefarm@btinternet.com www.woodcotefarm.com
Soil Association G4109. Woodcote Farm produces organic fat lamb and Aberdeen Angus beef. We also provide bed and breakfast and self-contained apartments for holidays or long lets.

WYEDEAN WHOLEFOODS

4 Royal Arcade, Pershore, WR10 1AG
Tel: 01386 556577
Hundreds of organic lines. Wholefoods, gluten- and dairy-free, cruelty-free cosmetics; SLS-free toiletries. Excellent range of vitamins, minerals and herbals. Wide range of chilled and frozen products.

NORTH-EAST

COUNTY DURHAM

ACORN DAIRY

Archdeacon Newton, Darlington, DL2 2YB
Tel: 01325 466999 Fax: 01325 464567 organic@acorndairy.co.uk www.acorndairy.co.uk
Process organic milk from own farm delivering to doorsteps in and around the Darlington area with organic bread, eggs, cheeses, youghurts, butter, fruit juices. Poultry once a month.

BUTTERBY

Low Butterby Farm, Croxdale, Durham, DH6 5JN
Tel: 0191 378 9193 info@butterby.co.uk www.butterby.co.uk
We run a box scheme in Durham city and its surrounding areas. The walled garden at Croxdale Hall is in organic conversion, we grow our own salad crops, summer vegetables, apples, pears, and plums. During the summer also offer cut flowers from the garden borders and honey from our own bees.

THE HEALTH WAREHOUSE

15 Post House Wynd, Darlington, DL3 7LU
Tel: 01325 468570 mjbarker2@hotmail.com
Large independent health store specialising in home-baked products and organic chilled and ambient foods. Also herbal and natural remedies and supplements.

THE LAND OF ROOTS LTD

17 Kingston Avenue, Bearpark, Durham, DH7 7DJ

Tel: 0191 373 5109

15-acre permaculture smallholding, 2 miles from Durham City, using sustainable methods to grow veg, salad and fruit. Also rare breed lamb produced on our wild flower pasture and wood products from our coppiced woodland.

PIERCEBRIDGE FARM

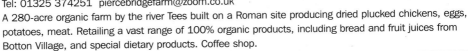

Piercebridge, Darlington, DL2 3SE

Tel: 01325 374251 piercebridgefarm@zoom.co.uk

A 280-acre organic farm by the river Tees built on a Roman site producing dried plucked chickens, eggs, potatoes, meat. Retailing a vast range of 100% organic products, including bread and fruit juices from Botton Village, and special dietary products. Coffee shop.

POLEMONIUM PLANTERY

Polemonium Plantery, 28, Sunnyside, Trimdon Grange,
Trimdon Station, TS29 6HF

Tel: 01429 881529 organic@polemonium.co.uk www.polemonium.co.uk

Specialist organic peat-free plant nursery selling flower plants and seeds, also organic bed and breakfast with local produce, garden visits, talks and garden plans. See website for full details.

NORTHUMBERLAND

A WORLD OF DIFFERENCE

13 Narrowgate, Alnwick, NE66 1JH

Tel: 01665 606005

Independent ethical retailer. Organic fresh produce, wholefoods, meat, dairy etc. Also a wide range of environmentally-friendly, recycled and fairly-traded gifts, clothing and household goods from around the world. Soil Association licence application submitted.

BURNLAW CENTRE

Burnlaw Whitefield, Hexham, NE47 8HF

Tel: 01434 345359 gvs38@hotmail.com www.burnlaw.org.uk

Smallholding – we also run retreats: courses in dance, painting, healing, mysticism and Baha'i wisdom. Good place for time out, come and stay, organic beef (very scrumptious!), fabulous setting and lots of (natural) enlightenment on tap!

CROPPED UP

Dilston College, Corbridge, NE45 5RJ

Tel: 07947 856641 Fax: 01434 633721

Soil Association G4553. Organic fruit and vet box scheme operating June 1st to Christmas only. All produce except potatoes grown on site. Local deliveries to Hexham, Haydon Bridge and Allendale.

THE GOOD LIFE SHOP

50 High St., Wooler, NE71 6BG

Tel: 01668 281700 goodlife_wooler@hotmail.com www.goodlifewooler.co.uk

Ours is a family-run business specialising in local and continental cheeses, wholefoods, organic ranges. Herbs and spices are weighed to order. Huge range of Ecover products.

NORTHUMBERLAND

THE GREEN SHOP

30 Bridge St., Berwick-upon-Tweed, TD15 1AQ
Tel: 01289 305566 Fax: 01289 305566
Complete and only green shopping since 1993. Organic seeds, clothing, toiletries, alcohol. Nearly 2,000 organic pre-packed foods, plus breads, chilled, frozen, fruit'n'veg & meat. 30 mile delivery. Fair trade. A very warm welcome.

HAVENS ORGANICS

The Havens Farm, Heatherwick, Otterburn, NE19 1LY
Tel: 01830 520806 Fax: 01830 520806
10-hectare S.D.A. small farm. Own veg in season box scheme, organic eggs, organic pedigree Dexter beef, small bulk veg sales to shops and other box schemes.

LUMBYLAW FARM
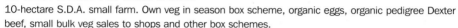
Lumbylaw Farm, Edlingham, Alnwick, NE66 2BW
Tel: 01665 574277 Fax: 01665 574277 holidays@lumbylaw.co.uk www.lumbylaw.co.uk
Two delightful cottages (self-catering), set in the most scenic countryside on our organic farm with pedigree prize winning South Devon cattle, and Lleyn sheep. Within the grounds are features such as medieval Edlingham Castle and a five-arch viaduct over the valley. Lumbylaw Cottage sleeps 6 (two bathrooms); Garden Cottage sleeps a couple. Both cottages have their own gardens, and are centrally heated. Our visitors return frequently.

THE MARKET SHOP

48 Bridge Street, Berwick-upon-Tweed, TD15 1AQ
Tel: 01289 307749 Fax: 01289 307749
Health food shop, wholefoods, herbs and spices.

NOAH'S PLACE
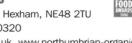
31 Main St, Spittal, Berwick-upon-Tweed, TD15 1QY
Tel: 01289 332141 info@noahsplace.co.uk www.noahsplace.co.uk
Family-run B&B and tea room close to sandy beach, historic town of Berwick-upon-Tweed, Holy Island, Scottish Borders. Organic food, natural bedclothes. English, French, German spoken. Children welcome, bicycle storage.

NORTH EAST ORGANIC GROWERS

Earth Balance, West Sleekburn Farm, Bomarsund, Bedlington, NE22 7AD
Tel: 01670 821070 Fax: 01670 821026 neog@care4free.net www.neog.co.uk
NEOG Ltd, a workers co-operative, has been running a box scheme since 1996 for vegetables, fruit and eggs, serving Tyneside and Northumberland and more recently County Durham. We grow a wide range of vegetables throughout the year including salads and brassicas and source also from the increasing number of local organic growers. We were commended in the Organic Box Scheme of the Year Awards 2003.

NORTHUMBRIAN QUALITY MEATS
Monkridge Hill Farm, West Woodburn, Hexham, NE48 2TU
Tel: 01434 270184 Fax: 01434 270320
enqs@northumbrian-organic-meat.co.uk www.northumbrian-organic-meat.co.uk
Distributor of organic beef, lamb and pork. Organic Food Awards 2004, 2006.

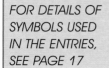 *FOR DETAILS OF SYMBOLS USED IN THE ENTRIES, SEE PAGE 17*

Joanne and Julian Spector sold their profitable water cooler business in 1998. They were interested in getting involved in environmental issues that affect us all.

They recognised in 1999 that in order to have a wider reach on the Internet, and create a distribution platform for innovative sustainable products, they needed to develop a solid, well-run, professional shopping channel. In this way they could reach the interested consumer and a wider public audience, whom they could engage in the subject of sustainability and encourage to make positive choices in their shopping habits.

Seven years on, they have just won the *Observer* Newspapers' Ethical Retailer of the Year Award. Their company, Green Dot Guides Ltd, mails out nearly two million of their catalogues, Natural Collection, to a fast-growing customer base, and they are now the largest non-food ecological retailer in Britain. Half their daily sales are now taken on their website, www.naturalcollection.com.

"The definition of environmentally friendly is always evolving," points out Julian. "So I tend to use the term environmentally considered."

Julian and Joanne are born optimists. "We believe that positive change will happen, and that shopping habits will improve accordingly," says Julian.

"We have a non-guilt vision. You've got to make it easy for people to want to change. Better than preaching to the converted, we have to reach the broader public and encourage them to think about their choices even in a small way."

Starting a new eco-business from scratch, at a time when online shopping was far less sophisticated and far fewer people had broadband, was challenging. "The first three years were a difficult learning curve," remembers Julian. "We have had to co-ordinate nearly 200 suppliers, and provide the customer with a seamless service, and at the same time express our positive message about sustainability through our catalogue and website. This took years to fine tune, but we now believe this is really working well."

ORCHARDFIELD ORGANICS

Pear Tree Cabin, Broomhaugh, Riding Mill, NE44 6EQ

Tel: 01434 682717 info@orchardfieldorganics.co.uk www.orchardfieldorganics.co.uk

Northumberland based organic fruit and vegetable box service. Delivered anywhere in the north-east of England. Seasonal, local, organic, fresh, low polluting and tasty! Mobile: 07952 783817.

ROCK MIDSTEAD
ORGANIC FARM

Rock Midstead, Rock, Alnwick, NE66 2TH

Tel: 01665 579225 Fax: 01665 579326 ian@rockmidstead.co.uk www.rockmidstead.co.uk

Rock Midstead is a small family-run organic farm situated near the unspoilt Northumberland coast. It has been run along traditional lines by the Sutherland family for 40 years; Beth and Ian Sutherland have branched out into high-quality B&B accommodation, livery stables and a farm shop with tea room. The farm supplies home-grown organic beef, lamb, pork, eggs and a variety of other produce to the farm shop (open 7 days a week) and to local outlets.

WHISTLEBARE

Bowsden, Berwick-upon-Tweed, TD15 2TG

Tel: 01289 388777 orders@whistlebare.co.uk www.whistlebare.co.uk

Artisan cured bacon, charcuterie and fresh pork from our pedigree Large Black pigs as well as beef from our grass-fed herd of pedigree Aberdeen Angus cattle. All meat is properly hung.

TYNE AND WEAR

GOSFORTH PARK FARM SHOP

within Chandlers Garden Centre, High Gosforth Park,
Newcastle-upon-Tyne, NE3 5EJ

Tel: 0191 236 5920 Fax: 0191 236 5920

the.farm.shop@btconnect.com www.gosforthfarmshop.co.uk

We run an organic box scheme which we deliver to work or home; extra items such as bread, milk and eggs are also available. We are also pleased to be able to offer organic meat packs which are supplied by Northumbrian Quality Meats. Within our shop there is wide variety of organic and fair trade produce.

NEAL'S YARD REMEDIES

19 Central Arcade, Newcastle-upon-Tyne, NE1 5BQ

Tel: 0191 232 2525 mail@nealsyardremedies.com www.nealsyardremedies.com

Neal's Yard Remedies manufactures and retails natural cosmetics in addition to stocking an extensive range of herbs, essential oils, homeopathic remedies and reference material.

OUT OF THIS WORLD

106 High St., Gosforth, Newcastle-upon-Tyne, NE3 1HB

Tel: 0191 213 5377 Fax: 0191 213 5378 info@ootw.co.uk www.outofthisworld.coop

Head office of small chain of ethical and organic supermarkets in Newcastle-upon-Tyne, Nottingham, York and Leeds. Selling over 5,000 products, most food products certified organic plus fairly traded crafts, recycled paper and body care products etc. Delivery scheme from Newcastle shop. Consumer co-op with over 17,500 members.

OUT OF THIS WORLD

Gosforth Shopping Centre, High St., Gosforth,
Newcastle-upon-Tyne, NE3 1JZ

Tel: 0191 213 0421 Fax: 0191 213 0429 info@ootw.co.uk www.outofthisworld.coop

Small chain of ethical and organic supermarkets in Newcastle-upon-Tyne, Leeds, York and Nottingham. Selling over 5,000 products, mostly certified organic food plus fairly traded crafts, recycled paper and body care products etc. Consumer co-op with over 17,500 members.

RISING SUN FARM

Kings Rd. North, Wallsend, NE28 9JL

Tel: 0191 234 0114 organics@risingsunfarm.freeserve.co.uk

Soil Association producer no. P1490. Cereals, horticultural, pigs, cattle. Urban fringe farm providing education, day service for special needs. Open farm for community. Livery yard for DIY liveries.

SCOTSWOOD NATURAL COMMUNITY GARDEN

John Marley Centre, Whickham View, Scotswood, Newcastle-upon-Tyne, NE15 6TT

Tel: 0845 4581653 Fax: 0845 4581654 office@sncg.org.uk www.sncg.org.uk

Award-winning urban permaculture garden with woodlands, ponds, meadows, orchards and vegetable plots. The two-acre site is a haven for local wildlife and an example of sustainable food production in an urban environment. We organise public open days in the summer and host visiting school and community groups throughout the year. Please see our website for more details.

TRAIDCRAFT PLC

Kingsway, Gateshead, NE11 0NE

Tel: 0191 491 0591 Fax: 0191 482 2690 joeo@traidcraft.co.uk www.traidcraft.co.uk

Importer and distributor of organic honey, tea, chocolate. Soil Association no. P2321.

EAST YORKSHIRE

ARTHUR STREET TRADING COMPANY LTD

Unit 2, 23 Arthur St., Hull, HU3 6BH

Tel: 01482 576374 arthursorganics@hotmail.com www.arthursorganics.com

A workers' co-operative that makes home deliveries in a solar powered veg-float, supplying comprehensive range of organic fruit & vegetables, eco-cleaning products, wholefoods, beers, wines and own brand range of organic hummus.

BARMSTON ORGANICS

Allison Lane End Farm, Lissett, Driffield, YO25 8PS

Tel: 01262 468128 Fax: 01262 468128 barmstontone@aol.com

Soil Association P5571 & G1855. 273-acre mixed farm selling vegetables, flour from our own wheat and lamb & beef. Box scheme and local farmers' markets.

CHANCE CAFÉ

209 Chanterlands Avenue, Hull, HU5 3TP

Tel: 01482 446815 Fax: 01482 446815 info@chancecafé.co.uk www.chancecafé.co.uk

An organic shop and vegetarian café supplying a selection of food and drink to eat in or take out, and a shop providing all your organic requirements.

DENSHOLME FARM

Great Hatfield, Hull, HU11 4UR
Tel: 01964 535315 denys_fell@wcg.org.uk
Member of the Soil Association Organic Farms Network.

FOSTON NURSERIES

Foston on the Wolds, Driffield, YO25 8BJ
Tel: 01262 488382
Soil Association W28N. Grower of organic produce. Gate sales, supplying three box scheme outlets, also sales at Driffield farmers' market. Self-contained holiday flat, sleeps 2.

GREEN GROWERS

1 Station Cottages, Wansford Rd., Nafferton, Driffield,
YO25 8NJ
Tel: 01377 255362 mail@greengrowers.fsnet.co.uk
Soil Association G2175. Green Growers is an organic nursery, retailing a wide variety of organic vegetables, fruit and wholefoods, specialising in fresh salads and herbs, and herb plants.

LOVE FOOD

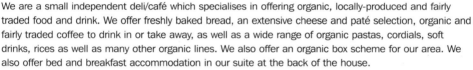

31 Market Place, Snaith, Goole, DN14 9HE
Tel: 01405 869629 love.food@ntlworld.com www.lovefoodsnaith.co.uk
We are a small independent deli/café which specialises in offering organic, locally-produced and fairly traded food and drink. We offer freshly baked bread, an extensive cheese and paté selection, organic and fairly traded coffee to drink in or take away, as well as a wide range of organic pastas, cordials, soft drinks, rices as well as many other organic lines. We also offer an organic box scheme for our area. We also offer bed and breakfast accommodation in our suite at the back of the house.

RACHEL'S GUEST HOUSE, BRIDLINGTON

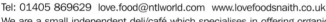

11 Richmond St., Bridlington, YO15 3DL
Tel: 01262 673652 rghbrid@btinternet.com uk.geocities.com/matthews620@btinternet.com/
Free pick-up by car from the Bridlington railway, coach or bus station, and return, by request. Tasty English or continental breakfast (organic). Small groups very welcome. Open all year!

SLATER ORGANICS

16 Cross St., Aldbrough, Hull, HU11 4RW
Tel: 01964 527519 slaterorganics@yahoo.co.uk
Soil Association G1917. Family business growing wide range of organic vegetables in walled garden at Rise Village. Working with other local growers, we supply box schemes in Hull, Beverley and local villages.

NORTH YORKSHIRE

ALLIGATOR

104 Fishergate, York, YO10 4BB
Tel: 01904 654525 www.alligatorwholefoods.com
Independent vegetarian & wholefood grocers and greengrocers offering a wide range of organic fruit, veg and groceries. Speciality diets catered for. Home delivery service within the York area.

BLUEBELL ORGANICS

Forcett Hall Walled Garden, Forcett, Richmond, DL11 7SB

Tel: 01325 718841 katrina@bluebellorganics.co.uk www.bluebellorganics.co.uk

Bluebell Organics run an all year round box scheme with quality local vegetables predominantly grown by themselves on 8 acres of land and in a growing partnership with S. J. Ward. Part of that land will be registered under the 'stock free' regulations so it is suitable for vegetarians and vegans. Also sell at local farmers' markets where they sell a range of home-made produce including organic apple juice, marmalade, pickles and preserves.

BRUNSWICK ORGANIC NURSERY

Appleton Rd., Bishopthorpe, York, YO23 2RF

Tel: 01904 701869 Fax: 01904 701869 jennifer@brunswickyork.org.uk

Soil Association G1903, HDRA member. Charity working with adults who have learning difficulties. Produce includes bedding plants, cottage garden plants, perennials, herbs, organic fruit and vegetables. All to Soil Association standards. Farm shop open weekdays in winter, seven days a week in summer. Organic Food Awards 2004 Fresh Fruit and Veg Highly Commended.

CAMPHILL VILLAGE TRUST – BOTTON VILLAGE

Danby, Whitby, YO21 2NJ

Tel: 01287 660871 botton@camphill.org.uk www.camphill.org.uk

Botton Village is a Camphill Village Trust community for adults with special needs. It has five mixed farms which are run on biodynamic principles, several craft and food processing workshops. Day visits are possible, and there is coffee bar (not a restaurant) on site.

CAMPHILL VILLAGE TRUST – LARCHFIELD COMMUNITY

Stokesley Rd., Hemlington, Middlesbrough, TS8 9DY

Tel: 01642 593688 Fax: 01642 595778

Producers of real organic meat, vegetables, seasonal fruit, bread, etc. Also handcrafts – weaving and wooden toys.

CASTLE HOWARD ESTATE LTD

The Estate Office, Castle Howard, York, YO60 7DA

Tel: 01653 648444 horchison@castlehoward.co.uk www.castlehoward.co.uk

Soil Association registered. Organic farmers. Producers of organic meats and arable crops. Telephone or check website for details of opening times.

CORNMILL LODGE VEGETARIAN GUEST HOUSE

120 Haxby Rd., York, YO31 8JP

Tel: 01904 620566 Fax: 01904 620566 cornmillyork@aol.com www.vegetarianyork.net

Vegetarian/vegan guest house using organic and fair trade produce where possible (80% organic), 15 minutes walk from York Minster, completely smoke-free, animal-free toiletries used.

EL PIANO

15-17 Grape Lane, York, YO1 7HU

Tel: 01904 610676 Fax: 01904 643049 info@elpiano.co.uk www.elpiano.co.uk

Open 10am–midnight Mon–Sat, Sundays midday–5pm. Licensed, hispanic, informal, vegetarian restaurant. Function rooms, event-catering inside or out. Children welcome all hours. Organic staples used in restaurant, Spanish foods. Wheat-free, gluten-free, vegan catered for. *Hand to Mouth: no ordinary cookbook* published.

FARMAROUND

The Old Bakery, Mercury Rd., Richmond, DL10 4TQ

Tel: 01748 821116 Fax: 01748 822007 info@farmaround.co.uk www.farmaroundnorth.co.uk

Organic Farmers & Growerrs UKP08009. From their base in Richmond, Farmaround delivers organic fruit and vegetables boxes to North and South Yorkshire, Tyne and Wear, County Durham and Cleveland. Also a fully organic vegetarian grocery range. Wholesale enquiries welcome.

FIRST SEASON

1 St. Ann's Lane, Whitby, YO21 3PF

Tel: 01947 601608 Fax: 01947 601608

Wholefood shop with a wide range of organic products including fresh fruit and vegetables, Botton Village bread and jams, and local eggs. Organic vegetable boxes can be ordered and collected from the shop.

GOOSEMOORORGANICS

Warfield Lane, Cowthorpe, Nr. Wetherby, LS22 5EU

Tel: 01423 358887 Fax: 01423 358887 vegebox@goosemoor.info www.goosemoor.info

Soil Association G802, P802. Goosemoor grows and distributes organic fruit, vegetables and vegetarian groceries to shops and restaurants throughout the north of England, as well as home deliveries via our vegebox scheme.

THE GREEN HOUSE

5 Station Parade, Harrogate, HG1 1UF

Tel: 01423 502580 Fax: 01423 505439

Shop selling arguably the best organic food and drink selection in North Yorkshire. Also vegetarian and special diet foods, nappies, toiletries, Ecover refill station. Delivery within 5 miles of shop.

GROWING WITH GRACE

Clapham Nurseries, Clapham, (Nr. Lancaster), LA2 8ER

Tel: 01524 251723 Fax: 01524 251548 info@growingwithgrace.co.uk www.growingwithgrace.co.uk

Soil Association G4295, P5562. We are a Quaker co-operative seeking to provide local people with home/locally produced vegetables and fair trade dried goods, through our bag scheme and farm shop. We cover north and east Lancashire, south-east Cumbria and the southern Yorkshire dales.

HAZELBROW VISITOR CENTRE

Low Row, Richmond, DL11 6NE

Tel: 01748 886224 info@hazelbrow.co.uk www.hazelbrow.co.uk

Organic working farm in Yorkshire Dales National Park producing lamb and milk, with visitor centre, shop and café open 11am–5pm five days a week, March to September (closed Mondays & Fridays).

HOOK HOUSE FARM

Hook House Farm, Kirkby Fleetham, Northallerton, DL7 0SS

Tel: 01609 748977 hookhousefarm@hotmail.co.uk

Small mixed farm in the Vale of York producing lamb, beef, Christmas turkeys and honey. Contact us to go on our mailing list.

HUNTERS OF HELMSLEY

13 Market Place, Helmsley, YO62 5BL

Tel: 01439 771307 Fax: 01439 771307 info@huntersofhelmsley.com www.huntersofhelmsley.com

High class food specialist stocking cooked meats, bacon, port and game pies, fish, cheeses, many varieties of jams, chutneys, teas, coffees, Belgian chocolates. We also offer mail order and specialist hampers.

NORTH YORKSHIRE

LARBERRY FARM SHOP

Larberry Pastures, Longnewton,
Stockton on Tees, TS21 1BN
Tel: 01642 583823 Fax: 01642 582249 larberry@farmersweekly.net

Farm shop selling our own home reared beef, lamb and organic free range eggs. Pork from Houghall Agricultural College, fruit and veg, groceries including flour, dairy, spreads, jams, herbs, spices – you name it, we do it. Also cater for special diets: gluten-free, dairy-free, wheat-free and diabetic products.

LENG'S GROCERS

36 Cold Bath Rd, Harrogate, HG2 0NA
Tel: 01423 503815 Fax: 01423 503815 lengsgrocers@btconnect.com

Traditional family-run grocers near the heart of Harrogate offering an ever expanding range of organic, locally produced, fair trade & wholefood goods. Free local delivery & organic box scheme.

THE LITTLE DELICATESSEN

3 High Street, Tadcaster, LS24 9AP
Tel: 01937 833244

High class delicatessen with a wide range of wholefoods, organic beer and organic lager.

LOW GILL BECK FARM

Low Gill Beck Farm, Glaisdale, YO21 2QA
Tel: 01947 897363

Home grown parsnips, carrots, turnips, brassicas, runner beans, dwarf beans, peas, potatoes. Strawberries & raspberries.

NATURE'S WORLD

Ladgate Lane, Acklam, Middlesborough, TS5 7YN
Tel: 01642 594895 Fax: 01642 591224 stuart@naturesworld.org.uk www.naturesworld.org.uk

The north of England's pioneering environmental centre with over 25 acres of organic demonstration gardens and wildlife areas. Open daily to the public, school groups and tours. Also farm shop, tea rooms and play areas. Monthly farmers' market.

THE ORGANIC FARM SHOP

Standfield Hall Farm, Westgate Carr Rd.,
Pickering, YO18 8LX
Tel: 01751 472249 Fax: 01751 472249
mike@theorganicfarmshop.com www.theorganicfarmshop.com

Soil Association PS21N. Specialist retailer or organic goods since 1984. Home produced vegetables and beef plus one of the biggest ranges of organic products in Yorkshire. Scarborough/Ryedale free delivery.

THE ORGANIC PANTRY

St.Helens Farm, Newton
Kyme, Tadcaster, LS24 9LY
Tel: 01937 531693 Fax: 01937 834062 office@theorganicpantry.co.uk www.theorganicpantry.co.uk

Family-run farm. Complete organic shop selling fruit, vegetables, meat, dairy, bread, wholefoods etc. box scheme, farm shop and website. Individual diets/special requirements and requests welcome. Deliveries throughout Yorkshire and Derbyshire. Farmers' markets.

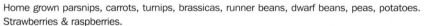

FOR DETAILS OF SYMBOLS USED IN THE ENTRIES, SEE PAGE 17

OUT OF THIS WORLD

25 George Hudson St., York YO1 6JL
Tel: 01904 627 963 info@ootw.co.uk www.outofthisworld.coop
Small chain of ethical and organic supermarkets in Newcastle-upon-Tyne, Leeds, York and Nottingham. Selling over 5,000 products, mostly certified organic food plus fairly traded crafts, recycled paper and body care products etc. Consumer co-op with over 17,500 members.

PADMORE, C F & E T

Bank House Farm, Glaisdale, Whitby, YO21 2QA
Tel: 01947 897297 Fax: 01947 897297 em-chris-padmore@onetel.net
Soil Association G1135. Organic beef and lamb and woodland reared pork. All meat home produced, butchered, bagged and labelled. Please phone regarding availability.

PASTURE COTTAGE ORGANICS

Pasture Cottage, Bog House Farm, Mickleby, Whitby, TS13 5NA
Tel: 01947 840075 jenny@yorkshireorganics.freeserve.co.uk
Soil Association G5723. On our small family farm we produce a wide range of seasonal vegetables and eggs for retail sale at our farm shop, through our box scheme and at local shops.

ROBINSON, DS

Fir Tree Farm, Northallerton, DL6 2RW
Tel: 01609 772032 mail@britishbeef.org www.britishbeef.org
Soil Association G4193. We are a specialist producer delivering organic beef from our pedigree herd of British White cattle direct to your home. We also produce organic pork and lamb.

SMITHY FARM SHOP

Baldersby, Thirsk, YO7 4BN
Tel: 01765 640676 Fax: 01765 640898
Meat, poultry, dairy, vegetables, bread and pasta. Large range of pulses, cereals, sauces, wines & beers.

WARD, SJ

Manor House Farm, Morton on Swale,
Northallerton, DL7 9RJ
Tel: 01609 773538 Fax: 01609 773538
Field-scale grower of wide variety of vegetables: potatoes, carrots, parsnips, onions, celeriac, beetroot, leeks and a variety of brassicas. Organic meat also available.

WENSLEYDALE DAIRY PRODUCTS LTD

Wensleydale Dairy Products Ltd, Gayle Lane, Hawes, DL8 3RN
Tel: 01969 667664 Fax: 01969 667638 creamery@wensleydale.co.uk www.wensleydale.co.uk
Producers of organic wensleydale Cheese. Originators & producers of organic Wensleydale cheese with cranberries. Visitor centre open seven days a week, specialist shop, museum, viewing gallery and fully licensed restaurant.

WILD GINGER VEGETARIAN BISTRO
Behind The Green House, 5 Station Parade, Harrogate, HG1 1UF
Tel: 01423 566122 www.wild-ginger.co.uk
100% vegetarian foods, freshly prepared and home-made. Large choice for vegans, also gluten/dairy/wheat/sugar-free and other exclusion diets catered for. Licensed, selling organic wines and beer. Regular gourmet evenings and special events. Good Food Best Restaurant in Yorkshire/Humberside 2004 by public vote from *Guardian/Observer*.

YORK BEER & WINE SHOP

28 Sandringham Street, Fishergate, York, YO10 4BA
Tel: 01904 647136 Fax: 01904 647136
ybws@york10.freeserve.co.uk www.yorkbeerandwineshop.co.uk
We are a specialist off-licence selling beer, wine, cider and cheese. We sell organic lines of all our categories.

SOUTH YORKSHIRE

BEANIES

205-207 Crookes Valley Road, Sheffield, S10 1BA
Tel: 0114 268 1662 Fax: 0114 268 1555 sheffield.wholefoods@virgin.net
Soil Association No R1731, Award-winning workers' co-operative. Shop open seven days a week. Box scheme delivery service within Sheffield, also Doncaster, Barnsley, Chesterfield, Rotherham. Organic greengrocery, wholefoods, bread, chilled and frozen produce, vegan and vegetarian produce, and speciality foods.

DOWN TO EARTH

406 Sharrowvale Rd, Hunters Bar, Sheffield, S11 8ZP
Tel: 0114 268 5220 dte@blueyonder.co.uk
Wholefood retailer with wide range of organic produce including dairy, spreads, nuts beans, pulses, rice, grains, cereals, etc – not fresh fruit and veg.

THE DRAM SHOP

21 Commonside, Sheffield, S10 1GA
Tel: 0114 268 3117
Specialist off licence wines, beers, ciders and spirits.

FIVE A DAY

5 Listerdale Shopping Centre, Rotherham, S64 3JA
Tel: 01709 532007
Fresh fruit & veg, vegetarian salads and meals, freshly juiced organic fruit, olive oils, sauces, etc, all organic.

HEELEY CITY FARM

Richards Rd, Sheffield, S2 3DT
Tel: 0114 258 0482 Fax: 0114 255 1400 farm@heeleyfarm.org.uk www.heeleyfarm.org.uk
A community environmental and horticultural project based on an inner city educational farm and environmental visitor attraction. Food produced using organic methods available in our farm café and from our garden centre during times of surplus. Local crafts, compost bins and gifts in farm shop.

THE WILD STAR FOOD CO. LTD

26-28 Bedford St., Sheffield, S6 3BT
Tel: 0114 276 3043 info@wildstarfood.com www.wildstarfood.com
The Wild Star Food Co. run an organic box delivery scheme to Yorkshire and Derbyshire. We supply a wide range of organic fruit and vegetable boxes as well as a range of organic and locally produced grocery items.

The Organic Delivery Company was started in 1997 by John Barrow, and yes, it is his real name. He was going to call his new company "Fresh from the Barrow", but decided against it because it didn't sound organic enough!

When anyone asks how my business got started, I always tell them, "Well, it all began with a pain in my back." There was an ad on TV in the 1970s which depicted a man in his garden pushing a wheelbarrow. Suddenly he bends forward with a look of agony on his face, as he clutches his lower back. A soft, soothing voice urges him to "Reeelaaax, in a Radox bath."

But when I suffered from chronic backache in the early 1990s, Radox was not enough to ease my aches and pains. I went to a series of specialists, all to no avail. As a last ditch effort, I tried a Taoist healing process. They advised me to eat macrobiotic and organic, to which I replied, "Organic – what's organic?"

That advice changed my life. After eating nothing but organic foods, within two weeks the back pain I had been suffering from for over six years simply vanished, and within a few years The Organic Delivery Company was in full swing. I was convinced that the wonders of organic food, still far from widely recognised, would certainly benefit people if only I could get the word out. A decade on, I have seen the organic market explode in size like I never would have imagined. More and more people are fed up (pun intended) with supermarket food that is often picked green and flown in from all over the world.

It is not just the air miles clocked up by supermarket food that concerns me, but also the road miles it travels as it is carried from airport to warehouse, to depot before arriving on the supermarket shelves, where there is further huge waste of energy on refrigeration. Finally it is collected from the supermarkets by individual car trips, causing further adverse impacts on the environment.

I was taken aback by the DEFRA research which showed that 70% of food miles are contributed by the consumer travelling to the shops. I take our food miles very seriously, so as well as not purchasing anything whatsoever that is transported by air, I have tried to keep our own vehicle emissions to a minimum by having my drivers do their deliveries in geographical order. It seems clear that it is better for one vehicle to deliver to 50 homes than for 50 consumers to go out shopping. That is the beauty of a home delivery service. Furthermore, we are currently trying out a bio-diesel fuel in some of our delivery vans. So that makes us the first to deliver our vegetables on vegetable oil!

Organically yours,
John Barrow

WEST YORKSHIRE

BEANO WHOLEFOODS

70 North St., Leeds, LS2 7PN
Tel: 0113 243 5737 Fax: 0113 243 5737 info@beanowholefoods.co.uk www.beanowholefoods.co.uk
Vegetarian and vegan wholefood shop, with specialism in organic products. Organic fruit and vegetables
delivered Monday, Tuesday and Thursday. Fair trade products stocked. Special diets catered for.

BEANSTALK ORGANIX

Unit 9, Townhead Trading
Centre, Main Street, Addingham, LS29 0PD
Tel: 01943 831103 Fax: 01943 839199 info@beanstalkorganix.co.uk www.beanstalkorganix.co.uk
Soil Association P4995. Yorkshire's leading organic home delivery service and one-stop organic shop of
fresh produce: groceries, meat and poultry, bread and cakes, eco-baby, personal care and household
products. We accept all major credit and debit cards.

BRADFORD WHOLEFOODS

The Cellar Project, The Old School, Farfield Rd., Shipley, BD18 4QP
Tel: 01422 202648 jackfirstgrove@aol.com
Specialist organic food retailer selling fresh vegetables and fruit, some locally grown in season, groceries,
eco-friendly toiletries and cleaning products.

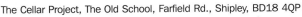

BRICKYARD ORGANICS

Brickyard Organic Farm, Badsworth, Pontefract, WF9 1AX
Tel: 01977 617327
Soil Association G598. Organic farm growing legumes, plants, salad, vegetables. Box scheme, shop open
on Saturdays 9.30–3.30 selling mainly own produce.

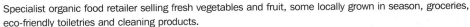

FOOD THERAPY

11 Northgate, Halifax, HX1 1UR
Tel: 01422 350826 Fax: 01422 362106
An award-winning store and restaurant with a huge range of organic wholefoods, cosmetic, toiletries,
cleaning products etc., etc.

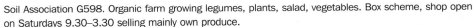

HALF MOON HEALTHFOODS

6 Half Moon St., Huddersfield, HD1 2JJ
Tel: 01484 456392 adrian@halfmoonhealthfoods.co.uk www.halfmoonhealthfoods.co.uk
We are a health food and wholefood store specialising in organic lines, vegetables, breads, dairy prod-
ucts, eggs, beers and wines. Our organic box scheme has been established 20 years.

KERSHAW'S GARDEN SHOPPING CENTRE

The Nurseries, Halifax Rd., Brighouse, HD6 2QD
Tel: 01484 713435
Garden centre stocking a range of organic composts, feeds, pest controls and seeds.

LOVE ORGANIC!

4 Regent St., Chapel Allerton, Leeds, LS7 4PE
Tel: 0113 266 3030
An organic and healthy food shop in the heart of Chapel Allerton. We stock all the organic essentials with a
fabulous range of groceries, fresh produce, meat, poultry and fish, baby, personal care and eco products.
We accept all major credit cards.

MEANWOOD VALLEY URBAN FARM

Sugarwell Rd., Meanwood, Leeds, LS7 2QG
Tel: 0113 262 9759 Fax: 0113 239 2551 info@mvuf.org.uk
Soil Association R27N. Member of the Organic Farm Network. City farm, combining organic market garden, environmental education services to schools. Farm animals, including rare breeds. Purpose-built environment centre, interactive displays. Shop café and play area. Registered charity, open every day to visitors. Member of the Soil Association Organic Farms Network.

NATURAL CHOICE

72 Westbourne Rd., Marsh, Huddersfield, HD1 4LE
Tel: 01484 513162 Fax: 01484 687466 graham.trudy@rush2001.freeserve.co.uk
Top quality organic fresh produce, also non-organic fresh produce. All the usual Suma-related products. Local deliveries.

NEAL'S YARD REMEDIES

20 County Arcade, Victoria Quarter, Leeds, LS1 6BN
Tel: 0113 243 8924 mail@nealsyardremedies.com www.nealsyardremedies.com
Neal's Yard Remedies manufactures and retails natural cosmetics in addition to stocking an extensive range of herbs, essential oils, homeopathic remedies and reference material.

ORG

79 Great George St., Leeds, LS1 3BR
Tel: 0113 234 7000 Fax: 0113 242 7201 novita@org-organics.org.uk www.org-organics.org.uk
Soil Association R6296. Treatment centre. Local fruit and vegetables, deliveries, hot & cold food, eat in & takeaway, dairy & dairy alternatives, meat and fish, juice bar, tea, coffees, groceries, cosmetics, frozen foods, household, alcohol, books, bulk grains, catering.

ORGANIC HOUSE

2 Market St, Hebden Bridge, HX7 6AA
Tel: 01422 843429 info@organic-house.co.uk www.organic-house.co.uk
Organic retail and refreshment, fresh fruit, veg, bread, dairy, dried goods, pulses, grains, nuts, cereals, coffees, teas, wines, beers, Fair Trade products, wide range of vegan, gluten-free and wheat-free produce. Also body care and organic clothing. Vegetarian café with wheat-free, gluten-free and vegan options always available.

OUT OF THIS WORLD

20 Newmarket St., Leeds, LS1 6DG
Tel: 0113 244 1881 Fax: 0113 234 1808 info@ootw.co.uk www.outofthisworld.coop
Small chain of ethical and organic supermarkets in Newcastle-upon-Tyne, Leeds, York and Nottingham. Selling over 5,000 products, mostly certified organic food plus fairly traded crafts, recycled paper and body care products etc. Consumer co-op with over 17,500 members.

SALTAIRE WINES & WHOLEFOODS

32 Bingley Rd, Saltaire, Shipley, BD18 4RU
Tel: 01274 583629 Fax: 01274 583629 len@thewolfes.freeserve.co.uk
Fine foods, luxury chocolates, wines, regional beers, whisky, liqueurs.

SNOWDEN, P A & S J

Hawthorne House Farm, Dunkeswick, Harewood, Leeds, LS17 9LP
Tel: 0113 288 6637 Fax: 0113 288 6754
Soil Association G1630. Organic arable farm growing milling wheat, field beans and fattening lambs. Selling potatoes, carrots, parsnips, leeks and other vegetables from the farm.

SWILLINGTON ORGANIC FARM

Garden Cottage, Swillington Organic Farm, Coach Rd., Swillington, LS26 8QA

Tel: 0113 286 9129 Fax: 0113 286 9129

jo@swillingtonorganicfarm.co.uk www.swillingtonorganicfarm.co.uk

Soil Association G5062. Mixed organic farm producing organic pork (commended 2004 Organic Food Awards), lamb, beef, chicken, eggs, and vegetables. Sold through farmers' markets and farm shop open Fridays 3pm–6pm and Saturdays 10am–4pm. Phone first at other times. Mobile: 07974 826876. Organic Food Awards 2004 Fresh Meat, Commended.

VALLEY GARDEN ORGANICS

31 Market St, Hebden Bridge, HX7 6EU

Tel: 01422 846651

Wide range of fresh organic fruit and veg, priority to local produce, wide range of other organic products including vegan, vegetarian, gluten-free. Organic meat, fair trade products, household and body care products.

WOW! FOODS

5 Victoria Square, Holmfirth, Huddersfield, HD9 2DN

Tel: 01484 682112 karen@wowfoods.co.uk www.wowfoods.co.uk

Organic box scheme delivering to West Yorkshire and South Yorkshire areas. Unique 'pick your own box' scheme in conjunction with the traditional picked £10/£15/£20 boxes. 100% vegetarian, 100% organic produce café, also special diets catered for.

NORTH-WEST

CHESHIRE

ABBEY LEYS FARM

Abbey Leys Farm, Peacock Lane, High Legh, Nr. Knutsford, WA16 6NS

Tel: 01925 753465 Fax: 01925 753465 tim@abbeyleys.co.uk www.abbeyleys.co.uk

Soil Association G4985. Organic free range hens including Speckledy and Hebden Black breeds. Free range duck eggs, home-grown Cheshire potatoes, fresh vegetables, fruit, farmhouse ice cream, home-made cakes, cheese and Abbey Leys honey. Local delivery available, not a box scheme. Abbey Leys Farmers' market and organic market on the 1st Sunday of the month 10 til 2pm. Farm shop open Mon-Sat 10 til 5pm, Sun 10 til 4pm, closed Bank Holidays.

AINSLEY'S – THE VERY FINEST ORGANIC BEEF

Park Farm, Wrexham Road, Ridley, Tarporley, CW6 9SA

Tel: 01829 261700 Fax: 01829 261700 ainsley@bakerconsulting.fsnet.co.uk

Our finest organic beef is slowly reared using native cattle breeds on our Cheshire farm. We firmly believe that the resulting tender, juicy, flavoursome beef will be some of the best that you've ever tasted! We only use our own native breeds such as Hereford, Aberdeen Angus or Welsh Black. All our boxes contain individually packaged and labelled beef from a selection of cuts ranging from tender steaks and roasting joints to sausages, burgers, mince and braising steak which is perfect for warming casseroles. Our beef is ideal for freezing and is delivered free of charge to your door in special insulated boxes to ensure that the meat reaches you in optimum condition. Large family box £140; smaller box £75. Please phone to order.

AROMART
28 Stockport Rd., Romiley, Stockport, SK6 4BN
Tel: 0161 406 7176 Fax: 0161 494 1129 aromart.romiley@ntlworld.com www.aromart.co.uk
We are a retail shop selling natural and organic products including herbs, spices and herbal teas.

BOOTHS SUPERMARKETS
Stanley Road, Knutsford, WA16 0BS
Tel: 01565 652522 Fax: 01565 652504
Supermarket with broad range of organic food, clearly labelled in store. Fresh produce, meat, dairy, Village Bakery products, many other groceries.

THE CHEESE SHOP
116 Northgate St., Chester, CH1 2HT
Tel: 01244 346240 Fax: 01244 314659
carole@chestercheeseshop.com www.chestercheeseshop.com
Specialist cheese shop with local delivery (not a box scheme). We promote local, organic and British cheeses, particularly cheeses sourced direct from the farm, matured and cared for in our cellars below the shop. Also organic wine, chutneys and biscuits.

CHESHIRE ORGANICS
5 Booths Hill Road, Lymm, WA13 0DJ
Tel: 01925 758575 Fax: 01925 758043 jackie@cheshireorganics.co.uk
Soil Association R2955. Over 1,000 product lines, fruit, vegetables, bread, dairy, grocery, gluten/dairy/sugar-free products, meat and poultry, homecare, wine and beer. All delivered direct to your home or office.

DAVENPORTS FARM SHOP
Bridge Farm, Warrington Road, Bartington, Northwich, CW8 4QU
Tel: 01606 853241 Fax: 01606 854900 davenports@fsbdial.co.uk www.davenportsfarmshop.co.uk
Farm shop selling organic, gluten-free and products suitable for diabetics. Farm applying for organic status with the Soil Association for growing vegetables and egg production.

DEER PARK FARM
Forty Acre Lane, Kermincham, Holmes Chapel, Crewe, CW4 8DX
Tel: 01477 532188 Fax: 01477 544638 martin.steer@lineone.net
Organic lamb (whole and half) available to order. Steer Ethelston Rural Ltd. Rural Chartered Surveyors, specialists in environmental and organic land management. Member of Soil Association Organic Farms Network.

DEMETER WHOLEFOODS LTD
12 Welles St., Sandbach, CW11 1GT
Tel: 01270 760445 demeter@gynger.co.uk
Retail outlet in Cheshire supplying the following organic merchandise: basic foodstuffs, drinks, culinary & medicinal herbs, nutritional supplements, environmentally sound cleaning products, recycled products. Trading in Sandbach since 1980 we have developed supply lines for a large number of obscure items which we increasingly despatch by post.

MARTON VILLA FARM
White Gate, Nr. Winsford, CW7 2QG
Tel: 01829 760289
Marton Villa is a 80-hectare mixed farm set in the heart of the Cheshire countryside. The farm converted to organic farming in 2001, with a long-term aim of being a mixed farm with laying hens and chickens, dairy cows, beef, sheep and bees. Marton Villa aims to sell much of its produce direct to the public and welcome visitors to the farm. Member of the Soil Association Organic Farms Network.

CHESHIRE

NATURE'S REMEDIES

10 Time Square, Warrington, WA1 2AR
Tel: 01925 444885 Fax: 01925 654821
Healthfood shop stocking wide range of organic foods.

NORTHERN HARVEST

Kenyon Hall Farm, Croft, Warrington, WA3 7ED
Tel: 0845 602 3309 Fax: 01942 608329 enquiry@northernharvest.co.uk www.northernharvest.co.uk
Award-winning home delivery service with over 3,000 products including fresh produce, dairy, meat, bakery, eco-friendly goods. We deliver to Cheshire, Greater Manchester, south Lancashire and Merseyside. Shop online at our website.

ORGANICFAIR

43 St. James St., Chester, CH1 3EY
Tel: 01244 400158 Fax: 01244 342228 mark@organicfair.co.uk www.organicfair.co.uk
Organicfair is the award-winning store specialising in organic, fairtrade and local products. We stock around 1,500 lines and run a highly popular veg box delivery service for Chester, Cheshire and north Wales. We are open 6 days a week from 10am–7pm.

ORGANIC GARDENS

Tel: 0161 285 8319 organicgardens@hotmail.co.uk www.theorganiclife.co.uk
Organic Gardens is a small local business that delivers garden maintenance which is fully organic.

ORGANIC ON THE HILL, BUTTERLANDS FARM

Butterlands Farm, Wincle, Macclesfield, SK11 0QL
Tel: 01260 227672 Fax: 01260 227672 jane@organiconthehill.com www.organiconthehill.com
Home reared organic beef, lamb and pork. Grazed on clover-rich meadows, giving an excellent taste and quality to the meat. Own processing facilities on the farm allowing us to give individual and personal attention at all times. All cuts available including our own recipe sausages and burgers. Local market in Macclesfield attended every Friday, plus other local Farmers' Markets on monthly basis. Please ring or email for further details and price list.

THE ORGANIC VEG. COMPANY LTD.

131 Walton Rd, Stockton Heath, Warrington, WA4 6NT
Tel: 01925 480895 theorganicvegcompany@hotmail.co.uk
The Organic Veg. Company is a local firm committed to offering you the consumer, fresh, quality organic, salad, fruit and vegetables. We offer this produce through our organic home delivery box scheme. Each week we select the best seasonal produce available, then deliver fresh to your door in a choice of three box sizes. Of course there will always be staple foods such as potatoes, carrots, onions and apples; however, the rest of the box's contents will vary according to the season. Regardless of the time of year, you will always receive the best service and finest quality produce. We also offer eggs and supply to the trade as well as to our domestic customers.

RIVERSIDE ORGANICS

Shipbrook Hill Farm, Manor Lane, Whatcroft, Northwich, CW9 7RH
Tel: 01606 46258 sales@www.riversideorganic.com www.riversideorganic.com
Family-run organic farmers, growers and retailers producing the finest beef, lamb and seasonal vegetables. Brilliant views, farm walks, picnic area and coffee shop.

STOCKLEY FARM ORGANICS

Smithy Farmhouse, Arley, Northwich, CW9 6LZ
Tel: 01565 777492 Fax: 01565 777501 organics@stockleyfarm.co.uk www.stockleyfarm.co.uk
Stockley farm organics grows, picks and delivers organic vegetables to your door. We also have an organic Aberdeen Angus herd. The beef is boxed and delivered to surrounding areas in Cheshire. The farm is open to the public for much of the year.

SUGARBROOK FARM

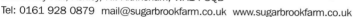   

Mobberley Rd., Ashley, Nr. Altrincham, WA14 3QB
Tel: 0161 928 0879 mail@sugarbrookfarm.co.uk www.sugarbrookfarm.co.uk
Soil Association G4603. Bed and breakfast with en-suite facilities from £25 per person, close to Manchester airport and Tatton Park. Sheep and arable farm welcoming educational access under Countryside Stewardship, i.e. free visits.

CUMBRIA

ALLEGARTH ORGANICS

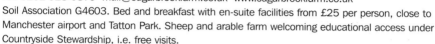

Allegarth, Roweltown, Carlisle, CA6 6JU
Tel: 01697 748065
Soil Association G797. A 12-acre smallholding offering unique holiday accommodation for up to 8 persons in a secluded and unspoilt part of North Cumbria. A member of Hadrian Organics.

ALSTON WHOLEFOODS LTD

Front St., Alston, CA9 3HU
Tel: 01434 381588
Workers co-operative shop with range of wholefoods and organic products. Speciality cheeses, dietary needs, local eggs, bread, cakes, mustards. Walkers' and cyclists' snacks, delicious ice creams. Cleaning products, deodorants, toothpaste, soap. Mon–Sat 9am–5pm. Sunday 11am–4pm.

ASKERTON CASTLE ESTATE

Askerton Castle, Brampton, CA8 2BD
Tel: 01697 73332 askerton.castle@btinternet.com www.askertoncastle.co.uk
Quality meat producer – our pedigree Belted Galloway cattle, Scottish Blackface and Kerry Hill sheep, eggs from traditional pure bred laying hens. We also do pork and bacon from Berkshire and Tamworths, alpaca fibre and Beltie rugs. Visit our website.

BOOTHS SUPERMARKETS

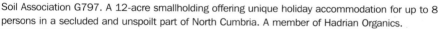

The Old Station, Victoria Street, Windermere, LA23 1QA
Tel: 015394 46114 Fax: 015394 88918 www.booths-supermarkets.co.uk
Organic fruit and veg, fresh meat, dairy, frozen burgers, frozen veg, wines, preserves, flour, bread, cakes.

EVA'S ORGANICS

Eva Botanicals Ltd., Medburn, Milton, Brampton, CA8 1HS
Tel: 01697 741906 Fax: 01697 741205
debbie.simpson@evabotanicals.co.uk www.evabotanicals.co.uk
We offer a wide range of fruit and vegetables in a box scheme with big savings for drop-off points. We also grow organic vegetables, culinary and medicinal herbs.

CUMBRIA

GILLAM'S TEA ROOM & RESTAURANT

64 Market St., Ulverston, LA12 7LT

Tel: 01229 587564 douglasgillam@btconnect.com

Gillam's is an organic and vegetarian traditional English tea room and restaurant. We serve loose leaf teas and fine coffees alongside excellent food in our beautiful 18th century building, with a garden to the rear.

HALF MOON WHOLEFOODS

14 Front St., Brampton, CA8 1NG

Tel: 01697 73775 chris@halfmoonwholefoods.co.uk www.halfmoonwholefoods.co.uk

Small but comprehensive wholefood store in north Cumbria. Stockists of Watermill organic flours, organic cheeses, ice creams, eco products, toiletries, supplements, homeopathic remedies, allergy testing, essential oils, creams, etc. Order service for products not in stock. Local delivery service.

HALLSFORD (A N & H S TOMKINS)

Hallsford Farm, Hethersgill, Carlisle, CA6 6JD

Tel: 01228 577329 Fax: 01228 577148 thefarm@hallsford.co.uk www.hallsford.co.uk

Soil Association G7042. Beef and lamb producer in North Cumbria. Pedigree beef Shorthorn cattle and one of the largest flocks of rare breed Llanwenog sheep. Top quality marbled Shorthorn beef and rare breed lamb via local farmers' markets, regional food fairs and nationally by mail order. Rare breed pork to be introduced in 2004. Visit the website.

HOWBARROW ORGANIC FARM

Cartmel, Grange-over-Sands, LA11 7SS

Tel: 015395 36330 Fax: 015395 36330

enquiries@howbarroworganic.co.uk www.howbarroworganic.co.uk

Grow and process medicinal herbs into tinctures and oils. 13-acre smallholding producing meat (lamb, beef, turkeys), eggs, vegetables and medicinal herbs. Supply local box scheme, farmers' markets and our award-winning Organic Farm Shop of the year, 2002. Demonstration farm, walks and displays. Soil Association licensed organic B&B and dinner. Member of the Soil Association Organic Farms Network.

ILOVEORGANICS

13 Wainwright's Yard, Kendal, LA9 4DP

Tel: 01539 721100 Fax: 01539 721100 info@iloveorganics.co.uk www.iloveorganics.co.uk

Large, ambient organic shop and café providing high quality health and beauty products, home and lifestyle, aromatherapy and well being, speciality foods, online shop and a stylish all-organic café.

KAN FOODS

9 New Shambles, off Market Place, Kendal, LA9 4TS

Tel: 01539 721190 lizkan@inthelight.info

A wholefood shop with high grade vitamins, herb, oils, organic make-up, juices, water filters, harmonisers, help and advice.

LADY JANE'S TEA ROOM

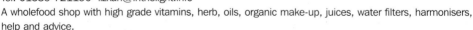

Cumbrian Antique Centre, St. Martin's Hall, Brampton, CA18 1NT

Tel: 07941 731255

Delicious home-made food prepared with locally grown organic and fair trade produce where possible. Outside catering a speciality. We are also a drop-off point for an organic produce box scheme.

LOW LUCKENS ORGANIC RESOURCE CENTRE

Low Luckens, Roweltown, Carlisle, CA6 6LJ

Tel: 01697 748186 lowluckensorc@hotmail.com www.lowluckensfarm.co.uk

The Organic Resource Centre is located in 220 acres of organically managed farmland. The centre provides self-catering accommodation, a range of events and courses and educational access. Organic meat and vegetables available.

LOW SIZERGH BARN FARM SHOP, TEA ROOM & CRAFT GALLERY

Low Sizergh Farm, Sizergh, Kendal, LA8 8AE

Tel: 01539 560426 Fax: 01539 561475 admin@lowsizerghbarn.co.uk www.low-sizergh-barn.co.uk

Soil Association G5843. Farm trail-part of the Organic Farms Network. Large farm shop with full range of fine locally produced food; cheese & ice cream made with the farm's milk; tea room (watch the cows being milked at 3.45pm); also crafts. Member of the Soil Association Organic Farms Network.

MANSERGH HALL FARM SHOP

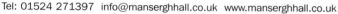

Mansergh Hall, Kirkby Lonsdale,
Carnforth, Cumbria, LA6 2EN

Tel: 01524 271397 info@manserghhall.co.uk www.manserghhall.co.uk

Organic lamb, pork, beef, mutton, milk and eggs are available from our farm shop, through our box scheme (which also offers fruit and vegetables) and by mail order. We also supply top quality farm shops and restaurants. Wholesale enquiries welcome.

SUNDANCE WHOLEFOODS

33 Main Street, Keswick, CA12 5BL

Tel: 01768 774712

Soil Association member. A wholefood shop with many organic lines.

THE VILLAGE BAKERY

Melmerby, Penrith, CA10 1HE

Tel: 01768 881811 Fax: 01768 881848 info@village-bakery.com www.village-bakery.com

Organic speciality breads, cakes, savoury biscuits, flapjacks, slices, Christmas goods. Special diet products. Mail order. Nationwide stockists. Baking courses. Organic Food Awards 2004 Cakes, Pastries, Biscuits Highly Commended.

THE WATERMILL

Little Salkeld, Penrith, CA10 1NN

Tel: 01768 881523 Fax: 01768 881047 organicflour@aol.com www.organicmill.co.uk

Soil Association (P632) and Biodynamic Agriculture Association registered. Specialist organic flours, milled by water power in our 18th century watermill to SA and BDAA standards. Mill shop, tea room, mill tours and baking courses.

WHITEHOLME FARM

Whiteholme, Roweltown, Carlisle, CA6 6LJ

Tel: 016977 48058 whiteholmefarm@hotmail.com www.whiteholmefarm.co.uk

Whiteholme Farm is an organic livestock farm situated in the north-east of Cumbria. Home reared organic beef, lamb and pork is prepared at our on-farm butchery from traditional breeds and sold to local customers through direct sales and farmers' markets. Accommodation, education and farm walks are all available. Member of the Soil Association Organic Farms Network.

LANCASHIRE

BOOTHS SUPERMARKETS

4-6 Fishergate, Preston, PR1 3LJ
Tel: 01772 251701 Fax: 01772 204316
admin@booths-supermarkets.co.uk www.booths-supermarkets.co.uk
Regional supermarket chain.

CHORLEY HEALTH FOOD STORE LTD
18 New Market St., Chorley, PR7 1DB
Tel: 0845 0560156 sales@yourhealthfoodstore.co.uk www.yourhealthfoodstore.co.uk
Town centre shop adjacent to main car park, taxi rank and bus station. We offer a wide variety of organic foods, drinks and supplements, special orders welcome. Open 6 days Monday–Saturday 8.15–5.15. Discount on full case orders.

EMINENCE ORGANICS
17B Boxer Place, Moss Side Ind Estate, Leyland, PR26 7QL
Tel: 07933 295936 info@eminenceorganic.co.uk www.eminenceorganic.co.uk
Organic box delivery scheme, delivering you fresh organic fruit, vegetables, meat, poultry and eggs direct to your door, hassle-free.

FAULKNER'S OF RAMSBOTTOM
12 Bolton St., Ramsbottom, Bury, BL0 9HX
Tel: 01706 823158 Fax: 0161 764 1799 order@faulknersorganics.co.uk www.faulknersorganics.co.uk
Local retail shop and box scheme service for the local people. Supplying the best available produce. Box schemes delivered as far as Rossendale, Haslingden, Helmshore, Bradshaw, Tottington, Bury, Turn Village etc, check our website for further details. Meat also available in-store from the 2nd Thursday of the month till the 2nd Sunday in the month only. Forward orders advisable. Come and see us soon!

FLINTOFF, LIBBY

Brook House Farm, Tarnacre Lane, St Michael's on Wyre, Preston, PR3 0TB
Tel: 01995 679728 Fax: 01995 679728 lib@theflintoffs.fsnet.co.uk
Soil Association G1898. Grower – mainly protected cropping including cucumbers, aubergines, french beans, celery and onions. Also some field vegetables.

THE GOOD LIFE
6 Frank St., Barnoldswick, BB18 5AE
Tel: 01282 850101
A wide range of organic and eco friendly products including dried fruits, cereals, fruit and veg, jams, soups, sauces, teas, coffees, flours, supplements, etc., in fact anything organic. Box scheme by Beanstalk.

GROWING WITH NATURE
Bradshaw Lane Nursery, Pilling, Nr. Preston, PR3 6AX
Tel: 01253 790046 Fax: 01253 790046
Soil Association S44N, RS44N. Grower's box scheme with seasonal vegetables and salads. Organic Food Awards 2004 Organic Trophy Winners.

FOR DETAILS OF SYMBOLS USED IN THE ENTRIES, SEE PAGE 17

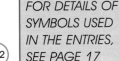

LYNCROFT FARM LTD

Lyncroft Farm, Butchers Lane,
Aughton Green, Ormskirk, L39 6SY

Tel: 01695 421712 Fax: 01695 422117 lyncroftfarm@tiscali.co.uk www.organic-veg.org

Here at Lyncroft Organic Farm we have been organic for over 25 years. The farm was founded by my father and I have recently acquired control. We are dedicated entirely to organic fruit and vegetable production on our 100+ acres of local land. We supply wholesale, retail and operate a local organic box delivery scheme, where we pride ourselves on our 24 hour turnaround: fresh organic vegetables are delivered direct from field to table within 24 hours.

MCKINSEY HEALTHY HERBS

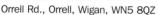 

Orrell Rd., Orrell, Wigan, WN5 8QZ

Tel: 01695 632825 Fax: 01942 736286

Organic herb nursery. We specialise in pot-grown and fresh-cut culinary and medicinal herbs. Browse our extensive stock, talk to our knowledgeable staff or relax in our tea room. Open Monday, Wednesday, Friday & Saturday 10am–4pm.

NATURE'S GARDEN

1 Tor View Rd., Haslingden, Rossendale, BB4 6PW

Tel: 01706 217832 shop@natures-garden.co.uk www.natures-garden.co.uk

Organic fruit and vegetables delivery box scheme covering the Rossendale valley and Rochdale areas. Box sizes to suit all households delivered free within 24 hours, supporting local growers and producers. All imported fruit is fair trade. Mobile: 07967 640434.

ONLY NATURAL

64 Standishgate, Wigan, WN1 1UW

Tel: 01942 236239

Health food shop selling a wide range of vitamins, body building, food supplements, cosmetics, wholefoods including organic ranges. Allergy testing once a month. Friendly and helpful staff.

PORTER, ROY

9 Bridge Rd., Chatburn, Clitheroe, BB7 4AW

Tel: 01200 441392 Fax: 01200 441096

Soil Association R4342. A very traditional butchers shop, whose products include organic meat and poultry. All meat is hung for 7–10 days depending on species and butchered to customers' individual requirements.

SINGLE STEP CO-OPERATIVE LTD

78A Penny St, Lancaster, LA1 1NN

Tel: 01524 63021

Wholefood co-op selling a wide range of organic and fair trade products, including fresh fruit and vegetables. Vegetarian and sugar-free policies.

SOW AND GROW ORGANICS

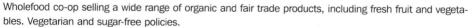

20 Hawthorn Avenue, Orrell, Wigan, WN5 8NQ

Tel: 01942 621729 sowandgroworganics@phonecoop.coop

Selling freshly harvested vegetables at McKinsey Healthy Herbs, Orrell, Wigan (Saturdays) and Fir Tree Farm Shop, Kings Moss, St Helens. Box scheme deliveries within five miles to drop-off points. Stockfree Organic Certified – no animal inputs.

WHALE TAIL CAFÉ

78A Penny St, Lancaster, LA1 1XN

Tel: 01524 845133

Spacious and friendly café offering home-made veggie and vegan food, and on Fridays an organic main meal option.

GREATER MANCHESTER

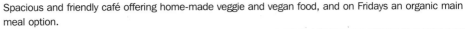

ARKADASH

103 Manchester Rd., Chorlton, M21 9GA

Tel: 0161 881 9500 hello@arkadash.co.uk www.arkadash.co.uk

We are a clothing shop selling only organic, fairtrade and sweatshop-free clothes for adults, kids and babies, as well as organic bedding, towels, make-up, body care, accessories, coffee and chocolate. We also sell through the web and at fairs and markets (see web for event details).

CHORLTON WHOLEFOODS

64 Beech Rd., Chorlton-Cum-Hardy, M21 9EG

Tel: 0161 881 6399 Fax: 0161 881 6399

Established in 1982, we sell organic fruit and veg, dairy produce, dried goods, herbal supplements etc. Home delivery within Greater Manchester. Practitioner visits and consultations.

CORNMELL, R.M. ORGANIC BUTCHER & FOOD SPECIALIST

459 Halliwell Rd., Bolton, BL1 8DE

Tel: 01204 846844

Our speciality organic foods: meats, bacon, ham, poultry, cheese, free range organic eggs, honey, jam, butter, herbs, spices, juices, bread, cakes and many more products (except vegetables) sold at the shop. Open Monday 9–5, Tuesday 9–5.30, Wednesday 9–2, Thursday at Altrincham farmers' market 9–4. Friday 9–6, Saturday 9–5.

DOJO ECOSHOP

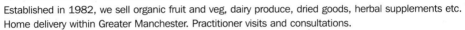

38 Mason St., Manchester, M4 5EZ

Tel: 0161 834 5432 Fax: 0161 834 5432 mail@dojoeco.co.uk www.dojoeco.co.uk

Hand-made mattresses, futons and cushions in all sizes using organic, natural and recycled materials. We also produce futon and bed frames using FSC timber and sell organic duvets, pillows, towels, bed linen, fabric, natural bath products, cosmetics, toiletries, eco paint, fairly traded toys, gifts, good coffee and much more.

EIGHTH DAY

111 Oxford Rd., Manchester, M1 7DU

Tel: 0161 273 4878 Fax: 0161 273 4869 mail@eighth-day.co.uk www.eighth-day.co.uk

Vegetarian health food shop, over 1,000 organic lines including foods and complementary remedies, vegetarian café and catering with some organic food.

HEALTH & VEGETARIAN STORE

33 Old Church Street, Newton Heath, Manchester, M40 2JN

Tel: 0161 683 4456

Health shop, all food vegetarian or vegan, special diets catered for. Herbal and homeopathic remedies, Hopi ear candles, chilled and frozen. Large selection of organic foods, cereals, nuts, seeds, pulses and fruit and vegetables, essential oils. Helpful friendly advice, local deliveries (not a box scheme).

LIMITED RESOURCES

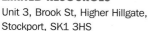   

Unit 3, Brook St, Higher Hillgate, Stockport, SK1 3HS

Tel: 0161 477 2040 Fax: 0161 226 3777 info@limited-resources.co.uk www.limited-resources.co.uk
Soil Association R1738. Free delivery service: organic fruit, veg, dairy, meat, fish, wholefoods, beers, wines, gardening and pet supplies, toiletries and cleaning products. Also mail order – ring for details.

MOSSLEY ORGANIC AND FINE FOODS

11–13 Arundel Street, Mossley, OL5 0NY
Tel: 01457 837743 Fax: 01457 837542

shop@mossleyorganicandfinefoods.co.uk www.mossleyorganicandfinefoods.co.uk
Huge range of natural food, many organic. Wide range of fresh, quality organic fruit and vegetables available. Chilled, frozen, dairy produce, deli counter. Many organic wines and beers. Specialist, individual friendly service. Fair trade products supported. Soil Association member. Free delivery/box scheme.

NEAL'S YARD REMEDIES

29 John Dalton St., Manchester, M2 6DS
Tel: 0161 835 1713 Fax: 0161 835 9322 mail@nealsyardremedies.com www.nealsyardremedies.com
Neal's Yard Remedies manufactures and retails natural cosmetics in addition to stocking an extensive range of herbs, essential oils, homeopathic remedies and reference material.

PUREHEALTH CLINIC

Purehealth Clinic, 91 High St., Uppermill, Oldham, OL3 6BD
Tel: 01457 877799 enquiries@purehealth2000.freeserve.co.uk www.purehealth.org.uk
We are a multi-disciplinary alternative health clinic with a full dispensary and shop. We have an extensive range of organic, non-toxic toiletries, allergen-free supplements and a small range of organic wheat-free and dairy-free foods.

UNICORN GROCERY

89 Albany Rd., Chorlton, Manchester, M21 0BN

Tel: 0161 861 0010 Fax: 0161 861 7675 office@unicorn-grocery.co.uk www.unicorn-grocery.co.uk
Soil Association GC5018, R2957. We are a large, friendly wholesome foodstore specialising in fresh and organic produce. Over 2,000 good value lines. We also cater for people with more specialised dietary needs.

MERSEYSIDE

CHURCH FARM ORGANICS

Church Farm, Church Lane, Thurstaston, Wirral, CH61 0HW

Tel: 0151 648 7838 Fax: 0151 648 9644 sales@churchfarm.org.uk www.churchfarm.org.uk
Soil Association G5381 & R2617. Picturesque farm with beautiful views, producing most vegetables for award-winning shop. 'Best Farm Shop' Organic Food Awards 2001 and second In the Radio 4 Food and Farming Awards 2004. Includes coffee bar. Bed and breakfast accommodation and holiday cottage. Wide range of seasons and events – see website for details.

FORSTER ORGANIC MEATS

Shoots Delph Farm, Birchley View, Moss Bank, St. Helens, WA11 7NU

Tel: 01942 831058 Fax: 01942 831867

info@forsterorganicmeats.co.uk www.forsterorganicmeats.co.uk

We produce our own beef and lamb. We sell and deliver locally fresh packs labelled and ready for eating or freezing. Farmers' Markets at Liverpool 1st and 3rd Saturdays every month, and now Bootle. We have our own butchery on the farm (very close to Carr Mill off the East Lancs Road). Customers are welcome to call by arrangement, or Thursdays when the butchery is open until 6.00pm. We prefer to sell directly the people who are going to enjoy our meat. We also make South African-style 'Biltong', which is very popular with S.A. ex-pats. We are proud to say that no finished livestock has been sold through a market for over 5 years. Please call Anne or Chris for more details.

ONLY NATURAL

48 Westfield St., St. Helens, WA10 1QF

Tel: 01744 759797

Health food shop selling a wide range of vitamins, body building, food supplements, cosmetics, wholefoods including organic ranges. Allergy testing once a month. Friendly and helpful staff.

ORGANIC DIRECT

57 Blundell St., Liverpool, L1 0AJ

Tel: 0151 707 6949 Fax: 0151 707 6949

Fresh organic fruit and vegetables, weekly deliveries direct to your door from £6. Also vegan organic wholefood deliveries, many organic lines.

PHYTOBOTANICA (UK) LTD

Greens Barn, Greens Lane, Lydiate, L31 4HZ

Tel: 01695 420853 info@phytobotanica.com www.phytobotanica.com

Producers of the first certified organic essential oils in th UK (lavender, peppermint, roman chamomile, German chamomile) and organic hydrosols. On-farm commercial hydrodistillation facilities, dispensary and conference centre for educational days (e.g. aromatherapy and holistic therapies).

WINDMILL WHOLEFOODS CO-OP

337 Smithdown Rd., Liverpool, L15 3JJ

Tel: 0151 734 1919 windmillorganic@hotmail.co.uk www.windmillorganic.co.uk

Grocery with a wide range of healthy, organic, vegan, vegetarian, and fair trade wholefoods. We also stock vegan/organic delights, like wines and chocolate. Ethical body care and cleaning products. Our veg box scheme delivers to the Liverpool area every Thursday.

NORTHERN IRELAND

ARKHILL FARM

25 Drumcroone Road, Garvach, Co. Londonderry, Northern Ireland, BT51 4EB

Tel: 028 2955 7920

Irish Organic Farmers and Growers license no. 1003. Box delivery service. Organic hen and duck eggs, pork, including bacon, sausages, ham, chops, fillets and roasts, lamb, chickens, turkeys, apples, fruit and veg. Open to groups e.g. schools etc.

BALLYLAGAN ORGANIC FARM

12 Ballylagan Rd., Straid, Ballyclare, Co. Antrim, Northern Ireland, BT39 9NF
Tel: 028 9332 2867 Fax: 028 9332 2129 ballylagan@aol.com www.ballylagan.com
Soil Association G1513. Farm shop selling home-produced meat and poultry products, fruit and vegetables,
plus full range of organic groceries. Shop opens: Thursday 2–6.30, Friday 9.30–6.30, Saturday 9.30–5.00.

CAMPHILL COMMUNITY – CLANABOGAN

Camphill Community Clanabogan, Omagh, Northern Ireland, BT78 1TJ
Tel: 028 8225 6111 Fax: 028 8225 6114 martinsturm@firenet.uk.net www.camphillclanabogan.com
Mixed biodynamic farm & renewables demonstration farm, with 320kw biomass district heating system,
20kw wind turbine, geothermal heating for polytunnel, solar panels, photovoltaic array, domestic wood
pellet boiler.

CAMPHILL COMMUNITY – HOLYWOOD

8 Shore Road, Holywood, Co. Down, Northern Ireland, BT18 9HX
Tel: 028 9042 3203 Fax: 028 9089 7818
camphillholywood@btconnect.com www.camphillholywood.co.uk
Organic retail dry goods and bakery, café serving all organic teas, coffees, soups and sandwiches.

DOWN-TO-EARTH

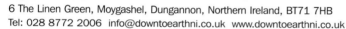

6 The Linen Green, Moygashel, Dungannon, Northern Ireland, BT71 7HB
Tel: 028 8772 2006 info@downtoearthni.co.uk www.downtoearthni.co.uk
Down-to-Earth provides produce for people of all ages and their dietary needs, offering foods such as
organic baby food to convenience foods, snacks for lunch boxes to ingredients for those exotic dishes.
Down-to-Earth strives to source local produce such as meat, dairy, fruit and vegetables from local farmers, cutting out the number of miles food has to travel contributing to the freshness of the produce as
well as supporting our local countryside.

HELEN'S BAY ORGANIC GARDENS

13 Seaview Terrace, Holywood, Co. Down, Northern Ireland, BT18 9DT
Tel: 028 9185 3122 organics2u@f2s.com www.helensbayorganicgardens.com
Weekly deliveries of fresh organic vegetables from our fields in Helen's Bay. Our delivery area covers
greater Belfast and North Down. We supply large, medium and small bags to cater for different needs.

LIFE TREE

37 Spencer Road, Derry, Co. Londonderry, Northern Ireland, BT47 6AA
Tel: 028 7134 2865 Fax: 028 7134 7880 lifetreeshop@hotmail.com
Health food shop run by qualified therapist with medical background, specialising in foods for special diets.

LITTLE EARTHLINGS

Riverton House, 151 Drumagarner Rd., Kilrea, Co. Derry,
Northern Ireland, BT51 5TW
Tel: 028 2954 1214 Fax: 028 2954 1498 info@littleearthlings.com www.littleearthlings.com
Specialising in the very best quality of organic cotton clothing, nappies and educational toys for babies up
to four. We also have a range of toiletries especially designed for pregnant mums.

NORTH WEST ORGANIC CO-OPERATIVE SOCIETY LTD

2 Foreglen Road, Killaloo, Northern Ireland, BT47 4HY
Tel: 028 7133 7950 Fax: 028 7133 7146 george@nworganic.com www.nworganic.com
The purpose of North West Organic is to co-ordinate the sale of locally produced organic food. All the
farmers in North West Organic are registered with either the Soil Association or Irish Organic Farmers and
Growers Association.

OAKDENE DAIRY/ORGANIC DOORSTEP

125 Strabane Rd., Castlederg, Co. Tyrone,
Northern Ireland, BT81 7JD
Tel: 0800 783 5656 Fax: 028 8167 9820 info@organicdoorstep.co.uk www.organicdoorstep.co.uk
We specialise in the production, processing, retailing of organic milk from the farm to the doorstep.

ORCHARD ORGANICS

Knockaconey, Allistragh, Armagh,
Northern Ireland, BT61 8DT
Tel: 028 3889 1506 Fax: 028 3889 1529 info@orchardorganics.com www.orchardorganics.com
Supply organic fruit and vegetables to supermarkets, box schemes, etc. Also deliver throughout Ireland
through our box scheme.

ORGANIC FOOD COMPANY

98 Flagstaff Rd., Newry, Co. Down, Northern Ireland, BT35 8NR
Tel: 028 3084 9000 Fax: 028 3084 9000 www.organicfoodcompany.co.uk
We operate a box scheme in Northern Ireland. Our specialty is locally grown, freshly picked produce
brought to your door throughout the year.

ULSTER WILDLIFE TRUST

John McSparran Memorial Hill Farm, Glendun, Cushenden,
Co. Antrim, Northern Ireland, BT44 0PZ
Tel: 028 2176 1403 Fax: 028 2176 1403 ulsterwt@glendunfarm.fsnet.co.uk
Soil Association G6697. Farming together with wildlife in a progressive and sustainable manner, producing
lamb and beef from traditional and native breeds. Native trees are also produced in our nursery.

SCOTLAND

ABERDEENSHIRE

BRIDGEFOOT ORGANICS

Bridgefoot, Newmachar, Aberdeenshire, AB21 7PE
Tel: 01651 862041 vegetables@bridgefootorganics.co.uk www.bridgefootorganics.co.uk
Soil Association nos. SG1071, SP5286. Producing vegetables, soft fruit and eggs. Home delivery service
for organic fruit, vegetables, eggs, mushrooms and meat in the Aberdeen area.

CORSHALLOCH ORGANICS

Corshalloch, Glass, Huntly, Aberdeenshire, AB54 4XT
Tel: 01466 700267 barbarasetterfield@hotmail.com
Small family farm producing vegetables and soft fruit, eggs, beef and lamb.

CROFT ORGANICS

Skellarts Croft, Daviot, Inverurie, Aberdeenshire, AB51 0JL
Tel: 01467 681717 croftorganics@hotmail.com www.croft-organics.co.uk
Soil Association SP6495, HDRA. Soil Association box scheme; vegetables and soft fruit grown on Soil
Association registered land. Farm shop sales, also free range eggs.

FRASER, J & M

Burnorrachie, Bridge of Muchalls, Stonehaven,
Aberdeenshire, AB39 3RU
Tel: 01569 730195
A 40-acre farm growing field veg for the wholesale market and local deliveries, specialising in supplying other box schemes. We also have 'meat days' when meat is available. Organic Food Awards 2004 Fresh Fruit and Veg Commended.

GREENESS ORGANICS

Rosebrae, Greeness, Cuminestown, Turriff, Aberdeenshire, AB53 8HY
Tel: 01888 544877
Soil Association G2381. Weekly box delivery of locally grown vegetables and occasionally fruit around Turriff, Banff, Aberchirder and their environs.

LEMBAS

Lorieneen, Bridge Of Muchalls,
Stonehaven, Aberdeen, Aberdeenshire, AB39 3RU
Tel: 01569 731746 Fax: 01569 739137
BDAA 307; Soil Association SP6660. Growers and distributors of Demeter and organically grown foods. We stock fresh fruit and vegetables, mushrooms, eggs, preserves, cheese and meat. Wholesale and retail service.

REID G & G

Canterland, Marykirk, Aberdeenshire, AB30 1XJ
Tel: 01674 840316 Fax: 01674 840316
Organic Aberdeen Angus beef, sold fresh at farmers' market, sold vacuum-packed and frozen from farm gate.

VITAL VEG

North Tillydaff Farm, Midmar, Inverurie, Aberdeenshire, AB51 7LS
Tel: 01330 833823 Fax: 01330 833823 info@vitalveg.co.uk www.vitalveg.co.uk
Vital Veg grow and supply mouthwatering organic vegetables, fruit and eggs, with the emphasis on flavour and freshness. We deliver boxes of veg and fruit to homes and offices in the Aberdeen area. We also grow and supply vegetable starter plants grown from organic seed in certified organic compost, so you can grow your own! We design vegetable gardens and potagers, and give advice and seminars on organic growing. Vital Veg is the complete organic vegetable service!

WYNFORD FARM

Wynford Farm, Kingswells, Aberdeen, Aberdeenshire, AB15 8RQ
Tel: 01224 744184 wynford4aabeef@btinternet.com
Prime 100% pedigree organic Aberdeen Angus beef. Farm shop open weekends and eves. Local deliveries. Please phone first.

ANGUS

ANGUS FARMERS' MARKET

Westby, 64 West High St., Forfar, Angus, DD8 1BJ
Tel: 01307 465454 jbrewster@ntlworld.com
Angus Farmers' Market is held 1st Sat of the month in Montrose and 2nd Saturday of the month in Forfar. Local farmers interested in selling contact Ruth Fairlie, secretary 07793 986082 (mobile) or email info@eqaccountants.co.uk

ANGUS

ANGUS ORGANICS LTD

Airlie Estate Office, Cortachy, Kirriemuir,
Angus, DD8 4LY
Tel: 01575 570103 sales@angusorganics.com www.angusorganics.com
Scottish organic certified Aberdeen Angus beef and Scottish organic lamb from our own farms.
Nationwide deliveries, mail order, retail and wholesale. Traditionally produced, traditionally butchered.

ANGUS ORGANICS LTD

East Memus, Forfar, Angus, DD8 3TY
Tel: 01307 860355 Fax: 01307 860356 sales@angusorganics.com www.angusorganics.com
See above.

ASHWHIN
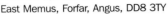

Dunstaffnage Mains Farm, Dunbeg by Oban, Argyll & Bute, PA37 1PZ
Tel: 01631 566192 Fax: 01631 566192 derby@ashwhin.com www.ashwhin.com
Ashwhin provides the space for you to reconnect with yourself, learn, relax and create the holiday of your
dreams, or simply enjoy a therapy session or workshop.

BEE-ORGANIC

The Fens, Dronley Rd., Birkhill, Angus, DD2 5QD
Tel: 01382 581548 roger@bee-organic.co.uk www.bee-organic.co.uk
Bee-Organic is a local Angus company that brings together the very best of Tayside's fruit and vegetable
producers and delivers seasonal boxes to your door or place of work. We deliver to Perth, Dundee,
Monifieth, Newport, Tayport and St. Andrews.

DUNDEE FARMERS' MARKET
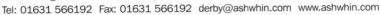

Economic Development Department, 3 City Square, Dundee, Tayside, DD1 3BA
Tel: 01382 434548 Fax: 01382 434457 lorna.mckenzie@dundeecity.gov.uk www.dundeecity.gov.uk
Dundee City Council organises monthly farmers' markets in Reform Street on the 3rd Saturday of every
month from January to November, with a special Christmas craft and produce market over the second
weekend in December. Produce includes venison, lamb, beef, pork, gluten-free sausages, cured bacon,
home baking, scottish wines, raspberry juice, smoked fish, salmon, cheeses, berries, organic vegetables,
fresh eggs, plants, fudge, honey and preserves and herbs. Regular traders include Arbroath Fisheries,
Barker's Highland Beef, Braes of Coul, Caithness Cheese, Cairn O'Mohr Fruit Wines, Caledonian
Homebakes, David Leslie Fruits, Deeside Truffles, DuckRUs, Ella Drinks, Inverness Fudge, Island Cheese
Company, Jemma's Plants, John Reid & Sons, Monarch Deer Farm, Puddledub Pork & Fifeshire Bacon,
Salad Thyme, Scottish Preserves, The Jute Co., The Thistle Soap Company and Tombuie Smokehouse.

HOPE TRUST (HOSPITALFIELD ORGANIC PRODUCE ENTERPRISE TRUST)

The plot next to Hospitalfield House, The Westway, Arbroath, Angus, DD11 4NH
Tel: 07837 862174 enquiries@hopegardentrust.org.uk www.hopegardentrust.org.uk
We grow a wide range of organic vegetables and fruit, and all produce is for sale. We operate a vegetable
box scheme and customers can have their box delivered or collect it from the garden. Customers can also
call in to purchase individual items. We also sell plants ad some craftwork. We are a registered charity,
and provide horticultural training to adults with learning disabilities. We are certified as organic with the
Soil Association. Open weekdays 2pm–4pm. Bus stop outside Hope on the Arbroath to Dundee route.
Car park facilities at Hope.

ARGYLL & BUTE

ARGYLL HOTEL

Argyll Hotel, Isle Of Iona, Argyll & Bute, PA76 6SJ

Tel: 01681 700334 Fax: 01681 700510 reception@argyllhoteliona.co.uk www.argyllhoteliona.co.uk

Small friendly hotel on the sea shore of Iona, with great views, open fires and celebrated restaurant serving home-grown organic vegetables and herbs, local seafood and organic meats. Garden certified by Soil Association.

THE FYNE ORGANIC COMPANY

Unit 16, Kilmory Estate, Kilmory, Lochgilphead,

Argyll & Bute, PA31 8RR

Tel: 01546 886378 www.fyneorganics.com

Distributor for the west coast of Scotland of organic fruit and vegetable box scheme and other goods. Trade enquiries welcome. UK delivery of hampers and gifts. We also run training courses on food and wine issues. External catering available for functions and events.

INVERAWE SMOKEHOUSES

Taynuilt, Argyll & Bute, PA35 1HU

Tel: 0870 423 0236 Fax: 01866 822274 info@inverawe.co.uk www.smokedsalmon.co.uk

Inverawe Smokehouses is a leading company supplying traditionally smoked seafoods and Scottish fine foods. Our range includes internationally award-winning organic smoked salmon, organic gravadlax and organic smoked salmon paté certified by the Soil Association.

KILDALLOIG FARM

Kildalloig, Campbelltown, Argyll & Bute, PA28 6RE

Tel: 01586 553192 Fax: 01586 553192 marycturner@btinternet.com www.kintyrecottages.com

Self-catering holiday cottages on organic farm. Organic beef and lamb to order. Organic breeding stock – Aberdeen Angus heifers, pedigree registered Blueface Leicester, Blackface and North Ronaldsay rams or ewe lambs.

MILLSTONE WHOLEFOODS

15 High St., Oban, Argyll & Bute, PA34 4BG

Tel: 01631 562704 Fax: 01631 562704

Fresh local organic vegetables and bread on Wednesdays to Fridays, wholefoods, herbal remedies, nutritional supplements, aromatherapy etc.

STONEFIELD FARM – T A GROVES

Glenmassan, Dunoon, Argyll & Bute, PA23 8RA

Tel: 01369 706640

Soil Association G2325. Organic: Blackface sheep, Highland mules, Highlander cattle. Meat, hay, soft fruit.

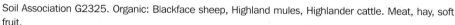

VERNON, R & H

Rashfield Farm, By Kilmun, Argyll & Bute, PA23 8QT

Tel: 01369 840237

Soil Association G768. Organically registered since 1985, specialising in the breeding of the original Black Highland cattle of the Western Highlands, reared in the traditional manner. Alternative therapies.

AYRSHIRE

DRUMSKEOCH FARM B&B

Drumskeoch Farm, Pinwherry, Girvan, Ayrshire, KA26 0QB
Tel: 01465 841172 drumskeoch@wildmail.com www.drumskeoch.co.uk
Organic, exclusively vegetarian/vegan B&B in beautiful hilly countryside, panoramic views, excellent local walks. Home cooked dinner/packed lunch available using some home grown produce, water from own underground source.

GLENDRISSAIG HOUSE
Glendrissaig By Girvan, Ayrshire, KA26 0HJ
Tel: 01465 714631 Fax: 01465 714631
Modern farmhouse with wonderful views. Peaceful location in Gulf Stream climate. Spacious en-suite rooms with one on ground floor. Home cooking with vegetarian option. Organic produce and spring water. Secure parking.

STAIR ORGANIC GROWERS

11 The Yetts, Tarbolton, Ayrshire, KA5 5NT
Tel: 01292 541369 info@organicgrowing.com www.organicgrowing.com
Box scheme and fruit and veg to order. Home delivery service. On line ordering, no credit cards needed. Locally produced in season.

BORDERS

ANCRUM ORGANIC VILLAGE STORE
Shiloh Cottage, Ancrum, Jedburgh, Roxburghshire, Borders, TD8 6UY
Tel: 01835 830509 Fax: 01835 830509 ancrumorganics@tiscali.co.uk
A beautiful quaint village store overlooking the historical and pretty Ancrum Village Green. The store stocks a wide range of completely organic, vegetarian and gluten-free foods, as well as eco-friendly cleaning products (some of which can be refilled – please phone to find out more).

CK ORGANIC
Midshiels, Denholm, Hassendean, Hawick, Borders, TD9 8RT
Tel: 07779 284379 rmc@ckorganic.com www.ckorganic.com
CK Organic is an organic foods company which exports from Argentina and South America and imports organic produce including wines, olives oils, jams, honey, cereals, dried foods and more into the UK.

ORGANIC ROOTS

25 Roxburgh St., Kelso, Borders, TD5 7DN
Tel: 01573 229107
Retailers of organic fruit, veg, meat, dairy, eggs, cosmetics and toiletries, clothes, non-food baby products.

DUMFRIES & GALLOWAY

CREAM O' GALLOWAY DAIRY CO LTD

Rainton, Gatehouse Of Fleet, Castle Douglas, Dumfries & Galloway, DG7 2DR
Tel: 01557 814040 Fax: 01557 814040 info@creamogalloway.co.uk www.creamogalloway.co.uk
Soil Association P2928. Farm-based manufacturer of organic ice cream and frozen yoghurt. Open to public with nature trails, tea room and adventure playground. Member of Soil Association Organic Farms Network.

FARM FUTURE – J M & P M ANDERSON

Netherfield Farm, Beeswing, Dumfries, Dumfries & Galloway, DG2 8JE
Tel: 01387 730217 www.netherfieldguesthouse.co.uk
BDAA/Demeter certification 325. Small farm guest house in Galloway Hills, offering own biodynamic and organic vegetarian-based catering. Hauschka massage with rest and care. Self-catering cottages available.

LOCH ARTHUR CREAMERY

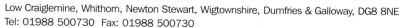

Camphill Village Trust, Beeswing, Dumfries,
Dumfries & Galloway, DG2 8JQ
Tel: 01387 760296 Fax: 01387 760296 creamery@locharthur.org.uk www.locharthur.org.uk
Producers of Demeter certified cheeses and yoghurt. Organic farm shop selling our own cheeses, meat, bread and vegetables and much more. Open Monday–Saturday. Also trade enquiries and mail order.

LOW CRAIGLEMINE FARM HOLIDAYS

Low Craiglemine, Whithorn, Newton Stewart, Wigtownshire, Dumfries & Galloway, DG8 8NE
Tel: 01988 500730 Fax: 01988 500730
enquiries@www.lowcraiglemine-farm-holidays.co.uk www.lowcraiglemine-farm-holidays.co.uk
BDAA Certificate No 354. Self-catering accommodation: organic family farm, cosy, comfortable cottage and bothy sleeping 6, 3. Warm welcome and peace await you. Biodynamic beef available. Bowen technique available.

SUNRISE WHOLEFOODS

49 King St., Castle Douglas, Dumfries & Galloway, DG7 1AE
Tel: 01556 504455
Wholefood shop, specialising in organic dried and fresh foods: organic meat, fruit and veg, cheese, wine, bread, books. Fresh veg from smallholding in summer.

FIFE

BELLFIELD ORGANIC NURSERY

Jamesfield Farm, Newburgh, Fife, KY14 6EW
Tel: 01738 850589 Fax: 01738 850085 order@bellfield-organics.com www.bellfield-organics.com
Bellfield organic nursery is a family-run grower of organic produce based in Abernethy. All our plants are grown from seed, ensuring delivery of the highest quality organic produce. We operate a box scheme that ensures regular essential supplies of organic produce direct to the door. We also sell organic bread, eggs, milk and bacon. Open 7 am–4 pm.

CRAIGENCALT ECOLOGY CENTRE

Craigencalt Farm, Kinghorn, Fife, KY3 9YG
Tel: 01592 891567 Fax: 01592 891567 cfec@free.uk.com www.cfec.org.uk
The Craigencalt Farm Ecology Centre is used by schools and adult groups for ecological studies, weekend study groups and various craft/arts workshops. Visitors are welcome to take part, walk, bird watch, chat to members, even pitch in with the various projects underway.

FOR DETAILS OF
SYMBOLS USED
IN THE ENTRIES,
SEE PAGE 17

JAMESFIELD ORGANIC CENTRE

Newburgh, Fife, KY14 6EW
Tel: 01738 850498 Fax: 01738 850741 jamesfieldfarm@btconnect.com www.jamesfieldfarm.co.uk
The Centre has its own butchery and processing unit, believed to be the most 'high tech' in Scotland. On site we manufacture everything from soups to ready made meals, and bake a wide range of breads and rolls (bakery to be certified). The computer system will give complete traceability in all manufactured products and meats. The centre also has a 100-seater restaurant overlooking the farm and Tay Estuary. Open 7 days a week. Regular bus service and parking for 100 cars.

PILLARS OF HERCULES FARM

Pillars Of Hercules, Strathmiglo
Road, Falkland, Cupar, Fife, KY15 7AD
Tel: 01337 857749 bruce@pillars.co.uk www.pillars.co.uk
Soil Association SB26C. Small farm producing wide range of vegetables, eggs and turkeys. Specialise in mixed salads. All produced to Soil Association standards. Run a well stocked farm shop selling wide range of organic fruit, vegetables, wholefoods, meat, dairy etc. Organically certified café serves simply healthy meals. Supply local restaurants and wholesalers. Open daily 9am–6pm. Car park on farm. Nearest bus stop 1 mile from Falkland. Member of the Soil Association Organic Farms Network.

SCOTMED HERBS

 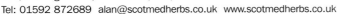 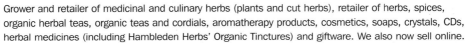

113/115 High Steet, Burntisland, Fife, KY3 9AA
Tel: 01592 872689 alan@scotmedherbs.co.uk www.scotmedherbs.co.uk
Grower and retailer of medicinal and culinary herbs (plants and cut herbs), retailer of herbs, spices, organic herbal teas, organic teas and cordials, aromatherapy products, cosmetics, soaps, crystals, CDs, herbal medicines (including Hambleden Herbs' Organic Tinctures) and giftware. We also now sell online.

HIGHLAND

BLACK ISLE BREWERY

Black Isle Brewery, Old Allangrange,
Munlochy, Highland, IV8 8NZ
Tel: 01463 811871 Fax: 01463 811875 greatbeers@blackislebrewery.com www.blackislebrewery.com
Soil Association registered. Black Isle Brewery is a small, intensely independent brewery in the heart of the Scottish Highlands producing a range of outstanding organic beers.

DONALDSON, MARJ

13 Newton Kinkell, Muir of Ord, Highland, IV6 7RB
Tel: 01349 861956
Sides of lamb from organic farm, butchered to your requirements, for your freezer.

EARTHSHARE CSA

65 Society Street, Nairn, Highland, IV12 4NL
Tel: 01667 452879 earthshare@macunlimited.net www.earthshare.co.uk
EarthShare is a community supported agriculture scheme, established in 1994. We are based in Moray and grow vegetables and soft fruit by organic methods for up to 200 local families. Subscribers join the scheme for a year at a time and during that year they receive an equal share of whatever is harvested. They are encouraged to come to the farm to help out, and in return they receive a discount off the cost of their weekly box. (Our field crops are Soil Association certified; our polytunnel crops and soft fruit are not, although they too are grown without the use of pesticides/herbicides/artificial fertilisers.)

THE HEALTH SHOP

20 Baron Taylor's Street, Inverness, Highland, IV1 1QG
Tel: 01463 233104 Fax: 01463 718144 healthshopinvern@aol.com
We are delighted to offer you a large range of organic products. Just get in contact and we'll do the rest!
Look forward to hearing from you.

HIDDENGLEN HOLIDAYS

Laikenbuie, Grantown Road, Nairn, Highland, IV12 5QN
Tel: 01667 454630 muskus@bigfoot.com www.hiddenglen.co.uk
Watch roe deer and woodpeckers from top quality holiday homes with beautiful outlook over loch amid
birch woods. Fun for children. Photos on website. Eggs, freezer-ready lamb and weaned calves sold.

HIGHLAND WHOLEFOODS

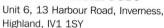

Unit 6, 13 Harbour Road, Inverness,
Highland, IV1 1SY
Tel: 01463 712393 sales@highlandwholefoods.co.uk www.highlandwholefoods.co.uk
Free delivery service throughout Northern Scotland. Cash and carry warehouse in Inverness. Over 800
organic lines stocked, including chilled and frozen. Soil Association reg. no. P2113.

MACLEOD ORGANICS

Kylerona Farm, Ardersier,
Inverness, Highland, IV2 7QZ
Tel: 01667 462555 Fax: 01667 461138 info@macleodorganics.com www.macleodorganics.com
Soil Association SP6506, SG8730. Main distributors for organic produce to and from the Highlands.
Organic farm centre including fully certified café, shop, box scheme and tourist accommodation.

MARCASSIE FARM

Marcassie Farm, Rafford, Forres, Highland, IV362RH
Tel: 01309 676865 Fax: 01309 676865 marcassie@marcassie.fsnet.co.uk
Based in Scotland (nr. Findhorn). Members of Association for Environmentally Conscious Builders,
Association of Scottish Hardwood Sawmillers. Sawmill & joinery shop (building components, bespoke joinery, lamp posts, street furniture & specialist commissions, all in Scottish grown timber), organic farm
(grains, wheatgrass, eggs, hay), commercial kitchen (being established), esoteric healing, self-catering
accommodation (for 4–6 people), educational courses (being established).

PHOENIX COMMUNITY STORES LTD

The Park, Findhorn Bay, Moray,
Highland, IV36 3TZ
Tel: 01309 690110 Fax: 01309 692124 store@findhorn.com www.findhorn.org/store/
Full service award-winning food shop plus café and organic bakery. The Phoenix also offers a wide range
of complementary products including apothecary, books, crafts, household, music and gifts.

RAASAY WALLED GARDEN

Isle of Raasay, By Kyle of Lochalsh, Highland, IV40 8PB
Tel: 01378 660345 raasaywalledgarden@btinternet.com
Soil Association GCS025, G5801; Skye & Lochalsh Horticultural Development Association, Highlands &
Islands Organic Association (HIOA). An organic garden growing a wide variety of fruits, vegetables, salads,
herbs, cut and dried flowers for sale in season, plus hardy plants, climbers and shrubs.

RHANICH FARM

Rhanich Rd., Edderton, Tain, Highland, IV19 1LG
Tel: 01862 821265
Fairly isolated hill farm offering camping in summer, farm gate sales (eggs, fruit, veg) in season. Mail
order organic coloured fleece for spinning or sheepskins.

WESTER LAWRENCETON

Wester Lawrenceton, Foray, Highland, IV36 2RH

Tel: 01309 676566 Fax: 01309 676162

Wester Lawrenceton is a 36-hectare mixed organic farm overlooking the Moray Firth to the mountains of Sutherland beyond. Member of the Soil Association Organic Farms Network.

LANARKSHIRE

CLYDE ORGANICS

Muirhouse Farm, Libberton, Carnwath, Lanarkshire, ML11 8LX

Tel: 01555 840271 Fax: 01555 841294 muirhouse@clydeorganics.co.uk www.clydeorganics.co.uk

We are a family-run, organic dairy farm that supplies wholesale and direct to the public. Our farm is in the Clyde Valley between Lanark and Biggar, and all of our milk is produced on our own farm from clover-rich pastures. Our milk is available in non-standardised full cream and semi-skimmed. Cream can be supplied as single cream or double cream. We supply to the retailing and wholesaling sectors and our milk and cream are available in a comprehensive range of packaging. We also grow a wide selection of vegetables and potatoes, which we sell at the farm.

LOTHIAN

CAMPBELL, ALLAN

47 Boswald Parkway, Edinburgh, Lothian, EH5 2BR

Tel: 0131 552 3486 Fax: 0131 552 3486

This is a high street shop selling organic meat and poultry, eggs and cheeses.

DAMHEAD ORGANIC FOODS

32A Damhead, Old Pentland Rd., Lothianburn, Edinburgh, Lothian, EH10 7EA

Tel: 0131 445 7425 Fax: 0131 445 7750 enquiries@damhead.co.uk www.damhead.co.uk

BDAA 238. Scotland's organic food specialists: award-winning home delivery service (Soil Association Highly Commended 2002), farm shop and wholesale division. Vast range of organic products available to order online at www.damhead.co.uk.

EAST COAST ORGANIC BOXES

24 Boggs Holdings, Pencaitland, Lothian, EH34 5BD

Tel: 01875 340227 Fax: 01875 340227

admin@eastcoastorganics.freeserve.co.uk www.eastcoastorganics.co.uk

East Coast Organics operate a highly successful & productive biodynamic farm. The box scheme 'Eco Box' was commended in the Soil Association Food Awards 2004 for its quality & good value. Various sizes of boxes are available & can include fruit, eggs, bread, etc. Free home delivery to Edinburgh & Lothians. Edinburgh farmers' market now every Saturday.

THE ENGINE SHED

19 St. Leonard's Lane, Edinburgh, Lothian, EH8 9SD

Tel: 0131 662 0040 Fax: 0131 667 5319 engineshed@aol.com www.engineshed.org.uk

Training centre for adults with learning disabilities. Training in catering setting towards employment. Five production workshops: café, bakery, outside catering, food processing and wholefood shop.

THE ENGINE SHED SHOP

123 Bruntisfield Place, Edinburgh, Lothian, EH

Tel: 0131 229 6494 engineshed@aol.com www.engineshed.org.uk

Small health food shop selling a range of organic dry products, organic fruit and veg, bread and cakes, etc., incorporating healthy, light snacks. Takeaway service.

THE GLENORA

14 Rosebery Crescent, Edinburgh, Edinburgh, Lothian, EH12 5JY

Tel: 0131 337 1186 enquiries@glenorahotel.co.uk www.glenorahotel.co.uk

The Glenora is one of the finest guesthouses in Edinburgh and has been awarded 4 stars by VisitScotland. Situated in Edinburgh's Haymarket district, the Glenora is close to the city's excellent shops and boutiques, the financial district and the top tourist attractions. It is in the ideal location for city breaks and business travellers. Our rooms are furnished and decorated thoughtfully and luxuriously. We offer a wide selection of locally sourced and organic produce in our dining room. The Glenora provides excellent accommodation and service at a reasonable price – in the very heart of the city.

GROW WILD

Unit 8, Block3, Whiteside Industrial Estate, Bathgate, Lothian, EH48 2RX

Tel: 0845 2263393 Fax: 01506 656543 sales@growwild.co.uk www.growwild.co.uk

Established in 1998, we are a company committed to supplying quality fresh organic produce at reasonable prices. To make it easier for the customer we deliver directly to your door – either at home or work; alternatively, we can leave it with a friend or neighbour. Freshness is key – so all produce is chilled throughout the supply chain. We believe strongly in providing a good service and have a customer-focused approach with a personal touch. Please see our website for full details.

HELIOS FOUNTAIN

7 Grassmarket, Edinburgh, Lothian, EH1 2HY

Tel: 0131 229 7884 Fax: 0131 622 7173 info@helios-fountain.co.uk www.helios-fountain.co.uk

A shop selling gifts, crafts, toys and beads. Our book selection includes most works by or about Rudolf Steiner.

NATURE'S GATE

83 Clerk Street, Edinburgh, Lothian, EH8 9JG

Tel: 0131 668 2067

Soil Association R1827. Wholefood shop with large organic range including bread, cereals, dried fruit, nuts, herbs, spices, coffees, teas, chilled and frozen, fresh fruit and vegetables, wines, toiletries, vitamin supplements and herbal remedies.

NEAL'S YARD REMEDIES

102 Hannover St., Edinburgh, Lothian, EH2 2LE

Tel: 0131 226 3223 Fax: 0131 225 9947 mail@nealsyardremedies.com www.nealsyardremedies.com

Retailer of organic essential oils and cosmetics and therapy room offering herbalist, homoeopath, massage and aromatherapy.

THE NEW LEAF

20 Argyle Place, Marchmont, Edinburgh, Lothian, EH9 1JJ

Tel: 0131 228 8840

Soil Association R3002. Vegetarian and organic wholefood shop dedicated to ethical trading. Fine selection of wholefoods including gluten- and dairy-free. Local fresh organic produce, eco friendly & cruelty-free products, and much more.

LOTHIAN / MULL

PHANTASSIE FOOD

Phantassie, East Linton, Lothian, EH40 3DF
Tel: 01620 860285 Fax: 01620 861531 veg@phantassie.co.uk www.phantassie.co.uk
Veg and egg producer operating local box scheme in Lothian and Borders, at local farmers' markets, and supplying wholesale to shops and caterers in Edinburgh and the Lothians.

THUJA – ORGANIC HEALTH & BEAUTY

37 Comiston Rd., Edinburgh, Lothian, EH10 6AB
Tel: 0131 447 7037 paulinehodge@hotmail.com
We are a small health and beauty clinic, shop and dispensary offering a full range of Dr. Hauschka beauty treatments and complementary therapies including herbal medicine consultations, using only organic or biodynamic products. We also insist on only using organically produced bedding and towels within our clinic rooms. Our shop stocks a range of products including Dr. Hauschka, Weleda, Green People, Essential Care and NHR oils.

THE WHOLEFOOD CONNECTION

49 Bernard Street, The Shore, Edinburgh, Lothian, EH6 6SL
Tel: 0131 476 3166 info@thewholefoodconnection.com www.thewholefoodconnection.com
A retail shop on The Shore in Edinburgh which sells organic, wholefoods, and GM/additive-free farm meats. We also stock a great selection of organic beer and wines, and an excellent choice of health supplements. You can also order online using our website at www.thewholefoodconnection.com. Food Certification (Scotland) certified.

THE WHOLE SHEBAG

South Cobbinshaw, West Calder,
Lothian, EH55 8LQ
Tel: 07931 738767 bags@thewholeshebag.com www.thewholeshebag.com
Fresh local produce delivered to your door. Family-run farm-based organic produce delivery service to Edinburgh, Glasgow, West Lothian, Lanarkshire, Inverclyde and Ayrshire. Products include fruit, vegetables, milk, eggs, wholefoods and meat. Minimum order £10. Self-catering accommodation also available.

ZONKER ORGANICS

66 Cumberland Street, Edinburgh, Lothian, EH3 6RE
Tel: 0131 558 1136 hilary@zonker.freeserve.co.uk www.zonker.co.uk
Small food shop located in New Town area of Edinburgh selling 100% organic food and drink. Items include fresh meat, pre-packed cold meats and charcuterie, some fresh vegetables, groceries and chocolates. Also espresso-based coffee-to-go, and sandwiches. Selection of wine and soft drinks. Nationwide sales via internet.

ISLE OF MULL

ARDALANISH ORGANIC FARM & ISLE OF MULL WEAVERS

Bunessan, Isle of Mull, PA67 6DR
Tel: 01681 700265 Fax: 01681 700674 info@ardalanishfarm.co.uk www.ardalanishfarm.co.uk
Traditional organic farm and tannery selling native Highland beef and Hebridean mutton. Weaving mill selling Hebridean tweed, throws, rugs, scarves, etc. woven on the farm. Sheepskins and cattle hides organically tanned on the farm. Local delivery – not a box scheme. Also at info@isleofmullweavers.co.uk and www.isleofmullweavers.co.uk. Member of the Soil Association Organic Farms Network.

FINDHORN FOUNDATION

Isle of Erraid, Fionphort, Isle of Mull, PA66 6BN
Tel: 01681 700384 bookings@erraid.fslife.co.uk www.erraid.com
Spiritual community living lightly on a tiny Hebridean island.

ORKNEY ISLANDS

ORCA HOTEL

76 Victoria St., Stromness, Orkney Islands, KW16 3BS
Tel: 01856 850447 info@orcahotel.com www.orcahotel.com
Two star guesthouse, six rooms (single, twins, doubles, family), all en-suite; situated in historic harbour village of Stromness, Orkney.

ORKNEY ORGANIC MEAT

New Holland Farm, Holm,
Orkney, Orkney Islands, KW17 2SA
Tel: 01856 872457 Fax: 01856 874960
info@orkneyorganicmeat.co.uk www.orkneyorganicmeat.co.uk
Organic farm producing Aberdeen Angus beef and lamb with emphasis on health for both animal and customer. Meat processed here on the farm by our own butcher. Mail order sales of beef, lamb, speciality sausages and ready meals, delivered throughout UK. Farm gate sales. Self-catering holiday cottage.

WHEEMS ORGANIC PRODUCE

Wheems Eastside, South Ronaldsay, Orkney,
Orkney Islands, KW17 2TJ
Tel: 01856 831537 Fax: 01856 831537
Small mixed family farm concentrating on vegetable production for the local market. Hostel accommodation for WWOOF helpers and other visitors: the site is half a mile above sandy bays and cliffs on northern Scottish island.

PERTH & KINROSS

ADAM AND WILSON

Struiehill Farm, Path of Condie, Forgandenny, Perth & Kinross, PH2 9DW
Tel: 01577 830303 Fax: 01577 830303
We are a smallholding of 75 acres specialising in rare breeds – Shetland cattle and Soay sheep, which we breed for their meat. We sell from the door or can deliver in the Perth/Edinburgh area. We will also sell our rare breeds to those interested in keeping them. We are members of the Soil Association. We let appox. 16 acres of good upland grazing for summer cattle pasture – well fenced and watered.

ALMOND VALLEY ORGANICS

4 Bridson Brae, Almondbank, Perth, Perth & Kinross, PH1 3JZ
Tel: 01738 582064 peter.fenton@virgin.net www.almondvalley.net
For the finest organic quality fresh fruit and vegetables you can join our weekly box scheme. You can choose from a range of boxes to suit your needs. You can order fruit and vegetables, freshly prepared and/or frozen vegetarian meals, pre-packed nuts, pulses, fruits and cereals and home-made sweets and cakes. See our website for further details.

THE BEAN SHOP

The Bean Shop, 67 George St., Perth, Perth & Kinross, PH1 5LB

Tel: 01738 449955 Fax: 01738 632693 sales@thebeanshop.com www.thebeanshop.com

The Bean Shop is an independent coffee roaster and tea specialist with a large range of gourmet organic coffees. We roast all our coffee by hand on the premises for optimum flavour and freshness.

BORLAND FARM / GAME CONSERVATION CONSULTANCY

Blacklunans, Blairgowrie, Perth & Kinross, PH10 7LA

Tel: 07789 301751 Fax: 01250 882214 kenneth@highlanddrovers.co.uk www.borlandfold.co.uk

Soil Association SG5245. Organic Highland beef, Hebridean lamb, pedigree Highland cattle and Hebridean sheep. National Delivery.

HIGHLAND HEALTH STORE

7 & 16 St. John St., Perth, Perth & Kinross, PH1 5SP

Tel: 01738 628102 Fax: 01738 447541

email@highlandhealth.fsnet.co.uk www.perthcitydirectory.com/healthstore/

Two vegetarian and health food shops – see our website for full details.

LURGAN FARM SHOP

Lurgan Farm, Drumdewan, By Aberfeldy, Perth & Kinross, PH15 2JQ

Tel: 01887 820808 info@lurganfarmshop.co.uk www.lurganfarmshop.co.uk

Soil Association SP6485. We sell our home-produced organic lamb and Aberdeen Angus beef. We make ready meals in our shop kitchen with our meats and bought-in organic vegetables. We have a huge range of organic wholefoods and dairy produce.

MEADOWHEAD FARM

By Cleish, Kinross, Perth & Kinross, KY13 0LP

Tel: 01577 850292 Fax: 01577 861323

Meadowhead is a small restored hill farm, declared as a SSSI where 132 plant varieties have been iden-tified.The stock include British White catte, Tamworth pigs and Soay and Pentland Croft Soay sheep. We sell half lambs and mutton butchered and packed for freezer, and beef frozen and vacuum packed. Occasionally there is pork for sale. All meat is processed at our on-site butchery. We also occasionally have yard stock and pedigree Tamworth weaners for sale. Phone for details.

PERTH FARMERS' MARKET

c/o source marketing, Algo Business Centre, Glenearn Road, Perth, Perth & Kinross, PH2 0NJ

Tel: 01738 450417 Fax: 01738 450460

info@perthfarmersmarket.co.uk www.perthfarmersmarket.co.uk

9am–2pm on first Saturday of every month in King Street, Perth. Perth Farmers' Market was the first of its kind in Scotland, and was initiated in 1999 by Jim Fairlie of Glenearn Lamb. Since its conception it has gone from strength to strength. The market now has around thirty-five stallholders each month. Running only on the first Saturday of each month, Perth boasts an abundance of fresh ingredients and quality products. From slabs of fresh red meat and slippery oysters to green, leafy vegetables to home-made cakes, pies and wines, you will find everything you need to create delicious meals.

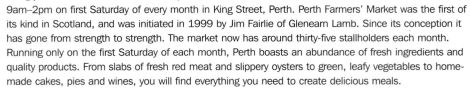

FOR DETAILS OF SYMBOLS USED IN THE ENTRIES, SEE PAGE 17

SOUTH WEST FULLARTON ORGANIC HUT

South West Fullarton, Meigle, Perth & Kinross, PH12 8SN
Tel: 01828 640391 Fax: 01828 640391
The Organic Hut stocks a variety of seasonal produce, much of which is home-grown or sourced locally and our raspberries are a summer speciality. We also stock eggs, a small selection of other foods, household items and a wide range of Ecover goods. Our box scheme currently serves Meigle, Alyth, Kirriemuir, Forfar, Friockheim and Arbroath. 1 mile south of Meigle on Dundee Road. Shop clearly signposted during opening hours.

STRATHMORE AND THE GLENS

PO Box 6621, Blairgowie, Perth & Kinross, PH12 8YF
Tel: 01828 640763 Fax: 01828 640763 sue@strathmoreglens.sol.co.uk www.strathmoreglens.org
The Community Market has a number of aims: to provide a source of healthy, affordable and tasty food for the residents of East Perthshire and Strathmore areas; to contribute to the health and sustainability of East Perthshire and Strathmore agriculture by providing an outlet for small local producers; to create a friendly, accessible and pleasing space where everyone can feel welcome – promoting links between all members for the community, the public, shoppers, business and visitors. Strathmore and the Glens host a Community Information Stall which contains a host of information on local initiatives. The markets are run on a not-for-profit basis, and live music is supplied by local schoolchildren.

SHETLAND ISLANDS

BALTA ISLAND SEAFARE LTD

Baltasound, Shetland Islands, ZE2 9DX
Tel: 01224 626261 salmac@mes.co.uk www.organic.shetland.co.uk
Soil Association G4733. Fish farm. Britain's most northerly fish farm producing salmon, certified organic since 1999. Minimum order 20kg salmon.

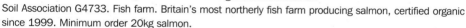

ISLE OF SKYE

ACHNACLOICH ORGANIC VEGETABLES

2 & 3 Achnacloich, Tarskavaig, Isle of Skye, IV49 8SB
Tel: 01471 855315 chris_marsh@madasafish.com
Soil Association GCS025/G2605. Established 1998, AOV supplies 50 households in South Skye with weekly vegetables (June–October). All produce grown by us on our 3-acre croft.

GLENDALE SALADS

19 Upper Fasach, Glendale, Isle of Skye, IV55 8WP
Tel: 01470 511349 Fax: 01470 511349
Salads, herbs, veg and soft fruit to hotels, restaurants and through a box-scheme. Varieties selected for flavour and attractiveness. Delivered chilled on regular runs several times a week. SA certificate G2263. Mail order throughout the UK. Organic Food Awards 2004 Fresh Fruit and Vegetables Winner.

RUBHA PHOIL FOREST GARDEN/ SKYE PERMACULTURE

Rubha Phoil, Armadale Pier, Isle of Skye, IV45 8RS
Tel: 01471 844700 sandyru@tiscali.co.uk www.skye-permaculture.org.uk
Soil Association GCS025/G4609, HDRA, Permaculture Association, Centre for Alternative Technology Ecosite. Herbs, vegetables, displays and demonstration of alternative systems, holiday accommodation, woodland walk, otter/bird hide, solitude in wilderness.

STIRLINGSHIRE

BALQUHIDDER BRAES HOLIDAY PARK

Balquhidder Braes Holiday Park, Balquhidder Station,
Lochearnhead, Stirlingshire, FK19 8NX
Tel: 01567 830293 enquiries@balquhidderbraes.co.uk www.balquhidderbraes.co.uk
Our on-site shop sells local organic beef and a good range of other organic items. We also sell local hill
lamb, venison, honey, jams, chicken and duck eggs (and goose eggs sometimes), sweets, etc, etc. We
are fully licensed and sell a range of beers, wines and spirits, including some organic ones.

STRATHCLYDE

EPO GROWERS

Kennels Cottage, Hardgate, Glasgow, Strathclyde, G81 5QR
Tel: 01389 875337 info@epogrowers.co.uk
We grow and sell organic vegetables, herbs and soft fruit under a Community Supported Agriculture sub-
scription system. Deliveries to households in Glasgow and NW area; we use compost, manure and rock
dust for fertility.

GRASSROOTS

20-22 Woodlands Rd, Charing Cross, Glasgow, Strathclyde, G3 6UR
Tel: 0141 353 3278 Fax: 0141 353 3078 www.grassrootsorganic.com
Vegetarian wholefood shop retailing organic produce and groceries. All your shopping needs, organic
where possible, fair trade if we can get it. Licensed and stocking a range of organic wines and beers.

GRASSROOTS CAFÉ

97 St. Georges Rd., Charing Cross, Glasgow, Strathclyde, G3 6JA
Tel: 0141 333 0534 www.grassrootsorganic.com
Grassroots café offers an informal atmosphere in which to enjoy a wide variety of vegetarian cuisine with
plenty of choice for vegans and those with special dietary requirements.

NEAL'S YARD REMEDIES

11 Royal Exchange Square, Glasgow, Strathclyde, G1 3AJ
Tel: 0141 248 4230 mail@nealsyardremedies.com www.nealsyardremedies.com
Neal's Yard Remedies manufactures and retails natural cosmetics in addition to stocking an extensive
range of herbs, essential oils, homeopathic remedies and reference material.

ROOTS & FRUITS, WHOLEFOODS & ORGANICS

455 Great Western Road, Glasgow, Strathclyde, G12 8HH
Tel: 0141 339 3097 Fax: 0141 334 3530
Stockists of over 1,000 organic products including fruit and vegetables, fresh meats and breads, dairy
and general provisions. A comprehensive range of baby foods and child care products. Box scheme and
delivery service throughout the Glasgow area.

TAPA COFFEE & BAKEHOUSE

21 Whitehill St, Dennistoun, Glasgow, Strathclyde, G31 2LH
Tel: 0141 554 9981 info@tapabakehouse.co.uk www.tapabakehouse.co.uk
Tapa Coffee and Bakehouse produces great breads and cakes from fine organic ingredients. We have a
range of delicious wheat-free bread and cakes. We make fresh sandwiches, soups and salads daily for
sale in our café and shop, and stock an ever-increasing range of organic groceries. We also roast rare
and organic coffees from around the world for superior freshness and flavour.

WALES

CARMARTHENSHIRE

CALON WEN ORGANIC FOODS

Unit 4, Whitland Industrial Estate, Spring Gardens, Whitland, Carmarthenshire, SA34 0HR

Tel: 01994 241368 Fax: 01994 241063 orderline@calonwen-cymru.com www.calonwen.co.uk

Calon Wen Organic Foods deliver fresh organic fruit, vegetables and dairy products direct to retailers, wholesalers and households across Wales and the Borders. We buy as much as possible from local Welsh farms, we ensure all our growers receive a fair price, and we pride ourselves our excellent service.

EADON, R H & E I

Esgairwen Isaf, Cwmann, Lampeter, Carmarthenshire, SA48 8HH

Tel: 01570 423285 eadon1@onetel.com

Soil Association G4623. Livestock farm producing lamb and beef supplied to the doorstep. Organic Welsh Food Certification.

FORDHAM, ANG & MDA

Dolgoch, Bregest, Newcastle Emlyn, Carmarthenshire, SA38 9EU

Tel: 01239 851466

Soil Association G2082. Dairy and vegetable farmer. Organic Farm Network farm. Tir Goval trail open to the public. Member of the Soil Association Organic Farms Network.

GONEGREEN LTD

2 Royal Oak Mews, Market Square, Newcastle Emlyn, Carmarthenshire, SA38 9AE

Tel: 01239 711841 info@gonegreen.co.uk www.gonegreen.co.uk

We are working to provide the widest range of organic, ethically produced, natural products available to help everyone get that bit greener. We have some great brands including Howies, Hug, Remarkable, Ecover and Green People. We sell everything from organic clothing for babies, kids and adults, including organic jeans, to eco-friendly cleaning products, books and solar gadgets.

IECHYD DA

11 Broad St., Llandovery, Carmarthenshire, SA20 0AR

Tel: 01550 720703

General health foods etc, organic fresh veg, dried fruit, yoghurts, coffee, cider vinegar, tofu, bread, tea, soya milk, rice, pasta, flour, oats and bran.

THE ORGANIC PANTRY

Margaret St., Ammanford, Carmarthenshire, SA18 3AB

Tel: 01269 596931 info@organics-online.co.uk www.organics-online.co.uk

Organic grocery shop selling local (where possible) fruit, salad, veg, milk, cheese & dairy products, wholefoods, jams & preserves, tea, coffee, juices & cordials, chocolate & snacks, pizzas, cakes, fresh bread, children's food & snacks, organic clothing, Ecover, and more. Delivery service also available.

ORGANICS TO GO

Werndolau Farm, Golden Grove, Carmarthen, Carmarthenshire, SA32 8NE

Tel: 0800 458 2524 enquiries@organicstogo.info www.organicstogo.info

Soil Association Cert G2644. We grow and supply 30-40 lines of fruit, veg and salad each week of the year. Set price order, or order from price list, in Bristol, Bath, south and west Wales, London and Manchester.

PEN PYNFARCH

Pen Pynfarch, Llandysul, Carmarthenshire, SA44 4RU

Tel: 01559 384948 enquiries@penpynfarch.co.uk www.penpynfarch.co.uk

Simple, cosy holiday cottage with woodburner, sleeps 4/6. Organic veggie breaks offered. Retreat/course centre with studio, accommodation and catering. Wooded valley with stream and lake, 30 mins to the sea.

PENRALLT HOME FARM

Pentrecwrt, Landysul, Carmarthenshire, SA44 5DW

Tel: 01559 370341 djwj@penrallt.freeserve.co.uk

Converted barns for self-catering holidaymakers. Mixed livestock. Member of the Soil Association Organic Farms Network.

S & J ORGANICS

Llwyncrychyddod, Llanpumsaint, Carmarthen, Carmarthenshire, SA33 6JS

Tel: 01267 253570 Fax: 01267 253562 info@sjorganics.co.uk www.sjorganics.co.uk

Soil Association certified poultry specialists. Producers of organic chickens, Muscovy ducks, Pekin ducks, geese, turkeys & guinea fowl. Whole birds & portions available. Supplying both retail & trade. Our poultry is processed through our low throughput, DEFRA registered, on-farm, Soil Association licensed abbatoir. Organic Food Awards 2004 Poultry Highly Commended.

CEREDIGION

CARPENTER, M B P & TWYFORD, C A

Ty Gwyn, Llwyn Rhydowen, Rhydowen, Llandysul, Ceredigion, SA44 4PX

Tel: 01545 590687 peasants@care4free.net

Soil Association G4267. Small registered flock Lleyn sheep, meat and breeding females available. All season mixed vegetables available at home or group stall at Ceredigion Farmers' markets.

CAWS CENARTH

Fferm Glyneithinog, Abercych, Ceredigion, SA37 0LH

Tel: 01239 710432 cenarth.cheese@virgin.net www.cawscenarth.co.uk

Soil Association G2093. Hand-made organic farmhouse cheese made on our Soil Association certified organic farm. Available in many varieties including Gold Award winners, suitable for vegetarians. Visitors welcome to watch the cheesemaking.

CERI ORGANICS

Llwyn Yr Eos, Rhydlewis, Llandysul, Ceredigion, SA44 5QU

Tel: 01239 851850

Soil Association G5980. Fresh organic vegetables and year round fruit and veg box scheme.

GARTHENOR
ORGANIC PURE WOOL

Garthenor, Llanio Road, Nr. Tregaron, Ceredigion, SY25 6UR

Tel: 0845 408 2437 Fax: 01570 493347

garthenor@organicpurewool.co.uk www.organicpurewool.co.uk

Soil Association G4388 & X8787. A small mixed farm producing eggs, lambs and wool from many traditional and rare breeds of sheep from our own and other Certified Organic flocks. Fleece: raw; washed; washed & carded. Beautiful knitting yarns in natural colours – undyed and unbleached: 4Ply; DK; Aran; Chunky and Super chunky. Others spun to your specification (for weaving etc.) subject to minimum order. Hand-knitted garments and babywear. Hand-woven floor rugs, hand-knitted & hand-woven cushions. Ex-stock or made to order. Commissions welcome. Visitors by appointment.

HARMONY HERD

Tel: 01239 810740 info@harmonyherd.co.uk www.organicpork.co.uk

Organic rare breed pork and wild boar x. We have two herds of pigs, one Oxford Sandy and Black and the other wild boar x. We have our own cutting unit and can cut to order, and we produce our own sausages, gammon and dry cure bacon which we sell at farmers' markets and food festivals in Wales. Organic Welsh Food Certification.

THE HIVE ON THE QUAY

Cadwgan Place, Aberaeron, Ceredigion, SA46 0BU

Tel: 01545 570445 hiveon.thequay@btinternet.com www.hiveonthequay.co.uk

Member of the Soil Association. A busy seasonal café/restaurant on the harbour specialising in regional dishes, local seafood from our own boat and honey ice creams.

JACOBS, CAROLE & ALLEN

Broniwan, Rhydlewis, Llandysul, Ceredigion, SA44 5PF

Tel: 01239 851261 Fax: 01239 851261 broniwan@beeb.net

A 45-acre (19 ha) grassland Aberdeen Angus suckler beef herd with 'tack' sheep. Small vegetables and soft fruit. A Tir Gofal Conservation Farm. Developing educational services. Farm guesthouse. Visits by appointment.

LIME FIRMS LTD

Corgam, Bwlchllan, Lampeter, Ceredigion, SA48 8QR

Tel: 01974 821624 Fax: 01974 821624 info@limefirmsltd.co.uk www.limefirmsltd.co.uk

Selling a range of eco-friendly building materials, including liners and paints.

LLUEST GROWERS

Lluest Y Conscience, Trefenter, Aberystwyth, Ceredigion, SY23 4HE

Tel: 01974 272218

Soil Association G2225. We produce organic eggs and seasonal organic vegetables and salads which are sold at the farm gate, through local shops and farmers' markets.

MAETH Y MEYSYDD

16 Chalybeate St., Aberystwyth, Ceredigion, SY23 1HX

Tel: 01970 612946 Fax: 01970 612946

Retail shop selling in season organic produce, eggs, bread, cheese and much more. Everything for vegetarian, vegan and special diets. Unique herb and spice room.

MENTRO LLUEST

Llanbadorn Fawr, Aberystwyth, Ceredigion, SY23 3AU

Tel: 01970 612114 Fax: 01970 612114 mentro.lluest@talk21.com

Soil Association G3081. Mentro Lluest teaches skills to people with special needs within a framework of organic growing, environmental sustainability and social cohesion. We specialise in producing salad, seasonal vegetables and herbs.

MULBERRY BUSH

2 Bridge Street, Lampeter, Ceredigion, SA48 7HG

Tel: 01570 423317 Fax: 01570 423317

Friendly wholefood vegetarian store, established 1974. Large range of organic cereals, grains, pulses, fruit, nuts and convenience foods, plus cosmetic, toiletries, natural remedies, cleaning products, books and excellent health advice. Organic fruit and veg, vegetarian and vegan café due late spring 2007.

NANTCLYD FARM PRODUCE

Nantclyd, Llanilar, Aberystwyth, Ceredigion, SY23 4SL

Tel: 01974 241543 liz.findlay@clara.co.uk

A small farm producing eggs, seasonal fruit and veg, e.g. strawberries, carrots, potatoes, cabbage, etc. and lemon curd. Produce available in Treehouse shop, Aberystwyth, and also from the farm. Visitors welcome – phone for details. Local delivery. Organic Food Awards 2004 Fresh Fruit and Veg Commended.

NANTGWYNFAEN ORGANIC FARM

Croeslan, Llandysul, Ceredigion, SA44 4SR

Tel: 01239 851914 Fax: 01239 851914 nantgwynfaen@hotmail.co.uk

We are a 62-acre mixed family farm. We sell our own poultry, eggs, beef and pork direct from the farm including sausages and burgers. Call first to make sure we are in. Local delivery, not a box scheme.

RIVERSIDE HEALTH

Adpar, Newcastle Emlyn, Ceredigion, SA38 9EE

Tel: 01239 711440

Wholefood shop, largely organic. Good stock of herbal supplements and essential oils. Therapy rooms upstairs. Fair trade products as much as possible.

TREBERFEDD FARM

  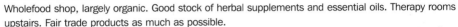

Treberfedd, Dihewyd, Lampeter,
Ceredigion, SA48 7NW

Tel: 01570 470672 Fax: 01570 470672 contactus@treberfedd.co.uk www.treberfedd.co.uk

There are four beautiful holiday cottages at Treberfedd including a wonderful Grade II listed thatched cottage. The farm produces beef and lamb from its organic rare breed sheep and cattle. The farm is rich in wildlife and over 14,000 new trees have been planted since 2002. Visitors can follow the nature trail around the farm and enjoy the stunning views over the Aeron Valley. The sandy beaches of Cardigan Bay are just a short drive away.

THE TREEHOUSE

14 Baker St., Aberystwyth, Ceredigion, SY23 2BJ

Tel: 01970 615791 adam@treehousewales.co.uk www.treehousewales.co.uk

A one-stop organic food shop stocked with over 1,000 products, many sourced locally. Call into our restaurant for coffee, lunch or tea. Our meals are made with fresh organic produce.

TREEHOUSE TLC

3 Eastgate, Aberystwyth, Ceredigion, SY23 2AR

Tel: 01970 625116 adam @treehousewales.co.uk www.info@treehousewales.co.uk

Non-food shop specialising in organic and natural cosmetics, organic clothing, babywear, books, paints and household products. All you need for a holistic lifestyle!

Accommodation	Day Visits	Manufacturers & processors	Restaurants, cafés & caterers
Alcoholic drinks	Farm Gate Sales	Importers & exporters	Retail shops
Baby goods	Farmers' market stall	Mail order suppliers	Textiles
Box schemes/ local deliveries	Garden and Farm Sundries	Pet supplies	Wholesalers
Cosmetics & toiletries	Household products	Producers	

CLWYD

NATURAL NATION

14 Central Arcade, Wrexham, Clwyd, LL11 1AG
Tel: 01978 264488 www.naturalnation.co.uk

Health food shop in a Victorian arcade stocking mainly organic foods, organic and natural skincare, baby-care, books, supplements and coffees. Open six days per week (late opening until 7.30 Thursdays). Espresso café bar and changing art exhibition. Health advice given.

CONWY

COUNTRY KITCHEN

10 Seaview Road, Colwyn Bay, Conwy, LL29 8DG
Tel: 01492 533329

General independent natural food store: vitamin supplements, organic products. Toiletries and cleaning products. Willing to order individual requirements. Free delivery possible within 5-mile radius of shop on orders over £25.

TY NEWYDD ORGANICS

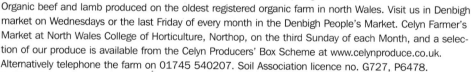

Ty Newydd Uchaf, Penmachno, Betws Y Coed, Conwy, LL24 0AJ
Tel: 01690 760350 clairebarnardburrows@yahoo.co.uk

Farm gate sales of organic hen, duck and goose eggs. Organically reared geese and ducks available for Christmas.

DENBIGHSHIRE

BRYN COCYN ORGANIC BEEF & LAMB

Bryn Cocyn, Llannefydd, Denbigh, Denbighshire, LL16 5DH
Tel: 01745 540207 info@bryncocynorganic.co.uk www.bryncocynorganic.co.uk

Organic beef and lamb produced on the oldest registered organic farm in north Wales. Visit us in Denbigh market on Wednesdays or the last Friday of every month in the Denbigh People's Market. Celyn Farmer's Market at North Wales College of Horticulture, Northop, on the third Sunday of each Month, and a selection of our produce is available from the Celyn Producers' Box Scheme at www.celynproduce.co.uk. Alternatively telephone the farm on 01745 540207. Soil Association licence no. G727, P6478.

CELYN PRODUCE LTD

Cadywn Clwyd, Llys Clwyd, Lon Parcwr Ind Park, Ruthin, Denbighshire, LL15 1NJ
Tel: 01824 707221 Fax: 01824 709853 info@celynproduce.co.uk www.celynproduce.co.uk

Celyn Produce supply locally produced food to customers in north-east Wales. We aim to reduce food miles, maximise quality and freshness. The core range of produce will be complemented by Organic, Fair Trade and Rainforest Alliance Certification.

HAFOD ELWY HALL

Bylchau, Denbigh, Denbighshire, LL16 5SP
Tel: 01690 770345 Fax: 01690 770180 enquiries@hafodelwyhall.co.uk www.hafodelwyhall.co.uk

Soil Association G6524. Peace and tranquillity among lakes and mountains in former shooting lodge on the edge of Snowdonia. Exclusive 4 Star WTB accommodation, with breakfast and evening meals using produce from our organic farm.

HOUSE OF RHUG

Rhug Estate Office, Corwen,
Denbighshire, LL21 0EH

Tel: 01490 413000 Fax: 01490 413300 contact@rhug.co.uk www.rhugorganic.com

The House Of Rhug is an organic café, farm butchery and shop on the A5, 2 miles west of Corwen on Lord Newborough's estate, centred around the estate's award-winning home reared meat. Alternative philiphughes@rhugorganicfarm.co.uk. Member of the Soil Association Organic Farms Network. Organic Food Awards 2004, 2006.

THE ORGANIC STORES

7 Mwrog St., Ruthin, Denbighshire, LL15 1LR

Tel: 01824 705796

We are a one-stop organic shop. We only sell organic goods. Fruit, veg, meat, fish, poultry and much more at sensible prices. We offer discounts for those on special diets such as the Gerson. You will always be welcomed by a friendly, helpful team, whose ambition is to help. Ample car parking space and carry-out service to your car; if it's too heavy, we don't expect you to lift a finger. Home delivery, not a box scheme. Established in 1996. Please feel free to give us a call – if we can help, we will.

FLINTSHIRE

THE ORGANIC STORES

Brooklyn Farm, Sealand Road, Deeside, Flintshire, CH5 2LQ

Tel: 01244 881209

We are a one-stop organic shop. We only sell organic goods. Fruit, veg, meat, fish, poultry and much more at sensible prices. We offer discounts for those on special diets such as the Gerson. You will always be welcomed by a friendly, helpful team, whose ambition is to help. Ample car parking space and carry-out service to your car; if it's too heavy, we don't expect you to lift a finger. Home delivery, not a box scheme. Established in 1996. Please feel free to give us a call – if we can help, we will.

GLAMORGAN

BEANFREAKS LTD

3 St. Mary St., Cardiff, Glamorgan, CF10 1AT

Tel: 029 2025 1671 kevin@swissherbalremedies.com www.swissherbalremedies.com

Fully stocked health food stores specialising in herbal medicine; advice line and mail order enquiries on 029 2041 7803. Online at www.swissherbalremedies.com. Stores at Cardiff, Newport, Cwmbran and Bridgend.

BUTTERFLY BABIES

34 Wellfield Rd., Cardiff, CF24 3PB

Tel: 029 2049 5800 emma@butterfly-babies.co.uk www.butterfly-babies.co.uk

Butterfly Babies – for natural, organic and fair trade products for mum and baby. We specialise in giving personal advice to both our online and retail customers about the wide range of washable nappies and baby carrying slings we have available. Organic lines we stock include organic clothes, soft toys, bedding and mattresses from Cut4Cloth, Cotton People Organic, Green Baby, miYim, ABACA and Aravore, as well as organic toiletries from the likes of Green People, Natalia, Earth Friendly Baby and Pure Potions.

GLAMORGAN

CHOCOLATE PINK HEALTH & BEAUTY

89 Whitchurch Rd., Heath, Cardiff, Glamorgan, CF14 3JP

Tel: 029 2061 9555 mail@choccypink.com www.choccypink.com

Chocolate Pink is an holistic health and beauty salon selling a wide range of organic body care products by Green People and Organic Blue.

GREEN CUISINE

Tel: 029 2039 4321 Fax: 029 2039 4321

info@greencuisineorganics.net www.greencuisineorganics.net

A customer choice home delivery service (no visitors) from twelve-page price list: meat, poultry, fish, eggs, dairy, frozen, chilled, deli, groceries, fruit, veg, baked goods, chocolates, body care, cleaning products.

JUST ORGANIC/CLYNGWYN ORGANIC FARM

Ystradfellte Rd, Pontneathvaughan, Neath, Glamorgan, SA11 5US

Tel: 01639 722930 Fax: 01639 722930 info@just-organic.com www.just-organic.com

Under new ownership – please check website for available produce. Bunkhouse accommodation set in glorious scenery in 'waterfall country'; sleeps up to 15.

LAMMAS ORGANICS

16 Holts Field, Murton, Swansea, Glamorgan, SA3 3AQ

Tel: 07765 377650 lammas@sustained.org.uk www.sustained.org.uk/lammas

Lammas Organics is a small market garden supplying high quality, freshly picked, seasonal vegetables direct to local customers. We aim to be fully sustainable by using only biodiesel for deliveries and our tractor.

MULDOONS – CARDIFF

Unit 4, The Old Brewery Quarter, Cardiff, Glamorgan, CF10 1FG

Tel: 029 2034 4949 www.muls.co.uk

Urban-style café, serving organic and fair trade produce in a dynamic and fun environment. Speciality coffees, sandwiches and smoothies.

MULTIPLE ORGANICS

Lake Farm Barns, St. Athan Rd, Cowbridge, Glamorgan, CF71 7HY

Tel: 01446 772964 Fax: 01446 772964 multipleorganics@btinternet.com

Organic herb and wild flower nursery, supplying plants, feed, composts; all organically registered. We have a catalogue, weekly 'looking good' list, and are open to the general public.

NEAL'S YARD REMEDIES

23-25 Morgan Arcade, Cardiff, Glamorgan, CF1 2AF

Tel: 029 2023 5721 mail@nealsyardremedies.com www.nealsyardremedies.com

Neal's Yard Remedies manufactures and retails natural cosmetics in addition to stocking an extensive range of herbs, essential oils, homeopathic remedies and reference material.

PENRHIW FARM ORGANIC MEATS

Penrhiw Farm, Trelewis, Treharris, Glamorgan, CF46 6TA

Tel: 01443 412949 penrhiw.farm@virgin.net

Producers of quality Aberdeen Angus beef and Welsh mountain lamb. Meat is sold at local farmers' markets. A local home delivery service is operated.

PULSE WHOLEFOODS LTD

171 Kings Road, Canton, Cardiff, Glamorgan, CF1 9DE
Tel: 029 2022 5873 Fax: 029 2023 1694 pulse@pulsewholefood.co.uk www.pulsewholefood.co.uk
We offer a wide range of organic fruit, vegetables, wines, beers, wholefoods and environmentally friendly products with a friendly and helpful service.

RIVERSIDE REAL FOOD MARKET

Fitzhamon Embankment, Riverside, Cardiff, Glamorgan, CF11 6AN
Tel: 029 2019 0036 Fax: 020 2025 0549 ken@riverside.org.uk www.riverside.org.uk
Riverside Community Market Association is a social enterprise run with the aim of improving access to fresh, local and organic produce. The company runs a weekly farmers' market and a community food growing project.

THE SOURCE

26, Cardiff Road, Caerphilly, Glamorgan, CF83 1JP
Tel: 029 2088 3236 Fax: 029 2088 3236 hebenlee@btopenworld.com www.healthstore24.co.uk
Retail store offering fresh organic fruit and veg box scheme with delivery service. Health foods, wholefoods, organic ranges, dairy and meat alternatives. Wheat/gluten-free ranges, organic food supplements.

SPICE OF LIFE

1 Inverness Place, Roath, Cardiff, Glamorgan, CF2 4RU
Tel: 029 2048 7146
Wholefood shop established 1980.

SWISS HERBAL REMEDIES

18 Nolton St., Bridgend, Glamorgan, CF31 1DU
Tel: 01656 661441 kevin@swissherbalremedies.com www.swissherbalremedies.com
Specialist herbal medicine store; advice line and mail order enquiries on 029 2041 7803. Online at www.swissherbalremedies.com. Stores at Cardiff, Newport, Cwmbran and Bridgend.

VENISON FROM THE VALE

Llantrithyd Park, Bonvilston, Glamorgan, CF5 6TQ
Tel: 01446 781900 adrianne@healthyvenison.co.uk www.healthyvenison.co.uk
Delicious prime organic venison, low in fat and cholesterol, available in a variety of boneless cut directly from our historic deer park in Bonvilston. Also available at farmers' markets in south Wales (Cowbridge, Penarth, Mumbles and Abergavenny). Check our website or call for details. Mobile: 07771 700606.

GWENT

BEANFREAKS LTD

7 Caradoc Rd., Cwmbran, Gwent, NP44 1PP
Tel: 01633 482507 kevin@swissherbalremedies.com www.swissherbalremedies.com
Fully stocked health food stores specialising in herbal medicine; advice line and mail order enquiries on 029 2041 7803. Online at www.swissherbalremedies.com. Stores at Cardiff, Newport, Cwmbran and Bridgend.

BEANFREAKS LTD

5 Chartist Towers, Up Dock St., Newport, Gwent, NP1
Tel: 01633 666150 kevin@swissherbalremedies.com www.swissherbalremedies.com
Fully stocked health food stores specialising in herbal medicine; advice line and mail order enquiries on 029 2041 7803. Online at www.swissherbalremedies.com. Stores at Cardiff, Newport, Cwmbran and Bridgend.

BROOKLANDS FARM

Chepstow Rd., Raglan, Gwent, NP15 2EN

Tel: 01291 690782 Fax: 01291 690782 brooklands-farm@raglan.fsbusiness.co.uk

Family-run organic farm 200 metres from Raglan village. Home-cooked breakfast and evening meal. Children welcome. Pets by appointment. Spacious garden and ample parking.

CARROB GROWERS

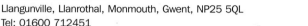

Llangunville, Llanrothal, Monmouth, Gwent, NP25 5QL

Tel: 01600 712451

Specialist fruit growers, some vegetables. Produce picked to order. Local deliveries to Monmouthshire and south Herefordshire.

HOLT-WILSON, A D & C M

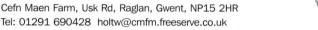 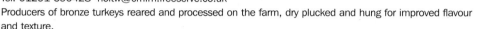

Cefn Maen Farm, Usk Rd, Raglan, Gwent, NP15 2HR

Tel: 01291 690428 holtw@cmfm.freeserve.co.uk

Producers of bronze turkeys reared and processed on the farm, dry plucked and hung for improved flavour and texture.

IRMA FINGAL-ROCK WINES

64 Monnow St., Monmouth, Gwent, NP25 3EN

Tel: 01600 712372 Fax: 01600 712372 tom@pinotnoir.co.uk www.pinotnoir.co.uk

Shop: wines our speciality. Also olive oil, eggs. Mail order and wholesale for wines.

LLANTHONY VALLEY ORGANICS

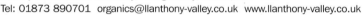 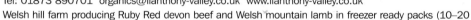 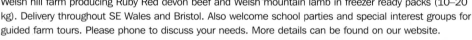

Maes-y-beran Farm, Llanthony, Abergavenny, Gwent, NP7 7NL

Tel: 01873 890701 organics@llanthony-valley.co.uk www.llanthony-valley.co.uk

Welsh hill farm producing Ruby Red devon beef and Welsh mountain lamb in freezer ready packs (10–20 kg). Delivery throughout SE Wales and Bristol. Also welcome school parties and special interest groups for guided farm tours. Please phone to discuss your needs. More details can be found on our website.

THE NURTONS

Tintern, Chepstow, Gwent, NP16 7NX

Tel: 01291 689253 Fax: 01291 689253 info@thenurtons.co.uk www.thenurtons.co.uk

Organic B&B, garden open 11am–5pm, Wednesday to Sunday, Easter to the end of September.

PEN-Y-LAN FARM & GOLDEN LAMB RUGS

Dingestow, Monmouth, Gwent, NP25 4DX

Tel: 01600 740252 Fax: 01600 740252 jamesandmary@yuleorganic.co.uk www.yuleorganic.co.uk

Local delivery by arrangement (not a box scheme) of freezer packs of organic Angus beef, lamb and organic eggs. Organic sheepskins, biodynamically tanned. Public footpaths. Visitors welcome to use the farmland as an educational resource.

RIVERFORD ORGANIC VEGETABLES

12 Lamb Lane, Ponthir, Newport, Gwent, NP18 1HA

Tel: 01633 431104 Fax: 01633 431105 anne@riverfordhomedelivery.co.uk www.riverford.co.uk

Home delivery of organic vegetables. Award-winning organic vegetable box scheme operating under license in the Newport and Cardiff areas. Various boxes for all households from single occupant to a large family. A selection of fruit, dairy products, eggs, fruit juices, wine etc. also available. Order weekly, fortnightly, or whenever you like. Can order online at www.riverford.co.uk or telephone 0845 600 2311. BBC Radio 4 Farmer of the Year 2005.

Charlotte Vøhtz first started her pioneering organic personal care and dietary health company in 1997. Little did she know that nine years on, Green People would be the leading organic health and beauty company, offering families more than one hundred chemical free products. The award-winning brand includes organic shampoos, a baby range, men's line, anti-ageing formulas and natural deodorants.

Charlotte's success came from having a suitable background that would steer her in the right direction. A qualified State Registered Nurse, she later went on to specialise in gastroenterology, dialysis and osteopathic diseases. After eleven years working in the pharmaceutical industry, Charlotte had gained substantial knowledge in the fields of chemistry, pharmacology and law. A further four years at the Commercial School of Business and Marketing resulted in qualifications in PR, marketing, sales, business management, accounts and administration. In the 1980s and early 1990s Charlotte attended the College of Phytotherapy, in order to undertake studies in herbal medicine.

There are many motivations behind the entrepreneurial spirit – to be your own boss, make money, or start something new. For Charlotte, that motivation came from wanting to help treat the eczema and allergies that her daughter Sandra suffered as a small child. As any modern parent of a child with severe skin problems will know, it can be a long and frustrating battle to find treatments that work.

After much research, it became clear that a focus on a more natural and holistic way of treating children's allergies and skin problems was the best approach.

While eating organically is a good start to helping fight allergies, it is often not enough as a cure. Green People's first product, Hawthorn & Artichoke Formula, came as the result of meeting a leading herbalist who introduced Charlotte to this herbal detox tonic. Combined with dietary changes, a daily dose of Omega oil and the removal of synthetic chemicals in personal care products, this cleansing tonic gave remarkable results in clearing up Sandra's eczema.

"From that moment I realised that we are all children of the chemical age, and that pollution, in combination with changing dietary habits, profoundly affects us all."

One of the most challenging tasks Charlotte faced was finding good quality and totally pure raw materials for the chemical-free products. Ingredients which met her high standards were expensive and difficult to source. Her refusal to accept diluted formulas with unnecessary bulking agents, as found in most conventional products, also threatened to put up the cost. An important part of Charlotte's mission, however, was to ensure that her organic products were affordable for families, and she was determined to work hard to make that aim a reality.

"I was horrified to realise that a product only had to contain as little as 1% natural ingredients to legally label itself 'natural'. I was determined to use only the best, organic ingredients in my products, but finding them required patience and persistence. As 60% of what is put on the skin is absorbed and can enter the bloodstream, it makes perfect sense to use skin care which is natural and organic."

In July 1997 the Green People Company was launched in the UK, with 32 products including herbal tonics and a range of personal care products, skin care, hair care and dental care products. Four health food stores stocked the goods, and purchases could also be made directly through mail order.

2003 was a turning point for the Company. The Good Shopping Guide awarded Green People with ethical company accreditation – the first time a beauty industry competitor has ever received this level of recognition. It soon became apparent that growth was excelling all expectations, and more staff and bigger premises were needed if supply were to meet the ever-increasing demand for toxic-free products. With a record number of people suffering from allergies, the need for gentle care for troubled skin was on the rise.

The company's aim is to offer hand-made health and beauty products that are 100% natural and certified organic. The use of toxins in many mainstream brands continues, but Green People's products are free from sodium lauryl/laureth sulphate (SLS), lanolin, propylene glycol, PABA-sunscreen, DEA, TEA, PEG's urea, ethyl alcohol, parabens, synthetic fragrances and petrochemicals. There is much documented evidence to indicate the harmful effects of such ingredients. They also operate a strict cruelty-free policy, and none of the Green People formulations have ever been tested on animals. All of the products are suitable for vegetarians, and most are also registered with the Vegan Society.

The range of products has continued to increase, and continuous development has resulted in ever higher levels of organic ingredients, confirmed by the fact that 37 of these products are now certified organic by the Soil Association or Organic Food Federation, and many more are awaiting approval.

Adopting a much 'greener' and more ethical approach to our lives goes further than simply buying natural and organic products. Green People sees its role as a provider of information and education on living an organic lifestyle. The catalogue and website give full declarations of all ingredients in each product and avoid the use of vague terms such as 'perfume' and 'fragrance', which often hide a cocktail of synthetic allergens.

Green People also take their social responsibilities very seriously, donating 10% of net profit to charity. A donation of 30p from the sale of a selected range of products is made to the Penny Brohn Cancer Care, a charity devoted to helping cancer sufferers cope with their disease.

WYEDEAN WHOLEFOODS

113 Monnow Street, Monmouth, Gwent, NP25 3EG

Tel: 01600 715429

Hundreds of organic lines. Wholefoods, gluten- and dairy-free, cruelty-free cosmetics; SLS-free toiletries. Excellent range of vitamins, minerals and herbals. Wide range of chilled and frozen products.

GWYNEDD

CHICKENSHACK

Brynllwyn, Rhoslefain, Tywyn, Gwynedd, LL36 9NH

Tel: 0845 456 5312 info@chickenshack.co.uk www.chickenshack.co.uk

Chickenshack is a housing co-operative and a fully mutual limited company. We own a 5-acre smallholding in Snowdonia which we have developed as a permaculture plot since 1995. We are not certified organic, as we only produce produce for ourselves. We run an annual permaculture design course each May, which lasts two weeks. We also host day visits for groups interested in low impact living, sustainable design etc. As well as offering some camping in our field, we have a holiday bungalow for let. It is a truly stunning area naturally, and an excellent to place to wind down, explore or study nature.

DIMENSIONS HEALTH STORE

15 Holyhead Rd., Bangor, Gwynedd, LL57 2EG

Tel: 01248 351562 info@dimensionshealthstore.com www.dimensionshealthstore.com

Soil Association no. P1857. Dimensions is an ethical retail store and online business dedicated to providing foods, supplements, remedies and other goods necessary to create health and well being.

FOREMAN, HELEN

Ysgubor Bach, Ffordd Cerrig Mawr, Caergeiliog, Holyhead, Anglesey, Gwynedd, LL65 3LU

Tel: 01407 742293

Seasonal organic box scheme, soft and top fruit, farmers' market stall.

LLANGYBI ORGANICS

Tel: 01766 819109 info@llangybi-organics.co.uk

www.llangybi-organics.co.uk

Offer: free welcome pack of organic seasonal vegetables grown on our farm. Restrictions: none.

THE NATIONAL TRUST WALES

Hafod Y Llan, Nant Gwynant, Beddgelert, Caernarfon, Gwynedd, LL5 4NG

Tel: 01766 890473 Fax: 01766 890473

Soil Association G7325. This is an upland holding extending to the summit of Snowdonia. Formed by the Trust, we are putting into practice the organic aims of our extensive beef and sheep enterprise. Member of the Soil Association Organic Farms Network.

PENTRE BACH HOLIDAY COTTAGES

Pentre Bach, Llwyngwril, Nr. Dolgellau, Gwynedd, LL37 2JU

Tel: 01341 250294 Fax: 01341 250885 cottages@pentrebach.com www.pentrebach.com

Holiday cottages (two with log fires) in Southern Snowdonia. Organic produce, free range eggs. Central heating, scenic Land Rover tours, train station nearby. Secluded, not isolated, between mountains and sea. Magnificent views. Winner, Wales Environment Award for Sustainable Tourism 2003. Special offers available October to May, outside school holidays.

PLAS LLANFAIR ORGANICS

Plas Llanfair, Tyn-Y-Gongl, Ynys Mon, Gwynedd, LL74 8NU

Tel: 01248 852316 mike@plasllanfair.freeserve.co.uk

Anglesey smallholding specialising in soft and top fruit and the processing thereof, jams, preserves and chutneys. Wide range of vegetable production on a small scale. Supply direct and local outlets.

RHOSFAWR CARAVAN PARK

Rhosfawr, Pwllheli, Gwynedd, LL53 6YA

Tel: 01766 810545

Small-scale home produced organic produce. Also touring caravan and camping park.

ROBERTS, M O & J S

Bron Heulog Farm, Llanddeusant, Holyhead, Anglesea, Gwynedd, LL65 4AU

Tel: 01407 730292

Soil Association G7296. Producing organic beef calves, Blonde x to sell as weaned calves and stores, possibility to finish some. Mobile: 07884 213217.

SAFFRON

48 High St., Llanberis, Gwynedd, LL55 4EU

Tel: 01286 871777 llanberisorganics@tiscali.co.uk www.llanberisorganics.co.uk

Organic shop with vegetarian deli counter and takeaway. Large range of organic wholefoods, fruit & veg, breads & cakes, frozen and chilled products. Environmentally friendly household and body care products and natural medicines.

THOMAS, G O

Blaen Y Nant, Nant Ffrancon, Bethesda, Gwynedd, LL

Tel: 01248 600400 Fax: 01248 600400

Traditional Welsh upland farm specialising in Welsh black beef/Welsh mountain lamb. Educational visits for organic and conservation information. Bed and breakfast. Located in panoramic views, mountains and lakes. Member of the Soil Association Organic Farms Network.

TY'N LON UCHAF

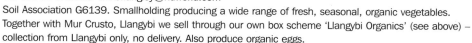

Ty'n Lon Uchaf, Llangybi, Pwllheli, Gwynedd, LL53 6TB

Tel: 01766 810915 mike.langley@ntlworld.com

Soil Association G6139. Smallholding producing a wide range of fresh, seasonal, organic vegetables. Together with Mur Crusto, Llangybi we sell through our own box scheme 'Llangybi Organics' (see above) – collection from Llangybi only, no delivery. Also produce organic eggs.

PEMBROKESHIRE

BLACKMOOR FARM

Ludchurch, Narberth, Pembrokeshire, SA67 8JH

Tel: 01834 831242 Fax: 01834 831242 ltecornth@aol.com www.infozone.com.hk/blackmoorfarm

Farm-backed tourism, grazing cattle and tack sheep.

BUMPYLANE RARE BREEDS

Shortlands Farm, Druidston, Broad Haven, Haverfordwest, Pembrokeshire, SA62 3NE

Tel: 01437 781234 info@bumpylane.co.uk www.bumpylane.co.uk

Soil Association G4793. Rare breed meat and black pudding. Recapture the real taste of lamb, mutton and beef from the traditional British breeds born and reared on our organic coastal farm overlooking St. Bride's Bay, Pembrokeshire. Self-catering cottage and holiday caravan to let.

PEMBROKESHIRE

CAERHYS ORGANIC FARM

Berea, St. Davids, Pembrokeshire, SA62 6DX
Tel: 01348 831244 Fax: 01348 831244 caerhysbandb@hotmail.com www.organic-holidays.co.uk
Organic farm holidays, B & B and self-catering cottage.

CLYNFYW COUNTRYSIDE CENTRE

Clynfyw, Abercych, Boncath,
Pembrokeshire SA37 0HF
Tel: 01239 841236 Fax: 01239 841236 jim.clynfyw@virgin.net www.clynfyw.co.uk
Soil Association G4192. Clynfyw is a residential, all access countryside activity, education, arts and respite care holiday centre set on a working organic farm. Animals include Welsh Black cattle and Saddleback pigs. With excellent Tourist Board approved cottages, Clynfyw makes the perfect holiday destination. Walk in the woods, help make charcoal, explore the decrepit wall garden or watch the badgers – there are few places more appealing! Member of the Soil Association Organic Farms Network.

DOVE COTTAGE, DYFFRYN ISAF

Dyffryn Isaf, Llandissilio, Pembrokeshire, SA66 7QD
Tel: 01437 563657 bettinab@dsl.pipex.com www.pembrokeshire-organic-holidays.co.uk
Small organic farm with self-catering holiday cottage. Shetland sheep, wool and crafts. Goats, chickens and honey. Quiet location close to Pembrokeshire coast and Preseli hills.

EVANS, D W & C M

Caerfai Farm, St. Davids, Haverfordwest,
Pembrokeshire SA62 6QT
Tel: 01437 720548 Fax: 01437 720548 chrismevans69@hotmail.com www.caerfai.co.uk
In the Pembrokeshire coast National Park, 140-acre organic dairy farm producing unpasteurised milk and home-made cheeses, early potatoes. Sales from farm shop (open daily from Whitsun to late September) and box schemes. Camping and self-catering cottages.

FFYNNONSTON ORGANICS

Ffynnonston, Dwrbach, Fishguard, Pembrokeshire SA65 9QT
Tel: 01348 873004 annhicks@waitrose.com
Small-scale organic producers located one mile from Pembrokeshire coast. Salads, herbs, vegetables and soft fruit. Also organically grown cut flowers. Self-catering units available.

FFYNNON SAMSON

Llangolman, Clynderwen, Pembrokeshire, SA66 7QL
Tel: 01437 532542 info@enjoypreseli.co.uk www.enjoypreseli.co.uk
Production of organic vegetables, fruit and eggs. Local box scheme. Please phone for all orders. Self-catering holiday cottage.

GROWING HEART WORKERS CO-OPERATIVE LTD

Henparcau Farm, Boncath, Pembrokeshire, SA37 0JY
Tel: 01239 841675 growingheart2@hotmail.com
Soil Association G6287. We grow fruit and vegetables on 7.5 acres, wholesaling and retailing locally. We have a fruit tree and bush nursery and specialise in planting edible forests. Vegetables delivered to cafés, festivals and events.

KNOCK FARM ORGANICS

Clarbeston Road, Pembrokeshire, SA63 4SL
Tel: 01437 731342
Deliver between Clarbeston Road and Cheltenham. Day visits by appointment. Produce: x Charolet suckler cow herd and Llanwennog sheep.

LATTER, T R E & A T

Penrhiw, Goodwick, Pembrokeshire, SA64 0HS
Tel: 01348 873315 Fax: 01348 873315 tom.latter@btopenworld.com
Beef, sheep, potatoes, eggs, and cereals. Self-catering visitor accommodation.

THE OLD RECTORY

The Old Rectory, Castlemartin, Pembrokeshire SA71 5HW
Tel: 01646 661677 Fax: 01646 661677
emma@torcastlemartin.freeserve.co.uk www.theoldrectoryweb.com
Comfortable old rectory offering organic B&B in wild Pembrokeshire. Sandy beaches and fabulous walking.
Two charming stone cottages available also for holidays.

SARRA, M R & T

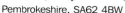

Peepout Farm, Portfield Gate,
Haverfordwest, Pembrokeshire, SA62 3LS
Tel: 01437 762323 Fax: 01437 762323 romeo@fwi.co.uk
150 acres specialising in a wide range of vegetables. Pembrokeshire new potatoes from May and all year
round. Delivered direct to box schemes, wholesalers. Retail shop, groceries, wines, fruit and veg.

WELSH HOOK MEAT CENTRE LTD

Woodfield, Withybush Road, Haverfordwest,
Pembrokeshire, SA62 4BW
Tel: 01437 768876 Fax: 01437 768877 sales@welshhook.co.uk www.welsh-organic-meat.co.uk
Wholesale and retail butchers specialising in organic pork, beef, lamb, veal, poultry, bacon and home-
made sausages. Deliveries local and M4 corridor to London. Mail order to anywhere in the UK. Organic
Food Awards 2004 Fresh Meat Highly Commended.

WHOLEFOODS OF NEWPORT

Bwydydd Cyflawn, East St., Newport, Pembrokeshire SA42 0SY
Tel: 01239 820773 Fax: 01239 820773 alinor@dial.pipiex.com
Lively general wholefood grocer, largely organic, healthy snacks, special diets, dairy-free, gluten-free,
wheat-free catered for. Welsh cheeses, cakes, confectionery, wines, beers, teas, coffees, Pembrokeshire
honey, conserves. Large selection of fresh fruit and vegetables. Complementary remedies. Body care
products. Bike hire.

POWYS

BACHELDRE WATERMILL

Churchstoke, Montgomery, Powys,
SY15 6TE
Tel: 01588 620489 Fax: 01588 620105 info@bacheldremill.co.uk www.bacheldremill.co.uk
17th century watermill, camping site and holiday cottages. Produce award-winning 'Bacheldre' stoneground organic flour. Organic Food Awards 2004, 2006.

BICYCLE BEANO VEGGIE CYCLING HOLIDAYS

Bicycle Beano, Erwood, Builth Wells, Powys, LD2 3PQ
Tel: 01982 560471 mail@bicycle-beano.co.uk www.bicycle-beano.co.uk
Sociable cycling holidays on the idyllic lanes of Wales and the Welsh Borders of England. Delicious vege-
tarian cuisine, using home-grown organic fruit and vegetables whenever available. Relaxed atmosphere.
All ages welcome.

CEFN GOLEU ORGANIC TURKEYS

Cefn Goleu, Pont Robert, Meifod, Powys, SY22 6JN

Tel: 01938 500128 cefngoleuturkeys@btclick.com

Registered packing station, eggs supplied to retail shops and direct farm gate sales. Oven-ready fresh Christmas turkeys, farm gate sales. Frozen turkeys, chickens throughout year. Lamb, pork when available.

CENTRE FOR ALTERNATIVE TECHNOLOGY

Machynlleth, Powys, SY20 9AZ

Tel: 01654 705950 Fax: 01654 702782 info@cat.org.uk www.cat.org.uk

Soil Association L09WW. Established in 1974, the Centre for Alternative Technology is Europe's leading eco-centre, with information on renewable energy, environmental building, energy efficiency, organic growing and alternative sewage systems. Services include a visitor centre open 7 days a week, practical and informative publications, a mail order service of 'green' books and products, educational services for schools, consultancy for individuals and businesses, residential courses, membership and a free information service.

THE CILIAU

The Ciliau, Erwood, Builth Wells, Powys, LD2 3TZ

Tel: 07887 656887

Organic breeding stock, pure breed beef and lamb. Private sales and deliveries. All feed stuff produced on farm for pedigree North Devons, Shropshire and Lleyn sheep.

THE CILIAU

Lower Porthamel,

Talgarth, Brecon, Powys, LD3 0DL

Tel: 07752 236773 Fax: 01874 711224 joeldurrell@yahoo.com

We encourage members of the public to our 400-acre farm and shop to enjoy the unique taste and environment of the upper Wye valley.

CLYRO HILL FARM

Clyro Hill Farm, Clyro, Powys, HR3 6JU

Tel: 01497 820520 Fax: 01497 820520 info@clyrohillfarm.co.uk www.clyrohillfarm.co.uk

Organic poultry, Hereford beef, Welsh lamb and pork raised on our farm. Free range chickens, turkeys, goose, duck, guinea fowl, pork, lamb and beef mail order. Eggs and vegetable boxes delivered locally.

DYFIGUEST ORGANIC B&B

Dyfiguest, 20 Ffordd Mynydd Griffiths, Machynlleth, Powys, SY20 8DD

Tel: 01654 702562 dyfiguest@yahoo.co.uk www.dyfiguest.co.uk

Luxurious W.T.B. 4* bungalow situated in the town of Machynlleth with spectacular views of the Dyfi valley and Snowdonia National Park, yet within 4 minutes walk of Machynlleth market town for evening meals. We serve organic breakfasts with most of the ingredients grown & produced in the Dyfi valley, a varied breakfast menu with home-made breads is available. We serve both traditional Welsh breakfasts also vegetarian & vegan. We are a few miles from the Centre for Alternative Technology; on a fine day it is a very pleasant walk. Our bungalow is just 200 yards from railway & bus station, and a free pick-up service is available. For further details see our website, or telephone. Finalist, Wales Environment Awards 2004, Green Dragon Environmental Award, level 2.

GEORGE & SON, S

Doll-Llugan, Bleddfa, Knighton, Powys, LD7 1NY

Tel: 01547 550208 Fax: 01544 230604

Soil Association G5456. A farm producing quality beef and lamb where extensive farming practices have always been exercised. Root vegetables are also grown.

GRAIG FARM ORGANICS

Dolau, Llandrindod Wells,
Powys, LD1 5TL

Tel: 01597 851655 Fax: 01597 851991 sales@graigfarm.co.uk www.graigfarm.co.uk

Award-winning organic meats, fish and other organic foods available by mail order, internet, retail outlets. Organic Retailer of the Year 2001/2. Winner Soil Association Home Delivery/Internet Service Award 2004; Organic Food Awards 1993–2004. Livestock supplies through producer group of 200 farmers across Wales and the borders. Organic Food Awards 2004, 2006.

GREAT OAK FOODS

12 Great Oak St., Llanidloes, Powys, SY18 6BU

Tel: 01686 413222 gareth@perpetualearth.com

Retail certified organic fruit and veg and non-certified locally grown produce using organic principles. We stock organic cheese, wine and spirits. Local production and low food miles are encouraged.

GWALIA FARM

Gwalia, Cemaes, Machynlleth, Powys, SY20 9PZ

Tel: 01650 511377 www.gwaliafarm.co.uk

Peaceful, remote small farm with goats, hens, sheep and large vegetable and fruit gardens. Vegetarian bed and breakfast. Beautiful views, spring water, tranquil lake, woods, birds and silence. Camping and self-catering caravan. The Centre for Alternative Technology is nearby.

MATTHEWS, RG & PARTNERS

Aberhyddnant, Crai, Brecon, Powys, LD3 8YS

Tel: 01874 636797 info@abercottages.co.uk www.abercottages.com

Two comfortable cottages sleeping 2 to 12 making an ideal location for short breaks and family holidays. Situated on 92 hectare, family-run, organic beef and sheep farm in Brecon Beacons National Park. Also member of Tir Gofal environmental scheme. Educational farm visits welcome by arrangement. Colour brochure. Member of the Soil Association Organic Farms Network. Organic Food Awards 2004 Commended.

NATURAL FOODS LLANIDLOES LTD

17 Great Oak St., Llanidloes, Powys, SY18 6BU

Tel: 01686 412306

We are retailers of organic health foods, dietary supplements, herbal remedies and other quality foods including a wide range of chilled and frozen foods. We also do bulk and special orders.

PENPONT

Penpont Estate, Brecon, Powys, LD3 8EU

Tel: 01874 636202 enquiries@penpont.com www.penpont.com

We offer bed and breakfast and self-catering accommodation in a historic listed mansion. We have two Victorian walled gardens where we grow registered organic vegetables. Visit our website for further details.

PENTWYN HERBS

c/o 1 Caerllan, Llanwrthwl, Llandrindod Wells, Powys, LD1 6NS

Tel: 01597 810113 susypeg@btopenworld.com

Grow herbs organically as crops (culinary and medicinal) and herbs in pots; herb collection of over 100 different herbs. Herb garden open to the public.

PRIMROSE ORGANIC & SACRED EARTH CENTRE

Felindre, Brecon, Powys, LD3 0ST

Tel: 01497 847636 enquiries@organic-sacred-earth.co.uk www.organic-sacred-earth.co.uk

A well established and thriving organic permaculture fruit and vegetable business offering a host of inspiring opportunities including volunteering and paid support work, education, accommodation, spiritual and sound healing workshops/retreats. Member of the Soil Association Organic Farms Network.

THE QUARRY SHOP & CAFÉ

13 & 27 Maengwyn St., Machynlleth, Powys, SY20 8EB

Tel: 01654 702624 (café), 702339 (shop) www.cat.org.uk

A vegetarian café and shop including some organic products. We are part of the Centre for Alternative Technology.

RAIKES, D

Treberfydd, Bwlch, Brecon, Powys, LD3 7PX

Tel: 01874 730205

Small organic Welsh Black suckler herd.

SMALL FARMS

Lower Porthamel, Talgarth, Brecon,
Powys, LD3 0BL

Tel: 01874 712125 Fax: 01874 712125 info@smallfarms.co.uk www.smallfarms.co.uk

A group of organic small farms with a shop & camping in the Upper Wye Valley producing organic beef, lamb, pork, poultry and vegetables. We deliver nationwide. We are committed to producing the highest quality food in an environmentally sound and sustainable way. The health and wellbeing of our animals is central to that. We want to re-engage people in the processes and practices of producing their food.

Accommodation	Day Visits	Manufacturers & processors	Restaurants, cafés & caterers
Alcoholic drinks	Farm Gate Sales	Importers & exporters	Retail shops
Baby goods	Farmers' market stall	Mail order suppliers	Textiles
Box schemes/ local deliveries	Garden and Farm Sundries	Pet supplies	Wholesalers
Cosmetics & toiletries	Household products	Producers	

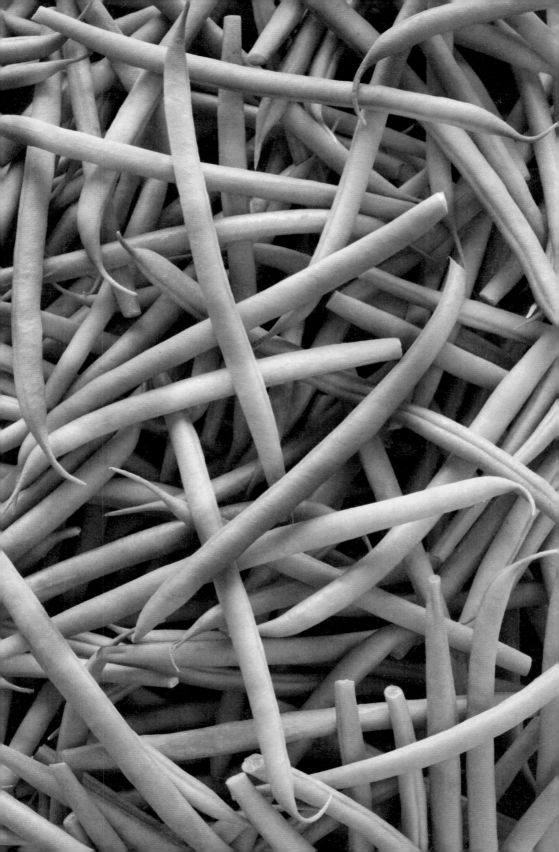

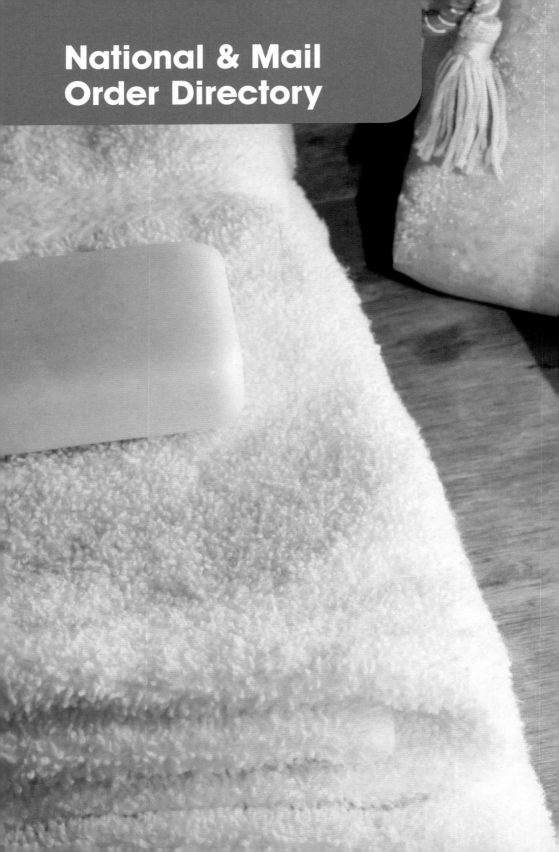

National & Mail Order Directory

ABACA LTD

Unit 1, Tycroes Business Park, Ammanford,
Carmarthenshire, SA18 3RD
Tel: 01269 598491   Fax: 01269 598492   info@abacaorganic.co.uk   www.abacaorganic.co.uk
Hand-made organic mattresses and hardwood beds. Abaca produces both luxury pocket sprung and
metal-free mattresses as well as cot mattresses and mattress pads. All standard sizes as well as a
bespoke service.

ABBEY ORGANICS

11 Almond Close, Abbeydale, Gloucester, Gloucestershire, GL4 5XY
Tel: 01452 423442   sales@abbeyorganics.co.uk   www.abbeyorganics.co.uk
We are a small nursery selling organic plants, mostly annuals, some biennials, perennials and shrubs.
These are available either as garden-ready large plugs or in 1 litre pots.

ABBOTT TREES, JAMES

1 Waterfall Cottages, Park Rd., Rivenhall, Witham, Essex, CM8 3PR
Tel: 01376 584576   james_abbott@btinternet.com
Trees and wild flowers. Supply of organic grown trees and wild flowers, mostly native. Price list available by post/email. Small orders welcome.

ABEL & COLE – *SEE LOCAL SECTION, p30*

ABEL & COLE – SEE LOCAL SECTION, p30

ABSOLUTE AROMAS LTD

6 Riverway, Newman Lane, Alton, Hampshire, GU34 2QL
Tel: 01420 540400   Fax: 01420 540401   relax@absolute-aromas.com   www.absolute-aromas.com
Aromatherapy products, available by mail order and from health food stores.

ADILI.COM

Adili Ltd, Blandford Hill, Milborne St. Andrew, Blandford Forum, Dorset, DT11 0HZ
Tel: 01258 837437   Fax: 01258 837563   adam@adili.com   www.adili.com
Adili brings together a community of producers, designers and customers who believe that fashion can
be both stylish and ethical. Adili.com offers the best brands in the ethical fashion market. You can buy
clothes that will benefit the people involved in their production or the environment, and in many cases,
both. Adili.com sells women's and children's clothes and accessories. Our ranges of organic clothing
and fair trade clothing include organic jeans, fair trade T-shirts and much more.

ALBATROSS GLOBAL LTD

Gowermead, Rowes Lane, East End, Lymington,
Hampshire, SO41 5SU
Tel: 08708 502098   Fax: 08708 502098   info@albatross-global.com   www.albatross-global.com
Soft & cosy organic cotton bedlinen (Skal certified). Luxurious organic cotton bath towels (Skal certified). Growing product range for you, your family & home.

ALL GREEN ORGANICS

PO Box 646, Haywards Heath, West Sussex, RH16 9AG
Tel: 0871 218 0887   Fax: 0871 288 4767   admin@allgreenorganics.com   www.allgreenorganics.com
Your one-stop online store for certified organic and all natural beauty products, including make-up,
perfume and nailcare as well as organic cotton baby clothes and gifts. We have vegetarian- and vegan-
friendly products, and all our packaging is either recyclable, re-usable or biodegradable.

A

ASKERTON CASTLE ESTATE

**Brampton
Cumbria CA8 2BD
Tel: 016977 3332
www.askertoncastle.co.uk
askerton.castle@btinternet.com**

Food To Taste
Quality Meats
Organic
Free Range
Rare Breeds

* Beef * Pork
* Lamb * Mutton
* Poultry * Eggs
*Alpaca Fibre
*Beltie Rugs

Born and Bred on the Farm

ALL THINGS ORGANIC LTD

66 Whalley Rd., Shuttleworth, Ramsbottom, Bury, Lancashire, BL0 0DE
Tel: 01706 829282 Fax: 01706 829282 info@allthingsorganic.ltd.uk www.allthingsorganic.ltd.uk
All Things Organic Ltd specializes in fresh organic fruit and vegetables, organic dried goods, and organic fruit and vegetable juices, where you can arrange a regular delivery of your choice. Also organic beauty products, and dietary health, with delivery the last Thursday of each month. We also have new additions to the range being sourced every month.

ALOE BABY

3 The Falcon, Watermead, Aylesbury, Buckinghamshire, HP19 0GE
Tel: 07944 485889 kerrie@aloebaby.com www.aloebaby.com
Aloe Baby provides an online niche portfolio of luxury organic baby skin care products and complementary organic accessories. All of our ranges are free from harmful chemicals, preservatives and animal testing.

A LOT OF CHOCOLATE

33 Douglas Road, Caversham, Reading, Berkshire, RG4 5BH
Tel: 0118 375 9375 info@alotofchocolate.co.uk www.alotofchocolate.co.uk
A great selection of organic and fair trade chocolates. Including Green & Blacks and Booja Booja. From single bars to fancy gift boxes.

A LOT OF COFFEE

Douglas House, 33 Douglas Rd., Caversham, Reading, Berkshire, RG4 5BH
Tel: 0118 901 2210 Fax: 0118 901 2210 info@alotofcoffee.co.uk www.alotofcoffee.co.uk
Quality freshly roasted organic and fair trade superior tasting coffees. For coffee drinkers who appreciate a first rate cup of coffee and have concerns about the environment.

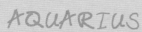
ANATOMY

165 Victoria Rd., Dartmouth, Devon, TQ6 9EF

Tel: 01803 839013 claire@anatomyfashion.co.uk www.anatomyfashion.co.uk

Anatomy is an organic/ethical women's clothing label. We use hemp, organic cotton, nettle fibres, linen and raw silk, as well as recycled and vintage fabrics. Any dyes that are used are either natural or low impact to reduce the risk to the environment and to our health and wellbeing. We do not use sweat shops or child labour, and our clothes are made in England. Anatomy wants you to look stylish and feel good in our clothes, having the same choice of contemporary cutting edge design as in the conventional fashion forum, but also having a clear conscience regarding the ethical environmental issues we all care about.

THE ANIMAL HEALING CENTRE

44 Woodlands Avenue, Berkhamsted, Herts, HP4 2JQ

Tel: 01442 878995 joy@animalhealing.org.uk www.animalhealing.org.uk

We educate about natural healing methods for pets, equines and farm animals, and sell 100% organic product remedies. We sell 100% organic wormers, probiotics and a variety of supplements.

AQUARIUS ORGANICS

12 Folly Hill, North Owersby, Market Rasen, Lincolnshire, LN8 3PW

Tel: 01673 828815 rosebram@aol.com www.aquariusorganics.co.uk

Internet mail order gift service supplying skincare products and confectionery packed in reusable wooden boxes. Hand-made recycled paper cards and Aquarius Easyfeed water-retaining plant food sachets for hanging baskets and containers.

ASKERTON CASTLE ESTATE

Askerton Castle, Brampton,
Cumbria, CA8 2BD

Tel: 01697 73332 askerton.castle@btinternet.com www.askertoncastle.co.uk

Quality meat producer: our pedigree Belted Galloway cattle, Scottish Blackface and Kerry Hill sheep, eggs from traditional pure bred laying hens. We also do pork and bacon from Berkshire and Tamworths, alpaca fibre and Beltie rugs. Visit our website.

ASSOCIATION KOKOPELLI (TERRE DE SEMENCES)

Ripple Farm, Crundale, Nr. Canterbury, Kent, CT4 7EB

Tel: Fax: 01227 730790 comments@organicseedsonline.com www.organicseedsonline.com

Organic vegetable and flower seed suppliers. Over 1,000 varieties available. Certification is by the French certifier 'Ulase'.

A–B

ATHOLL GLENS ORGANIC MEAT

Mains of Killiechangie, Pitlochry, Perth & Kinross, PH16 5NB
Tel: 01796 481482 Fax: 01796 482297 info@athollglens.co.uk www.athollglens.co.uk
The highest quality organic beef and lamb direct from the Atholl region in Highland Perthshire, one of the largest Special Protection Areas in the United Kingdom. Atholl Glens' objective is to produce the highest quality organic beef and lamb available, full of taste and tender to perfection.

ATOMIC GIFTS

Unit N3, Gate 4, Meltham Ind. Estate, Meltham,
Holmfirth, West Yorkshire, HD9 4DS
Tel: 01484 854842 enquiries@atomicgifts.co.uk www.atomicgifts.co.uk
We stock a range of high quality organic cotton baby items that can be embroidered with the name of your child. Our product range includes baby blankets, babygrows, vests, pyjamas, toys and towels.

AURO UK

Cheltenham Rd., Bisley, Nr. Stroud, Gloucestershire, GL6 7BX
Tel: 01452 772020 Fax: 01452 770104 sales@auro.co.uk www.auro.co.uk
Importers of natural organic paints 100% free from petrochemicals and their derivatives. The range includes emulsions, glosses, eggshells, woodstains, floor finishes, waxes, varnishes and adhesives, all of which are uncompromising in their use of natural ingredients.

AUTHENTIC BREAD CO

Unit 2, Strawberry Hill Business Park, Strawberry Hill,
Newent, Gloucestershire, GL18 1LH
Tel: 01531 828181 Fax: 01531 828151 breadbaron@authenticbread.co.uk www.authenticbread.co.uk
Established producer of high quality organic bakery and Christmas products. Everything from bread to pasties are lovingly hand-made in our Gloucestershire bakery. Winners of 6 Soil Association Good Food awards. Soil Association symbol no. P1912. Organic Food Awards 2004 Puddings Winner.

AVEA ORGANIC

PO Box 121, Chepstow, Gwent, NP16 6WP
Tel: 0800 027 1102 Fax: 0709 202 1615 info@avea.co.uk www.avea.co.uk
Avea sells organic cosmetics and skin care products online. All the products are paraben-free and do not contain petrochemicals, synthetic preservatives or colourants, phthalates or sodium laureth sulphate. We stock different ranges and cater for every skin type, including babies.

BABY JOY LTD

Tel: 0800 013 7030 www.babyjoygifts.co.uk
Buying the perfect new organic baby gift is easy with our friendly, reliable service. Our luxurious range of traditional baby gift baskets & personalised gifts will bring a smile to any child's face. All are beautifully delivered in the UK within 48 hours.

BABY-O

210 Church Rd., Hove, East Sussex, BN23 2DJ
Tel: 0870 760 7552 dave@baby-o.co.uk www.baby-o.co.uk
Organic cotton baby clothes, blankets, bedding and babycare products.

G. BALDWIN & CO – *SEE LOCAL SECTION, p31*

BALM BALM LTD

PO Box 830A, Thames Ditton, Surrey, KT1 9BB
Tel: 020 8339 0696 Fax: 020 8339 0811 info@balmbalm.com www.balmbalm.com

A 100% organic skincare company producing multi-purpose lip & face balms.

O R G A N I C

THE
AUTHENTIC
BREAD COMPANY

The Authentic Bread Company is an established family business with over a decade of organic baking experience. Using traditional methods and the very best organic ingredients we produce an extensive range of national award-winning baked goods.

t +44 (0)1531 828181
e info@authenticbread.co.uk
www.authenticbread.co.uk

BARWINNOCK HERBS

Barwinnock Herbs, Barrhill, Ayrshire, KA26 0RB

Tel: 01465 821338 herbs@barwinnock.com www.barwinnock.com

Garden and nursery with hardy plants from a cool climate, propagated and grown without any chemical fertilisers or pesticides. Culinary and medicinal herbs available by mail order.

BATH ORGANIC FARMS – *SEE LOCAL SECTION, p92*

BEAMING BABY

Unit 1, Place Barton Farm, Moreleigh,

Totnes, Devon, TQ9 7JN

Tel: 0800 0345 672 Fax: 01548 821589 sales@beamingbaby.com www.beamingbaby.com

Beautiful organic baby clothes, the best choice of washable nappies, eco-disposable nappies, natural wipes, organic and natural baby toiletries. Eco-friendly toys, natural bedding. Essentials for mother, and many treats too.

BEANS AND HERBS

The Herbary, 161 Chapel Street, Horningsham, Warminster, Wiltshire, BA12 7LU

Tel: 01985 844442 info@beansandherbs.co.uk www.beansandherbs.co.uk

Organic seed – specialising in herbs and vegetables. Very large number of unusual varieties of french bean seed, both climbing and dwarf. Also many herbs. All seeds suitable for the home grower or allotment holder. Mail order all year. Visit our website, or send A5 first class SAE for current catalogue.

BEAUTY IN A BOX

2 Greenways Crescent, Shoreham by Sea, West Sussex, BN43 6HS
Tel: 01273 491475 sales@beautyinabox.co.uk www.beautyinabox.co.uk
Organic skincare products for all the family delivered to your door! From body lotions to shampoos, from shaving cream to baby nappy cream! Luxury products at great prices.

BELLE & DEAN

22 The Mount, Reading, Berkshire, RG1 5HL
Tel: 0118 986 9552 info@belleanddean.com www.belleanddean.com
Belle & Dean is a Singapore-based online organic clothing shop offering adult and baby wear in simple, plain or hand-drawn designs. They focus on high quality and timeless clothing made in the most sustainable way. Belle & Dean's website also contains environmental news, views and photos along with their products.

BIOBABY

Tel: 01264 354015 info@bio-baby.co.uk www.bio-baby.co.uk
BioBaby is a small company providing a range of beautiful organic baby clothes by Cut4Cloth, Disana and other manufacturers. We sell both locally and worldwide through our website. We aim to provide excellent quality organic clothes, manufactured through ethical means, at a reasonable price. We are always looking out for ranges that are baby-proof (we have our own little one to test them on), beautiful, practical and fun to wear.

BIOWISE

Hoyle Depot, Graffham, Petworth, West Sussex, GU28 0LR
Tel: 01798 867574 Fax: 01798 867574
Soil Association approved biological controls for gardeners and growers.

BORN – *SEE LOCAL SECTION, pp27, 66 & 93*

BRITISH ECO

Northgate House, St. Marys Place, Newcastle Upon Tyne, Tyne & Wear, NE1 7PN
Tel: 0191 209 4161 britisheco@hotmail.com www.britisheco.com
Online shop selling solar powered lights, panels, water features and rechargers. Wildlife products, organic fertiliser, mulch and lawn feed, wind-up radios, composters, garden furniture plus loads more.

BROUGHTON PASTURES ORGANIC FRUIT WINE CO – *SEE BUSINESS SECTION, p307*

BUMPYLANE RARE BREEDS

Shortlands Farm, Druidston, Broad Haven, Haverfordwest, Pembrokeshire, SA62 3NE
Tel: 01437 781234 davidandpam@btconnect.com www.bumpylane.co.uk
Soil Association G4793. Rare breed meat and black pudding. Recapture the real taste of lamb, mutton and beef from the traditional British breeds born and reared on our organic coastal farm overlooking St. Bride's Bay, Pembrokeshire. Self-catering cottage and holiday caravan to let.

BUTTERFLY BABIES – *SEE LOCAL SECTION, p198*

BUTTERWORTHS ORGANIC NURSERY

Garden Cottage, Auchinleck Estate, Cumnock, Ayrshire, KA18 2LR
Tel: 01290 551088 butties@webage.co.uk www.butterworthsorganicnursery.co.uk
SOPA 625G. Fruit tree nursery specialising in northern conditions. 70 apple varieties plus some pears, plums and cherries. Mail order, visitors by arrangement, see internet catalogue or send 2 x 1st class stamps please. Mobile 07732 254300.

BUY ORGANICS

54 Broadcroft Avenue, Stanmore, Middlesex, HA7 1PF
Tel: 020 8952 1424 mail@buyorganics.co.uk www.buyorganics.co.uk
Organic living specialists dedicated to selling pure, toxin-free products. Stockists of the best organic goods; Essential Care, Earthbound, Miessence, Organics for Kids, Tatty Bumpkin, Simply Gentle cotton, Natracare, herbs, spices, mattresses, gifts.

BY NATURE
71 Avoca Rd., London, London, SW17 8SL
Tel: 020 8488 3556 info@bynature.co.uk www.bynature.co.uk
We sell diverse products from foods to textiles. Some are certified SKal, IMO, Ecocert, OFF.

CAMBRIAN ORGANICS

Horeb, Llandysul, Ceredigion, SA44 4JG
Tel: 01559 363151 Fax: 01545 581071 info@cambrianorganics.com www.cambrianorganics.com
Soil Association P7702. Co-operative of organic livestock farmers from Wales selling beef, pork and lamb by mail order. Native breed specialities include Welsh mountain lamb and Welsh Black beef. Organic Food Awards 2004 Prepared Dishes Winner.

CANINE ORGANICS
117 Hoylake Rd., Sale, Manchester, Cheshire, M33 2XJ
Tel: 08450 750393 mike@canineorganics.co.uk www.thedogbiscuitshop.co.uk
All our organic biscuit dog treats are made using only the finest natural, healthy, organic human grade food available. We do not use any additives, preservatives or artificial colourings. All our treats are hand-made and baked to order.

CAP-IT-ALL LTD

Cue House, Chapel Lane, Stockton Heath, Warrington, Cheshire, WA4 6LL
Tel: 08703 306252 info@ecothefriendlyfrog.co.uk www.ecothefriendlyfrog.co.uk
Suppliers of compostable, biodegradable and recycleable catering disposables. Range includes plates, bowls and containers. Made from renewable sources: pulped reed or sugar cane fibres, totally food safe, suitable for microwaving, conventional ovens, freezable to -25°C, lightweight and incredibly strong.

CAVIP UK LTD
2 Sheraton St, Soho, London, W1F 8BH
Tel: 0870 366 6145 Fax: 0870 140 0377 cavipuk@cavipuk.co.uk www.cavipuk.co.uk
Skal International Inspection & Certification.

THE CELTIC HERBAL CO LTD

Baldwins Moor, Manorbier,
Tenby, Pembrokeshire, SA70 7TY
Tel: 01758 701883 info@celticherbs.co.uk www.celticherbs.co.uk
We grow a wide selection of herbs organically, and incorporate these in a range of beautiful hand-made herbal soaps and other bath products.

CERES NATURAL FOODS LTD – *SEE LOCAL SECTION, p94*

CHASE ORGANICS/THE ORGANIC GARDENING CATALOGUE

Riverdene Business Park, Molesey Rd., Hersham, Surrey, KT12 4RG
Tel: 01932 253666 Fax: 01932 252707
enquiries@chaseorganics.co.uk www.organiccatalogue.co.uk
The Organic Gardening Catalogue contains mail order seeds and gardening products suitable for organic gardening and allotments. Catalogue produced in association with the HDRA.

CHEEKY RASCALS

Stone Barn, 1 Brows Farm, Farnham Rd, Liss,
Hampshire, GU33 6JG

Tel: 0870 873 2600 Fax: 0870 873 2800 sales@cheekyrascals.co.uk www.cheekyrascals.co.uk
Importers of baby and toddler nursery equipment. In particular, washable nappies and kiddy and buggy boards. Member of the Real Nappy Association. National delivery.

CHEGWORTH VALLEY JUICES

Water Lane Farm, Chegworth, Harrietsham,
Kent, ME17 1DE

Tel: 01622 859272 Fax: 01622 850918 info@chegworthvalley.com www.chegworthvalley.com
A range of award-winning drinks including apple juice and pear juice and blended juices with strawberries, raspberries, rhubarb, blackcurrants, blackberries and cranberries grown and pressed on our family farm in Kent. All are full of natural goodness and free from added sugars, sweeteners, concentrates, artificial colourings, flavourings or preservatives and presented in 250ml and 1litre wine-shaped glass bottles featuring stunning photography from the farm. We supply direct to private customers through numerous farmers' markets and by mail order service, and also to quality independent retailers nationwide. Please visit our website to find out more.

CHILDHAY MANOR ORGANICS

Childhay Manor, Blackdown, Beaminster, Dorset, DT8 3LQ

Tel: 01308 868709 Fax: 01308 868119 lucy@childhaymanor.com www.childhaymanor.com
We produce our own organic pork, bacon and beef, which we supply, as well as organic lamb and chickens from other local farmers. We deliver to butchers throughout the South of England, and operate an overnight hamper delivery scheme to the general public, nationwide.

CHILTERN SEEDS

Bortree Stile, Ulverston, Cumbria, LA12 7PB

Tel: 01229 581137 Fax: 01229 584549 info@chilternseeds.co.uk www.chilternseeds.co.uk
Chiltern Seeds catalogue lists over 4,600 items including an organic vegetable section. There are also flowers, trees, shrubs, annuals, houseplants, exotics for your greenhouse, unusual vegetables and herbs.

CHILTERNS ORGANIC COMPANY

Tel: 01494 459040 enquiry@chilternsorganic.com www.organic-direct.co.uk
Organic health and beauty products and gifts delivered direct to your door anywhere in the UK.

THE CHOCOLATE ALCHEMIST LIMITED

Units 1&2 Langham Stables, Lodsworth, West Sussex, GU28 9BU

Tel: 01798 860995 Fax: 01798 860996

info@thechocolatealchemist.co.uk www.thechocolatealchemist.co.uk
Award-winning, hand-made, organic, single origin chocolate products. They taste great too!

CIDERSTORE

Unit 2 Stroud Enterprise Centre, Bath Rd., Stroud, Gloucestershire, GL5 3NL
Tel: 01453 759057 / 835634 sales@ciderstore.com www.ciderstore.com
Online cider retailer specialising in independently produced craft ciders including certified organic ciders from Heron Valley, Luscombe, Sheppy's and Weston's. The majority of our other ciders are real ciders made without additives etc.

CLEAN & PURE

13 Raglan Close, Frimley Green, Camberley, Surrey, GU16 8YL

Tel: 01252 669950 info@cleanandpure.co.uk www.cleanandpure.co.uk/page/943722

100% organic oils. Our healthy organic natural vegetable seed oils can provide the essential fatty acids often lacking in the modern diet. UK produced. All products are in dark glass bottles.

CLEAN SLATE (SCHOOL UNIFORMS)

19 Dig St., Ashbourne, Derbyshire, DE6 1GF

Tel: 01335 343917 Fax: 01335 300485

enquiries@cleanslateclothing.co.uk www.cleanslateclothing.co.uk

Our supplier is certified to IMO control (Cert. No. 24003). Fairtrade mark (FLO 4581) and ECO Sustainable Textile Standards (C803805-TEX-01.2006). They are also working towards the Global Organic Textile Standards. In addition Clean Slate is currently pursuing FLO and Soil Association certification. We sell the UK's first range of organic and fair trade school uniforms and PE kits. All our garments are made from 100% organic cotton. The age range is from 4 to 12 years. Schools and PTAs may buy uniforms and PE kits directly from us at a wholesale price with embroidery services provided. Parents can purchase individual items from our online shop or group together to form a co-operative buying club to receive further discounts. Alternative telephone: 0845 337 2963.

CLIPPER – *SEE BUSINESS-TO-BUSINESS SECTION, p280*

CLOTHWORKS

P.O. Box 3233, Wiltshire, BA15 2WB

Tel: 01225 309218 clothworks.info@virgin.net www.clothworks.co.uk

Linda Row believes that designing clothes in this century requires an awareness of the environmental impact of all raw materials used, from growing the fibre to manufacturing and colouring the cloth. Using organic cotton, organic linen and hemp, her aim is to combine good design with ethical manufacture and change the perception of 'Green Clothing'.

CLYRO HILL FARM – *SEE LOCAL SECTION, p208*

COCOA LOCO

1 Maple Cottage, High Street, Partridge Green, West Sussex, RH13 8EW

Tel: 01403 713130 Sarah@Cocoaloco.co.uk www.cocoaloco.co.uk

Scrumptious organic chocolate brownies and truffles. Perfect as a gift for any occasion. From a single brownies in a box, right up to a party box of 24! Free UK delivery.

COMPLETE ORGANICS

Lilacs, Mount Pleasant, Lymington, Hampshire, SO41 9LS

Tel: 01590 678409 info@completeorganics.org www.completeorganics.org

Certified by USDA, ACO, and JAS and BFA (United States, Austalia and Japan).The world's first certified organic complete range of body care, skincare, toiletries, shampoos, toothpastes, probiotics and cosmetics. Miessence and MiVitality, manufactured in Australia, newly available in the UK.

COTSWOLD SEEDS LTD

The Cotswold Business Village, London Rd., Moreton-in-Marsh, Gloucestershire, GL56 0JQ

Tel: 01608 652552 Fax: 01608 652256 info@cotswoldseeds.com www.cotswoldseeds.com

Soil Association P5985. Cotswold Seeds is a supplier of seeds: grass, clover, wild flowers and green manures. Next day delivery service to most parts of the UK.

CUMBRIA GARDENS & PETS DIRECT

Seaview Nurseries, Nethertown, Egremont, Cumbria, CA22 2UQ
Tel: 01946 820412 Fax: 01946 824091 enquiries@cumbriagardensandpetsdirect.co.uk
www.cumbriagardensandpetsdirect.co.uk
Pet food and gardening supplies.

CUMFYBUMFY

10 Joules Court, Shenley Lodge, Milton Keynes, Buckinghamshire, MK5 7BA
Tel: 01908 660096 info@cumfybumfy.co.uk www.cumfybumfy.co.uk
Organic washable nappies and baby clothes to order.

CUT4CLOTH

4 Fore St., Constantine, Falmouth, Cornwall, TR11 5AB
Tel: 01326 340956 Fax: 01326 340956 kurt@cut4cloth.co.uk www.cut4cloth.co.uk
Cut4Cloth offer an extensive range of bright and funky, organic cotton baby and children's clothing.
Retailing via www.cut4cloth.co.uk and wholesale by request.

DAMHEAD ORGANIC FOODS – SEE LOCAL SECTION, p186

DAMSELFLY LIMITED

Littlecroft, Village Street, Petersfield, Hampshire, GU32 2AH
Tel: 0870 9192762 damselfly@fsmail.net www.damselfly.co.uk
Children's organic T-shirts with creative and individual designs.

DAVENPORT VINEYARDS

Limney Farm, Castle Hill, Rotherfield, Crowborough,
East Sussex, TN6 3RR
Tel: 01892 852380 info@davenportvineyards.co.uk www.davenportvineyards.co.uk
Producers of organic English wine, sold under the Limney label. Specialities include a dry white
'Horsmonden' single vineyard wine and Limney Estate bottled fermented sparkling wine.

DAYLESFORD ORGANIC FARMSHOP

Daylesford Organic Farmshop, Daylesford,
Nr. Kingham, Gloucestershire, GL56 0YG
Tel: 01608 731700 Fax: 01608 658009
enquries@daylesfordfarmshop.com www.daylesfordorganic.com
At Daylesford we offer the freshest food in season, from our fully organic estates; we have a passionate commitment to quality. We practise compassionate farming and sustainability: organic beef, lamb,
venison and poultry; heritage variety vegetables and fruits; award-winning hand-made organic cheeses;
organic breads, pastries, and much more. Discover the authentic taste of the best organic food from
Daylesford – to take home or to enjoy in our café which was awarded Organic Restaurant of the Year in
the Organic Food Awards 2004; Prepared Dishes Highly Commended; Soups and Sauces Winner;
Sweet Preserves and Spreads Winner.

DEFENDERS LTD

Occupation Rd., Wye, Ashford, Kent, TN25 5EN
Tel: 01233 813121 Fax: 01233 813633 help@defenders.co.uk www.defenders.co.uk
Defenders supplies a comprehensive range of biological controls and integrated control products to
gardeners by mail order.

daylesfordorganic

Daylesford Organic: a way of life

At Daylesford, we start at first principles: food must be organic, local, seasonal and sustainable. Organic beef, lamb, venison, pork and poultry are reared to full, compassionate, Soil Association standards. Our heritage varieties of vegetables, fruit and herbs are exceptional, and our hand-made organic cheeses have won top British Cheese Awards. Daylesford's organic bakery, organic kitchens and cafés – in the Cotswolds and in London – offer real food, served with respect for natural ingredients.

D

Mail order with nationwide delivery is available – telephone 0800 083 1233 or visit us online at www.daylesfordorganic.com Daylesford Organic Farmshop, Daylesford, Nr Kingham, Gloucestershire GL56 0YG Tel 01608 731700.

Daylesford Organic is also available in London:
Selfridges Food Hall, Oxford Street; Clifton Nurseries, Little Venice; Bamford and Sons, Sloane Square and Pimlico Road, Pimlico.

D–E

DELFLAND NURSERIES LTD

Benwick Road, Doddington, March,
Cambridgeshire, PE15 0TU
Tel: 01354 740553 Fax: 01354 741200 jill@delfland.co.uk www.organicplants.co.uk
Vegetable, salad, herb, strawberries and ornamental plants for outdoor and greenhouse/polytunnel production. Wholesale deliveries made all over the UK. Retail shop and mail order for gardeners and allotment holders – online catalogue at www.organicplants.co.uk.

DEMETER SEEDS STORMY HALL

Stormy Hall Farm, Botton Village, Danby, Whitby, YO21 2NJ
Tel: 01287 661368 Fax: 01287 661369 stormy.hall.botton@camphill.org.uk
Producer, processor, and retailer of biodynamic and organic, vegetable, herb and flower seeds.

DOT RUN SHOP

Designers on the Run, The Drill Hall, 30-38 Dalmeny Street,
Edinburgh, Lothian, EH8 8DW
Tel: 0131 553 6223 enquiries@dotrunshop.co.uk www.dotrunshop.co.uk
We supply limited edition organic cotton T-shirts that are hand screen printed locally in Edinburgh with our own in-house, exclusive designs. Our tees are the softest, kindest and funkiest tees around. So come visit our website, soon! Mobile: 07984 601114.

DRAPER'S ORGANIC COTTON

PO Box 588, Godstone, Surrey, RH9 8WX
Tel: 08452 60 35 60 care@drapersorganiccotton.co.uk www.drapersorganiccotton.co.uk
Retailer of Demeter certified organic Egyptian cotton baby clothes, real nappies and toys. Retailer and wholesaler of contemporary 100% hemp home interiors, including mix and match tableware & curtains, shower curtains, ladies' wraps and children's sun screen throws.

EARTHBOUND ORGANICS

The Toll House, Dolau, Llandrindod Wells,
Powys, LD1 5TL
Tel: 01597 851157 sales@earthbound.co.uk www.earthbound.co.uk
Hand-made organic skin care products sold online.

EASTBROOK FARMS ORGANIC MEAT – *SEE LOCAL SECTION, p63*

ECO4

25 Ivory Close, Faversham, Kent, ME13 7RS
Tel: 01795 538929 nick@eco4.co.uk www.eco4.co.uk
Eco4 wholesale provides single-origin certified organic coffees to caterers, at work and at home. Eco4 events caters for events with organic coffees.

ECOBOO LTD

Alexander Cottage, Station Road, Heighington, Newton Aycliffe,
Co. Durham, DL5 6PU
Tel: 01325 316202 Fax: 01325 316202 contact@ecoboo.co.uk www.ecoboo.co.uk
Ecoboo offers an organic, eco, fair trade collection of clothing, toiletries, gifts and a re-usable nappy system and accessories for 0-4 years and for pregnancy. The organic lavender products are certified by Ecocert, the French certifier, the nappies are oeko-tex certified, many of the toiletries contain organic ingredients and do not contain synthetic additives/ paraben preservatives and SLS. Website, secure online payment, phone/fax orders.

ECO ECO LTD

2 Bagshaw Lane, Sparrowpit, Buxton, Derbyshire, SK17 8EU
Tel: 01298 816235 info@eco-eco.co.uk www.eco-eco.co.uk
Eco fashion for women, young children (up to the age of 5) and men. We aim to stock clothes and accessories that are as environmentally friendly and ethical as we can find – organic wherever possible (especially for the children's wear). We have a wide range of clothing, from casual to smart, that is suitable for all occasions. Please note: to visit our shop, please look in the regional section in Derbyshire for the address.

ECO-LOGIC BOOKS

Mulberry House, 19 Maple Grove, Bath, Somerset, BA2 3AF
Tel: 01225 484472 Fax: 0117 942 0164 info@eco-logicbooks.com www.eco-logicbooks.com
Publish and sell mail order books that promote practical solutions to environmental problems, organic gardening, permaculture and sustainability.

ECOS PAINTS

Unit 34, Heysham Business Park, Middleton Rd., Heysham, Cumbria, LA3 3PP
Tel: 01524 852371 Fax: 01524 858978 mail@ecospaints.com www.ecospaints.com
Organic odourless solvent-free paints, varnishes and other related products.

EQUOP

Unit 4, Old Malthouse, Little Ann Street, Bristol, Bristol, BS2 9EB
lynn@equop.com www.equop.com
equop is a modern, design-led, fair trade organic (Skal, Agrocel) clothing company and a promoter of public talent. Based online (www.equop.com), it offers a truly unique collection of exciting products, services and communities. It works in partnership with a variety of fair trade and ethical organisations to promote responsible trade and living to everyone. equop promotes public talent through the production of 'limited edition' garments, allowing the public to send in designs which are voted for by site users and may become limited edition clothing, earning the designer 25% of the profits. The 'illustrated' section of the equop site is a free platform for designers, artists, musicians and writers to show of their work.

FOR DETAILS OF SYMBOLS USED IN THE ENTRIES, SEE PAGE 17

E–F

ESSENTIAL CARE – *SEE BUSINESS-TO-BUSINESS SECTION, p295*

THE ETHICAL FOOD COMPANY

Verney Junction Business Park, Units 4–5, Verney Junction,
Buckingham, Buckinghamshire, MK18 2LB
Tel: 01296 733737 enquiries@ethicalfoods.co.uk www.ethicalfoods.co.uk
The Ethical Food Company is an online grocery store that sells food and drink produced to high standards, including organics, animal welfare, fair trade and local/sustainable production. We guarantee excellent quality products and outstanding customer service. Orders can be taken by internet, phone, email and fax and delivered to your door. We currently deliver locally with our own vehicles and nationally by courier.

ETHICAL JUICERS

3 Coronation Hill, Epping, Essex, CM16 5DT
Tel: 0845 330 6781 Fax: 0870 706 2744 info@livingearth.co.uk www.ethicaljuicers.co.uk
We supply juicers, blenders, soya milk making machines, tofu making kits, UK-grown organic soya beans, UK-grown organic soya beans, sprouters and a wide selection of organic sprouting seeds.

ETHICALONESTOPSHOP.COM

PO Box 40067, London, N6 5SN
Tel: 0870 850 6552 enquiries@ethicalonestopshop.com www.ethicalonestopshop.com
ethicalonestopshop.com has been launched from growing ethical concerns regarding trade and consumerism and an increasing awareness of our impact on the planet and its inhabitants. The aim of ethicalonestopshop.com is to make it as easy as possible for people to make the changes they would like to make in regard to environmental, animal and human-friendly shopping. ethicalonestopshop.com has done all the research for you, and they provide a wide range of ethical products in one shop, making it easier for you to shop ethically. We believe that all economic activity should be politically, socially and environmentally responsible, and work towards the building of a fair society in a sustainable, natural economy for the environment and our future. If you are interested in fair trade, natural, organic, hemp and recycled products, then take a look at ethicalonestopshop.com. You will find these and many more ethical goods for you and your home.

EVERSFIELD ORGANIC – *SEE LOCAL SECTION, p81*

EVERYBODY ORGANIC LTD

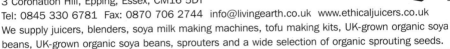

110 East Duck Lees Lane, Enfield, Middlesex, EN3 7SR
Tel: 0845 345 5054 Fax: 020 8804 1657
enquiries@everybodyorganic.com www.everybodyorganic.com
Soil Association P7703. Supplying the finest organic fruits, vegetables and groceries with delivery direct to your door. National coverage.

FACE OF FLOWERS

Unit 20 Llambed Business Park,
Tregaron Road, Lampeter, Ceredigion, SA48 8LT
Tel: 01570 423523 info@faceofflowers.com www.faceofflowers.com
An organic internet site providing a wide range of organic items (any non-organic items are clearly marked as such) both food and non-food. As well as an eco-friendly range of cleaning products. Offer a national overnight courier service as well as a local (Carmarthen/Ceredigion) delivery service. Also the public are welcome to come and shop in person.

FAIRPLAY SEED

P.O. Box 209, Woodbridge, Suffolk, IP12 1JD
Tel: 01394 610341 Fax: 01394 610341 info@fairplayseed.co.uk www.fairplayseed.co.uk
Take a look at our collection of easy-to-grow beautiful wildflowers from around the globe, which include a growing number of fragrant flowers. Most of the seed we produce ourselves in the UK, without using any chemicals or artificial fertilizers in the process. We then have the joy of hand-picking the seed at just the right moment! As part of our commitment to organic seed production, all our land is in conversion to the Soil Association's organic standards. We are also commercial members of Garden Organic (formerly known as the Henry Doubleday Research Association). We also sell the UK's first fair trade flower seed, produced by two unique growers in South Africa. Our seed packets are available through our secure online shop at www.fairplayseed.co.uk, Traidcraft, Woodbridge and Snape Farmers' markets in Suffolk, and selected Notcutts garden centres.

FERRYMAN POLYTUNNELS LTD

Bridge Rd., Lapford, Crediton, Devon, EX17 6AE
Tel: 01363 83444 Fax: 01363 83050 info@ferryman.uk.com www.ferryman.uk.com
Manufacturers of polytunnel greenhouse kits for private and commercial growers.

FESTIVAL WINES

P.O. Box 5088, Brighton & Hove, East Sussex, BN52 9BZ
Tel: 0800 024 2969 ben@festivalwines.co.uk www.festivalwines.co.uk
Importer of biodynamic and organic wines from around the world. Our website has an extensive database of vegan and vegetarian wines from our small producers. Next day delivery within the UK.

1516 BEER COMPANY

P.O Box 320, Crewe, Cheshire, CW2 6WY
Tel: 01270 668718 Fax: 01270 668801 sales@1516beer.co.uk www.1516beer.co.uk
1516 Beer Company is a specialist mail order and online retailer specialising in the sale of quality organic bottled beers.

THE FINE CHEESE CO – *SEE LOCAL SECTION, p95*

FINE FAYRE

260 Drake Avenue, Worcester, Worcestershire, WR2 5RZ
Tel: 01905 425480 Fax: 01905 425480 michele@finefayre.co.uk www.finefayre.co.uk
Fine Fayre offers businesses selling high quality, traditional, hand crafted, organic, eco-friendly, eco-therapeutic or locally produced items a free service, making their products available for customers to buy online.

FISHLEIGH ESTATE – *SEE LOCAL SECTION, p81*

FLORAME

Mill Pightle House, Hollow Lane, Stiffkey, Norfolk, NR23 1QQ
webmaster@florame.co.uk www.florame.co.uk
Florame is a supplier of certified organic essential oils, carrier oils, massage oils and other aromatherapy products.

FORD FARM, ASHLEY CHASE ESTATES

Parks Farm, Litton Cheney, Dorchester, Dorset, DT2 9AZ
Tel: 01308 482580 Fax: 01308 482608 cheese@fordfarm.com www.fordfarm.com
Soil Association P4414. Traditional West Country farmhouse cheese producers. Organic, kosher and flavoured cheeses are our speciality, including traditional cloth-wrapped cheddar.

FOUNTAIN VIOLET FARM

Mount Ridley Rd., Kingswear, Devon, TQ6 0DU
Tel: 01803 752363 Fax: 01803 752885 ed@fvfarm.freeserve.co.uk
Soil Association registered. Organic beef from pure breed South herd available via mail order or box scheme.

FREE RANGE KIDS

Garstang Rd. East, Poulton-Le-Fylde, Lancashire, FY6 8HJ
Tel: 01253 896290 info@freerangekids.co.uk www.freerangekids.co.uk
One-stop shop for baby slings, carriers, real washable nappies, organic and fair trade clothing and toys from around the world. Family-run business. Carefully researched products, thoroughly tested, beautiful and practical.

FRESH-COCONUT

145A Wembley Park Drive, Wembley, Middlesex, HA9 8HQ
directory@fresh-coconut.com www.fresh-coconut.com
IMO BIO – Siegel virgin coconut oil, hemp seed oil, flax oil, etc.

THE FRESH NETWORK

The Fresh Network Ltd., PO Box 71, Ely, Cambridgeshire, CB6 3ZQ
Tel: 0870 800 7070 Fax: 0870 800 7071 info@fresh-network.com www.fresh-network.com
The Fresh Network – trying to eat more healthily? We are here to help. We specialise in promoting and supplying organic raw and living foods and publish *Get Fresh!* magazine, hold an annual Fresh Festival featuring many of the world's leading authorities on natural healthy living, and offer an extensive range of specialist books, foods and kitchen equipment by mail order, including juicers, sprouting equipment, dehydrators and much more.

GARTHENOR ORGANIC PURE WOOL – *SEE LOCAL SECTION, p194*

GLENDALE SALADS – *SEE LOCAL SECTION, p191*

GLOBALKIDS.CO.UK

  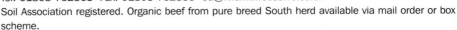

13 Buckhurst Road, Frimley Green, Camberley, Surrey, GU16 6LH
Tel: 020 8133 8533 info@globalkids.co.uk www.globalkids.co.uk
Online retailer of organic baby and toddler clothes, baby basics, hand-made natural and organic baby skincare, fair trade toys and gifts and hand-made natural wood personalised gifts. Free delivery in the UK on orders over £45.

GLO4LIFE LTD

83 Llandeilo Rd., Upper Brynamman, Ammanford, Carmarthenshire, SA18 1BE
Tel: 01269 824695 damian@glo4life.com www.glo4life.com
Glo4life wholesale and retail high-quality certified 100% organic cotton T-shirts, made to their own designs, printed with cool urban graphic designs. Glo4life care about what they do. Skal certified.

FOR DETAILS OF
SYMBOLS USED
IN THE ENTRIES,
SEE PAGE 17

GOODNESSDIRECT

South March, Daventry,
Northamptonshire, NN11 4PH

Tel: 01327 704197 Fax: 01327 703179 lesley.cutts@goodness.co.uk www.goodnessdirect.co.uk
Distributor of hundreds of organic products by wholesale and mail order. The one-stop organic supermarket delivered to your door.

GOODNESS FOODS

South March, Daventry, Northamptonshire,
NN11 4PH

Tel: 01327 706611 Fax: 01327 300436 lesley.cutts@goodness.co.uk www.goodness.co.uk
Soil Association P1636. We carry a fantastic range of organic foods, thousands of products including frozen and chilled foods. We deliver throughout the the UK. Phone for details or look at our websites – trade: www.goodness.co.uk or retail: www.GoodnessDirect.co.uk.

GOODNESS KNOWS

14 Francis St., Cheltenham,
Gloucestershire, GL53 7NY

Tel: 01242 238762 Fax: 01242 525178

enquiries@goodnessknows.co.uk www.goodnessknows.co.uk

Freshly made organic fruit and vegetable baby purées for sale and delivery. 9 'Mix and Match' pots to aid weaning for babies from 6 months. Free local home delivery, not a box scheme!

GRAIG FARM ORGANICS

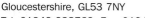

Dolau, Llandrindod Wells,
Powys, LD1 5TL

Tel: 01597 851655 Fax: 01597 851991 sales@graigfarm.co.uk www.graigfarm.co.uk
Award-winning organic meats, fish and other organic foods available by mail order, internet and through retail outlets. Organic Retailer of the Year 2001/2. Winner Soil Association Home Delivery/Internet Service Award 2004; Organic Food Awards 1993-2004. Livestock supplies through producer group of 200 farmers across Wales and the borders. Organic Food Awards 2004, 2006.

GRANARY HERBS

The Granary, Milgate Park, Ashford Road,
Bearsted, Kent, ME14 4NN
Tel: 01622 737314 Fax: 01622 739781
Mail order only (no callers). Tinctures, fluid extracts and creams made from fresh organic home grown herbs. Swedish bitters.

THE GREEN APPLE

Tel: 02476 511056 mickey@the-green-apple.co.uk www.thegreenapple.eu
Eco and ethical one-stop online shop. Products include handbags made from recycled bicycle inner tubes, creatures made from recycled sweaters, a wide range of organic cotton clothing, fair trade accessories plus much much more!

GREEN BABY CO LTD – *SEE LOCAL SECTION, p28*

GREEN BABY CO LTD – *SEE LOCAL SECTION, p28*

GREEN BOOKS LTD

Foxhole, Dartington, Totnes, TQ9 6EB
Tel: 01803 863260 Fax: 01803 863843 john@greenbooks.co.uk www.greenbooks.co.uk
Besides publishing *The Organic Directory*, we have a wide range of other books on organic living, including *Organic Places to Stay in the UK*, *The Organic Baby & Toddler Cookbook*, and *Gaia's Kitchen: Vegetarian Recipes For Family And Community*. Also books on eco-building, organic gardening, green politics and economics, etc. Mail order and trade catalogues available on request.

GREENFIBRES

99 High St., Totnes, Devon, TQ9 5PF
Tel: 01803 868001 Fax: 01803 868002 mail@greenfibres.com www.greenfibres.com
Organic clothing, bedding, fabrics, household linen and mattresses made from organic raw materials (organic cotton, organic linen, organic wool) under fair and safe working conditions. Feel and look good while supporting organic agriculture and ethical work practices. We also stock organic cleaning products.

THE GREEN GLUTTON

30 Oakdene Rd., Brockham, Betchworth, Surrey, RH3 7JX
info@thegreenglutton.com www.thegreenglutton.com
Website devoted to selling the highest quality food and gourmet gifts, offering the organic and fair trade option where possible. Olive oil, balsamic vinegar, honey, teas and infusions, chocolates, biscuits, food accessories etc.

GREEN HOUSE ORGANICS

5 Thorncliffe Terrace, Gordon Rd., Tideswell, Derbyshire, SK17 8PS
Tel: 01298 872801 annette@greenhouseorganics.co.uk www.greenhouseorganics.co.uk
Sell chemical-free, organic skin care products via the internet. Green House Organics itself hasn't been certified organic, but the companies whose products we sell have been certified by the Soil Association.

GREENLIFE DIRECT

11 The Paddocks, Totnes Ind. Park, Totnes, TQ9 5XT
Tel: 01803 868733 Fax: 01803 864948 enquiries@greenlife.co.uk www.greenlife.co.uk
Greenlife Direct retail a wide range of nutritional supplements including competitively priced own label and hard-to-find products. Practitioner discounts. Established 1989. Now the largest independent health/wholefood shop in the Westcountry.

G–H

GREEN PEOPLE

Pondtail Farm, West Grinstead,
West Sussex, RH13 8LN
Tel: 08702 401444 Fax: 01403 741810 organic@greenpeople.co.uk www.greenpeople.co.uk
Manufacturer of hand-made organic health and beauty products for all the family. Sun care, dental care, body care, baby care, skin care, hair care and home care products. No petrochemicals, sodium lauryl sulphate or parabens. Approved by the Vegan Society. Call for a free catalogue and trial sachet.

THE GREEN SHOP, BISLEY – *SEE LOCAL SECTION, p127*

GREEN YOUR OFFICE

483 Green Lanes, London, N1 4BS
Tel: 0845 456 4540 Fax: 0870 112 6339 info@greenyouroffice.co.uk www.greenyouroffice.co.uk
Green Your Office is your convenient one-stop shop for everything you need to manage your office, from stationery to office cleaning and food. Everything we sell is socially and environmentally responsible. Organic and fair trade food, teas, coffees & milk and bottled water supplied.

GREMBO ORGANICS UK

Banks Farm Cottage, Staynall Lane, Hambleton,
Poulton-Le-Fylde, Lancashire, FY6 9DT
Tel: 01253 701518 Fax: 01253 700523 info@grembo.co.uk www.grembo.co.uk
Producers of beautiful organic cotton sleeping bags from birth to 4 years of age. Made in the USA from the highest quality organic cotton, they are excellent in design and are a must for all children. Choose from winter, spring and summer bags, six different designs.

HUGH GRIERSON

Newmiln Farm, Tibbermore, Perth,
Perth & Kinross, PH1 1QN
Tel: 01738 730201 Fax: 01738 730201
enquiries@hughgrierson.co.uk www.the-organic-farm.co.uk
Finest Aberdeen Angus beef, lamb and pork from your local farm. All our food is grass-fed and properly hung for maximum tenderness and flavour. We deliver nationwide or locally to your home in the evenings. Traditional local produce safeguards local jobs.

GROWERS ORGANIC PLANT CENTRE – *SEE LOCAL SECTION, p82*

THE HAMPSTEAD TEA & COFFEE COMPANY

P.O. Box 52474, London, NW3 9DA
Tel: 020 7431 9393 Fax: 020 7431 3700 info@hampsteadtea.com www.hampsteadtea.com
Organic Food Award winners 98 & 99 for our high quality range of biodynamic and fair trade teas. Certified by BDAA. Products at health food stores and by mail order.

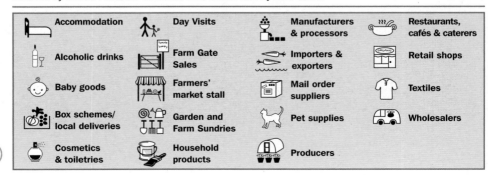

Accommodation		Day Visits		Manufacturers & processors		Restaurants, cafés & caterers
Alcoholic drinks		Farm Gate Sales		Importers & exporters		Retail shops
Baby goods		Farmers' market stall		Mail order suppliers		Textiles
Box schemes/ local deliveries		Garden and Farm Sundries		Pet supplies		Wholesalers
Cosmetics & toiletries		Household products		Producers		

Ethical and Organic

Natural and organic beauty for healthy skin and hair

GREENPEOPLE

Made without Sodium lauryl sulphate, parabens, lanolin, petrochemicals and perfume

For a **FREE** catalogue and sachet
visit www.greenpeople.co.uk
or call 01403 740350

HANDMADE HAMMOCKS LTD

Unit 10 Kempleton Mill, Kempleton Mill, Twynholm,
Kirkudbright, Dumfries & Galloway, DG6 4NJ
Tel: 01557 860000 Fax: 01557 860255
sales@handmadehammocks.co.uk www.handmadehammocks.co.uk
Fair trade hammocks in organic cotton certified by Control Union Certifications (formerly Skal International). Accompanied by our own FSC hardwood hammock stands and all the suspension accessories you need.

HEALTHQUEST LTD

9th Floor, 112 Station Rd., Edgware, HA8 7BJ

Tel: 020 8424 8844 Fax: 020 8424 8222 info@healthquest.co.uk www.healthquest.co.uk
HealthQuest supplies the stylish Organic Blue range of wellbeing products (aromatherapy, bodycare and herbal supplement ranges), the award-winning Earth Friendly Baby range (natural baby toiletries) and Natalia aromatherapy range (pregnancy).

HEALTHY LIFESTYLE ORGANICS LTD

Unit 2, Stockwood Business Park, Stockwood, Nr.
Redditch,Worcestershire, B96 6SX

Tel: 01386 791555 Fax: 01789 730056 orders@hlorganics.co.uk www.hlorganics.co.uk
We are an organic and earth-friendly shopping delivery company. We deliver in our own temperature controlled vehicles direct to your door.

HEALTHYORGANICS

73 Savoy Court, King Edward Close, Calne, Wiltshire, SN11 9RQ

Tel: 01249 817486 rrobson10@ntlworld.com www.healthyorganics.net
The Miessence certified organic range is the first range of skin, hair and body care products to bear the seal of approval of leading organic certifying bodies: USDA, Australian Certified Organic.

HEAVEN SCENT HERBS

Unit 9, Gidleys Meadow, Christow, Exeter, Devon, EX6 7QB

Tel: 01647 252847 Fax: 01647 252847
enquiries@heavenscentherbs.co.uk www.heavenscentherbs.co.uk
Hand-made herb and spice mustards – 12 distinctively flavoured organic varieties available in a selection of sizes. Contact for nearest stockists. Starter packs available for retail outlets. Mail order service.

HEDGEROW HERBALS

9 Simpson Rd., East Mains Ind Estate, Broxburn, Lothian, EH52 5NP
Tel: 0870 118 2010 www.hedgerowherbals.com
Herbaria makes organic and natural herbal hand-made soaps and other bath & body products. For trade customers can supply own range or make to order under your own label. Shoppers can purchase directly from www.hedgerowherbals.com.

HEHLIS HOLISTICS

17 Lansdowne Court, Brighton Rd., Purley, Surrey, CR8 2BD
Tel: 020 8660 7954 info@hehlis-holistics.com www.hehlis-holistics.co.uk
Grain mills, flakers and accessories to make your own fresh flour, cereals and porridge. Teas, spices, yoga mats, pet care.

HEJHOG

Freepost RLSB-GZKT-CUGG, hejhog, Goole,
East Yorkshire, DN14 8HY
Tel: 01724 798747 Fax: 01724 798785 info@hejhog.co.uk www.hejhog.co.uk
Natural and organic babywear, sleeping bags, soft toys, baby slings, products by Engel, Lana, Simply Soaps, Badger – all highly regarded throughout Europe for their outstanding quality and ecological standards. Hand-shaped and hand-painted wooden toys. For a free colour catalogue call 0845 606 6487 or visit www.hejhog.co.uk. Open Monday–Friday 9.30am–3.30pm.

THE HEMP SHOP LTD

PO Box 396, Brighton,
East Sussex, BN1 1SX
Tel: 0845 123 5869 Fax: 0845 123 5896 mailorder@thehempshop.co.uk www.thehempshop.co.uk
The UK's leading hemp retailer: we carry the largest range of organic hemp foods, hemp clothes, hemp body care products, hemp paper, hemp interiors, hemp luggage and hemp accessories in the UK. You can order from our website, by phone, and we have a mail order catalogue and post to anywhere in the world.

THE HERBARY

The Herbary, 161 Chapel Street, Horningsham,
Warminster, Wiltshire, BA12 7LU
Tel: 01985 844442 info@beansandherbs.co.uk www.beansandherbs.co.uk
Organic seed – specialising in herbs and vegetables. Very large number of unusual varieties of french bean seed, climbing and dwarf. Suitable for the home grower or allotment holder. Mail order all year. Visit our website, or send A4 first class SAE for catalogue.

HERBS, GARDENS & HEALTH

27 Northdown Rd., St. Peter's, Broadstairs, Kent, CT10 2UW
Tel: 01843 600201 Fax: 01843 863134
juliet@herbsgardenshealth.com www.herbsgardenshealth.com
Mostly organic health foods, special diet foods, natural and organic toiletries, Ecover, herbal remedies, vitamins, minerals and supplements, organic veg-in-a-box from Wingham, etc.

HERITAGE PRIME – EARNESTLY BRITISH MEATS OF RARE QUALITY

Shedbush Farm, Muddy Ford Lane, Stanton St. Gabriel,
Bridport, Dorset, DT6 6DR
Tel: 01297 489304 Fax: 01297 489304 heritageprime@aol.com www.heritageprime.co.uk
Biodynamic farming – food more carefully produced than the highest organic standard. All produce to Demeter biodynamic standards: lamb, beef, pork and occasional poultry. Domestic boxes, all joints and cuts butchered, with Slow Food recipes. Mail order only, nationwide. Favourite of the finest chefs in England – where Nigella buys her meat! Organic Food Awards 2004 Commended.

HIGHER FINGLE FARM

Higher Fingle Farm, Crockernwell, Exeter,
Devon, EX6 6NP
Tel: 01647 281281 intray@higherfingle.co.uk www.higherfingle.co.uk
Organic free range ducks, chickens, geese and turkeys direct from the farm. Processed in our high welfare licensed abattoir to our unique dry plucked & hung methods. Suppliers direct to public and wholesale to a range of nationwide outlets.

HIGHLAND DROVERS

2 – 4 Mercian Buildings, Shore Road,
Perth, Perth & Kinross, PH2 8BD
Tel: 01738 561523 Fax: 01738 628497 sales@highlanddrovers.co.uk www.highlanddrovers.co.uk
Highland cattle supplied throughout the country. Parking available. Nearest train station is in Perth.

HINDON ORGANIC FARM – *SEE LOCAL SECTION, p96*

HI PEAK FEEDS LTD – *SEE BUSINESS-TO-BUSINESS SECTION, p299*

HNP DIRECT.COM

Everthorpe Grange, Common Lane, North Cave, East Yorkshire,
HU15 2PE
Tel: 01430 425531 Fax: 01430 423196 info@hnpdirect.com www.hnpdirect.com
Internet company supplying Coia coir composts, fertilisers, magna therapy.

HOBBS HOUSE BAKERY – *SEE BUSINESS-TO-BUSINESS SECTION, p306*

HOLZ TOYS
Holz Toys, The Creamery, Lostwithiel, Cornwall, PL22 0HG
Tel: 0845 130 8697 laura@holz-toys.co.uk www.holz-toys.co.uk
Organic clothing.

HOWBARROW ORGANIC FARM – *SEE LOCAL SECTION, p170*

IEKO NATURAL PAINTS – *SEE LOCAL SECTION, p46*

ILOVEORGANICS – *SEE LOCAL SECTION, p170*

IMPLEMENTATIONS
P.O. Box 2568, Nuneaton, Warwickshire, CV10 9YR
Tel: 0845 330 3148 enq@implementations.co.uk www.implementations.co.uk
Beautiful hand-crafted copper garden tools. Hard-wearing, kind to the soil, hand-made in Austria by craftsmen coppersmiths, with shafts of European hardwoods and bronze blades, hand-beaten for added durability. Alternative telephone: 024 7639 2497.

INVERAWE SMOKEHOUSES – *SEE LOCAL SECTION, p181*

JAMESFIELD ORGANIC CENTRE – *SEE LOCAL SECTION, p184*

JAMES WHITE DRINKS LTD – *SEE BUSINESS-TO-BUSINESS SECTION, p296*

JA ORGANICS

The Limes, 19 Hazelville Close, Dovercourt, Harwich, Essex, CO12 3TQ
Tel: 01255 242387 Fax: 01255 242387 jacqui@jaorganics.com www.jaorganics.com
The world's first extensive range of certified organic, skin, health, hair, cosmetic and personal care products. Certified to international food grade standards by USDA. Unique in their production. Safe and toxin-free.

JEKKA'S HERB FARM

Rose Cottage, Shellards Lane, Alveston, Bristol, BS35 3SY
Tel: 01454 418878 Fax: 01454 411988 farm@jekkasherbfarm.com www.jekkasherbfarm.com
Soil Association G5869. This farm grows over 500 different varieties of herb and native wild flowers. The transplants are grown to Soil Association Standards. The herb displays have won RHS Gold Medals at the Chelsea Flower Show in 1995–1997 and 1999–2006. The farm also has Open Days throughout the year and runs herb workshops.

KANIKER NATURAL HEALTH

Kaniker Natural Health Centre, Blythe Bridge, Staffordshire, ST11 9JG
Tel: 01782 396467 rebecca@kanikernaturalhealth.co.uk www.kanikernaturalhealth.co.uk
We offer a fabulous range of cosmetics and toiletries made from natural ingredients, many of which are certified organic by the Soil Association. All products are free from harmful chemicals and toxic ingredients and can be safely used by the whole family.

KEER FALLS FOREST FARM

Arkholme, Carnforth, Lancashire, LA6 1AP
Tel: 015242 21019 Fax: 015242 21730 philip@keerfalls.co.uk www.keerfalls.co.uk
Soil Association G7569. Producers of delicious organic lamb and beef, rare breed lamb, forest ducklings, herbs, hardwood timber and firewood. See our web site for more details.

KINGS SEEDS

Monks Farm, Coggeshall Rd., Kelvedon, Essex, CO5 0PG
Tel: 01376 570000 Fax: 01376 571189 sales@kingsseeds.com www.kingsseeds.com
Soil Association P5847. Leading supplier of organic seed suitable for UK climatic conditions.

KITCHEN GARDEN PRESERVES – *SEE BUSINESS-TO-BUSINESS SECTION, p307*

LANGLEY CHASE ORGANIC FARM

Kington Langley, Chippenham, Wiltshire, SN15 5PW
Tel: 01249 750095 Fax: 01249 750095 post@langleychase.co.uk www.langleychase.co.uk
Soil Association G4302. Pedigree flock of rare breed Manx Loghtan sheep carefully reared to produce organic whole, half lambs or joints. Nationwide delivery. Please phone to discuss your requirements. Farm visits welcome. Organic Food Awards 2001, 2002, 2004, 2006.

LAVERA (UK) LTD

Conchieton Business Centre, Kirkudbright,
Dumfries & Galloway, DG6 4TA
Tel: 01557 870203 Fax: 01557 870403 info@lavera.co.uk www.lavera.co.uk
Manufacture and supply organic and natural bodycare, facial cosmetics, hair care, sun care and world's
first anti-ageing range, to BDIH standards with certified organic ingredients. See www.bdih.co.uk.

LAZY DOG TOOL COMPANY LTD

Hill Top Farm, Spaunton, Kirkbymoorside, North Yorkshire, YO62 6TR
Tel: 01751 417351 Fax: 01751 417351 philip@lazydogtoolco.co.uk www.lazydogtoolco.co.uk
Specialist hand tools for removing individual plants (weeds).

LEAVE ONLY FOOTPRINTS

36 Arlington Drive, Macclesfield, Cheshire, SK11 8QL
Tel: 07738 952635 info@lofootprints.co.uk www.lofootprints.co.uk
Website selling a range of ethical, organic and fair trade products for babies and toddlers.

LIFE CHANGES LTD

2nd Floor, 28-30 Belle Vue Terrace, Great Malvern, Worcestershire, WR14 4PZ
Tel: 0800 043 6309 dawn@lifechanges.co.uk www.saferwithorganics.net
Products of unrivalled purity for skin, hair, body, oral care & cosmetics.International organic certification
to food grade standards – USDA, IFOAM, ACO and JAS. No synthetic chemicals, just cold processed,
nutrient-rich high quality ingredients. New to UK since Feb 05. Available mail order and online.
Distributors required across UK & Eire.

LITTLE GREEN ANGELS

Tel: 0121 288 2010
mail@littlegreenangels.com www.littlegreenangels.com
We are an online shop specialising in eco-friendly, organic and fair trade products for babies and children,
including eco nappies and wipes, organic mattresses and bedding, baby slings, organic soft toys and more.

LIV

21 Stockwood Business Park, Stockwood, Nr. Redditch, Worcestershire, B96 6SX
Tel: 01386 791038 Fax: 01386 791011 enquiries@liv-uk.com www.liv-uk.com
Stylish organic clothing, bedlinen and bath towels for the eco-conscious. Liv is working with suppliers in
India, Turkey, Germany and Egypt to produce a range of beautiful organic certified textiles in cotton,
linen and hemp. Products can be purchased through the company's website and mail order facility. Liv
claims a socially responsible ethos.

THE LOCAL FOOD COMPANY

Orchard House, Galpin St., Modbury, Devon, PL21 0QA
Tel: 01548 831183 Fax: 01548 831183 www.thelocalfoodcompany.co.uk
Web based company delivering a wide range of organic products.

LONDON TEA COMPANY

1 Ballards Lane, Finchley, London, N3 1LQ
Tel: 020 8349 8089 Fax: 020 8141 3248 info@londontea.c.uk www.londontea.co.uk
We produce a novel range of organic fruit infused speciality teas and teasans, using only the finest
100% organic ingredients from around the world. All the teas in the London Tea range are Fairtrade
certified. Our current range includes teas that are created with premium organic black and green teas
which are then blended with freshly picked and dried fruit, exotic flowers, herbs and spices to create a
variety of delightfully flavoured and aromatic teas.

L–M

LOVELY ORGANIC LTD

6 Goostrey Lane, Cranage, Cheshire, CW4 8HE

Tel: 07966 434632 victoria@lovelyorganic.com www.lovelyorganic.com

We are a company who specialise in organic beauty products, sourcing organic beauty products from around the world. Our mission is to raise awareness of the harm that we are causing to our bodies and our planet by using chemicals. The team at Lovely Organic is dedicated and passionate about how we can start to change the world by being organic, natural, eco-friendly and by using fair trade ethics.

LOWER HURST FARM – *SEE LOCAL SECTION, p109*

LUMA

PO Box 28894, Barnes, London, SW13 0WH

Tel: 0845 094 2598 alison@lumadirect.com www.lumadirect.com

A range of bed linens of the finest quality organic cottons made by leaders in fair trade practices. Luma currently offers 7 different lines of Skal certified organic cotton bed linens in simple, classic designs as well as organic cotton blankets and towels. All have been priced to be great value for money compared with conventional cotton products of similar quality.

MAESYFFIN MUSHROOMS

Tel: 0845 458 1258 enquiries@maesymush.co.uk www.maesymush.co.uk

Grower and supplier of fresh and dried organic shiitake mushrooms.

MAISON PLASSE

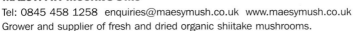

2 Sovereign Place, Wallingford, Oxfordshire, OX10 9GF

Tel: 01491 834699 sandrine@maisonplasse.com www.maisonplasse.com

Online French organic gourmet food catered by a family business in the Auvergne. The organic pâtés and cooked dishes are available in glass jars with a shelf life of a year. Certified in France by Ecocert SASF32600. European certification: F.63.040.28 CEE.

MANGO MUTT

Millbrook House, Wayside Avenue, Harrogate, North Yorkshire, HG2 8NP

Tel: 01423 545787 info@mangomutt.co.uk www.mangomutt.co.uk

Online shopping experience for dog owners who are looking for natural and organic dog accessories. We offer certified organic dog treats in four delicious flavours; peanut butter, parmesan and mint, honey and ginger, and lambs liver and cheddar cheese, made by hand in our Yorkshire kitchen with locally sourced ingredients wherever possible. Come visit our site for more information – we hope you stop by soon!

MANNA ORGANIC

Unit 11F, Hybris Business Park, Warmwell Rd., Dorchester, Dorset, DT1 2NH

Tel: 01305 851551 mail@mannaorganic.co.uk www.mannaorganic.co.uk

Award-winning, chef-prepared ready meals and desserts made using the finest Westcountry ingredients. Mail order & wholesale available across the UK. Our range includes gluten-free and dairy-free options.

MANSE ORGANICS

The Manse, Capel Isaac, Llandeilo, Carmarthenshire, SA

Tel: 01558 669043 info@graftedwalnuts.co.uk www.graftedwalnuts.co.uk

Soil Association G7180. Organic Scheme for Wales member. Specialists in fruiting and ornamental walnut trees. Native, European and American (black walnut) varieties and hybrids are grafted on to sturdy walnut rootstocks selected for UK conditions. Range of sizes available.

MARIPOSA ALTERNATIVE BODYCARE

15a Shelldale Rd., Portslade, East Sussex, BN41 1LE
Tel: 01273 242925 Fax: 01273 242925
enquiries@mariposa.co.uk www.mariposa-alternative-bodycare.co.uk
Organic and natural skin care as well as baby care, feminine hygiene, organic cotton wool and fair trade products. Order online or by phone.

MARTINA GEBHARDT NATURAL SKIN CARE UK

12 The Butts, Aldbourne, Wiltshire, SN8 2DE
Tel: 01672 541690 martin@trueaffinity.co.uk www.trueaffinity.co.uk
Martina Gebhardt Natural Skincare is 100% natural, certified by BDIH. More than 95% of the raw materials are from certified organic cultivation or Demeter contract cultivation. 17 Demeter certified products. Distributed in the UK by True Affinity Limited.

MATERIA AROMATICA

London House, 42 Upper Richmond Road West, London, SW14 8DD
Tel: 020 8392 9868 Fax: 020 8255 7126
info@materia-aromatica.com www.materia-aromatica.com
Aromatherapy, essential oils and skin care products. Certified organic essential oils and vegetable oils, 100% natural skin and body care made with organic ingredients, free from chemicals and preservatives.

MATTHEWS LTD, FWP – THE COTSWOLD FLOUR MILLERS – *SEE LOCAL SECTION, p134*

THE MAY ORGANIC FARMS

Panteg, Cellan, Lampeter, Carmarthenshire, SA48 8HHN
Tel: 01570 423080 Fax: 01570 423080 geoff@themay.co.uk www.themay.co.uk
All the organic highland beef, lamb and mutton that we produce comes exclusively from our small farms. You do your bit for conservation when you buy from us as our animals graze some 80 hectares of conservation land in Wales. We produce only five times a year, so visit our website and put yourself on the mailing list to receive an order form.

MCARD (SEEDS), SM

39 West Rd, Pointon, Sleaford, Lincolnshire, NG34 0NA
Tel: 01529 240765 Fax: 01529 240765 seeds@smmcard.com www.smmcard.com
Organic seeds, vegetables, flowers and herbs. Unusual vegetables.

MIDDLE CAMPSCOTT FARM – *SEE LOCAL SECTION, p86*

MIDDLE WHITECLEAVE – *SEE LOCAL SECTION, p86*

MIESSENCE & MIVITALITY

46a Stanger Road, South Norwood, London, SE25 5JZ
Tel: 020 8656 0754 herbalpatsy@aol.com www.onegrp.com/?HERBALIST
The world's first and internationally certified organic skincare range. Excellent for all skin types, especially problem skin. Certified organic by authorities in the USA, Japan and the International Federation of Organic Agricultural Movements (IFOAM).

MILLERS OF SPEYSIDE

Strathspey Ind. Estate, Grantown On Spey, Highland, PH26 3NB
Tel: 01479 872520 Fax: 01479 872892 info@millersofspeyside.co.uk www.millersofspeyside.co.uk
Millers of Speyside are a small private abattoir situated in the Highlands of Scotland. Suppliers of quality beef, lamb and pork to the catering and retail trade.

M–N

MONTEZUMA'S CHOCOLATES – *SEE LOCAL SECTION, pp 46, 50 & 52, and BUSINESS-TO-BUSINESS SECTION, p278*

MOORLANDS FARM SHOP – *SEE LOCAL SECTION, p86*

MORE THAN SKIN DEEP

7 Elizabeth Way, Eye, Suffolk, IP23 7HR
Tel: 01379 870147 lara@morethanskindeep.co.uk www.morethanskindeep.co.uk
Certified organic skincare, cosmetics, health care, hair care and oral care. Certification bodies: USDA organic, JAS (Japan), ACO (Australia).

MOTHER EARTH

Birkrow Cottage, Blawith, Ulverston, Cumbria, LA12 8EG
Tel: 01229 885266 enquiries@motherearth.co.uk www.motherearth.co.uk
I created Mother Earth for two main reasons, one of which was to offer people a natural alternative to skin care made with artificial chemicals. The other guiding principle of the business is that we aim to provide products that combine therapy with everyday living. In this way you can experience the emotional and spiritual benefits of flower essences & aromatherapy oils whilst cleansing and moisturising, making a room smell nice or even when you wash your hands!

MULADULA – *SEE LOCAL SECTION, p128*

MYBEINGWELL

2B Tregoniggie, Falmouth, Cornwall, TR11 4SN
Tel: 01326 377555 Fax: 01326 377555 info@mybeingwell.com www.mybeingwell.com
mybeingwell has brought together the very best organic skincare and natural cosmetics. All our products are 100% free from petrochemicals, synthetic colours, fragrances and preservatives. They do not contain GMO ingredients and are not animal tested.

MYRIAD NATURAL TOYS & CRAFTS

The Buckman Building, 43 Southampton Road,
Ringwood, Hampshire, BH24 1HE
Tel: 01725 517085 Fax: 01725 517152 veronica@myriadonline.co.uk www.myriadonline.co.uk
Natural toys made from wood, wool and cotton. Dolls made from organic cotton and wool. Plant-dyed organic wool craft products. Plant dye paints, crayons and colouring pencils. Environmentally aware products for children and families. Wide range available by mail order. Free catalogue.

NATURAL ALTERNATIVE PRODUCTS

PO Box 313, Whitefield, Lancashire, M45 6WS
Tel: 0161 798 0671 sales@natural-alternative-products.co.uk
www.natural-alternative-products.co.uk
One-stop shop for natural and organic products for all the family. Vast range of skincare, eczema, head lice and hayfever products. Instant hand sanitizers, Pure Emu Oil, Acai berry, goji berries, Aloe vera juice, Geo Thermal mud spa products and even snoring sprays.

NATURAL CHOICE, ASHBOURNE – *SEE LOCAL SECTION, p111*

NATURAL COLLECTION

Green Dot Guides Ltd, 6 Monmouth Place,
Bath, Somerset, BA1 2AT
Tel: 0870 331 3333 Fax: 0870 331 3334 info@naturalcollection.com www.naturalcollection.com
Natural Collection is a large showcase of unusual and beautiful lifestyle products chosen with a fairer planet in mind, including certified organic, natural, eco, fairly traded and hand-crafted products.

N

NATURAL DYE COMPANY

Stanbridge, Wimborne, Dorset, BH21 4JD
Tel: 01258 840549 Fax: 01258 840958
naturaldyecompany@boltblue.com www.naturaldyecompany.com
The Natural Dye Company offers hand-knitted jackets, coats and cardigans in silk, wool and cashmere,
coloured with our famous natural, organic dyes.

NATURAL HOUSE PRODUCTS LTD

Sherwood House, 7 Gregory Boulevard,
Nottingham, Nottinghamshire, NG7 6LB
Tel: 0115 960 4038 Fax: 0115 960 4116 info@natural-house.co.uk www.natural-house.co.uk
We specialise in organic homecare products. We have the first ever Soil Association certified organic
cleaning products. Our range is designed to reduce the burden of potentially harmful chemicals in the
home. Made from organic/natural ingredients and perfumed with essential oils.

NATURALLY YOURS

Horse and Gate, Witcham Toll, Ely, Cambridgeshire, CB6 2AB
Tel: 01353 778723 orders@naturally-yours.demon.co.uk www.naturally-yours.co.uk
Suppliers of organic and additive-free foods including meat, fish, fruit and vegetables and groceries.
Full traditional butchery service. Fruit and vegetable box scheme. Free delivery within defined area.

THE NATURAL NURSERY – *SEE LOCAL SECTION, p67*

NATURAL WAY, PAIGNTON – *SEE LOCAL SECTION, p86*

NATUREMADE OASIS

East Johnstone, Bish Mill, South Molton, Devon, EX36 3QE
Tel: 01769 573571 Fax: 01769 573571 sales@naturemade.co.uk www.naturemade.co.uk
Soil Association P1741. Vegetarian food manufacturers. Small family business manufacturing and distributing vegetarian foods. Mail order available. Also producing cows milk yoghurts, drinking yoghurts and cream, organic goats milk and products.

NATURESENSE

14 Shirley Parade, Gomersal, Cleckheaton, West Yorkshire, BD19 4WR
Tel: 0870 850 1797 Fax: 0870 850 1797 stephen@naturesense.co.uk www.naturesense.co.uk
Naturesense is a pure organic skin care company, sourcing organic skin care products from around the world.

NATURISIMO.COM

Unit 10, 28 Old Brompton Road, London, London, SW7 3SS
Tel: 020 7584 7815 info@naturisimo.com www.naturisimo.com
Naturisimo.com – natural and organic skin care products from exceptional organic brands including Living Nature, The Organic Pharmacy, Weleda, Green People, Spiezia Organics and Suki's Naturals.

NEAL'S YARD REMEDIES (HEAD OFFICE)

8-10 Ingate Place, Battersea, London, SW8 3NS
Tel: 020 7498 1686 Fax: 020 7498 2505
mail@nealsyardremedies.com www.nealsyardremedies.com
Neal's Yard Remedies manufactures and retails natural cosmetics in addition to stocking an extensive range of herbs, essential oils, homeopathic remedies and reference material. Customer Services: 020 7627 1949, cservices@nealsyardremedies.com. Are you interested in complementary medicine? Neal's Yard Remedies runs courses on Natural Medicine, Organic Nutrition, Aromatherapy, Herbalism, Flower Remedies and Homeopathy. Contact Emma Thomson on 020 7574 0031 for further information.

NEWBABYBASKETS.CO.UK

Tel: 01275 818275
sales@newbabybaskets.co.uk www.newbabybaskets.co.uk/
We are an online baby goods and gift shop specialising in organic baby gift baskets, organic baby clothes and eco-friendly nappies and toiletries.

NEW SEASONS

The Old Post Office, Lockinge, Wantage, Oxfordshire, OX12 8QD
Tel: 01235 821110 Fax: 01235 834294 jb@newseasons.co.uk www.newseasons.co.uk
Essential oils, vegetable oils, flower waters, massage oils, bath oils, bath milk, bath salts, face & body spritzers, room sprays, creams and lotions.

NHR ORGANIC OILS

5 College Terrace, Brighton, East Sussex, BN2 0EE
Tel: 0845 310 8066 Fax: 0845 310 8068 r@nhr.kz www.nhrorganicoils.com
The purest organic essential oils at affordable prices, beautifully presented in clear glass bottles within elegant metal tubes. The largest Soil Association certified range of the finest aromatherapy oils – over 80 types available.

FOR DETAILS OF SYMBOLS USED IN THE ENTRIES, SEE PAGE 17

THE NICE NAPPY COMPANY

Tel: 08453 457193

info@nicenappy.co.uk   www.nicenappy.co.uk

Vegan owned WAHM business selling washable nappies and covers, organic and fair trade children's clothes, washable sanitary products and slings. Products in cotton, bamboo and hemp, organically produced wherever possible, small wholesale range. Toy range imminent.

NORDTANG®
THE SEAWEED COMPANY

Warren Virgate, Plummers Plain, West Sussex, RH13 6PD

Tel: 01444 400403 Fax: 01444 400493 seaweed@seagreens.com www.seagreens.com

Products: wild seaweed harvesting business, supplying bulk bags of dried granules, powders and liquid forms. Outstanding arctic wild wrack seaweeds. Customers: manufacturers of food/animal feed/horticultural products, merchants & wholesalers of bulk ingredients, farmers for animals/plants and soil. Special offer: organic farms entitled to 15% off our trade price.

NORTHERN HARVEST – *SEE LOCAL SECTION, p168*

NORTHERN TEA MERCHANTS – *SEE LOCAL SECTION, p111*

NORTHUMBRIAN QUALITY MEATS – *SEE LOCAL SECTION, p153*

NUTSHELL NATURAL PAINTS

KBS House, 41 Marsh Green Road West, Exeter, Devon, EX2 8PN

Tel: 08700 331140 Fax: 01392 208200 info@nutshellpaints.com www.nutshellpaints.com

Nutshell Natural Paints manufacture and distribute a range of ecological household paints, wood finishes and cleaning products. We offer a beautiful range of non-poisonous and light-fast earth and mineral pigments. Nutshell uses traditional paint recipes and British-sourced ingredients wherever possible, and is still a family owned business (established 1990). Nationwide efficient and friendly mail order service via telephone or website. Retail and wholesale enquiries welcome.

OCEANS OF GOODNESS

Warren Virgate, Plummers Plain, West Sussex, RH13 6PD

Tel: 0845 064 0040 Fax: 01444 400493

post@oceansofgoodness.com www.oceansofgoodness.com

Internet retailer of Seagreens® wild seaweed food products to consumers, healthcare practitioners and patients and caterers.

OLDS, VIVIAN LTD – *SEE LOCAL SECTION, p75*

ONE (ORGANIC, NATURAL & ETHICAL) FOOD LTD

19 Austin Way, Royal Oak Trading Estate, Daventry, Northamptonshire, NN11 5QY

Tel: 0870 871 1112 Fax: 0870 871 1113 enquiries@onefood.co.uk www.onefood.co.uk

One (organic, natural and ethical) produces, wholesales and markets the largest range of fresh organic fruit, vegetables, meat and grocery to the UK. All of its range including Seafresh (sustainable) Fish can be prepared for the restaurateur, retailer, distributor, school, hospital or private home delivery – all from source to your door in 48 hours.

OLIVE OIL STORE

Tel: 01375 483863 sales@oliveoilstore.co.uk www.oliveoilstore.co.uk

Online retail and wholesale. We are an Essex-based supplier of organic olive oil, organic olives and condiments. Our products have been hand-picked from a large variety of manufacturers for their quality and appeal. The core function of our business is high quality organic products and continued customer satisfaction.

OLIVEORGANIC

The Warren, Highfield Way, Yardley Hastings,
Northampton, Northamptonshire, NN7 1HQ

Tel: 0845 838 2893 mail@oliveorganic.com www.oliveorganic.com

OliveOrganic.com – your one-stop shop for chemical-free affordable organic and natural skincare needs. Organic skincare, naturally fragranced shampoos, products for bouncing babies, shaving care and manly moisturisers. Eczema and psoriasis creams. We stock all the products on our site, no waiting around, most orders despatched same day.

ORGANIC-ALLY

118 Nibthwaite Rd., Harrow, Middlesex, HA1 1TG

shopkeeper@organic-ally.co.uk www.Organic-Ally.co.uk

Only UK retail website for organic cotton hankies, table napkins, bath mitts, dishcloth and other earth-friendly alternatives to plastic and paper such as string bags (to replace plastic carriers), gift bags (to replace single-use paper wrapper) and washable reusable cosmetic pads (to replace cotton wool/tissue paper). Low or no P&P charged for some items to encourage customers to start on their green journey. All goods are ethically sourced.

ORGANIC ANGEL

30 Riverbank Way, Ashford, Kent, TN24 0PZ

Tel: 01233 612484 angela@organic-angel.com www.organic-angel.com

The world's first extensive range of certified organic skincare, haircare, toothcare, personal care, cosmetics and health care products.Not only are these products certified organic, but they are certified to food grade standards. No harmful chemicals or synthetics. Over 80 products with a 15 day money back guarantee.

ORGANIC BODIES

75 Gaskell Rd., Highgate, London, N6 4DU

Tel: 020 7267 8383 nicole.duffy@springstudios.com www.onegrp.com/?ukorganic

Ukorganic & Organic Bodies specialise in the distribution of Australian-made and certified organic Miessence products in the UK & EU. Our 80-product range of skin, body, health range are fully certified organic to food standards by ACO Australian Certified Organic & the USDA. Distributors, agents, consultants are required to market our unique range into the UK marketplace. Contact Nicole Duffy Mob 0011 4477 9383 7081 daytime 020 7267 8383 c/o Spring Studios London.

ORGANIC BOTANICS

PO Box 2140, Hove, East Sussex, BN3 5BX

Tel: 01273 773182 Fax: 01273 773182 richfield@cwctv.net www.organicbotanics.com

Manufacturer/supplier of organic skin care. Superb organic skin care made with organic, cold-pressed plant oils and extracts. Organic essential oils, natural vitamins, natural UV filter. Telephone 01273 773182 for further information and free sample.

THE ORGANIC CHOCOLATE CAKE COMPANY

The Lodge, Oxford St., Kingsdown, Bristol, Bristol, BS2 8HH

Tel: 0117 927 3954 mail@toccc.co.uk www.toccc.co.uk

We produce 100% organic and nut-free chocolate cakes for weddings and celebrations. Our wonderful chocolate cake is soaked on vintage organic port before being layered with buttercream and home-made plum jam and encased in the finest organic chocolate and decorated to your specifications.

THE ORGANIC COUNTRY STORE – *SEE LOCAL SECTION, p20*

THE ORGANIC COUNTRY STORE – *SEE LOCAL SECTION, p20*

THE ORGANIC DELIVERY COMPANY

68 Rivington St., London, EC2A 3AY

Tel: 020 7739 8181 Fax: 020 7613 5656 info@organicdelivery.co.uk

www.organicdelivery.co.ukLarge range of organic vegetarian and vegan groceries of the highest quality delivered to you, throughout London and nationwide. Affordable and convenient. Order by telephone or securely online. Highly commended in the Soil Association awards, and registered with them. Licence no. P8888.

ORGANIC ESSENCE

Organic Essence (Correspondence), 9 Orford Rd., London, E18 1PY

info@organicessence.co.uk www.organicessence.co.uk

Luxury organic skincare, bodycare, and haircare. Also included organic products for use during pregnancy, birth, and for the mother after giving birth, as well as for babies. Current brands are John Masters, Skincare Café, Earth Mama Angel Baby, Henry Tianus.

THE ORGANIC FLOWER COMPANY

Jubilee House, Kinnerley, Oswestry, Shrewsbury, Shropshire, SY10 8DF

Tel: 01691 683866 Fax: 01743 358856 felicity@tofc.co.uk www.tofc.co.uk

Beautiful, fresh organic cut flowers sent for next day delivery in the UK. Call us or order online and chose from organic, locally grown or fair trade flowers, all delivered to your door.

THE ORGANIC GIFT HAMPER COMPANY

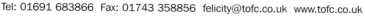

Banks Farm Cottage, Staynall Lane, Hambleton,
Poulton-le-Fylde, Lancashire, FY6 9DT

Tel: 01253 701518 info@theorganicgifthampercompany.co.uk

www.theorganicgifthampercompany.co.uk

Exclusive luxury and everyday hampers. Gifts for every occasion, beautifully packaged and delivered straight to your door or that of a loved one. Products include Japanese, Italian, Greek, chocolate, champagne and Christmas hampers. Also specialise in organic new baby hampers.

ORGANIC GIFTS DIRECT

Evergreen, Jubilee Rd., Pensilva, Liskeard, Cornwall, PL14 5QL

Tel: 08708 635225 info@organicgiftsdirect.co.uk www.organicgiftsdirect.co.uk

Organic Gifts Direct is an online shop based in Cornwall, supplying organic and natural toiletries and associated products as gift packages. Our range includes gifts for babies, ladies, children and men. Our gift sets are packed into reusable jute gift bags and packaged using environmentally friendly materials.

ORGANIC-GIFTS.CO.UK

Aylesbury, Bucks, Buckinghamshire, HP21 7EU

www.organic-gifts.co.uk

Unique organic and recycled gifts for special occasions – sole UK distributors of 'The Green Lacewing' clothing range. Recycled paper greeting cards with vegetable ink.

THE ORGANIC HAMPER COMPANY

PO Box 1407, Bristol, Somerset, BS41 9WZ
Tel: 08701 997061 Fax: 07092 040276
info@organichampercompany.com www.theorganichampercompany.com
The Organic Hamper Company offers luxurious gifts in stylish boxes – ideal for business clients, friends and family at any time of the year. Not just a seasonal gift, these hampers are an original and indulgent alternative to everyday presents. We cater for all occasions – birthdays, anniversaries, Valentine's, Mother's Day, Easter and Christmas etc., packaging each hamper by hand and organising delivery to any-where in the country. The hampers come in four price ranges: £59, £79, £99 & £159, and the hessian bags come in two sizes: £15 & £25, plus delivery costs. We are also happy to bespoke any gift to suit your individual need. Simply visit our website or call us on 08701 997061 to discuss your requirements.

ORGANICKERS.COM

13 Overbury Road, London, London, N15 6RH
Tel: 07737 053127 jo@organickers.co.uk www.organickers.com
Organic cotton clothing made in India, certified by Skal. We focus on pattern development and quality manufacturing levels ensured by our experience in the clothing industry. Our clothing is designed for comfort in exercise, specifically yoga. We aim to provide essential elements of the wardrobe for every-day wear.

ORGANIC PRINCESS
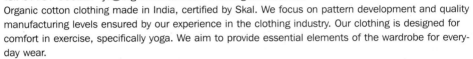
6 Ayleswade Road, Salisbury, Wiltshire, SP2 8DR
tanya@organicprincess.com www.organicprincess.com
Australia Certified Organic (ACO). Following a United States Department of Agriculture (USDA) ruling, we have the only skin care range that meets the USDA requirements for organic food production.

THE ORGANIC SALON

Tel: 0845 355 1157 info@theorganicsalon.com www.theorganicsalon.com
Our mantra 'Beautiful Body, Beautiful Earth' means you won't find any nasties here – just pure and effective natural products that really are just that. TheOrganicSalon.com strives to supply only the high-est-quality products derived from an ethical and safe source. Many of these are at the forefront in the development of certified organic face, body, hair and cosmetic products. Almost all are chock-full of ingredients that are actually beneficial to your health.

ORGANIC THERAPIES

info@organictherapies.co.uk www.organictherapies.co.uk
Organic Therapies can supply the complementary therapist with everything needed to provide superior organic treatments using quality organic products: from organic aromatherapy essential oils to organic flower essences. Visit our web site at www.organictherapies.co.uk.

THE ORGANIC TOWEL COMPANY LTD

TRB2 Trowbray House, 108 Weston St., London, SE1 3QB
Tel: 020 7378 7259 Fax: 0870 762 2371 tamae@organictowel.co.uk www.organictowel.co.uk
The Organic Towel Company offers luxurious towels made of organic cotton (IMO certified) and natural bodycare products using organic ingredients.

ORIGIN COFFEE

Mill House, Trewardreva Mill, Constantine, Falmouth, Cornwall, TR11 5QD
Tel: 01326 340320 Fax: 01326 340660 tom@origincoffee.co.uk www.origincoffee.co.uk
Origin Coffee trade in outstanding environmentally and ethically sound coffees in volumes suitable for catering and retail. Origin organic coffee is shade grown in Papua New Guinea. It has an intense, well rounded fruit flavour, with lush nutty chocolate overtones. Available in espresso bean, espresso grind and cafetière grind.

The Organic Delivery Company

Great value organic groceries to you

Ethical Affordable Local

Call now for your free brochure

020 7739 8181

or order securely online

www.organicdelivery.co.uk

Evening and daytime deliveries to London

ORIGINAL ORGANICS LTD

Unit 9 Langlands Business Park, Uffculme, EX15 3DA
Tel: 01884 841515 Fax: 01884 841717 sales@originalorganics.co.uk www.originalorganics.co.uk
Manufacturer of the world famous 'Original Wormery' and Rotol Composter.

ORIGO HOME

2 Coldgrove Cottages, Taplow, Buckinghamshire, SL6 0HD
Tel: 020 7386 0856 Fax: 020 7385 8056 alan@origohome.co.uk www.origohome.co.uk
We've been making beautiful natural goods for more than 15 years in Europe. We believe in classic designs but we also really like our planet, so we make our products from organic and natural materials. We strive to ensure that our products are produced with the best interests of the environment in mind, and also the people living in it. Because we use certified organic cottons and wools, and woods from sustainable forestry, you can enjoy our products knowing that you've made a positive difference to the world and its environment. What's more, our products aren't that expensive, which just goes to show that products don't have to cost the earth for you to help look after it.

PAGEANT WINES LIMITED

12 Pageant Place, Framlingham, Suffolk, IP13 9BX
Tel: 01728 622018 Fax: 01728 622018 enquiries@pageantwines.com www.pageantwines.com
Specialist wine merchant supplying the best organic and biodynamic wines from around the world. We offer a friendly, efficient service to trade and retail home delivery customers nationwide. We also offer an organic wine club. Contact us for further information, for a wine list, or visit our website.

PEOPLE TREE

Studio 7, 8-13 New Inn St., London, Middlesex, EC2A 3PY
Tel: 020 7739 0660 rachel.neame@peopletree.co.uk www.peopletree.co.uk
People Tree is a pioneering fair trade and ecological fashion company, making beautiful clothing and accessories for women, men, children and babies. People Tree products are made to the highest fair trade and environmental standards from start to finish, and consistently prove that it is possible to wear stylish, exciting and affordable fashion, at the same time as respecting people and planet. People Tree is the first UK fashion company to carry both Fairtrade and Soil Association accreditation on their designs, with over 50% of the collection made from organic and Fairtrade certified cotton.

PET ORGANIC

PO Box 23625, 4/11 Constitution Street, Edinburgh, Lothian, EH6 7YY
Tel: 0131 555 6366 Fax: 0131 555 6366 sales@petorganic.com www.petorganic.com
Make the organic choice for your pet. We offer a range of organic pet food and products for dogs, cats, small animals, horses and birds. Quality organic and natural grooming supplies, toys and bedding also available. Pet care advice and product information available. Secure online purchase with delivery throughout the UK.

THE PIONEERING FOOD COMPANY

Unit 51/52 Fairways Business Park, Lammas Road,
Leyton, London, E10 7QB
Tel: 020 8556 1155 info@organicbutchers.net www.organicbutchers.net
Organic butchers – you can now enjoy the real taste of the countryside with our range of top quality organic meat fresh from the farm, which we will deliver to your door. Ranging from superb roasts for special occasions to a selection of great tasting organic cuts.

PITFIELD BEER SHOP & BREWERY – *SEE LOCAL SECTION, p29*

POLEMONIUM PLANTERY
Polemonium Plantery, 28, Sunnyside, Trimdon Grange,
Trimdon Station, Co. Durham, TS29 6HF
Tel: 01429 881529 organic@polemonium.co.uk www.polemonium.co.uk
Specialist organic peat-free plant nursery selling flower plants and seeds, also organic bed and break-fast with local produce, garden visits, talks and garden plans. See website for full details.

POSTLETHWAITE'S HERBAL PRODUCTS
The Field, Eardisley, Herefordshire, HR3 6NB
Tel: 0870 240 3379 Fax: 0870 240 3379 paul.herbs@ntlworld.com
Soil Association PR10M. We supply a wide range of tinctures and other herbal products in retail sizes with the familiar gold label. Most are fresh tinctures made using home grown herbs, and we offer an own label service for large and small runs. Mail order also available.

PROVENANCE FINE FOODS
Wakes End Farm, Eversholt, Bedfordshire, MK17 9FB
Tel: 01525 288252 info@provenancefinefoods.co.uk www.provenancefinefoods.co.uk
Based in the heart of rural Bedfordshire, Provenance Fine Foods is an online food store recommended by the Good Web Guide, selling a mouthwatering range of the finest organic and traditionally produced foods and drinks including meat, fish, cheese, preserves, yoghurts, compôtes, fruit juices, cordials, herbs and spices. We deliver nationwide. The producers that we work with are some of the most talented in the UK and have received many accolades and awards for their products. Please visit our website to find out more.

P

PROVIDENCE FARM ORGANIC MEATS – *SEE LOCAL SECTION, p87*

PUKKA HERBS LTD
The Old Sawmill, The Home Farm, Barrow Court Lane,
Barrow Gurney, Bristol, BS48 3RW
Tel: 01275 461950 Fax: 01275 464165 bolyn@pukkaherbs.com www.pukkaherbs.com
Providers of delicious award-winning organic herbal teas and ayurvedic remedies that have proven traditional usage over thousands of years. Pukka Herbs is committed to fair trade, organic farming and personal wellbeing.

PUMPHREYS COFFEE LTD – *SEE BUSINESS-TO-BUSINESS SECTION, p317*

PURE NUFF STUFF
The Egyptian House, 6 Chapel St., Penzance, Cornwall, TR18 6AJ
Tel: 01736 366008 Fax: 01736 366008 helen@purenuffstuff.co.uk www.purenuffstuff.co.uk
100% natural skincare, toiletries and cosmetics with pure essential oils and organic ingredients. Free of SLS, paraben, synthetic fragrance, synthetic colours.

PURE ORGANICS
4 Larkspur Close, Tanfield Lea, Stanley, Co. Durham, DH9 9UH
Tel: 01207 284754 Fax: 01207 284754 sales@pure-organics.co.uk www.pure-organics.co.uk
Organic clothing for babies and children, organic toys and organic skincare for babies, children, men and women.

PURE SKIN CARE
12 Trevanion Road, Liskeard, Cornwall, PL14 3QN
care@pureskincare.co.uk www.pureskincare.co.uk
Online retailer of pure, natural and organic skin, hair and body care products.

P–R

PURE WINE

Ocean House, 51 Alcantara Crescent,
Ocean Village, Southampton, Hampshire, SO14 3HR
Tel: 023 8023 8214 Fax: 023 8023 8186 service@purewine.co.uk www.purewine.co.uk
Organic wine merchant supplying organic wines from around the world by mail order, via printed catalogue or web. To contact, either Freephone 0808 100 3123 or visit the website. The Pure Wine company also runs wine clubs for third party organisations with organic or environmentally minded cutomers and supporters.

PUR NATURAL SKINCARE

Unit 4 Hubert John Yard, Pant Industrial Estate,
Dowlais, Glamorgan, CF48 2SR
Tel: 029 2055 2691 linda@purskincare.co.uk www.purskincare.co.uk
Gentle spa and skincare products brimming with natural and organic extracts, minerals, and herbal compounds.

QUENBY HALL ORGANIC FOODS – *SEE LOCAL SECTION, p114*

RAVENSBOURNE WINE

Unit 602, Bell House, 49 Greenwich High Rd., London, SE10 8JL
Tel: 020 8692 9655 Fax: 020 8692 9655 sales@ravensbournewine.co.uk
Wine merchant. Retail/wholesale, delivery and mail order of select range of organic wines and beers. Free delivery of mixed cases of wine and beers and Decantae bottled mineral water to London addresses.

REAL FARM FOODS

Blandys Farmhouse, Letcombe Regis, Wantage, Oxfordshire, OX12 9LJ
Tel: 08080 067426 Fax: 01235 772526 info@realfarmfoods.com www.realfarmfoods.com
Real Farm Foods delivers fresh organic meat, poultry, eggs, fruit, vegetables and groceries from Soil Association certified farms as well as fresh fish direct to your door, with no delivery charge, throughout the UK. Call Freephone 08080 067426 for a catalogue.

RED POLL MEATS

Cherry Tree House, Hacheston, Woodbridge, Suffolk, IP13 0DR
Tel: 01728 748444 Fax: 07050 600079 info@redpollmeats.co.uk www.redpollmeats.co.uk
Red Poll Meats supply organic Norfolk Black & Bronze turkeys, organic lamb, organic beef, organic pork, free-range venison and organic fruit & vegetables nationwide. We try where possible to use unusual or rare breeds.

RE LTD

207 Christchurch Road, Ringwood, Hampshire, BH24 3AN
Tel: 08700 419 432 feelgood@be-re.com www.be-re.com
Retailer of a wide and stylish range of eco-ethically sourced home furnishings, bed and bath-linens, clothing, babywear and accessories. Re pursues fair trade and fair play principles when choosing its products.

REVITAL HEALTH AND BEAUTY – *SEE LOCAL SECTION, p124*

RIVERSIDE ORGANICS – *SEE LOCAL SECTION, p168*

ROBERT WILSON'S CEYLON TEAS

Stonehaven, Nuttree, North Perrott,
Crewkerne, Somerset, TA18 7SX
Tel: 01460 77508 Fax: 01460 77508 info@wilstea.com www.wilstea.com
Organic Farmers & Growers UKP 030485. Packers and shippers. Our business in Sri Lanka works with single estates to have special dry season manufacture made to our specific requirements. We import for UK distribution or export internationally from Colombo. Retail shop on the web.

RODANDBENS – *SEE LOCAL SECTION, p89*

ROUNDHURST FARM LTD

Tennysons Lane, Haslemere,
Surrey, GU27 3BN
Tel: 01428 656445 Fax: 01428 656380 roundhurstfarm@virgin.net www.roundhurstfarm.com
Producing organic beef from pedigree pure bred Sussex herd. Beef is well hung and sold at farmers' markets, at the farm, and by mail order.

SAFER ALTERNATIVE – ORGANIC & NATURAL PRODUCTS

16 Smithwell Lane, Hebden Bridge, West Yorkshire, HX7 7NX
Tel: 08708 921899 (national rate) saferalternative@yahoo.co.uk www.saferalternative.com
Local and global (via internet shop) suppliers of the extensive range of certified organic body, hair, skin care & cosmetics, plus a growing selection of nutritional probiotics and household products. Imported directly from ONEgroup, the manufacturers, these products are certified by Australian Certified Organic. Telephone number is national rate.

SANDS, D & PJ

Blossom Farm, New Inn, Pencader, Carmarthenshire, SA39 9AY
Tel: 01559 384621
Soil Association G6750. Welsh Black beef and Suffolk lambs delivered nationwide. Mutton available seasonally.

SAVE THE BACON – *SEE LOCAL SECTION, p119*

SCOTMED HERBS – *SEE LOCAL SECTION, p184*

SEAGREENS®

Warren Virgate, Plummers
Plain, West Sussex, RH13 6PD
Tel: 084506 400403 Fax: 01444 400493 post@seagreens.com www.seagreens.com
Products: natural consumer products and remedies from seaweeds, sustainably wild harvested and produced to Demeter (Biodynamic Agricultural Association) and Soil Association standards, for use in organic foods. Outstanding complete nutritional profile and balance. Customers: retailers & wholesalers, healthcare practitioners, catering, manufacturers (ingredients), biodynamic and organic farms. For local high street stockists or mail order phone Seagreens Information Service on 084506 400403.

SEASALT ORGANIC COTTONS

Unit 18, Kernick Business Park,
Annear Road, Penryn, Cornwall, TR10 9EW
Tel: 01326 379451 Fax: 01326 378580 neil@seasaltcornwall.co.uk www.seasaltcornwall.co.uk
Bright, fashionable, and fun organic cotton clothing. We are the first fashion company in the UK to have organic clothes certified to Soil Association standard. Visit our website to see and buy our latest collections.

SEASONED PIONEERS LTD

Unit 8, Stadium Court, Stadium Rd.,
Plantation Business Park, Wirral, Merseyside, CH62 3RP
Tel: 0800 068 2348 info@seasonedpioneers.co.uk www.seasonedpioneers.co.uk
We supply authentic spice blends, herbs, chillies and peppercorns. Mail order, retail, food service and manufacturing. Highly commended by many top UK food writers.

SEDLESCOMBE ORGANIC VINEYARD – *SEE LOCAL SECTION, p48*

SENSITIVE SKINCARE CO

7 Whitecross St., Monmouth, Gwent, NP25 3BY
Tel: 01600 719774 Fax: 01600 715967
amanda@sensitiveskincareco.com www.sensitiveskincareco.com
I run a small skincare company, directly catering for sensitive skins. I use only natural sourced, sustainable and organic aromatherapy quality ingredients.

SGORGANICS

The Old Barn, Walnut Court, Faringdon, Oxfordshire, SN7 7JH
Tel: 01367 241966 Fax: 01367 244726 sue@sgorganics.com www.sgorganics.com
100% natural and organic, certified to food grade standards by Australian Certified Organics and USDA. Absolutely pure and unique skin care and personal care products using certified organic cold-pressed and unrefined oils and therapeutic grade herb and flower extracts.

SHARPHAM PARTNERSHIP LTD – *SEE LOCAL SECTION, p89*

SHEEPDROVE ORGANIC FARM

Warren Farm, Sheepdrove, Lambourn,
Hungerford, Berkshire, RG17 7UU
Tel: 01488 674721 Fax: 01488 73335 manager@sheepdrove.com www.sheepdrove.com
Driven by a passionate concern for animal welfare, wildlife preservation and a sustainable rural economy, we produce our own organic beef, lamb, mutton, chicken and pork. We hang and cut all our meat on the farm and offer a bespoke service with nationwide delivery. Organic and environmentally sound, The Kindersley Centre combines exceptional surroundings with state of the art technology for meeting, conferences and events for between 8 and 200 delegates. Member of the Soil Association Organic Farms Network. Organic Food Awards 2004, 2006.

SHIPTON MILL LTD – *SEE BUSINESS-TO-BUSINESS SECTION, p307*

SILKWING

45 Gloucester Square, London, London, W2 2TQ
info@silkwing.co.uk www.silkwing.co.uk
A line of luxury designer clothing for women using exclusively all-natural materials that have not been chemically dyed or finished, such as hand-woven plant-dyed wild and cultivated silks, organic naturally pigmented cotton and baby alpaca, as well as naturally coloured cashmere. Also a small baby range available featuring hand-knitted organic cotton and pure undyed cashmere. Certification by Skal in the Netherlands.

SKINCARE CAFÉ LTD

Riverbank House, Putney Bridge, London, SW6 4JD
Tel: 0870 443 2744 customercomments@skincarecafe.com www.skincarecafe.com
Quality organic skincare range, certified by Ecocert, Vegan and Vegetarian Society approved. 100% plant origin. Suitable for sensitive skin. Cleanser, moisturiser, facemask, body lotion, anti-ageing treatment, bodywash, all-in-one shampoo and conditioner.

S

SKYDANCER ORGANICS

283 Nantwich Road, Crewe, Cheshire, CW2 6PF
Tel: 01270 652727 info@skydancerorganics.co.uk www.skydancerorganics.co.uk
The world's first extensive range of certified organic skin, body, hair, oral & health care products – certified by Australian Certified Organic (ACO) and the United States Department of Agriculture (USDA) to the highest international food standards. We offer an innovative product range of unrivalled purity and effectiveness combined with an ethical, unique and versatile business model that rewards all those associated with us through a financially stable, soundly managed company.

THE SLING STORE LTD

Tel: 023 9234 7581 jo@theslingstore.co.uk www.theslingstore.co.uk
Baby slings and fair trade and organic baby clothes and cloth nappies, organic and fair trade toys.

SMILECHILD

Units 3 & 10, Callington Business Park, Tinners Way, Moss Side
Industrial Estate, Callington, Cornwall, PL17 7SH
Tel: 0800 1956 982 Fax: 01579 383050 customerservices@smilechild.co.uk www.smilechild.co.uk
Online shopping for the planet-conscious parent. Smilechild offers a full range of fair-trade and organic clothes, wooden toys, natural toiletries, eco-nappies and more. Founded in 2000, this family-run business has dedicated itself to bringing the best for mother, baby and the environment to your door. Backed by the Prince's Youth Business Trust and finalists in the Gloucestershire Environmental Business Awards, Smilechild are setting a new standard for positive, ethical small business.

SOMERSET ORGANICS – *SEE LOCAL SECTION, p99*

SO ORGANIC

John Humphries House, 4-10 Stockwell St.,
Greenwich, London, London, SE10 9JN
Tel: 0800 169 2579 Fax: 020 8465 5599 enquiries@soorganic.com www.soorganic.com
Online one-stop shop offering organic cosmetics, skin care, body care, toiletries, toothpaste, deodorant. Organic cotton baby, toddler and children's clothing, towels, toys, feminine hygiene sanitary products, washable nappies and environmentally friendly disposables children's skincare. Silk duvets and remedies for sensitive skin, eczema and allergy sufferers. Eco-friendly household cleaning products and a wide vegan range. Many certified organic brands including Spiezia, Essential Care, Green People, Organic Blue and Natracare . . . because organic living is more than just a food choice!

S–T

SPIEZIA ORGANICS LTD

Dove House, Tregoniggie, Falmouth,
Cornwall, TR11 4SN
Tel: 0870 850 8851 Fax: 01326 377712 info@spieziaorganics.com www.spieziaorganics.com
100% organic skin care, body care and healing ointments, hand-made in Cornwall by Dr Mariano
Spiezia. Infusions of herbs and flowers in oils to make highly concentrated, water-free ointments. For
all skin types, especially sensitive and delicate. Also soaps and home fragrances.

SPIRIT OF NATURE

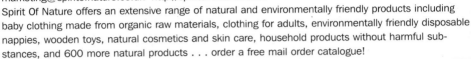

Unit 7, Hannah Way, Gordleton Industrial Park,
Lymington, Hampshire, SO41 8JD
Tel: 0870 725 9885 Fax: 0870 725 9886
marketing@spiritofnature.co.uk http://spiritofnature.co.uk
Spirit Of Nature offers an extensive range of natural and environmentally friendly products including
baby clothing made from organic raw materials, clothing for adults, environmentally friendly disposable
nappies, wooden toys, natural cosmetics and skin care, household products without harmful sub-
stances, and 600 more natural products . . . order a free mail order catalogue!

SPRINGSLADE ORGANICS

Teddesley Home Farm, Penkridge, Stafford,
Staffordshire, ST19 5RJ
Tel: 01785 712595 Fax: 01785 714558
ejbuxton123@btinternet.com www.springsladeorganics.co.uk
Arable and livestock farmer. Soil Association G6375. Top quality milling wheat, premium organic lamb
and organic potatoes, available locally with free delivery or online. For more details, visit our website.

STONELINK FARM

Stonelink Farm, Stubb Lane, Brede, Rye, East Sussex, TN31 6BL
Tel: 01424 882747 Fax: 01424 882584 sian@stonelinkfarm.co.uk www.stonelinkfarm.co.uk
Organic sloe gin.

STONE MILLS ORGANIC OILS

A1 Seed Bed Centre, Davidson Way, Romford, Essex, RM7 0AZ
Tel: 01708 724378 stonemills@globalnet.co.uk www.stonemills.co.uk
Stone Mills Organic Oils produces the highest quality flax oil and evening primrose oil.

SUFFOLK HERBS

Monks Farm, Coggeshill Rd., Kelvedon, Essex, CO5 9PG
Tel: 01376 572456 Fax: 01376 571189 sales@suffolkherbs.com www.suffolkherbs.com
Leading supplier of organic produced seed for the home gardener and professional user.

THE SUSSEX WINE COMPANY

47 South Street, Eastbourne, East Sussex, BN21 4UT
Tel: 01323 431143 info@thesussexwinecompany.co.uk www.thesussexwinecompany.co.uk
Specialist Sussex wine merchant supplying quality wine and spirits from around the world online.
Organic wine and spirits, English fruit and sparkling wine, champagne, whisky, gift items, hand-made
Sussex chocolates, glassware and discounted mixed cases. No minimum order and UK delivery.

SWADDLES ORGANIC – *SEE LOCAL SECTION, p119*

SWADDLES ORGANIC – *SEE LOCAL SECTION, p119*

TAMAR ORGANICS – *SEE LOCAL SECTION, p90*

TATTY BUMPKIN LTD.

Allens Farm, Allens Lane, Plaxtol, Sevenoaks, Kent, TN15 0QZ
Tel: 01732 812212 Fax: 01732 812219 info@tattybumpkin.com www.tattybumpkin.com
Skal certified fun, practical clothes and accessories for kids – inspired by yoga and an organic lifestyle.
Range includes: long and short sleeve T-shirts, trousers, skirts, sweatshirts, bamboo clothing, sun-
shirts, pyjama sets, bed linen sets, quilted cotton yoga mat; toys and a unique bendy yoga doll.

TERRAMAR ORGANICS

50 Gordon Rd., Mannofield, Aberdeen, Aberdeenshire, AB15 7RL
Tel: 07999 613982 peter@terramar.co.uk www.terramar.co.uk
Ethical fairly traded organic clothing. Online shop with limited edition printed T-shirts and classic
basics. We specialise in customising clothing for business with printing and embroidery. Stylish clothing
that doesn't cost the earth.

THERE MUST BE A BETTER WAY

9 Thetford Mews, Caversham Park Village, Reading, Berkshire, RG4 6SN
sales@theremustbeabetterway.co.uk www.theremustbeabetterway.co.uk
We sell natural, organic skincare & cosmetics, free from all harsh synthetic chemicals for a healthy,
balanced lifestyle.

THINK ORGANIC

3 Edith Road, London, London, N11 2QW
Tel: 020 8365 8472 veronicasamuels@msn.com www.thinkorganics.co.uk
Miessence beauty products, the world's first certified organic skin, body, hair and oral health care,
developed in Australia, now available in the UK. 100% synthetic-chemical-free products.

THOMPSON & MORGAN ORGANIC SEEDS

Poplar Lane, Ipswich, Suffolk, IP8 3BU

sworth@thompson-morgan.com www.seeds.thompson-morgan.com/uk/en/list/organics

A range of organic vegetable seeds, including beetroot, carrots, cauliflowers, courgettes, leeks, lettuce, onions, spinach, tomato and more. Also a a range of organic seed potatoes can be found in our potato catalogue at http://potatoes.thompson-morgan.com/uk/en/list/organics.

TLC IN A BOTTLE

Lormor, Tregoyne, East Cliff, Porthtowan, Cornwall, TR4 8AW

Tel: 01209 890910 Fax: 01209 203001 nicolle@tlcinabottle.co.uk www.tlcinabottle.co.uk

Natural health and beauty products made with love, in small batches, in Cornwall. Ingredients mostly organic, otherwise sourced locally or sustainably. Green People and Urtekram products also available.

TREVARNO ORGANIC SKINCARE

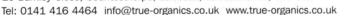

Trevarno Manor, Helston,

Cornwall, TR13 0AB

Tel: 01326 555977 Fax: 01326 574282 enquiry@trevarno.co.uk www.trevarno.co.uk

We produce a wide range of natural skin care products including facial cleansing, toning and moisturising. Hand care, body care and a dedicated baby care range. A full range of natural organic soaps is also available.

TRUE ORGANICS

10 Barnley Close, Countesthorpe, Leicester, Leicestershire, LE8 5SD

Tel: 0141 416 4464 info@true-organics.co.uk www.true-organics.co.uk

True Organics specialises in certified organic skin and body care products from Mother Earth, Essential Care, Balm Balm, Trevarno, Green People and Natura. On our website we also have a discussion forum and 'News and Views', where visitors can submit their own articles.

EDWIN TUCKER & SONS LTD – *SEE LOCAL SECTION, p90*

TURTLE BAGS

1, Hardcastle Villas, Worcester Rd.,

Stourport on Severn, Worcestershire, DY13 9PA

Tel: 01299 827092 turtle_bags@yahoo.co.uk www.turtlebags.co.uk

Turtle Bags sells alternative to plastic bags. The organic cotton string bags have been audited by Skal International. Turtle Bags is so-named to highlight the problem of plastic bags finding their way into leatherback turtles. Leatherback turtles travel up the Gulf Stream in search of jellyfish from the Caribbean. They come in the summer months, and have been coming in increasing numbers and further north with rising sea temperatures. Many thousands of plastic bags find their way from landfill sites, streams and rivers into the oceans. They represent a hazard to the turtles who, not being intelligent animals, mistake the upturned bags for jellyfish.

UK JUICERS LTD

Unit 3 Waterline Estate, Acaster Malbis, York, North Yorkshire, YO23 2UY

Tel: 01904 704705 Fax: 01904 771007 enquiries@ukjuicers.com www.ukjuicers.com

UK Juicers are stockists of high quality juice extractors, blenders, water purifiers, food dehydrators and other healthy products perfect for making good use of organic produce.

UKORGANIC

73 Gaskell Rd., Highgate, London, N6 4DU
Tel: 07793 837081 kymkayla@bigpond.com.au www.ukorganic.biz
World's first fully certified organic skincare, hair, body health and cosmetics, new to the UK and EU, Miessence is now available via online buying. Receive up to 50% off if you own a retail/online store; earn a second income and become a distributor/agent and start your own organic enterprise, and be the first to take it into retail in the UK & EU. For your free information pack and samples call today or visit www.ukorganic.biz. Nicole Duffy 020 8348 5366.

ULULA – ORGANIC BABY FOOD

Jordan House, Whitwell, Reepham, Norfolk, NR10 4RQ
Tel: 01362 688060 mail@ulula.co.uk www.ulula.co.uk
Certified organic and biodynamic baby food. Includes diet plan and allergy-aware baby food. Our unique range of baby foods includes brands from Holle, Sunval and ErdmannHAUSER, all producers truly devoted to healthy, natural and pure products and with long traditions of producing biodynamic baby food for up to 70 years.

UNWINS SEEDS LTD

Histon, Cambridge, Cambridgeshire, CB4 9LE
Tel: 01223 236236 colin.hambidge@unwins-seeds.co.uk www.unwins-mailorder.co.uk
Soil Association P4413. Seedsman. Supplier of vegetable and flower seeds to gardeners.

THE VILLAGE BAKERY – *SEE LOCAL SECTION, p171*

U–V

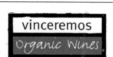

vinceremos
Organic Wines

Twenty years experience providing over 300 organic drinks at competitive prices, direct to your door

0800 107 3086
www.vinceremos.co.uk

VINCEREMOS WINES AND SPIRITS LTD

74 Kirkgate, Leeds, West Yorkshire, LS2 7DJ
Tel: 0800 107 3086 Fax: 0113 288 4566 info@vinceremos.co.uk www.vinceremos.co.uk
Longest established organic wine specialist with the largest range in the UK. You can mix your own case with delivery to your door. We also supply organic beers, ciders, spirits and soft drinks. Organic Food Awards 2004, 2006.

FOR DETAILS OF SYMBOLS USED IN THE ENTRIES, SEE PAGE 17

V-W

VINTAGE ROOTS LTD

Farley Farms, Bridge Farm, Reading Road,
Arborfield, Berkshire, RG2 9HT
Tel: 0118 976 1999 Fax: 0118 976 1998 info@vintageroots.co.uk www.vintageroots.co.uk
Specialist shippers of the finest organic wines, beers, ciders, spirits and other products from around
the world. Call for free brochure (Freephone 0800 980 4992) or visit our website. The organic wine
specialists: trade@vintageroots.co.uk. Organic Food Awards 2004, 2006.

WALCOT ORGANIC NURSERY

Lower Walcot Farm, Walcot Lane,
Drakes Broughton, Pershore, Worcestershire, WR10 2AL
Tel: 01905 841587 Fax: 01905 841587 enquiries@walcotnursery.co.uk
Soil Association G5594. Producers of organically grown fruit trees. Available bare-root November to
March, and in containers. Mail order anywhere in mainland UK. Visitors welcome by appointment.
Catalogue available.

THE WATERMILL, PENRITH – *SEE LOCAL SECTION, p171*

THE WEARDALE ORGANIC SOUP COMPANY LTD

Elm Cottage, Westgate-in-Weardale, Co. Durham, DL13 1LP
Tel: 01388 517384 Fax: 01388 517384 weardalesoup@aol.com
Artisan organic soups, all vegetarian, vegan and gluten-free. Licensed with Coeliac UK. We also produce home-made organic gluten-free quiches. Available from farmers' markets, retail outlets in northern England and by mail order in 500ml cartons and also 5-litre pails for the trade.

WELEDA (UK) LTD – *SEE BUSINESS-TO-BUSINESS SECTION, p300*

WELL HUNG MEAT CO – *SEE LOCAL SECTION, p90*

WELSH FRUIT STOCKS

Llanerchir, Bryngwyn, via Kington, Herefordshire, HR5 3QZ
Tel: 01497 851209 Fax: 01497 851209 sian@welshfruitstocks.co.uk www.welshfruitstocks.co.uk
Propagators of top quality soft fruit plants, including organic strawberry plants, raspberry canes,
black/red/white currant bushes, gooseberry bushes, jostaberry bushes. Mail order gardeners' list and
growers' list available.

WELSH HOOK MEAT CENTRE LTD – *SEE LOCAL SECTION, p207*

THE WESTCOUNTRY CURRY CO LTD

Units 8/9, Knighton Business Centre, Wembury, Devon, PL9 0ED
Tel: 01752 863123 Fax: 01752 863123
enquiries@westcountrycurry.com www.westcountrycurry.com
Hand-made curry pastes, marinades and dipping sauces. All created using authentic recipes, following
traditional methods, with no additives or flavourings. All made with care in our south Devon kitchen.

WESTCOUNTRY ORGANICS

Oak Farm, Tedburn St. Mary,
Exeter, EX6 6AW
Tel: 01647 270056 Fax: 01647 61491
enquiries@westcountryorganics.co.uk www.westcountryorganics.co.uk
National mail order of organic foods including a range of vegetables and fruit, dairy products, drinks
and vegetarian products.

WEST RIDING ORGANICS

Unit 3 Near Bank, Shelley, Huddersfield, West Yorkshire, HD8 8LS
Tel: 01484 609171 Fax: 01484 609166 julian@wrorganics.co.uk www.wrorganics.co.uk
Manufacturers of Nature's Own and Bio-Pak organic composts (Soil Association registered). Module, blocking, potting and grow bags all supplied. Volcanic rock dust. Trade enquiries welcome.

WHITEHOLME FARM – *SEE LOCAL SECTION, p171*

WIGGLY WIGGLERS

Lower Blakemere Farm, Blakemere, Herefordshire, HR2 9PX
Tel: 01981 500391 Fax: 01981 500108 david@wigglywigglers.co.uk www.wigglywigglers.co.uk
Wiggly Wigglers supply natural gardening products including worm and conventional composters, garden bird food and feeders including live feed, insect and mammal habitats and wild flowers.

WILLEY WINKLE PURE WOOL BEDDING MANUFACTURERS

Offa House, Offa St., Hereford, Herefordshire, HR1 2LH
Tel: 01432 268018 Fax: 01432 268018
Traditional mattress makers using organic wool filling and organic outer cover ticking. Also suppliers of organic bedding sheets, duvets, pillows, towelling etc.

WILD & WONDERFUL

Tel: 01273 734344 info@wildwonderful.co.uk www.wildwonderful.co.uk
Luxurious organic cotton certified by Skal, hemp and silk bedlinen and a unique range of hand-made cushions using eco-friendly fabrics.

WILD OATS WHOLEFOODS – *SEE LOCAL SECTION, p70*

WINES NATURALLY UK

221 Alfreton Rd., Little Eaton, Derbyshire, DE21 5AA
Tel: 01332 830200 Fax: 0845 456 5315 enquiries@winesnaturally.com www.winesnaturally.com
Online organic and biodynamic wine retailer. Excellent choice of wines, spirits and soft drinks from all around the world. Free UK mainland delivery. Excellent service. Go Organic!

WINTERSHALL PARTNERSHIP

Bramley, Surrey, GU5 0LR
Tel: 01483 892167 Fax: 01483 898709 susan@huntleygroup.com www.wintershall-estate.com
We are producers of Aberdeen Angus beef and lamb, available retail through our box scheme delivered to the door. We also sell wholesale and produce several arable crops.

WONDERMESH LTD

Redford Farm, Garvock, Laurencekirk, Aberdeenshire, AB30 1HS

Tel: 01561 377946 Fax: 01561 378389 info@wondermesh.co.uk www.wondermesh.co.uk

Wondermesh is recognised in the UK as the leading supplier of quality insect netting for the agricultural and horticultural industries.

WOODEN WONDERS

Farley Farm House, Chiddingly, East Sussex, BN8 6HW

Tel: 01825 872856 Fax: 01825 872733 info@woodenwonders.co.uk www.woodenwonders.co.uk

Wooden Wonders was the first wooden craft gift manufacturer in the UK with Forest Stewardship Council accreditation making practical and ornamental gifts – all suitable for customisation with our in-house laser engravers.

WORLD OF NZ

info@worldofnz.co.uk www.worldofnz.co.uk

Your online specialist store & information on our quality products: Comvita Active Manuka honey and Living Nature skin and body care, made from organic and wildcrafted ingredients from the native healing plants of New Zealand.

WWW.CRYSTALSPRING.CO.UK

Fir Tree Farmhouse, Fir Tree Lane, Horton Heath, Eastleigh, Hampshire, SO50 7DF

Tel: 023 8069 5550 Fax: 023 8069 5444 sales@crystalspring.co.uk www.crystalspring.co.uk

Crystal Spring is a retailer of natural and organic products on the internet and by mail order.

WWW.ECOBTQ.COM

Flat 5, 87/89 St Aubyns, Hove, East Sussex, BN3 2TL

Tel: 07966 369499 contact@ecobtq.com www.ecobtq.com

I stock Ciel fashion who are Soil Association verified.

WWW.INFOODWETRUST.COM

335 City Road, London, London, EC1V 1LR

Tel: 020 7729 6992 john@infoodwetrust.com www.infoodwetrust.com

The world's first climate-neutral luxury organic online food shop.

WWW.NATURALLYTEJAS.COM

74 Beattyville Gardens, Ilford, Essex, IG6 1JY

Tel: 020 8551 6948 Fax: 020 8518 1326 josephine@naturallyTejas.com www.naturallyTejas.com

www.naturallyTejas.com is an online store for natural and organic personal care products. Many of our suppliers are Soil Association certified organic. Please visit our website for further information about all our suppliers.

WWW.STIRRUPHOES.CO.UK

Unit 4 Emsworh House Close, Emsworth, Hampshire, PO10 7JR

stirruphoe@tiscali.co.uk www.stirruphoes.co.uk

Specialist supplier of stirrup hoes for professional growers.

Business-to-Business Directory

LONDON & THE SOUTH EAST

ESSEX

ADM MILLING
Kingsgate, 1 King Edward Rd., Brentwood, Essex, CM14 4HG
Tel: 01277 262525   Fax: 01277 200320   sales_milling@admworld.com   www.admmilling.co.uk
Manufacturer of high quality flours, improvers, premixes and concentrates, including organic flours.

DOUBLE DRAGON CO
4 Tring Close, Barkingside, Ilford, Essex, IG2 7LQ
Tel: 020 8554 3838   Fax: 020 8554 3883   info@doubledragon.co.uk   www.doubledragon.co.uk
Soil Association P6143. Importer of organic Green Tea, China Green Tea, Pure Ginseng Tea, Pure Ginkgo Biloba Tea, Jasmine Tea, Green Tea with Ginkgo Biloba Tea. We are a wholesaler of Ginseng, Royal Jelly, essential balm etc. Beautiful packaging, reasonable prices.

FARMER KIT ORGANICS
Little Bowsers Farm, Bowsers Lane, Little Walden,
Saffron Walden, Essex, CB10 1XQ
Tel: 01799 527315   Fax: 01799 527315   sales@farmerkit.co.uk   www.farmerkit.co.uk
Soil Association G2143. Little Bowsers Farm produces organic free range eggs and organic top fruit, apples, pears, plums. Also organic soft fruits. We deliver regularly to London wholesalers.

FUERST DAY LAWSON LTD
Unit 4, Fourth Avenue, Bluebridge Ind. Estate, Halstead, Essex, CO9 2SY
Tel: 01787 473826   Fax: 01787 475029   mclarke.halstead@fdl.co.uk   www.fdl.co.uk
We are a processor of dried cereals, fruit and seeds.

HALSTEAD FOOD SERVICES LTD
Unit 1, 1st Avenue, Bluebridge, Halstead, Essex, CO9 2EX
Tel: 01787 473222   Fax: 01787 479026   halsteadfoods@hotmail.com
Soil Association registered. We clean, dice and pack organic nuts, dried fruits, seeds and cereals.

HART WORLDWIDE LTD
Mill House, Riverway, Harlow, Essex, CM20 2DW
Tel: 01279 639669   Fax: 01279 635257   ahowe@hartww.com
Soil Association P6778. Importer of organic top fruit.

MANNINGTREE ORGANIC GROWERS
83 Hungerdown Lane, Lawford, Manningtree, Essex, CO11 2LY
Tel: 01206 231399   marina_oconnell@onetel.com
We are a group of 4 growers producing top fruit and soft fruit, salads and eggs, lavender oils and associated cosmetic products in the Stour valley. Wholesale and Stoke Newington farmers' market.

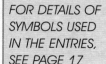
*FOR DETAILS OF
SYMBOLS USED
IN THE ENTRIES,
SEE PAGE 17*
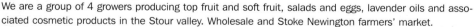

ESSEX

PRODEK LIMITED

26 White Hart Lane, Hawkwell, Hockley, Essex, SS5 4DQ

Tel: 01702 202123 Fax: 01702 202932 linbjo1@aol.com

Supply eco-friendly slurry tank, water containment, capping for slurry waste, liners for fish farms, bund lining using EPDM heat-welded lining.

SAWDON, J M

Peldon Hall, Peldon, Nr. Colchester, Essex, CO5 7PU

Tel: 07973 750367 Fax: 01206 735791 john@peldonhall.com www.peldonhall.com

Store, bag, dress, clean, dry and blend wheat, barley, triticale, oats, beans, peas, maize, lucerne and bran.

SIMPLY DELICIOUS

Baxters Colchester, Halifax Way, Earls Colne Business Park,

Earls Colne, Essex, CO6 2NS

Tel: 01787 222250 Fax: 01787 222484

ccl-customer.service@baxters.co.uk www.simplydelicious.co.uk

Manufacturers of the Simply Delicious range of premium quality organic mayonnaise, condiments and salad dressings.

TRUST ORGANICS LTD

Jubilee House, The Drive, Great Warley, Brentwood, Essex, CM13 3AR

Tel: 01277 725282 Fax: 01277 725001 sales@trustorganics.co.uk www.trustorganics.co.uk

Manufacturer, processor and packer of organic fruit juices, organic fruit smoothies and organic milk drinks. Manufacturing facility: Bevendean Farm, Woodingdean, Brighton, East Sussex, BN2 6AF. Tel: 01273 819300, Fax: 01273 818136. ian.matthews@trustorganics.co.uk.

USHER, JENNY

Green Oaks, Threshers Bush, Nr. Harlow, Essex, CM17 0NS

Tel: 01279 444663

Soil Association U02E. Organic fruit, veg, herbs and plants. Direct marketing consultant, especially practical advice.

KENT

AUSTRALIS DISTRIBUTION LTD

21 Almond Close, Ashford, Kent, TN25 4PA

Tel: 0845 456 0639 Fax: 020 7504 8099

lara@australisdistribution.com www.australisdistribution.com

We import Australian personal care products that are naturally based, organic, free from harmful additives and free from harmful by-products in manufacture.

BARKER LTD, J J

Hook Place Farm, Southfleet, Gravesend, Kent, DA13 9NH

Tel: 01474 833555 Fax: 01474 834364 sales@jjbarker.co.uk

UK-based grower and importer, packer and distributor of organic produce – mainly salads and legumes primarily for the UK multiples. Soil Association no. P2380.

ESSEX / KENT

CANON GARTH LTD

Alexander House, 31-39 London Rd., Sevenoaks, Kent, TN13 1AR
Tel: 01732 228500 Fax: 01732 743444 david.kelman@ctcs-ltd.co.uk
Bulk trader and importer/exporter of groundnuts, treenuts and dried fruit. Peanuts, almonds, cashews, hazlenuts, sultanas and walnuts.

DAVIES & DAVIES, JEFFREY LTD

Arctic House, Rye Lane, Dunton Green, Sevenoaks, Kent, TN24 5HL
Tel: 01732 450948 Fax: 01732 452012 info@ www.davies-davies.co.uk
Jeffrey Davies & Davies Ltd are a pork processing and export company, trading in a wide variety of meats, throughout Great Britain, Europe and the Far East.

ECO4

25 Ivory Close, Faversham, Kent, ME137RS
Tel: 01795 538929 nick@eco4.co.uk www.eco4.co.uk
Eco4 wholesale provides single-origin certified organic coffees to caterers, at work and at home. Eco4 events caters for events with organic coffees.

GALA COFFEE & TEA LIMITED

Mill House, Riverside Way, Dartford, Kent, DA1 5BS
Tel: 01322 272411 Fax: 01322 278600 gala@gala-coffee-tea.co.uk www.gala-coffee-tea.co.uk
Gala is a unique company focused on the special requirements of both retailers and food service companies, producing coffee and tea under private label.

GOOD FOOD WINES LTD

No. 3 Warehouse, Whitewall Rd., Strood, Kent, ME2 4EW
Tel: 01634 290592 Fax: 01634 716617 info@goodfoodwines.com www.goodfoodwines.com
Suppliers of ingredients to the food industry for wines, beers, spirits and vinegars: organic and non-organic.

GREENCELL LTD

St. Johns House, 37-41 Spital St., Dartford, Kent, DA1 2DR
Tel: 01322 425555 Fax: 01322 425500 info@greencell.com www.greencell.com
Fresh imported organic fruit sourced to give 12 month continuity. We store, condition, pack and distribute to retailers, wholesalers, food service providers and processors through the UK.

HERBAL HEALTH LTD

PO Box 114, Sissinghurst, Cranbrook, Kent, TN17 2XQ
Tel: 01580 713613 Fax: 01580 712714 joe.d@qi-teas.com www.qi-teas.com
Supplier of top quality organic China tea under the Qi (chee) label, including traditional loose leaf teas and green tea blends with abundant organic fruit and herbs.

HORTON PARK FARM

The Pent, Postling, Hythe, Kent, CT21 4EY
Tel: 01303 862436 Fax: 01303 863723 cr.reynolds@farmline.com
Soil Association G4082. 900 acre mixed farm, 100 sucklers, 160+ ewes. Angus x South Devon beef freezer packs available by prior booking, also whole or half lambs during the summer months. Arable crops grown for seed.

KENT

INTERNATIONAL PRODUCE LTD

Sheerness Produce Terminal,
Spade Lane, Sittingbourne, Kent, ME9 7TT
Tel: 01634 269200 Fax: 01634 269269
info@internationalproduce.com www.internationalproduce.com
International importers of organic and non-organic produce.

LUDDESDOWN ORGANIC FARMS LTD

Court Lodge, Luddesdown, Nr. Cobham,
Kent, DA13 0XE
Tel: 01474 813376 Fax: 01474 815044
organic@luddesdown.u-net.com www.luddesdownorganicfarms.co.uk
Soil Association S38S. 950 acres producing cereals, beans, red clover for seed, forage, beef and vegetables. All grown to Soil Association standards. Wholesaler and retailer, including vegetable box scheme delivery scheme and home produced beef. Member of the Soil Association Organic Farms Network.

MACK BANANAS

Mack Multiples Division, Transfesa Road, Paddock Wood, Kent, TN12 6UT
Tel: 01892 831224 Fax: 01892 837670 elliot.mantle@mackmultiples.com www.mwmack.co.uk
Importers & ripeners of bananas: organic and Fairtrade organic.

MICHAELS WHOLEFOODS

Units 1, 5 & 7, Northdown Ind. Park, St. Peters, Broadstairs, Kent, CT10 3JP
Tel: 08451 306307 Fax: 01843 604603
enquiries@michaels-wholefoods.co.uk www.michaels-wholefoods.co.uk
Dried foods hand packed to order. Own label available.

ROWCLIFFE, ANTHONY & SON LTD

Unit B, Paddock Wood Distribution Centre, Paddock Wood, Kent, TN12 6UU
Tel: 01892 838999 Fax: 01892 836585 arowcliffeinfo@aol.com www.rowcliffe.com
Nationwide distributors of dairy products.

THE SO REAL ICE COMPANY

Lodge Rd., Staplehurst, Kent, TN12 0QY
Tel: 01580 892200 Fax: 01580 893414 mira@realiceco.co.uk
Manufacturer of private label organic ice cream for major retailers and food service.

WINTERWOOD FARMS

Chartway St., East Sutton, Maidstone, Kent, ME17 3DN
Tel: 01622 844286 Fax: 01622 844274 organics@winterwood.co.uk www.winterwood.co.uk
Soft fruit grower/packer. Main customers are UK multiples. Also actively growing in Poland, France, Spain and South Africa.

LONDON-EAST

CLEAN BEAN

170 Brick Lane, London, E1 6RU
Tel: 020 7247 1639 Fax: 020 7247 1639 cleanbean@ssba.info
Soil Association P2200. Clean Bean manufactures fresh organic tofu which is supplied to restaurants and wholefood stores in the London area, and directly from our stalls at Borough Market every Saturday and Spitalfields Organic Market every Sunday.

KENT

FUERST DAY LAWSON LTD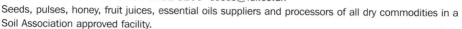

Devon House, 58-60 St. Katherine's Way, London, E1 9LB

Tel: 020 7488 0777 Fax: 020 7702 3200 seeds@fdl.co.uk

Seeds, pulses, honey, fruit juices, essential oils suppliers and processors of all dry commodities in a Soil Association approved facility.

NAPIER BROWN & CO LTD

1 St. Katharine's Way, London, E1W 1XB

Tel: 020 7335 2500 Fax: 020 7335 2502 sales@napierbrown.co.uk www.napierbrown.co.uk

Napier Brown are the largest independent sugar distributor in the UK. We offer a wide range of organic sugars and syrups in both industrial and retail packs from factories approved by the Soil Association. Deliver nationally.

TWIN TRADING LTD

Third Floor, 1 Curtain Road, London, EC2A 3LT

Tel: 020 7375 1221 Fax: 020 7375 1337 info@twin.org.uk

Soil Association licensed. Fairtrade importer of coffee, cocoa, nuts etc.

WAKEFIELD, DR & COMPANY LTD

Mitre House, 12–14 Mitre Street, London, EC3A 5BU

Tel: 020 7621 9345 Fax: 020 7621 9420 coffee@drwakefield.com www.drwakefield.com

Importer of organic raw coffee from many producing countries sourcing directly from the farmer.

LONDON-NORTH

ALARA WHOLEFOODS

108-112 Camley St., London, NW1 0PF

Tel: 020 7387 9303 Fax: 020 7388 6077 alexsmith@alara.co.uk www.alara.co.uk

Alara are specialist manufacturers and packers of cereals, especially muesli, with over 50 different types of organic muesli currently produced in our BRC A-grade factory. Branded and own label available, catering to over twenty-five international markets.

BLISS ORGANICS LTD

102B Belgravia Workshops, 157-163 Marlborough Rd., London, N19 4NF

Tel: 020 7281 7995 Fax: 020 7281 7995

Soil Association P7529. Organic cakes and patisserie made to order. Specialities include cakes without wheat, sugar, dairy etc.

THE CELTIC BAKERS

42B Waterloo Rd., Cricklewood, London, NW2 7UH

Tel: 020 8452 4390 Fax: 020 8452 8235 info@thecelticbakers.co.uk www.thecelticbakers.co.uk

A dedicated organic vegetarian bakery specialising in most aspects of hand-made bread production (including 100% ryes and sourdough methods), cakes, pastries and savouries.

COMMUNITY FOODS LTD

Micross, Brent Terrace, London, NW2 1LT

Tel: 020 8450 9411 enquiries@communityfoods.co.uk www.communityfoods.co.uk

Soil Association no. P1422. We are an importer and distributor of a large range of natural products including several hundred organic lines. Bulk dried fruit, nuts, pulses etc. plus brands like Sanchi, Crazy Jack, Nature's Path, Eunature, Emile Noel, Monki, Shady Maple, Rebar and many more.

DAY PLUS ONE LTD

Unit 11A&B, Crusader Ind. Estate,
167 Hermitage Rd., London, N4 1LZ
Tel: 020 8802 1088 Fax: 020 8802 3862 enquiries@dayplusoneltd.co.uk
Soil Association P1469. Packer of organic wholefoods under the Organic Day's brand and customers own label. Supplier of a large range of organic pre-packs in a wide variety of sizes. Product range includes, amongst others, nuts, dried fruit, rice, pulses, grains, cereals and snacks.

ETHICAL EDIBLES

The Hub, 5 Torrens St., London, EC1V 1NQ
Tel: 08454 565493 Fax: 020 7841 8999 info@ethicaledibles.co.uk www.ethicaledibles.co.uk
Ethical Edibles – importers and wholesalers of Italian organic and artisan food and wine sourced from small producers and family-run enterprises preserving traditional forms of agriculture. We currently stock unique wines, some of the best olive oils from Tuscany and Sicily, low or no sugar jams and unusual pestos.

HONEY ROSE BAKERY

6 Fortune Way, London, NW10 6UF
Tel: 020 8960 5567 Fax: 020 8960 5598 cakes@honeyrosebakery.com www.honeyrosebakery.com
Dedicated organic operation hand-baking award-winning muffins, brownies, cookies, and cakes. Beautifully packaged for retail and to go, or unwrapped for foodservice. We derive great satisfaction in preserving time-honoured baking crafts.

MARIGOLD HEALTH FOODS

102 Camley St., London, NW1 0PF
Tel: 020 7388 4515 Fax: 020 7388 4516
sales@marigoldhealthfoods.com www.marigoldhealthfoods.com
Soil Association P2604, OF&G UK2 P0015. Producer of vegetarian food, drinks, nutritional supplements and animal-free products particularly strong in organic and chilled. Distribute to south-east England; Marigold Bouillon Powder and Yogi Teas stocked by wholesalers throughout UK.

ORGANIC LOGISTICS

Rosebery Industrial Park, Phase One, Units 1-8, Rosebery Avenue, London, N17 9SR
Tel: 020 8886 0812 Fax: 0118 901 2702 info@newburyphillips.co.uk www.newburyphillips.co.uk
We mainly supply wholesale/stockists and organisations involved in food manufacturing with organic products and ingredients. Our product range includes herbs and spices to dried fruits and products such as organic pitta bread, manufactured and packed under own label (Newbury Phillips).

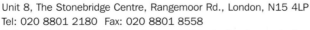

SAN AMVROSIA HEALTH FOODS

Unit 8, The Stonebridge Centre, Rangemoor Rd., London, N15 4LP
Tel: 020 8801 2180 Fax: 020 8801 8558
Soil Association P4139. Manufacturers of fresh dips (vegetarian).

SIMPLY BREAD

Building E, The Chocolate Factory, Western Road, London, N22 6UY
Tel: 020 8889 7159 Fax: 020 8889 2428 info@simply-bread.co.uk
Soil Association P2628. Wholesale bakery specialising in organic rye bread, organic wholemeal, organic white and organic croissants.

SKOULIKAS, GEORGE LTD

Unit 5, 998 North Circular Rd, Coles Green Rd., London, NW2 7JR
Tel: 020 8452 8465 Fax: 020 8452 8273 info@skoulikas.com
Imports and distribution of mediterranean organic foods including olives, olive oil, tahini, halva, sesame bars, orange, lemon and lime juice, pesto and polenta.

SOUTH LONDON BAKERS & NATURAL RISE FOODS

21 Bernard Rd., London, N15 4NE
Tel: 020 8808 2007 Fax: 020 8808 2007 inder333@aol.com
Organic craft bakers since 1981, specialising in hand-moulded organic yeasted and sourdough breads produced without additives, flour improvers and preservatives. Deliveries available throughout the Greater London area.

LONDON-SOUTH

EASTERN VENTURE LTD

Zeal House, 8 Deer Park Rd., London, SW19 3GY
Tel: 020 8543 6227 Fax: 020 8296 9799 info@eastern-venture.com www.eastern-venture.com
The Organic Tulsi Tea Collection: tulsi (holy basil), the legendary 'Incomparable One', now available as a deliciously soothing organic herbal tea in original, tulsi green, tulsi ginger, tulsi chai, tulsi brahmi (gobu kole), tulsi darjeeling.

FOOD BRANDS GROUP LTD

9-10 Calico House, Plantation Wharf, Battersea, London, SW11 3TN
Tel: 020 7978 5300 Fax: 020 7924 2732 www.fbg.co.uk
Food Brands Group Ltd trades in teas and coffees (Percol), soft drinks (Santa Cruz Organic) and wines. Organic Food Awards 2004, 2006.

GREENWICH CAKES LTD

17 Anchorage Point, Anchor & Hope Lane, London, SE7 7SQ
Tel: 020 8269 0409 Fax: 020 8269 0417
office@greenwichcakes.co.uk www.greenwichcakes.co.uk
Delicious cakes.

GREEN & BLACKS

2 Valentine Place, London, SE1 8QH
Tel: 020 7633 5900 Fax: 020 7633 5901
enquiries@greenandblacks.com www.greenandblacks.com
Green & Black's make award-winning, quality organic chocolate combining the highest environmental and ethical standards. Their delicious range of organic chocolate products includes chocolate bars, hot chocolate, cocoa, ice creams, chocolate-covered almonds and chocolate hazelnut spread. Certified by the Soil Association and available nationwide at supermarkets, good health food stores and delicatessens. Now part of Cadbury Schweppes. Organic Food Awards 2004 Chocolate Highly Commended.

FOR DETAILS OF SYMBOLS USED IN THE ENTRIES, SEE PAGE 17
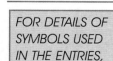

LANGRIDGE ORGANIC PRODUCTS LTD

Unit A55-57, New Covent Garden Market, Nine Elms Lane, London, SW8 5EE
Tel: 020 7622 7440 Fax: 020 7622 7441 sales@langridgeorganic.com www.langridgeorganic.com
Soil Association P7570. Langridge specialise in the wholesale supply of organic fruit, vegetables and
dairy products to independent retailers, box schemes, restaurants, schools and hospitals. Our produce
is sourced from our network of growers throughout the UK, Europe and the rest of the world. Langridge
operates a policy of buying the most locally available organic produce at all times.

LEILA CONTINENTAL CANNERS

Unit 6, Chelsea Fields Industrial Estate, London, SW19 2QA
Tel: 020 8648 2778 Fax: 020 8648 2779 canners@fsbdial.co.uk
A family-owned canned food manufacturer in business for over a decade. We have our own well established 'Natura' brand of organic pulses, soups and ready meals, and also contract pack for other companies. Our BRC accreditation ensures our products are of the highest quality and we are always open
to suggestions for the development of further products. We have the capability to produce a few pallets or even a whole container load of products.

MONMOUTH COFFEE COMPANY

2 Park St, London, SE1 9AB
Tel: 020 7645 3585 Fax: 020 7645 3565
beans@monmouthcoffee.co.uk www.monmouthcoffee.co.uk
Coffee roasters, wholesalers and retailers.

O&F CONSULTING

The Old Bakery, 8A Replingham Rd., London, SW18 5LS
Tel: 020 8870 5383 Fax: 020 8870 8140 simon@organicandfair.com www.organicandfair.com
Simon Wright is founder of O&F Consulting. Since 1986 Simon has specialised in the manufacturing,
retailing, legislation and marketing of organic and Fairtrade food and drink, working with companies
throughout Europe and in the USA. Clients range from small manufacturers of natural foods through to
one of the UK's largest multiple retailers. For more information please visit www.organicandfair.com.

ORGANIC TRADE LTD

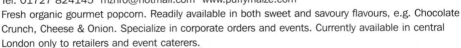

Premier House, 325 Streatham High Road, Streatham, London, SW16 3NT
Tel: 020 8679 8226 Fax: 020 8679 8823 rshah@organictrade.co.uk www.organictrade.co.uk
Import wholesalers of all organic edible nuts, dried fruits, pulses, seeds and cereals. Delivery to all of UK.

PUFFY MAIZE POPCORN

4 Montpelier Street, Knightsbridge, London, SW7 1EE
Tel: 01727 824145 mzhro@hotmail.com www.puffymaize.com
Fresh organic gourmet popcorn. Readily available in both sweet and savoury flavours, e.g. Chocolate
Crunch, Cheese & Onion. Specialize in corporate orders and events. Currently available in central
London only to retailers and event caterers.

RDA ORGANIC

118 Putney Bridge Rd, London, SW15 2NQ
Tel: 0870 833 8732 Fax: 020 8875 0370 juice@rdaorganic.com www.rdaorganic.com
RDA Organic is an award winning range of 100% fresh, pure, organic juices and smoothies. The range
consists of 5 delicious juices, including 'The UK's Best Organic Soft Drink' and the UK's only fresh,
pure organic fruit smoothies. Each bottle provides you with your recommended daily allowance (RDA)
of vitamin C and contains the juice from your recommended daily intake of fruit. RDA Organic contains
nothing but organic fruit – no added sugar, no water, no flavourings – just premium organic fruit.
Organic Food Awards 2004 Non-alcoholic Drinks Highly Commended.

RUDE HEALTH FOODS

PO Box 56501, London, SW18 9AX

Tel: 0845 202 0777 enquiries@rudehealthfoods.co.uk www.rudehealthfoods.co.uk

Rude Health Foods – always delicious, always nutritious. We use the best organic ingredients to create our range of totally natural mueslis, crunchy cereal and porridge. The whole range is wheat-free with no added sugar or salt.

SCAN FOODS UK LTD

1A Amies St., London, SW11 2JL

Tel: 020 7228 4046 Fax: 020 7223 4534 www.swedishkitchen.co.uk

Soil Association P6027. Supplier of Swedish organic meat and processed products including organic Swedish meatballs.

TODAY WAS FUN LTD

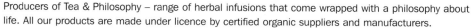

PO Box 47072, London, SW18 1XU

Tel: 0870 240 0092 sharyn@todaywasfun.com www.todaywasfun.com

Producers of Tea & Philosophy – range of herbal infusions that come wrapped with a philosophy about life. All our products are made under licence by certified organic suppliers and manufacturers.

WESTFALIA MARKETING (UK) LTD

Market Towers, 1 Nine Elms Lane, London, SW8 5NQ

Tel: 020 7720 8544 Fax: 020 7720 4209 simon@westfaliauk.co.uk www.westfaliauk.co.uk

Soil Association registered. Importation of conventional and organic avocados and mangos, primarily from parent company in South Africa, but also other sources. Newly added Fairtrade ranges introduced.

WINDMILL ORGANICS LTD

Unit 4, Atlas Transport Estate, Bridges Court, London, SW11 3QS

Tel: 020 7294 2300 Fax: 020 7223 8370 sales@windmillorganics.fsnet.co.uk

Production and distribution of organic foods-dairy products, tofu, margarine, bakery goods, pasta, canned pulses, juices etc. Main brand: Biona.

LONDON-WEST

BONTERRA VINEYARDS

Brown-Forman Wines, Regent Arcade House, 19-25 Argyll St., London, W1F 7TS

Tel: 020 7478 1300 Fax: 020 7287 4661 caroline_park@b-f.com www.bonterra.com

Bonterra Vineyards are one of the world's leaders in organic viticulture, producing a range of premium wines from organically grown grapes. Organic Food Awards 2004 Wines Commended.

BUXTON FOODS LTD/STAMP COLLECTION/PETER RABBIT ORGANICS

12 Harley St., London, W1G 9PG

Tel: 020 7637 5505 Fax: 020 7436 0979

customerservices@buxtonfoods.com www.buxtonfoods.com

We also produce Peter Rabbit Organics, a range of children's foods with no added salt or sugar, and the Stamp Collection range of organic, wheat-free, dairy-free foods.

CLEARSPRING LTD

19A Acton Park Estate, London, W3 7QE

Tel: 020 8749 1781 Fax: 020 8746 2259 info@clearspring.co.uk www.clearspring.co.uk

Soil Association P1474. Clearspring traditional and organic Japanese and European foods regularly win awards for their great taste. They are produced to vegan standards on a small scale and to the highest quality.

ECO ALLIANCE LTD

Durham House, Durham House Street, London, WC2N 6HG

Tel: 020 7930 3538 Fax: 020 7839 3137 www.eco-all.com

Soil Association P7377. Importer, broker and distributor of organic foods from Chile. Eco owns and distributes Aimara organic oils and food products (www.aimara.co.uk), and represents over 60 Chilean organic producers.

FRESH! NATURALLY ORGANIC

Unit 3a, Westwood Business Centre, 98 Victoria Road,
London, NW10 6NB

Tel: 020 8795 2117 info@ freshnaturallyorganic.co.uk www.freshnaturallyorganic.co.uk

Makers of damn fine sandwiches, wraps, salads, soups and cakes. Organic Food Awards 2004, 2006.

JENKIM UK LTD

48 Boston Rd., Hanwell, London, W7 3TR

Tel: 020 8840 8687 Fax: 020 8840 8687 jenkim@onetel.com www.agrologistic.com

Distributor and supplier of Agroneem organic insecticide emulsifiable concentrate and Agroneem organic fertiliser. Product extracted from the neem tree. Organic Material Review Institute (OMRI) listed and US EPA approved.

LUPPOLO LTD

42 Westbourne Terrace, London, WC2 6QE

Tel: 020 7262 4562 Fax: 020 7262 9078 luppolo@tiscali.co.uk

Importing products for the catering industry, day walks on organic farms, cookery and dietetic courses. Teaching in Tuscany on local wild herbs, expert on ECC 2092/91.

ORGANIC MONITOR LTD

79 Western Rd, London, W5 5DT

Tel: 020 8567 0788 Fax: 020 8567 7164

postmaster@organicmonitor.com www.organicmonitor.com

Organic Monitor provides business research and consulting on the international organic and natural products industry.

TASTE MATTERS LTD.

Impress House, Mansell Rd., London, W3 7QH

Tel: 020 8811 2555 Fax: 020 8811 2666 info@tastematters.co.uk www.tastematters.co.uk

Taste Matters Ltd. produces a premium range of chilled 'food to go' products sold under the Taste Matters brand through leading independent organic food retailers, health food stores, food halls and delicatessens. Organic Food Awards 2004, 2006.

LONDON—WEST

FOR DETAILS OF SYMBOLS USED IN THE ENTRIES, SEE PAGE 17

URBAN KITCHEN

63-65 Goldney Road, London, W9 2AR
Tel: 020 7286 1700 Fax: 020 7286 1709
events@urban-productions.co.uk www.urban-productions.co.uk

Urban is a bespoke event-making company with full event production services and a luscious kitchen in-house. We are accredited by the Soil Association to provide organic menus for every occasion. Clients include BBC, MTV, Deutsche Bank, Sony, M&C Saatchi, Armani and Marks & Spencer, along with a large number of private clients.

SURREY

BIG OZ ORGANIC

126 Acre Road, Kingston-upon-Thames, Surrey, KT2 6EN
Tel: 020 8541 3636 Fax: 020 8541 5850 bigozorganic@btconnect.com www.bigoz.co.uk

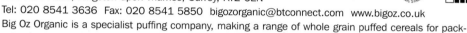

Big Oz Organic is a specialist puffing company, making a range of whole grain puffed cereals for packaging in our own brand, Morning Puffs, and for selling in bulk to other producers.

CONFOCO (UK) LTD

Duncan House, High Street, Ripley, Surrey, GU23 6AY
Tel: 01483 211288 Fax: 01483 211388 confocouk@confocouk.com www.confocouk.com

Supplier of organic food ingredients to the baking, confectionery and breakfast cereal industries.

DUCHY ORIGINALS

The Old Ryde House, 393 Richmond Road,
East Twickenham, Surrey, TW1 2EF
Tel: 020 8831 6800 Fax: 020 8538 9991 office@duchyoriginals.com www.duchyoriginals.com
Duchy Originals embodies HRH The Prince of Wales's commitment to what he calls a 'virtuous circle' of providing natural, high-quality organic and premium products, while helping to protect and sustain the countryside and wildlife. This in turn helps generate profits for charity rather than for commercial gain.

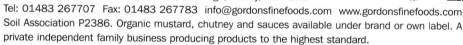

GORDON'S FINE FOODS

Gordon House, Littlemead Ind. Estate, Cranleigh, Surrey, GU6 8ND
Tel: 01483 267707 Fax: 01483 267783 info@gordonsfinefoods.com www.gordonsfinefoods.com
Soil Association P2386. Organic mustard, chutney and sauces available under brand or own label. A private independent family business producing products to the highest standard.

GROVE FRESH LIMITED

Saxley Court, 121-129 Victoria Rd, Horley, Surrey, RH6 7AS
Tel: 01293 820832 Fax: 01293 822741 customer.services@grovefresh.co.uk www.grovefresh.co.uk
Soil Association P1814. Manufacturer of organic fruit juices.

KALLO FOODS LTD

Coopers Place, Combe Lane, Wormley, Surrey, GU8 5SZ
Tel: 01428 685100 Fax: 01428 685800 marketing@kallofoods.com www.kallofoods.com
Kallo Foods is the UK's leading supplier of organic breadsticks, organic crackers and biscuits and organic stocks and gravies, as well as organic chocolate and gluten-free products.

LATIN AMERICAN PRODUCE LTD

30 Westmeads, Onslow Village, Guilford, Surrey, GU2 7ST
Tel: 01483 561719 Fax: 01483 571035 lap@mssn.freeserve.co.uk
LAP Ltd is an import house with many contacts in Latin America. We aim to help Latin American producers to sell organic fresh produce (fruit and vegetables) both in the UK (supermarkets) and European marketplace.

THE ORGANIC SPIRITS CO LTD

Meadow View House, Tannery Lane, Bramley, Surrey, GU5 0AB
Tel: 01483 894650 Fax: 01483 894651 office@londonandscottish.co.uk
We supply world medal-winning organic spirits: Juniper Green Organic Gin, UK5 Organic Vodka, Highland Harvest Organic Scotch Whisky, Papagayo Organic Siced Rum, Papagayo Organic White Rum, Utkins Fairtrade White Rum. Websites: www.junipergreen.org and www.uk5.org.

OUR TOWN CATERING

26 Wodehouse Place, 41 Epsom Rd., Guildford, Surrey, GU1 3HX
Tel: 07706 558513 lunches@ourtowncatering.com www.ourtowncatering.com
We provide freshly prepared local and organic sourced food for corporate breakfasts and lunches. Sandwich trays and buffet sandwich bar available, home-made and organic cakes. Fresh, delicious and ethical food for your company.

SINGLE MARKETING LTD

Hipley House, Hipley Street, Woking, Surrey, GU22 9LQ
Tel: 01483 771152 Fax: 01483 766808 singlemktg@aol.com
Complete sales and marketing service to regional and national retail chains.

WHOLE EARTH FOODS LTD

Kallo Foods, Coopers Place, Combe Lane,
Wormley, Godalming, Surrey, GU8 5SZ
Tel: 01428 685100 Fax: 01428 685800 marketing@kallofoods.com www.wholeearthfoods.com
Since 1976 Whole Earth Foods have led and guided the movement to organic food. We offer a wide range of organic products: peanut butters, spreads, breakfast cereals, canned goods, and soft drinks. Available nationally in major supermarkets and good health food stores.

WILSON & MANSFIELD

Headley House, Headley Rd., Grayshott, Surrey, GU26 6TU
Tel: 01428 601140 Fax: 01428 607851 sales@wmjuice.co.uk www.wmjuice.co.uk
Fruit juices/purées. Wilson & Mansfield are recognised as leaders in the importation of organic fruit juices and purées. Serving the UK and other continental European markets.

EAST SUSSEX

COURT LODGE FARM

Court Lodge Farm, Horsewalk, Nr Hailsham,
Wartling, East Sussex, BN27 1RY
Tel: 01323 832150 Fax: 01323 831984
info@courtlodgeorganics.co.uk www.courtlodgeorganics.co.uk
We are organic dairy farmers and make a range of yogurt smoothies, using fresh whole milk from our pedigree dairy herd.

DAVENPORT VINEYARDS

Limney Farm, Castle Hill, Rotherfield,
Crowborough, East Sussex, TN6 3RR
Tel: 01892 852380 info@davenportvineyards.co.uk www.davenportvineyards.co.uk
Producers of organic English wine, sold under the Limney label. Specialities include a dry white
'Horsmonden' single vineyard wine and Limney Estate bottled fermented sparkling wine.

HENLEY BRIDGE INGREDIENTS LTD

Cocoa House, 22, Bell Lane, Bellbrook Ind. Est., Uckfield,
East Sussex, TN22 1QL
Tel: 0845 880 0799 Fax: 0845 880 0833 sales@hbingredients.co.ukl www.hbingredients.co.uk
Suppliers of organic & conventional ingredients to food processors: sugar, sugar syrups, chocolate, cereal
syrups, cocoa powder, cocoa butter, dextrose, praline paste, marzipan, fondant, milk powders, etc, etc.

HERONS FOLLY GARDEN

Herons Folly, Fletching Street, Mayfield, East Sussex, TN20 6TE
Tel: 01435 873608
Organic vegetable and fruit crops in season. We sell mainly wholesale and for schools, restaurants
etc., disease-resistant varieties of apple trees.

INFINITY FOODS COOPERATIVE LTD

67 Norway St., Portslade, Brighton, East Sussex, BN41 1AE
Tel: 01273 424060 Fax: 01273 417739 sales@infinityfoods.co.uk www.infinityfoods.co.uk
Leading UK wholesaler of organic foods. Soil Association no. P1465. Over 3500 organic lines in stock
offering the most comprehensive range of organic products available anywhere. Delivery to the trade
throughout the UK.

KAI ORGANIC

Unit 10, The Knoll Business Centre, Old Shoreham Rd., Hove, East Sussex, BN3 7GS
Tel: 01273 414146 info@kaiorganic.co.uk www.kaiorganic.co.uk
Kai Cakes is an exciting range of hand made organic cakes produced by Kai Organic. The cakes are
hand-baked to order in small batches ensuring quality, taste and freshness. The range includes wheat-
and gluten-free options. The gluten-free Rich Chocolate Cake was judged 'Highly Commended' and
awarded a Certificate of Excellence in the 2004 Soil Association Organic Food Awards. The cake also
won a Gold in the 2005 Great Taste Awards. Our Lemon Drizzle Loaf won Silver and the Coconut &
Lime won Bronze.

OAKWOOD FARM

Poppinghole Lane, Robertsbridge, East Sussex, TN32 5BL
Tel: 01580 830893 Fax: 01580 830201
Soil Association G2575 & P6079. Top fruit, soft fruit, single variety apple juice, pear juice, apple &
blackberry, pear & raspberry, cider and perry. Also attend Lewes Farmers' market. We supply box
schemes and wholesale markets around the country.

ORCHIDWOOD MUSHROOMS LTD

Hobbs Lane, Beckley, East Sussex, TN31 6TS
Tel: 01797 260411 Fax: 01797 260603
nathan.goodsell@orchidwood.co.uk www.orchidwood.co.uk
Soil Association P4568. Processing of IQF sliced, diced, whole mushrooms for supply to food manufacturers.

THE ORGANIC CAKE COMPANY

The Clocktower, Highgate Works, Tomtits Lane, Forest Row, East Sussex, RH18 5AT

Tel: 01342 823564 sales@theorganiccakecompany.co.uk www.theorganiccakecompany.co.uk

Delicious organic cakes, freshly baked with local and fair trade ingredients. Supremely tangy lemon sponge. Very chocolatey chocolate sponge. Luscious carrot cake with local cheese topping. A rare fruit cake made with porter that tastes like fruit cake should, and lasts 3 months. Available at farmers' markets, retailers and online. Gluten-free, dairy-free available. Delivery across south-east and national courier service.

SEASONS FOREST ROW LTD

10-11 Hartfield Rd., Forest Row, East Sussex, RH18 5DN

Tel: 01342 824673 Fax: 01342 826119

sales@seasons-forest-row.co.uk www.seasons-forest-row.co.uk

Two shops. Large range of wholefoods and fresh produce, most organic, many biodynamic. Also natural cosmetics, wooden toys, large range of books on biodynamics and anthroposophy. Separate shop for organic fruit and vegetables. Wholesale to shops, restaurants and institutions in Sussex. Business owned by charitable trust.

WEST SUSSEX

FARGRO LTD

Toddington Lane, Littlehampton, West Sussex, BN17 7PP

Tel: 01903 721591 Fax: 01903 730737 info@fargro.co.uk www.fargro.co.uk

Horticultural wholesaler providing organic fertiliser and a full range of biological and organic pest control products.

G&G FOOD SUPPLIES LTD

Vitality House, 2-3 Imberhorne Way, East Grinstead, West Sussex, RH19 1RL

Tel: 01342 311401 Fax: 01342 301904 jstephens@gandgvitamins.com www.gandgvitamins.com

Soil Association approved contract encapsulator of herbal and vitamin capsules. Own label product range created: see www.gandgcontract.com. EssentialFood, a certified organic superfood, excellent for boosting energy levels: see www.essentialfood.co.uk. For mail order, internet and distributors see www.gandgvitamins.com.

THE GOODWOOD ESTATE CO LTD

Home Farm, Goodwood, Chichester, West Sussex, PO18 0QF

Tel: 01243 755150 Fax: 01243 755155 farm@goodwood.co.uk www.goodwood.co.uk

Producers of beef, lamb, pork, milk and cream for retail or wholesale. Native breeds finished to a high standard.

GREEN PEOPLE

Pondtail Farm, West Grinstead, West Sussex, RH13 8LN

Tel: 08702 401444 Fax: 01403 741810 organic@greenpeople.co.uk www.greenpeople.co.uk

Manufacturer of hand-made organic health and beauty products for all the family. Sun care, dental care, body care, baby care, skin care, hair care and home care products. No petrochemicals, sodium lauryl sulphate or parabens. Approved by the Vegan Society. Call for a free catalogue and trial sachet.

Infinityfoods/Wholesale
organic & natural foods

Distribution

Manufacture

Wholesale

- Over 4000 Lines - Many Organic.
- Full range of commodities and branded goods (including 'Infinity' own label).
- Efficient national delivery service.

Wholesale Contact Tel : 01273 424060
Fax : 01273 417739
www.infinityfoods.co.uk

HIGH WEALD DAIRY

Tremains Farm, Horsted Keynes, Haywards Heath,
West Sussex, RH17 7EA
Tel: 01825 791636 Fax: 01825 791641 info@highwealddairy.co.uk www.highwealddairy.co.uk
Soil Association P1772. High Weald make a wide range of cheeses from organic sheep milk and
organic cows milk, and supply outlets throughout the UK. Telephone for your nearest stockist.

KPS COMPOSTING SERVICES LTD

Awbrook Park Farm, Ham Lane, West Sussex, RH17 7PR
Tel: 01444 831010 Fax: 01444 831340 ed@kps.uk.com www.kpscomposting.com
Contract hire of green waste processing machinery. Organic compost also supplied.

MONTEZUMA'S CHOCOLATES

Birdham Business Park, Birdham, West Sussex, PO20 7BT
Tel: 0845 450 6304 Fax: 0845 450 6305 jo.delaney@montezumas.co.uk www.montezumas.co.uk
Soil Association P6067. Manufacturer and retailer of award winning British organic chocolate. Highly
acclaimed, innovative and exciting products.

PASTA REALE

Fleming Way, Crawley, West Sussex, RH10 9JW
Tel: 01293 649700 Fax: 01293 649741 info@pastareale.com www.pastareale.com
Soil Association P5554. Pasta Reale specialise in the manufacture of fresh pasta and fresh sauce to
the retail sector. All products are made using natural ingredients.

STEEPWOOD FARM

Broadford Bridge Rd., Adversane,
Billingshurst, West Sussex, RH14 9EG
Tel: 01403 785434 Fax: 01403 784730 val@steepwoodfarm.fsnet.co.uk
Soil Association G7049. Producer wholesaler and retailer of the finest quality meat and game.

VAL'S NATURAL BAKERY

Langham Stables, Lodsworth, West Sussex, GU28 9BU
Tel: 01798 860900 val@valsnaturalbakery.co.uk www.farretti.co.uk
We produce Farretti organic baked hand-made spelt crisps. Main ingredients: spelt flour and extra virgin olive oil. Yeast-free. Made from a traditional Italian recipe. Flavours: plain no salt (wholemeal
spelt), rosemary and garlic (wholemeal spelt), chilli and chives (white spelt), tomato and basil (white
spelt), cheddar (white spelt). Format: bags of 75g, sold by boxes of six bags. Shelf life: six months.
Baked crisps, very tasty on their own and great for dipping. Ideal to accompany appetizers.

THE SOUTH

BERKSHIRE

DOVES FARM FOODS LTD

Salisbury Rd., Hungerford, Berkshire, RG17 0RF
Tel: 01488 684880 Fax: 01488 685235 mail@dovesfarm.co.uk www.dovesfarm.co.uk
Soil Association PD03. Growers and manufacturers of a large range of organic cereal-based foods
including home baking flour, breakfast cereal, biscuits, cookies, cereal bars and flapjacks, several of
which are ethical trade or fair trade certified. Also produce a sperate range of special diet and gluten-
free foods. Organic Food Awards 2004 Breakfast Cereals Winner; Cakes, Pastries Biscuits Commended.

ORGANICO

60-62 Kings Rd, Reading, Berkshire, RG1 3AA
Tel: 0118 951 0518 Fax: 0118 951 0519 info@organico.co.uk www.organico.co.uk
Import and distribution of authentic high quality produce supplying the specialist organic and wholefood trade as well as fine food stores. Winner of 10 Great Taste Awards 2003. Wide range of quality organic brands and food products: juices, pasta, sauces, babyfoods, tinned fish, dairy and gluten-free products, veggie spreads, cordials, jams, fruit purees, oils, vinegars, soups.

PRODUCT CHAIN LTD

Twyford Mill, 55 High St., Twyford, Berkshire, RG10 9AJ
Tel: 0118 934 4944 Fax: 0118 934 1399 info@productchain.com www.productchain.com
Soil Association P5339; Organic Food Federation 00424/01. Product Chain is the foremost broker/agent in the UK, having been personally involved in the movement since 1974. Associated with most of the key brands and players, including Martlet, Grove Fresh, Tim's Dairy, Amy's Kitchen and more to come.

ROCKS ORGANICS

Loddon Park Farm, New Bath Rd., Twyford, Berkshire, RG10 9RY
Tel: 0118 9342344 Fax: 0118 934 4539 hugh@rocksorganic.com www.rocksorganic.com
Soil Association P2150. A specialist producer of organic dilutable drinks, we are a dedicated organic producer only.

WISTBRAY TEAS LTD

P.O. Box 125, Newbury, Berkshire, RG20 9LY
Tel: 01635 278648 Fax: 01635 278672 info@wistbray.com www.elevenoclocktea.com
Wistbray Teas is an exciting and innovative family business with over 100 years of passionate tea experience. Eleven O'Clock Rooibosch Tea is the original caffeine-free tea, and the Dragonfly Organic speciality range offers high quality teas for every taste. Alternative website: www.dragonfly-teas.com.

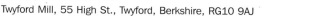

DORSET

ORGANIX BRANDS LTD

Knapp Mill, Mill Road, Christchurch, Dorset, Dorset, BH9 2SD
Tel: 01202 479701 Fax: 01202 479712 marie.vanhagen@organix.com www.organix.com
Organix Brands are manufacturers of organic baby and children's foods. Its range for babies includes, infant cereals, fruit purees for weaning and developing babies, rice cakes, fruity wheels and jumbo breadsticks to encourage self-feeding. Its 'Goodies' range for children from 12 months includes savoury snacks, chewy fruit & cereal bars, fruit purees, fruit dippers, animal biscuits and gingerbread men. All Organix Goodies snacks for children are made without any adulteration. They do not contain any added processed sugars, additives, colourings, preservatives or flavourings. They taste great – go on, give them a try!

BARTON MEADOWS

Barton Meadows Farm, Dorchester Rd., Cerne Abbas, Dorset, DT2 7JS
Tel: 01300 341336 Fax: 01300 341336 bartonmeadows@tiscali.co.uk
Soil Association G956. We sell prime Angus beef, pork, lamb and mutton. Both fresh and frozen, plus honey and Romney fleece for spinners. Also available are organic watercolours and prints by Elizabeth Bairstow.

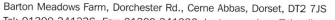

DORSET

CHILDHAY MANOR ORGANICS

Childhay Manor, Blackdown, Beaminster, Dorset, DT8 3LQ
Tel: 01308 868709 Fax: 01308 868119 lucy@childhaymanor.com www.childhaymanor.com
We produce our own organic pork, bacon and beef, which we supply, as well as organic lamb and chickens from other local farmers. We deliver to butchers throughout the south of England, and operate an overnight hamper delivery scheme to the general public, nationwide.

CLIPPER

Beaminster Business Park, Beaminster, Dorset, DT8 3PR
Tel: 01308 863344 enquiries@clipper-teas.com www.clipper-teas.com
Clipper is one of Britain's favourite organic brands, with a huge range of great tasting organic Fairtrade tea, coffee, hot chocolate and infusions. Check out the full range on our website. Organic Food Awards 2004 Coffee Highly Commended.

DORSET FARMS

Littlewindsor, Beaminster, Dorset, DT8 3QU
Tel: 01308 868822 Fax: 01308 868973
Soil Association P2595. Producers of quality organic ham and bacon. Ham available on or off the bone and pre-packed. Bacon sliced in packs of 2.27kg or pre-packed.

MANNA ORGANIC

Unit 11F, Hybris Business Park, Warmwell Rd.,
Dorchester, Dorset, DT1 2NH
Tel: 01305 851551 mail@mannaorganic.co.uk www.mannaorganic.co.uk
Award-winning, chef-prepared ready meals and desserts made using the finest Westcountry ingredients. Mail order & wholesale available across the UK. Our range includes gluten-free and dairy-free options.

MANOR FARM ORGANIC MILK LTD

Manor Farm, Godmanstone, Dorchester, Dorset, DT2 7AH
Tel: 01300 341415 Fax: 01300 341170
pam@manor-farm-organic.co.uk www.manor-farm-organic.co.uk
Producers of organic cartonned, pasteurised whole milk, semi-skimmed milk and cream. Distribution over the south of England. Member of the Soil Association Organic Farms Network. Organic Food Awards 2004 Fresh Meat Commended.

RESPECT ORGANICS

31 Bell St., Shaftesbury, Dorset, SP7 8AR
Tel: 01747 851561 Fax: 01747 851715 info@respectorganics.com www.respectorganics.com
Owner of the Respect brand, specialising in the ambient cake market. We license other manufacturers to produce our cakes for us.

STOATE, NR AND SONS

Cann Mills, Shaftesbury, Dorset, SP7 0BL
Tel: 01747 852475 Fax: 01747 851936 michael@stoatesflour.co.uk www. stoatesflour.co.uk
Traditional stoneground flour millers since 1832, producing a full range of organic flour for all your baking requirements.

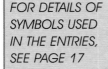
FOR DETAILS OF SYMBOLS USED IN THE ENTRIES, SEE PAGE 17

WOODLANDS PARK DAIRY LTD

Woodlands, Wimborne, Dorset, BH21 8LX

Tel: 01202 822687 Fax: 01202 826051 sales@woodlands-park.co.uk www.woodlands-park.co.uk

Soil Association P5037. Producers of live sheep and goats milk yoghurts, goats milk butter and organic sheeps milk powder. No GMOs. Organic Food Awards 2004 Sheeps Milk Yoghurt Winner.

HAMPSHIRE & ISLE OF WIGHT

ABSOLUTE AROMAS LTD

6 Riverway, Newman Lane, Alton, Hampshire, GU34 2QL

Tel: 01420 540400 Fax: 01420 540401 relax@absolute-aromas.com www.absolute-aromas.com

Aromatherapy products. Available by mail order and from health food stores.

BRIDGEGUILD LTD

Budbridge Manor Nursery, Merstone, Newport, Isle of Wight, PO30 3DH

Tel: 01983 840623 Fax: 01983 840225 www.wightsalads.com

Organic glasshouse-grown cherry and beef tomatoes, sold through our marketing company 'Wight Salads Ltd' to UK supermarkets.

FUNDAMENTALLY FUNGUS

Mycomarketing Ltd, Meon Hill Farm, Stockbridge, Hampshire, SO23 0QD

Tel: 01264 811170 Fax: 01264 811170

jdfungus@mycomarketing.fsnet.co.uk www.fundamentallyfungus.co.uk

Soil Association P5809. Speciality mushrooms. Growers and sellers of fresh speciality mushrooms to catering and restaurant trade. Retail packs of mixed and single variety speciality mushrooms for shops.

LYME REGIS FINE FOODS LTD

Station Ind. Estate, Liphook, Hampshire, GU30 7DR

Tel: 01428 722900 Fax: 01428 727222 info@lymeregisfoods.com www.lymeregisfoods.com

Soil Association P4348. Manufacturers of natural and organic healthy snack bars, particularly fruit, cereal and marzipan bars, sold in health food shops and major supermarkets. Organic Food Awards 2004, 2006.

MATSOFRESH LTD

Fenwick Harrison Building, 16-20 Camp Rd.,

Farnborough, Hampshire, GU14 6EW

Tel: 08702 405420 Fax: 01252 669009 sales@matsofresh.co.uk www.matsofresh.co.uk

Soil Association P6392. Growers, importers and distributors to processors, catering, retail and packers.

PETTY, WOOD & CO

P.O. Box 66, Livingstone Rd., Andover, Hampshire, SP10 5LA

Tel: 01264 345500 Fax: 01264 332025 info@pettywood.co.uk www.pettywood.co.uk

Petty Wood sells, distributes and markets speciality ambient food products to the retail and wholesale sectors. Portfolio includes Duchy Originals, Yarrah Pet Food, Sacla, Baxters and our own 'Epicure Organics'.

POLLEN ORGANICS LIMITED

Three Firs House, Bramshott Chase, Hampshire, GU26 6DG

Tel: 01428 608870 Fax: 01428 608890

richard.pollen@pollenorganics.com www.pollenorganics.com

Soil Association registered. Organic sauces, relishes, dressings, nuts and nibbles. Pollen Organics has established a strong brand identity in organic grocery foods such as Soil Association award-winning pesto sauces, mayonnaise and hollandaise sauces, pasta sauce, red onion marmalade and Seville orange marmalade with exceptional taste, dressings, nuts and nibbles. Organic Food Awards 2004 Condiments Commended.

RASANCO LTD

The Estate Office, Sutton Scotney, Hampshire, SO21 3JW

Tel: 01962 761935 Fax: 01962 761860 ras@rasanco.com www.rasanco.com

Soil Association P2960. Rasanco is a specialist organic ingredients supplier offering the food and drink manufacturer a one-stop shop for their organic raw materials. We subscribe to a 'from field to finished foods' ethic.

TURF CROFT ORGANIC HERBS

Turf Croft Cottage, Burley, Ringwood, Hampshire, BH24 4DF

Tel: 01425 403502 Fax: 01425 403502

Soil Association W165 and BDAA member. Wholesale specialists in fresh culinary herbs all year round. Extensive range, home produced in season, imported out of season. A range of packet sizes and styles available.

THE WINCHESTER BAKERY

51 Hatherley Rd., Winchester, Hampshire, SO22 6RR

Tel: 01962 861477

Soil Association P5584. Organic home-made bread, available through local shops and farmers' markets.

MIDDLESEX

BOMBAY HALWA LTD

Unit G, Bridge Road Ind. Estate, Southall, Middlesex, UB2 4AB

Tel: 020 8571 0237 Fax: 020 8843 2179 www.bombayhalwa.com

Soil Association P2936. Meat-free site for organic and conventional ready meals, snacks, chutneys, desserts and speciality ethnic foods; Indian, Asian, Mexican, Italian.

DMB47 LTD & BODEGA VINECOL – 'VINOS ORGANICOS'

'Rancho Alegre', 47 Sonning Gardens, Hampton, Middlesex, TW12 3PN

Tel: 020 8255 3420 davidbennett47@yahoo.co.uk

We work with an organic vineyard in Mendoza, Argentina (Bodega Vinecol) and import their wines into the UK. We sell both wholesale & retail. The wines and vineyard are certified by 'Letis', an organisation in Argentina, and all documentation is provided for HM Customs for clearance into the UK.

HORIZON FOOD LTD.

Unit 21 & 25, Redburn Ind. Estate, Woodall Road, Enfield, Middlesex, EN3 4LE

Tel: 020 8443 3455 Fax: 020 8443 5040 cos@horizonfood.co.uk www.horizonfood.co.uk

Organic dried fruit including organic stuffed dried fruit. Packers for major distributors.

HAMPSHIRE & IOW / MIDDLESEX

NEAL'S YARD BAKERY LIMITED

Unit 1, Swan Island, Strawberry Vale, Twickenham, Middlesex, TW1 4RP
Tel: 020 8744 1992 Fax: 020 8744 2992 info@nealsyardbakery.co.uk www.nealsyardbakery.co.uk
Neal's Yard Bakery was established in 1976 and bakes a wide range of tasty and healthy organic breads, cakes and pastries.

WILTSHIRE

AGRALAN GARDEN PRODUCTS

The Old Brickyard, Ashton Keynes, Swindon, Wiltshire, SN6 6QR
Tel: 01285 860015 Fax: 01285 860056 sales@agralan.co.uk www.agralan.co.uk
Agralan offer a range of non-poisonous and effective treatments for many pest problems: vegetables can be grown without pesticides. New products allow control of slugs, ants and flies. Distribute Biobest biological controls and bumblebees.

BERKELEY FARM DAIRY

Berkeley Farm, Swindon Rd., Wroughton, Swindon,
Wiltshire, SN4 9AQ
Tel: 01793 812228 Fax: 01793 845949 berkeleyfarmdairy@fwi.co.uk
Soil Association G4670, P4891. Organic dairy and arable farm, organic Guernsey milk processed on farm for Abel & Cole. Contract processing of organic milk.

DBWT (UK)

47 Portway Lane, Warminster, Wiltshire, BA12 8RE
Tel: 01985 220491 info@denisebirdwoventextiles.com www.denisebirdwoventextiles.com
Organic, ecological and eco-therapeutic textile (and fashion) design solutions. End products are not certified organic, but most of the fibres used to create them are certified organic by Skal on their EKO label. DBWT (UK) is collaborating with fair trade overseas manufacturers of ecological textiles in an attempt to provide UK / EU consumers with the high quality, fashionable ecological products which they are demanding at affordable prices. Denise is based in the UK and also works on a commission basis with private clients.

HAXNICKS

Beaumont Business Centre, Woodlands Road, Mere, Wiltshire, BA12 6BT
Tel: 0845 241 1555 Fax: 0845 241 1550 philippa@haxnicks.co.uk www.haxnicks.co.uk
Market leaders in 'chemical-free' garden plant protection. Haxnicks manufacture and distribute an innovative range of quality gardening products, including FSC certified hardwood plant houses and cloches, Victorian bell cloches, polythene, fleece and net tunnel cloches. Haxnicks are also the UK distributor for the DuPont GreenVista range of weed and root barrier fabrics.

PERTWOOD ORGANIC CEREAL CO LTD

Lord's Hill Barn, Longbridge Deverill,
Warminster, Wiltshire, BA12 7DY
Tel: 01747 820499 Fax: 01985 841919 www.pertwood.co.uk
Range of organic breakfast cereals processed from own produce: oat-based, wheat-free, GMO-free muesli with delicious fruits, porage oats, crunchy with raisins and almonds, crunchy with mixed nuts. UK coverage. Large quantities available. Member of the Soil Association Organic Farms Network.

MIDDLESEX / WILTSHIRE

PURE ORGANICS LTD

Stockport Farm, Stockport Rd., Amesbury, Wiltshire, SP4 7LN
Tel: 01980 626263 Fax: 01980 626264 pauline@pureorganics.co.uk www.pureorganics.co.uk
Soil Association P2269. We specialise in the production of organic, additive-free foods for children. Our products are minimally processed using the very best ingredients providing popular alternatives to mass produced convenience foods. In our EC/BRC (higher level) approved factory we produce chicken nuggets, burgers, sausages and vegetarian products. We specialise in addressing dietary intolerances which are causing increasing difficulties for many children and adults, testing to levels as low as 3 parts per million for gluten and dairy proteins. We produce under our own brand 'For Georgia's Sake' and also produce own label products for two of the major multiples. Recently we have started to produce food for school meal services, ensuring children are getting the best possible nutrition by controlling fat and salt levels and developing innovative recipes which bring further nutrition and protein to traditional favourites.

SAGE ORGANIC LTD

Clench Lodge, Wootton Rivers, Marlborough, Wiltshire, SN8 4NT
Tel: 01672 811777 Fax: 01672 811888 info@sageorganic.com www.sageorganic.com
We produce a high quality range of food supplements with the inclusion of organic ingredients. The right combination of organic herbs, vitamins, minerals and other nutrients available in our easy to use Dual Pack range.

STONEGATE LTD

Corsham Rd., Lacock, Wiltshire, SN15 2LZ
Tel: 01249 730700 Fax: 01249 732200 enquiries@stonegate.co.uk www.stonegate.co.uk
Soil Association P6229, Organic Farmers & Growers 12UKCP030028. Stonegate Ltd currently produce, pack and deliver organic eggs to the UK. We supply all large retailers and specialise in special breed organic eggs such as Columbian Blacktail and Speckledy.

THE TRACKLEMENT COMPANY LTD

The Dairy Farm, Pinkney Park,
Sherston, Wiltshire, SN16 0NX
Tel: 01666 840851 Fax: 01666 840022 info@tracklements.co.uk www.tracklements.co.uk
Soil Association P4261. Manufacturers of high quality chutneys, sauces, jellies, mustards and dressings (accompaniments to meat, fish and cheese). Organic Food Awards 2004 Condiments Winner.

TRAFALGAR FISHERIES

Barford Fish Farm, Downton, Wiltshire, SP5 3QF
Tel: 01725 510448 Fax: 01725 511165 info@trafish.com www.trafish.com
Soil Association G4381, P5061. Fish farm/processors. Producers and processors of organic rainbow and brown trout for the table.

T SHIRT AND SONS LTD

11 Washington Rd., West Wilts Trading Estate, Westbury, Wiltshire, BA13 4JP
Tel: 01373 301645 sales@tshirtandsons.co.uk www.tshirtandsons.co.uk
T Shirt and Sons Ltd, the UK's only Soil Association certified T-shirt printer, produces high quality printed and embroidered promotional clothing for a broad range of high profile clients, specialising in fairtrade T-shirts and organic T-shirts.

WARMINSTER MALTINGS LTD

39 Pound St., Warminster, Wiltshire, BA12 8NN
Tel: 01985 212014 Fax: 01985 212015 info@warminster-malt.co.uk www.warminster-malt.co.uk
Soil Association P5961. Manufacture of malt from cereal (barley/wheat) using traditional floor malting process. For use in brewing and food.

WILTSHIRE ORGANIC MILK

Housecroft Farm, Edington, Nr. Westbury, Wiltshire, BA13 4NN
Tel: 01380 870985 Fax: 01380 870985 pf.josborne@tinyworld.co.uk
Produce and sell wholesale pasteurised organic milk, whole and semi-skimmed, also organic cream; ideally to shops, boxes, milkmen, restaurants, cafes, hotels etc. in Wiltshire.

WINCANTON GROUP LTD

Methuen Park, Chippenham, Wiltshire, SN14 0WT
Tel: 01249 710000 Fax: 01249 710001 enquiries@wincanton.co.uk www.wincanton.co.uk
Soil Association P6716. Wincanton Group are specialists in warehousing and distribution activities including organic milk collected for numerous customers.

THE SOUTH-WEST

BRISTOL COUNTY BOROUGH

BART SPICES LTD

York Road, Bristol, BS3 4AD
Tel: 0117 977 3474 Fax: 0117 972 0216 bartspices@bartspices.com www.bartspices.com
Bart Spices produces a range of organic herbs and spices destined for multiple retailers. We also have a range of organic pastes. Bart Spices is a member of the Soil Association.

BOCM PAULS LTD

1st Avenue, Royal Portbury Dock, Bristol, BS20 7XS
Tel: 01275 378384 Fax: 01275 373828 mike.thompson@bocmpauls.co.uk www.bocmpauls.co.uk
Soil Association P2091. BOCM Pauls manufacture approved feeds for dairy cows, youngstock, beef, sheep, pigs and poultry. The products are supported by specialist management services for organic producers in England, Wales, Scotland and Northern Ireland.

BODYMATTER

PO Box 2514, Bristol, BS6 9AP
Tel: 07900 693468 dympna@bodymatter.com www.bodymatter.com
Blenders of organic and award winning wheat-free cereals that are free of anything artificial! Basically, if it's not healthy and it doesn't taste delicious, we won't use it.

BRITISH SEED HOUSES LTD

Portview Rd., Avonmouth, Bristol, BS11 9JH
Tel: 0117 982 3691 Fax: 0117 982 2198 seeds@bshavon.co.uk www.britishseedhouses.co.uk
Soil Association P5945. Seed merchants producing and supplying both the agricultural and amenity seed trade with conventional and organic seeds of grass, clover and cereal varieties.

ESSENTIAL TRADING CO-OPERATIVE LTD

Unit 3 & 4, Lodge Causeway Trading Estate,
Fishponds, Bristol, BS16 3JB
Tel: 0117 958 3550 Fax: 0117 958 3551
sales@essential-trading.coop www.essential-trading.coop
Trade only. Essential trading is a natural foods wholesaler supplying the independent retail sector. Our product range is entirely vegetarian, and we carry only GMO-free products. Aiming for totally organic product range. Registered with OF&G and BDAA. Customer careline 0845 458 1459.

FIRST QUALITY FOODS

Unit 29, The Beeches, Lavenham Road, Yate, Bristol, BS37 5QX

Tel: 01454 880044 Fax: 01454 853355 fqf@mail.com www.firstqualityfoods.co.uk

Sammy's Organic couscous in 3 varieties: Mediterranean tomato, French Provençale, Italian pesto; Ma Baker organic cereal bars in 4 varieties: date & walnut, almond, apricot, apple & sultana.

HEART OF DEVON ORGANICS

Albert Crescent, Bristol, BS2 0XM

Tel: 01395 233660 Fax: 01395 233660

Soil Association P6946. The largest sole wholesaler of quality organic fresh fruit and vegetables in the south-west. Working closely with local and near continent growers. Deliveries from M4 to Lands End.

NATRACARE – BODYWISE (UK) LTD

Unit G, 7A4 Business Centre, Victoria Rd., Avonmouth, Bristol, BS11 9DB

Tel: 0117 982 3492 Fax: 0117 982 3489 info@natracare.com www.natracare.com

Soil Association I303. Feminine hygiene products. Natracare organic cotton tampons, feminine pads and baby wipes made from natural and disposable materials available from health stores and super-markets nationwide.

PERFECTA LTD

Ashmead Enterprise centre, Ashmead Rd., Keynsham, Bristol, BS31 1SX

Tel: 0117 986 8800 Fax: 0117986 1687 sales@perfecta.ltd.uk www.perfecta.ltd.uk

Suppliers of organic herbs, spices and other ingredients. Manufacturers of organic seasonings and blends including sausage, burger, bakery and vegetarian products. Kosher production available.

R & B (BRISTOL) LTD

Unit 4, Bristol Distribution Park, Hawkley Drive, Bradley Stoke, Bristol, BS32 9BF

Tel: 01454 456700 Fax: 01454 456710

We are a Soil Association certified site (P2492) and produce organic pasta sauces for retail.

CHANNEL ISLANDS

JERSEY DAIRY

Five Oaks Dairy, St. Saviour, Jersey, Channel Islands, JE2 7UD

Tel: 01534 818500 Fax: 01534 818535 customer.services@ jerseydairy.je www.jerseydairy.je

Soil Association P4608. Dairy product range. Manufacture, supply and marketing.

CORNWALL

CARLEYS ORGANIC FOODS LTD

The Parade, Truro, Cornwall, TR1 1UJ

Tel: 01872 270091 Fax: 01872 270092 sales@carleys.co.uk www.carleys.co.uk

We manufacture our own 'Carleys' brand products.

THE GRANARY

Newham Road, Truro, Cornwall, TR1 2ST

Tel: 01872 274343 Fax: 01872 223477

sales@granarywholefoods.co.uk www.granarywholefoods.co.uk

Wholesale distributors of healthfoods, natural foods, delicatessen producrs throughout Cornwall, Devon, Somerset, parts of Wiltshire and Dorset.

HEART OF DEVON ORGANICS

c/o 37 Jubilee Street, Newquay, Cornwall, TR7 1LA

Tel: 01395 233660 Fax: 01395 233660

The largest sole wholesaler of quality organic fresh fruit and vegetables in the south-west. Working closely with local and near continent growers (visit website). Deliveries from M4 to Lands End.

HELSETT FARM CORNISH ICE CREAM

Helsett Farm, Lesnewth, Boscastle, Cornwall, PL35 0HP

Tel: 01840 261207 helsett.icecream@lineone.net

Manufacturer of real Cornish ice cream made in small batches, no stabilisers or emulsifiers, all added ingredients e.g. butterscotch, fruit purée, prepared in the dairy.

MICROTECH PRODUCTION HOLDINGS PLC

Microtech Production Holdings plc,

13D Cardrew Industrial Estate, Redruth, Cornwall, TR15 1PS

Tel: 01209 314734 Fax: 01209 314694 cgates@microtechph.com www.microtechph.com

Manufacturer of seaweed-based plant feeds and fertilisers for horticultural, agricultural and gardening markets sold under the ShoreGrow logo. Microtech also manufacture non-toxic, non-chemical insect traps including indoor and outdoor fly traps, wasp traps and a cockroach trap.

OIL IN THE RAW

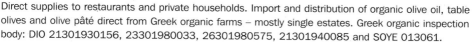

Dilletts Cottage, St. Dominick, Cornwall, PL12 6TE

Tel: 01579 351178 dina@oilintheraw.co.uk www.oilintheraw.co.uk

Direct supplies to restaurants and private households. Import and distribution of organic olive oil, table olives and olive pâté direct from Greek organic farms – mostly single estates. Greek organic inspection body: DIO 21301930156, 23301980033, 26301980575, 21301940085 and SOYE 013061.

THE ORGANIC BREWHOUSE

Unit 1, Higher Bochym Rural Workshops, Cury Cross Lanes,

Helston, Cornwall, TR12 7AZ

Tel: 01326 241555 orgbrewandy@tiscali.co.uk

Soil Association registered. Brewery producing solely organic real ales in cask and bottle-conditioned form.

SCILLY ORGANICS

Middle Town, St. Martins, Isles Of Scilly, Cornwall, TR25 0QN

Tel: 01720 423663 enquiries@scillyorganics.co.uk www.scillyorganics.co.uk

Scilly Organics is a small scale market garden producing a wide range of vegetables, fruit and herbs for local sales. Run on permaculture principles, we use seaweed and compost as fertiliser, and diversity of crops is paramount to the success of our sustainable system. Produce is available at our roadside stall in Middle Town. Visitors welcome, by appointment please.

DEVON

BUCKFAST ORGANIC BAKERY

Hamlyn House, Mardle Way, Buckfastleigh, Devon, TQ11 0NR

Tel: 01364 642279 Fax: 01364 642279 sallycarson@clivespies.co.uk www.clivespies.co.uk

Soil Association P2974. Producers of 'Clive's' pies and cakes – delicious organic vegetarian pies in wholemeal pastry and gluten-free pastry – also luxury gluten-free cakes and organic flapjacks.

CORNWALL / DEVON

CHIMAN'S

Cleave Farm, East Down, Barnstaple, Devon, EX31 4NX
Tel: 01271 883864 Fax: 01271 882843 sallyagarwal@chimans.co.uk www.chimans.co.uk
Soil Association P5692. A unique range of 16 spice blends from authentic Indian recipes, ready to cook at home.

COTONS CONTINENTAL CHOCOLATES

Unit 1, Island Square, Island St., Salcombe, Devon, TQ8 8DP
Tel: 01584 844004 robin@cotonschocolates.co.uk www.cotonschocolates.co.uk
Hand-made chocolates using Belgian organic chocolate. Cotons brands include award-winning plain and milk chocolate 100g bars. We also make truffles, Easter egg and Christmas models.

DEVON FOODS LTD

Old Hill, Cullompton, Devon, EX15 1RW
Tel: 01884 33272 Fax: 01884 33272 sales@devonfood.co.uk www.devonfood.co.uk
Specialise in production of Soil Association organic day-old chicks, table birds, duck, guinea fowl, hatching eggs and point of lay pullets.

DRAGONFLY FOODS

2A Mardle Way, Buckfastleigh, Devon, TQ11 0NR
Tel: 01364 642700 Fax: 01364 644485 info@beanydiet.co.uk www.beany.co.uk
Manufacturer of organic chilled soya bean products, including tofu, Beanys, Soysage and Tatty, a potato and rice cake. Sold to independent health food shops in the UK. Organic Food Awards 2004 Soya Foods Winner.

ECO SCI – WEST COUNTRY COMPOST

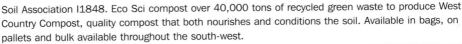

Wolfson Laboratories, Higher Hoopern Lane, Exeter, Devon, EX4 4SG
Tel: 01392 424846 Fax: 01392 425302 mail@ecosci.co.uk www.ecosci.co.uk
Soil Association I1848. Eco Sci compost over 40,000 tons of recycled green waste to produce West Country Compost, quality compost that both nourishes and conditions the soil. Available in bags, on pallets and bulk available throughout the south-west.

HEART OF DEVON ORGANICS

Langridge Farm, Crediton, Devon, EX17 5HH
Tel: 01395 233660 Fax: 01395 233660
The largest sole wholesaler of organic fresh fruit and vegetables in the south-west. Working closely with local and near continent growers (visit website). Deliveries from M4 to Lands End.

HERON VALLEY CIDER AND ORGANIC JUICE

Crannacombe Farm, Hazelwood, Loddiswell,
Kingsbridge, Devon, TQ7 4DX
Tel: 01548 550256 Fax: 01548 550256
National award winning producers of organic apple-based fruit juices and sparkling and traditional still organic ciders, pressed from hand-selected fruit at our farm based in stunning river Avon valley. Organic Food Awards 2004 Non Alcoholic Drinks Highly Commended.

LUSCOMBE ORGANIC DRINKS

Luscombe Farm, Colston Road, Buckfastleigh,
Devon, TQ11 0LP
Tel: 01364 643036 Fax: 01364 644498 enquiries@luscombe.co.uk www.luscombe.co.uk
Soil Association P2222. Produce and bottle the most genuine soft drinks using all organic ingredients and great attention to detail. From apple juice through ginger beer, elderflower to Sicilian lemonade.

MAUNDER LTD, LLOYD

Willand, Cullompton, Devon, EX15 2PJ

Tel: 01884 820534 Fax: 01884 821404 adrian.blyth@lloydmaunder.co.uk www.lloydmaunder.co.uk
Lloyd Maunder supply organic lamb and organic chicken to the major multiples to Soil Association standards.

MILK LINK LTD

Plym House, 3 Longbridge Rd, Plymouth, Devon, PL6 8LT

Tel: 01752 331805 Fax: 01752 331812 lee.richards@milklink.com www.milklink.co.uk
Milk Link is the UK's third largest integrated dairy business with the capacity to process and add value to up to 80 per cent of our members' milk, allowing them to benefit from a long term secure outlet for their milk, together with the additional margins available from processing it into added-value products. Milk Link also manufacture a wide range of dairy products including long life milk, fresh milk and creams, extended shelf life products, flavoured milks, custards, milk powders, soft cheeses and cultured ingredients supplying all the UK's major food retailers, many of its largest food processors, and food services organisations as well as being the second largest cheese producer in the UK, making a comprehensive range of award winning British cheeses. Milk Link is also able to supply specialist milks including organic, Channel Islands, Ayrshire and kosher milks. Milk Link is the leading supplier of Channel Islands milk and the second largest supplier of organic milk in the UK. The majority of Milk Link's organic milk is produced in Devon, Cornwall, and Somerset and distributed, via Arla Foods to Tesco stores nationwide. Organic milk is also supplied to a number of specialist cheese makers.

OLD CUMMING ORGANIC FARM

Old Cumming Organic Farm, Colston Road,
Buckfastleigh, Devon, TQ11 0LP

Tel: 01364 642672
Soil Association G2495. Family-run organic farm producing high quality fresh pre-packed organic produce. Salad packs, leaf vegetables and fruit juice. Organic Food Awards 2003, 2004, 2006.

ORGANIC LYNX

31 Bowden Hill, Newton Abbot, Devon, TQ12 1BH

Tel: 01626 200706 Fax: 01626 200706 vivani@hotmail.co.uk www.vivani.de
UK agents for award-winning 'Vivani' organic chocolate.

ORGANIC POULTRY EQUIPMENT LTD

Peterhales House, Trinity, Cullompton, Devon, EX15 1PE

Tel: 07974 353073 Fax: 01884 35004

organicpoultryequipment@yahoo.co.uk www.organicpoultryequipment.co.uk
Suppliers of well insulated, low cost, modular poultry housing, developed by organic table bird producers. Features include a highly efficient feeding system, excellent welfare standards and a very durable structure. Secondary telephone number: 01884 33218.

OTTER VALLEY POULTRY

Spurtham Farm, Upottery, Honiton, Devon, EX14 9QD

Tel: 01404 861209 Fax: 01404 861715
Soil Association P5599. Family-run poultry abattoir, offering a personal service to customers, specialising in the processing of all aspects of organic poultry.

ROCOMBE FARM FRESH ICE CREAM LTD

Old Newton Rd., Heathfield, Newton Abbot, Devon, TQ12 6RA

Tel: 01626 834545 Fax: 01626 835777 info@rocombefarm.co.uk www.rocombefarm.co.uk
Luxury organic dairy ice cream, organic frozen yoghurt and organic fruit sorbet. Soil Association P1006.

DEVON

SKYSPROUTS

Gosworthy Cottage, Harberton, Totnes, Devon, TQ9 7LP
Tel: 01364 72404 Fax: 01364 72404 skysprouts@ic24.net
Growers of organic beansprouts, alfalfa sprouts, alfalfa and broccoli sprouts, alfalfa and fenugreek sprouts, mung, aduki, lentil, chickpea, sunflower and sunflower salads. Supplying wholesalers, shops and veggie box schemes throughout the UK.

TIDEFORD ORGANIC FOODS LIMITED

Unit 5, The Alpha Centre, Babbage Road, Totnes, Devon, TQ9 5JA
Tel: 01803 840555 Fax: 01803 840551 tideford@btconnect.com www.tidefordorganics.com
Soil Association P2178. Tideford produces award-winning soups, sauces, pestos and puddings.

TOPRACK

Throwcombe, Stoodleigh, Nr. Tiverton, Devon, EX16 9QQ
Tel: 01884 881471 sales@toprack.co.uk www.toprack.co.uk
Prime tender organic park venison, cutting and packing information, cooking instructions and recipes. Selling points: lowest in fat, high in iron, contains Omega 3 fatty acids, etc.

WYLDE HERBS

Oak Cottage, Poundsgate, Ashburton, Devon, TQ13 7NU
Tel: 01364 631233 wyldeherbs@btinternet.com
Growing and researching organic/biodynamic herbs. Supply to herbalists, researchers. Consultancy and training in production of medicinal herbs, lectures, writing, project feasibility studies, report production. Related business advisory service.

SOMERSET

BIOSELECT UK

Bindon Home Farm, Langford Budville, Wellington, Somerset, TA21 0RU
Tel: 01823 401500 Fax: 01823 401501
laurence.hasson@organicpotatoes.co.uk www.organicpotatoes.co.uk
Soil Association (PH06W), NASPM (Natural Association Seed Potato Merchants). Organic seed potatoes, onions, garlic shallot sets. Bioselect UK Ltd manage the production and marketing of organic seed potatoes and import/export. Mobile: 07775 938472.

BOWERINGS ANIMAL FEEDS LTD

The Docks, Bridgwater, Somerset, TA6 3EX
Tel: 01278 458191 Fax: 01278 445159 ben@boweringsfeeds.co.uk
Soil Association P2246. Manufacturers of organic compound feed for all stock. Suppliers of blends, straights and seeds.

COOMBE FARM

Coombe Farm, Roundham, Crewkerne, Somerset, TA18 8RR
Tel: 01460 279500 Fax: 01460 77349 info@coombefarm.com www.coombefarm.com
Producers and distributors of organic cheese, butter, cream, milk and also bespoke fruit recipes for the food industry.

CRABTREE & EVELYN

Tylers End, Highbridge, Somerset, TA9 4JS
Tel: 01278 780913 Fax: 01278 795461 www.crabtree-evelyn.co.uk
Manufacturer of high quality organic preserves, marmalades and sauces. Soil Association reg.no. P4419.

DAISY AND CO

Tree Tops Farm,
North Brewham, Bruton, Somerset, BA10 0JS
Tel: 01749 850254 Fax: 01749 850815 sales@daisyandco.co.uk www.daisyandco.co.uk
Dairy farm (Jersey cows). Cheese makers – wholesale/retail via internet/farmers markets/farm gate.
Soft 'Camembert'-style cheese – plain; covered in crushed peppercorns; or oak smoked. Hard cheese.

THE ELMS ORGANIC DAIRY

Friars Oven Farm, West Compton,
Shepton Mallet, Somerset, BA4 4PD
Tel: 01749 890371 Fax: 01749 890371 elms.organic.dairy@care4free.net
OF&G registered. Producers of organic sheep and cow dairy products.

GODMINSTER

Godminster Farm, Bruton, Somerset, BA10 ONE
Tel: 01749 813733 Fax: 01749 812059 sales@godminster.com www.godminster.com
Godminster is a mixed organic farm with a dairy herd, free range organic chickens, apple orchards and
fruit and vegetable gardens. Our milk goes into making the renowned Godminster Vintage organic
cheddar and we also supply eggs, table birds, jams, chutneys and flavoured vodkas – made with
organic produce from the farm. We supply shops, mail order and local farmers' markets. Visitors for
farm gate sales please ring in advance.

HAMBLEDEN HERBS

Rushall Organic Farm, Devizes Rd., Rushall, Wiltshire, SN9 6ET
Tel: 01980 630721 Fax: 01980 630712 lyn@hambledenherbs.co.uk www.hambledenherbs.co.uk
The Hambleden Herbs range of over 135 organic herbal products includes teas, culinary herbs and
spices, infusions, tinctures and Christmas products. The range has won over 30 trade and consumer
awards in the last nine years. High quality, unadulterated herbal products ethically produced and traded, using only essential processing and minimal recycled packaging. Hambleden Herbs are produced
on a working organic farm in Somerset and can be purchased from health food stores, organic farm
shops and delicatessens.

HEART OF DEVON ORGANICS

c/o Croxley Sutton Road, Somerton, Somerset, TA11 6QL
Tel: 01395 233660 Fax: 01395 233660
The largest sole wholesaler of quality organic fresh fruit and vegetables in the south-west. Working
closely with local and near continent growers (visit website). Deliveries from M4 to Lands End.

HUEGLI INDUSTRIAL FOODS

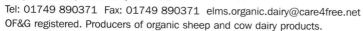

Prioryfield House, 20 Canon St., Taunton, Somerset, TA1 1SW
Tel: 01823 350950 Fax: 01823 350953 huegli2@btconnect.com www.huegli.com
Soil Association P6844, OF&G UKP0092. HIF is the European market leader in the organic bouillon
sector. Products include organic bouillons, sauces, soups, generic seasonings, mustards and desserts.

ILCHESTER CHEESE CO LTD

Somerton Rd., Ilchester, Somerset, BA22 8JL
Tel: 01935 842800 Fax: 01935 842801 sales@ilchester.co.uk www.ilchester.co.uk
Speciality and traditional cheese manufacturer producing traditional organic cheeses for the UK and
export markets.

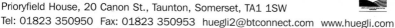

SOMERSET

SOMERSET

LUBBORN CHEESE LTD

Manor Farm, Cricket St. Thomas, Chard, Somerset, TA20 4BZ
Tel: 01460 30736 info@lubborn.co.uk www.lubborn.co.uk
Sole makers of Somerset Brie, Somerset Camembert and Capricorn goats cheese, all traditionally
ripened for full flavour and a creamy texture. Organic Food Awards 2004 Cheese Highly Commended.

MARKUS PRODUCTS LTD

Murray Way, Wincanton Business Park, Wincanton, Somerset, BA9 9RX
Tel: 01963 435270 Fax: 01963 435271 info@markusproducts.co.uk www.markusproducts.co.uk
Soil Association P4162. Manufacturer of flavoured butters, flavoured soft cheese portions, crumb coat-
ings, flavoured oils and stuffings in IQF format.

MILES, DJ & CO LTD

The Vale Yard, High St., Porlock, Somerset, TA24 8PU
Tel: 01643 703993 Fax: 01643 706303 info@djmiles.co.uk www.djmiles.co.uk
40 organic teabags, 80 organic teabags manufactured in Somerset.

MOLE VALLEY FARMERS LTD
Huntworth Mill, Marsh Lane, Bridgwater, Somerset, TA6 6LQ
Tel: 01278 444829 Fax: 01278 446923
feeds@molevalleyfarmers.com www.molevalleyfarmers.com
Soil Association P2332, Organic Farmers & Growers UKP 030463. Manufacturers of organic feeds for
dairy, beef, cattle, sheep, pigs and poultry, and suppliers of seeds, fertilisers and other inputs for
organic farmers.

THE ORGANIC HERB TRADING COMPANY
Milverton, Somerset, TA4 1NF
Tel: 01823 401205 Fax: 01823 401001
info@organicherbtrading.com www.organicherbtrading.com
Soil Association P938. The leading UK supplier of organic raw materials including herbs and spices,
essential oils, tinctures, macerated oils and flower waters for use in food, beverages, herbal medicines
and cosmetics. Quantities from ½ kilo/litre to container. NOP certification for the American markets.
Member of the Soil Association Organic Farms Network.

ORGANIC MILK SUPPLIERS CO-OPERATIVE LTD
Court Farm, Loxton, Nr. Axbridge, Somerset, BS26 2XG
Tel: 01934 750244 Fax: 01934 750080 enquiries@omsco.co.uk www.omsco.co.uk
UK-wide supplier of organic milk.

QUEENSWOOD NATURAL FOODS LTD
Bristo Rd., Bridgwater, Somerset, TA6 4AW
Tel: 01278 423440 Fax: 01278 424084
sales@queenswoodfoods.co.uk www.queenswoodfoods.co.uk
Soil Association P1559. Supplies of bulk and pre-packed organic commodities, along with a wide
range of branded, chilled and frozen products, with weekly deliveries throughout a large area. Organic
ingredients also available.

ROBERT WILSON'S CEYLON TEAS

Stonehaven, Nuttree, North Perrott, Crewkerne, Somerset, TA18 7SX
Tel: 01460 77508 Fax: 01460 77508 info@wilstea.com www.wilstea.com
Organic Farmers & Growers UKP 030485. Packers and shippers. Our business in Sri Lanka works with
single estates to have special dry season manufacture made to our specific requirements. We import
for UK distribution or export internationally from Colombo. Retail shop on the web.

STILLMANS (SOMERSET) LTD

Staplergrove Mill, Staplegrove, Taunton, Somerset, TA2 6PX
Tel: 01823 272661 Fax: 01823 332270
peter@stillmansbutchers.co.uk www.stillmansbutchers.co.uk
Soil Association P3014. Stillmans is a small welfare-friendly farm abattoir providing a service to local farmers.

TRUUULY SCRUMPTIOUS ORGANIC BABY FOOD

Edford Farm, Edford Hill, Holcombe, Radstock, Somerset, BA3 5HQ
Tel: 01761 239300 Fax: 01761 239300
sales@bathorganicbabyfood.co.uk www.bathorganicbabyfood.co.uk
Award-winning frozen organic baby and toddler food. Entire range is Soil Association certified. Winners of the Soil Association Organic Food Awards in 2002 and 2004. Our range includes such delights as salmon and broccoli pie, sweetcorn chowder and apple and mango. Organic Food Awards 2004 Baby Food Winner.

THE YEO VALLEY ORGANIC CO LTD

Cannington Creamery, Cannington, Somerset, TA5 2ND
Tel: 01761 462798 Fax: 01761 462181 enquiries@yeo-organic.co.uk www.yeo-organic.co.uk
Soil Association P2168. This family-owned independent business won The Queen's Award for Enterprise for Sustainable Development in 2001. Now the UK's biggest organic dairy brand, products include yogurts, desserts, butter and ice cream. Organic Food Awards 2004, 2006.

ZUMO ZEST

Hayeswood Rd., Timsbury, Bath, Somerset, BA2 0FQ
Tel: 01761 470523 Fax: 01761 471018 info@zumazest.com www.zumazest.com
A family-run business in the heart of the West Country making 'to order' organic citrus zest and juice, for use as an ingredient to enhance the quality of puddings, cakes etc., by the trade.

EAST ANGLIA

NORFOLK

ALL NATURAL

Unit 61 E+F, Gorse Industrial Estate, Barnham, Thetford, Norfolk, IP24 2PH
Tel: 01842 890891 michael@allnaturalbakery.co.uk www.allnaturalbakery.co.uk
Organic and biodynamic sourdough bread with emphasis on speical dietary needs such as low carb, no baker's yeast, dairy-free, no modern wheat, gluten-free, vegan, low sodium. All Natural supplies independent health food shops, wholefood stores, delicatessens and farm shops throughout East Anglia and in London.

BARRIER ANIMAL HEALTHCARE

36 Havescroft Ind. Estate, New Rd., Attleborough, Norfolk, NR17 1YE
Tel: 01953 456363 Fax: 01953 455594 sales@barrier-biotech.com www.footrot.co.uk
Manufacturer of animal health products and agricultural healthcare products. Specialist manufacturers of high quality non-toxic, non-irritant healthcare products. Our effective range of agricultural products are designed for intensive farming and also suitable for organic farming systems. Call 01953 456363 or visit www.ragwort.com.

THE BOOJA BOOJA COMPANY

Howe Pits, Norwich Rd., Brooke, Norfolk, NR15 1HJ

Tel: 01508 558888 Fax: 01508 557844

Soil Association P4181. Manufacturers of organic dairy-free, vegetarian, vegan, wheat- and gluten-free chocolates.

EARWIG ORGANICS

30, Blenheim Close, Sprowston, Norwich, Norfolk, NR7 8AN

Tel: 01603 405420 sales@ earwig-organics.co.uk www.earwig-organics.co.uk

Mail order retailer of Rockdust, a product to remineralise the soil. Available UK-wide as mail order.

GERMAIN'S TECHNOLOGY GROUP UK

Hansa Rd., Hardwick Ind. Estate, Kings Lynn, Norfolk, PE30 4LG

Tel: 01553 774012 Fax: 01553 773145 info@germains.com www.germains.com

Soil Association P7187. High performance seed technology products for organic use under the brand 'ProBio', including coatings, pellets, steeping, priming and non-chemical disinfection. Wide range of agricultural and horticultural seeds handled.

KETTLE FOODS LTD.

Barnard Rd, Bowthorpe Industrial Estate, Norwich, Norfolk, NR5 9JB

Tel: 01603 744788 Fax: 01603 740375 info@kettlefoods.co.uk www.kettlechips.co.uk

Kettle Foods supply Kettle® Organics, a range of organic hand cooked potato chips, available in two varieties: lightly salted and sea salt with crushed black peppercorns. Plus the perfect accompaniment, an organic salsa dip.

THE METFIELD ORGANIC BAKERY LTD

The Stores, The Street, Metfield, Harleston, Norfolk, IP20 0LB

Tel: 01379 586798 Fax: 01379 586798

Soil Association R1531. Bakery. Producers of hand-crafted organic bread, cakes and savouries.

NATIONWIDE FOOD PACKING LTD

13 Norwich Road Ind. Estate, Watton, Thetford, Norfolk, IP25 6DR

Tel: 01953 885735

Soil Association P2619. Contract packers, bulk to retail. Mostly dry canning of bouillon gravy granules.

THE ORGANIC FEED COMPANY

Norfolk Mill, Shipdham, Thetford, Norfolk, IP25 7SD

Tel: 01362 822903 Fax: 01362 822910 sales@organicfeed.co.uk www.organicfeed.co.uk

Soil Association registered. Organic feed for layers, poultry, pigs, sheep, goats and cattle. Vegetarian Society Approved. Available nationally through retail outlets, in 20kg sacks.

ORGANICS-ON-LINE LTD

Park House, Gunthorpe Hall, Melton Constable, Norfolk, NR24 2PA

Tel: 0845 052 0777 info@organics-on-line.com www.organics-on-line.com

Business-to-business internet trading site. Organics-on-line offers a large range of organic products. The site acts as a means of facilitating trade direct from the producer to the buyer and is targeting business-to-business trade in organics.

FOR DETAILS OF SYMBOLS USED IN THE ENTRIES, SEE PAGE 17

PEARCE LTD, ALFRED G

Garage Lane Ind. Estate, Common Lane,
Setchey, Kings Lynn, Norfolk, PE33 0BE
Tel: 01553 810456 Fax: 01553 811464 info@alfredgpearce.co.uk www.alfredgpearce.co.uk
Soil Association P5559. Suppliers of prepared and semi-prepared root vegetables, and a selection of IQF vegetables to the manufacturing and food service industry. We process products giving full traceability by using dedicated growers to ensure the continuity of supply.

PLACE UK (R & JM PLACE LTD)

Church Farm, Tunstead, Norfolk, NR12 8RQ
Tel: 01692 536225 Fax: 01692 536928 admin@placeuk.com www.placeuk.com
Soil Association P1734. Growers and processors of soft fruit, vegetables, beansprouts and carbohydrate products. Processing facility for IQF, bulk freezing, rehydrated, blanching, puréeing, cutting and slicing.

TRADITIONAL NORFOLK POULTRY

Garage Farm, Hargham Road, Shropham, Norfolk, NR17 1DS
Tel: 01953 498434 Fax: 01953 498962 enquiries@tnpltd.com
We are producers and processors of organic chicken and turkeys all year round. We are members of OF&G, no. 31UKF120071.

WESTFARM FOODS LTD

Unit 44, Bergen Way, North Lynn Industrial Estate, King's Lynn, Norfolk, PE30 2JG
Tel: 01553 772522 Fax: 01553 776860 sales@qualitopsuk.co.uk www.qualitopsuk.co.uk
EEC organic certified products including: salami, chorizo, pâtés, frankfurters, fine meat products, Belgian salami, Ganda ham, goats cheeses and vegetarian tians.

SUFFOLK

ASPALL

The Cyder House, Aspall Hall, Stowmarket, Suffolk, IP14 6PD
Tel: 01728 860510 Fax: 01728 861031 info@aspall.co.uk www.aspall.co.uk
Founder members of the Soil Association and organic producers of apple juice, cyder and cyder vinegar for over 57 years. Our products are widely available through good retail food outlets.

ASTON ORGANIC ORCHARDS

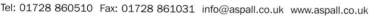

The Orchard, Welham Lane, Risby, Bury St Edmunds, Suffolk, IP28 6QS
Tel: 01284 811668 Fax: 01284 700011 tonyfuller@btinternet.com
Soil Association registered organic apple orchard. The following varieties are grown (mainly for the wholesale market). Dessert apples: Spartan & Lord Lambourne. Cooking apples: Bramley & Grenadier.

BARENBRUG UK LTD

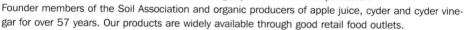

33 Perkins Rd., Rougham Ind. Estate, Bury St. Edmunds, Suffolk, IP30 9ND
Tel: 01359 272000 Fax: 01359 272001 info@baruk.co.uk www.barenbrug.co.uk
Soil Association P6199. Barenbrug are specialist grass and forage seed producers who produce organic grass seed mixtures, specifically designed for organic farmers. These include the new white clover Barblanca, which is extremely productive.

CHURCH (BURES) LTD, WA

High St., Bures, Suffolk, CO8 5JQ
Tel: 01787 227654 Fax: 01787 228325
organicseed@churchofbures.co.uk www.churchofbures.co.uk
Soil Association P7482. All organic grass mixtures available: vetch, mustard, red clover, white clover and all organic seed mixtures.

DE FACTO SOFTWARE
The Rutherford Centre, 8 Dunlop Road, Ipswich, Suffolk, IP2 0UG
Tel: 01473 417200 Fax: 01473 417201
enquiries@defactosoftware.com www.defactosoftware.com
De Facto Software provides fully integrated accounting, ERP, MRP and CRM solutions to mid-sized food enterprises (SMEs). Our solution is utilised by distributors, importers, wholesalers, manufacturers, processors, packers, mail order, traders and agents. De Facto S5 incorporates financials, logistics, production, CRM, e-commerce and costings. Deploying the system typically delivers significant customer gains in such areas as productivity, cost advantage, management awareness, and competitive edge. Our customer base covers produce, wine and drinks trade, food, packaging, building and construction, electronics and components, engineering and more.

ESSENTIAL CARE

26 James Carter Rd., Mildenhall, Suffolk, IP28 7DE
Tel: 01638 716593 info@essential-care.co.uk www.essential-care.co.uk
From the purest plant oils, herbs and floral waters we create organic skin & body care and the only Soil Association certified shampoo. Hand-made and formulated without unnecessary synthetics, especially for sensitive and eczema-prone skin. We are a caring & friendly, family-run company.

GOBBLIN WHOLEFOODS LTD
Station Rd. Ind. Estate, Elmswell, Bury St. Edmunds, Suffolk, IP30 9HR
Tel: 01359 241841 Fax: 01359 241841
Soil Association P5476. Manufacturer of vegetarian wholefoods, including organic sweet and savoury lines, for delivery within the M25 and throughout the east of England, to retail, catering and licensed outlets.

HORIZON SEEDS
Unit 3, Airfield Industrial Park, Langton Green, Eye, Suffolk, IP23 7HN
Tel: 01379 873377 Fax: 01379 873373 info@horizonseeds.com www.horizonseeds.com
Retailers of organic seed: grass leys, forage maize, cereals, pulses and fodder crops. We supply to farms throughout the country.

JAMES WHITE DRINKS LTD
Whites Fruit Farm, Ashbocking, Ipswich, Suffolk, IP6 9JS
Tel: 01473 890111 Fax: 01473 890001 info@jameswhite.co.uk www.jameswhite.co.uk
James White press and bottle a range of organic and non-organic apple and pear juices at their site in Suffolk. These include apple & crushed ginger, carrot & apple, cranberry & apple and raspberry & pear. They are available from specialist retailers and caterers throughout the UK and also can be ordered by phone or via the web site for home delivery.

KOPPERT UK LTD

Homefield Business Park, Homefield Road, Haverhill, Suffolk, CB9 8QP
Tel: 01440 704488 Fax: 01440 704487 info@koppert.co.uk www.koppert.co.uk
Biological pest control.

MICROCIDE

Shepherds Grove, Stanton, Bury St. Edmunds, Suffolk, IP31 2AR

Tel: 01359 251077 Fax: 01359 251545 microcide@microcide.co.uk www.microcide.co.uk

Soil Association I1616. Manufacturers of vegetable oil adjuvants which maximise the performance of plant protection products and increase droplet deposition, spread and uptake. Reduces drift and improves rain fastness. They are biodegradable.

NORTON ORGANIC GRAIN LTD

Castlings Heath Cottage, Groton, Sudbury, Suffolk, CO10 5ES

Tel: 01787 210899 Fax: 01787 211737

john.norton@nortonorganic.co.uk www.nortonorganic.co.uk

Organic grain/pulse supplier, sourcing organic grains and pulses from UK farms and European/third country sourced soya, oilseeds, grains etc. Soil Association licence P1674, OFF SAL/97. International coverage.

OMEGA INGREDIENTS LIMITED

Cygnus House, Orion Court, Great Blakenham, Suffolk, IP6 0RL

Tel: 01473 836400 Fax: 01473 836478

sales@omegaingredients.co.uk www.omegaingredients.co.uk

Essential oils, natural extracts, flower and herb waters, fruit juices, flavours and fragrances, ingredients for flavours and fragrances, aloe vera, dried aloe flowers. Mobile 07775 581444.

PAGEANT WINES LIMITED

12 Pageant Place, Framlingham, Suffolk, IP13 9BX

Tel: 01728 622018 Fax: 01728 622018 enquiries@pageantwines.com www.pageantwines.com

Specialist wine merchant supplying the best organic and biodynamic wines from around the world. We offer a friendly, efficient service to trade and retail home delivery customers nationwide. We also offer an organic wine club. Contact us for further information, a wine list or visit our website.

ST. PETER'S BREWERY

St. Peter's Brewery Co Ltd, St. Peter's Hall, St. Peter South Elmham, Bungay, Suffolk, NR35 1NQ

Tel: 01986 782322 Fax: 01986 782505 colin@stpetersbrewery.co.uk www.stpetersbrewery.co.uk

Soil Association P5891. Organic brewery. Production of organic beers and ales using organic barley and organic hops, presented in cask or bottle for shipment around the world.

EAST MIDLANDS

CAMBRIDGESHIRE

THE BILLINGTON FOOD GROUP LIMITED

Dugar Wy, Peterborough PE2 9AY

Tel: 01733 422368 Fax: 01733 422990 enquiries@billingtons.co.uk www.billingtons.co.uk

Billington's supplies a range of organic cane sugars to retail and manufacturing sectors, both within UK and worldwide. All products are certified by the Soil Association.

BOKOMO FOODS (UK) LTD

38-40 Stapledon Rd., Orton Southgate, Peterborough, Cambridgeshire, PE2 6TD

Tel: 01733 362900 Fax: 01733 394111 abrand@bokomo.co.uk www.bokomo.co.uk

Manufacture and packing of breakfast cereals including traditional blended mueslis and baked crunchy products and porridge. Able to supply in bulk or in retail units, cartons or bags, especially own-label.

SUFFOLK / CAMBRIDGESHIRE

BRITISH SUGAR PLC

Oundle Rd., Peterborough, Cambridgeshire, PE2 9QU

Tel: 0870 240 2314 Fax: 0870 240 2729 rcogman@britishsugar.co.uk www.britishsugar.co.uk

British Sugar Plc manufactures LimeX products which are ideal for rapid, persistent correction of acidity. LimeX contains useful nutrients and may be used in organic systems. Flexible service options meet the needs of individual customers. coproducts@britishsugar.co.uk

BRITISH SUGAR PLC

Oundle Road, Peterborough, Cambridgeshire, PE2 9QU

Tel: 08000 688022 Fax: 01733 422916 sales@britishsugar.co.uk www.britishsugar.co.uk

British Sugar's organic range includes granulated, cane, icing and liquid sugars. The range is supplied to meet all your product requirements and provides all the functionality expected from quality sugars.

GREENVALE AP

Floods Ferry Road, Doddington,

March, Cambridgeshire, PE15 0UW

Tel: 01354 672059 Fax: 01354 677561 phil.britton@greenvale.co.uk www.greenvale.co.uk

Greenvale AP is the UK's largest handlers of organic potatoes, supplying fresh organic potatoes and organic dehydrated potato flake accross the UK and Europe.

GREENVALE FOODS LTD

Boleness Rd., Wisbech, Cambridgeshire, PE13 2RB

Tel: 01945 469840 Fax: 01945 581414 www.greenvale.co.uk

Soil Association P2334. Manufacturer and supplier of dehydrated drum-dried potato flake for use in snacks, potato mash and other food preparations and dishes.

G'S MARKETING LTD

Barway, Ely, Cambridgeshire, CB7 5TZ

Tel: 01353 727200 Fax: 01353 624388 info@gs-marketing.com www.gs-marketing.com

Soil Association P4445. Growers and packers of organic salads and vegetables. Growing in Cambridgeshire and the West Midlands producing the finest quality organic produce. Sourcing product worldwide when out of the UK season.

JDM INGREDIENTS LTD

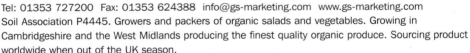

Broad End Rd., Walsoken, Wisbech, Cambridgeshire, PE14 7BQ

Tel: 01945 465556 Fax: 01945 465796 www.garlicandginger.com

Soil Association P6068. Producers of garlic purée, ginger purée, roasted vegetables.

LANDAUER HONEY LTD

Top Barn, Fowlemere Rd., Newton, Cambridge, Cambridgeshire, CB2 5PG

Tel: 01223 872444 Fax: 01223 872512 honey@ landauergroup.co.uk www.landauergroup.co.uk

Honey refiner supplying the food manufacturing industry.

MASTEROAST COFFEE COMPANY LTD

50–54 Ivatt Way Business Park, Westwood, Peterborough, Cambridgeshire, PE3 7PN

Tel: 01733 842000 Fax: 01733 266934 info@masteroast.co.uk www.masteroast.co.uk

Soil Association P2995. Roasting, grinding and packing of fresh coffee beans to customers' requirements.

CAMBRIDGESHIRE

NORGROW INTERNATIONAL LTD

Grange Farm Lodge, Leverington Common,
Wisbech, Cambridgeshire, PE13 5JG
Tel: 01945 410810 Fax: 01945 410850 sales@norgrow.com www.norgrow.com
Food ingredients, wide range: soya products, sugar and natural sweetners, beans, peas, pulses, seeds, nuts, fruit, vegetables, culinary and medicinal herbs and spices, essential oils, oleoresins, plant extracts and powders. Bulk and wholesale only. See our website for full range of products.

OAKLEY FARMS

Hall Rd., Outwell, Wisbech, Cambridgeshire, PE14 8PE
Tel: 01945 773387 Fax: 01945 774101 admin@oakleyfarms.co.uk www.oakleyfarms.co.uk
Growers and packers of organic vegetables, specialising in courgettes, pumpkins and broccoli.

PRO-VEG SEEDS LTD

6 Shingay Lane, Sawston, Cambridge, Cambridgeshire, CB2 4SS
Tel: 01293 833001 Fax: 01293 833006 johnburrows@provegseeds.com www.provegseeds.com
Whoolesale and retail vegetable seed suppliers, supplying to other seed companies, including packet seed companies, and professional growers.

DERBYSHIRE

ARTISAN BISCUITS

Blenheim Rd., Ashbourne, Derbyshire, DE6 1HA
Tel: 01335 342373 Fax: 01335 346394 john@artisanbiscuits.co.uk
Soil Association registered. An award-winning independent family-run biscuit baker specialising in production of traditional hand-baked biscuits using only the purest natural ingredients, including a developing range of organic sweet and savoury biscuits. Organic Food Awards 2004 Cakes, Pastries, Biscuits Winner.

DOVEDALE CONFECTIONERY LTD
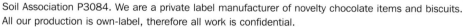
Vernon Street Industrial Estate, Shirebrook, Derbyshire, NG20 8SL
Tel: 01623 742277 Fax: 01623 743020 dovedale@o2.co.uk
Soil Association P3084. We are a private label manufacturer of novelty chocolate items and biscuits. All our production is own-label, therefore all work is confidential.

ENGLISH ORGANIC FOODS PLC
The Old Vicarage, 226 Ashbourne Rd., Turnditch, Derbyshire, DE56 2LH
Tel: 01773 550173 Fax: 01773 550855
Organic matching agency.

HI PEAK FEEDS LTD

Hi Peak Feeds Mill, Sheffield Rd.,
Killamarsh, Derbyshire, S21 1ED
Tel: 0114 248 0608 Fax: 0114 247 5189 info@hipeak.co.uk www.hipeak.co.uk
Manufacturers and distributors of organic and UKROFS permitted animal feeds for all farm livestock, horses and dogs. Nationwide delivery and mail order. Soil Association licence no. P2486, OF&G licence no. 11UKP090258. We supply farmers and smallholders.

NEW LAND OWNER MANAGEMENT SERVICES

Aston House Farm, Sudbury, Nr. Ashbourne, Derbyshire, DE6 5AG

Tel: 01283 585410 r.jeffery@btconnect.com www.newlandowner.co.uk

Management consultancy set up to provide a helping hand to those who are new to rural land owner-ship. We offer a completely flexible range of services to fit in with your needs, lifestyle and aspirations.

WELEDA (UK) LTD

Heanor Road, Ilkeston, Derbyshire, DE7 8DR

Tel: 0115 944 8200 Fax: 0115 944 8210 info@weleda.co.uk www.weleda.co.uk

Demeter certified. Weleda produces natural medicines and body care products, using ingredients from our Demeter certified gardens.

WRIGHT LTD, FRANK

Blenheim House, Blenheim Rd., Ashbourne, Derbyshire, DE6 1HA

Tel: 01335 341155 Fax: 01335 341171 rachel.fowers@frankwright.com www.frankwright.com

Soil Association P6918. Manufacturers of Soil Association approved mineral supplements for organic ruminant livestock, which are essential to maintain performance, health and welfare. Also available as bespoke formulations for specific farm needs.

LEICESTERSHIRE

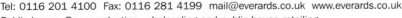

AMBROSIAN VEGETARIAN FOODS

Highfields Lodge, 69 Occupation Rd., Albert Village, Leicestershire, DE11 8HA

Tel: 01283 225055 Fax: 01283 550536

ambrosian@btopenworld.com www.synergynet.co.uk/ambrosian/

Soil Association P6694. Manufacturer of high quality home made vegan organic food. The range includes pies, pasties, sos rollo, burgers, sosages and sosage and burger mixes. All products are regis-tered with the Vegan Society and produced under organic standards.

CLAYBROOKE MILL

Frolesworth Lane, Claybrooke Magna, Leicestershire, LE17 5DB

Tel: 01455 202443 claybrookemill@yahoo.co.uk

Soil Association P1578. We are a 300-year-old working watermill producing high quality flours and mueslis. Over 40 different varieties of flour and mueslis.

EVERARDS BREWERY

Castle Acres, Narborough, Leicestershire, LE19 1BY

Tel: 0116 201 4100 Fax: 0116 281 4199 mail@everards.co.uk www.everards.co.uk

Public house. Beer production, wholesaling and public house retailing.

LONG CLAWSON DAIRY LTD

West End, Long Clawson, Melton Mowbray, Leicestershire, LE14 4PJ

Tel: 01664 821732 Fax: 01664 823236 enquiries@clawson.co.uk www.clawson.co.uk

Stilton-blended cheese manufacturers (dairy). Organic Food Awards 2004 Cheese Winners.

OSBASTON KITCHEN GARDEN

Osbaston Hall, Osbaston, Nr. Nuneaton, Leicestershire, CV13 0DR

Tel: 01455 440811

Soil Association G1523. Walled kitchen garden (1 acre) growing organic fruit, vegetables and herbs.

PAUL'S TOFU/SOYFOODS LTD

66-68 Snow Hill, Melton Mowbray, Leicestershire, LE13 1PD
Tel: 01664 560572 Fax: 01664 410345 paul@soyfoods.co.uk www.soyfoods.co.uk
Wholesale supplier of organic fruit and vegetables and baked goods.

S & D AROMA LTD

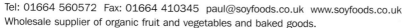

The Manor, Tur Langton, Leicester, Leicestershire, LE8 0PJ
Tel: 01858 545837 Fax: 01858 545761 sales@sdaroma.com www.sdaroma.com
Producers of organic essential oils, carrier oils and butters that promote the welfare and structure of villages in Nepal, India, Ghana, Malawi, South Africa and several others.

SEEDS OF CHANGE

Freeby Lane, Waltham On The Wolds, Leicestershire, LE14 4RS
Tel: 0800 952 0000 www.seedsofchange.co.uk
Seeds of Change offer accessible day to day products, all 100% certified organic. The range includes dried pasta, pasta sauces, ethnic sauces, stir-in sauces, soups and cereal bars.

WHISSENDINE WINDMILL

Melton Road, Whissendine, Leicestershire, LE15 7EU
Tel: 01664 474172
OF&G P080027. Traditional windmill producing a range of stoneground meals: white, wholemeal flours, rye, spelt, oats, barley.

LINCOLNSHIRE

AGRIMARCHE LIMITED

2nd Floor, 2 St Mary's Hill, Stamford, Lincolnshire, PE9 2DP
Tel: 01780 484640 Fax: 01780 481737 stephen.tutt@agrimarche.co.uk www.agrimarche.co.uk
Suppliers of organic soybeans for manufacturing and wholesale. All grades supplied from animal feed to tofu. Also suppliers of organic soya oil and soya expeller.

CHATEAU PAPILLON ESTATES

Unit H, Holmes Court, Boston Road Ind Estate,
Horncastle, Lincolnshire, LN9 6AS
Tel: 0845 838 1790 Fax: 0870 131 3172
simon@chateau-papillon.com www.chateau-papillon.com
UK importer, international distributor and UK wholesaler of organic & biodynamic wine, champagne and port. All wine is certified organic and/or biodynamic and comes from among the best producers in France and Portugal (port).

CHEERS NURSERIES

Eleven Acre Lane, Kirton, Boston, Lincolnshire, PE20 1LS
Tel: 01205 724258 Fax: 01205 724259 henry@cheersnurseries.co.uk
Raise organic vegetable transplants.

DUNN COMMODITIES LIMITED

The Priory, St. Chad, Barrow upon Humber, Lincolnshire, DN19 7AU
Tel: 01469 533355 Fax: 01469 533353 richard@dunncomm.co.uk
Approved supplier of organic soya meal and organic crude soya expellar oil for animal feeds.

LINCOLNSHIRE

ENTERPRISE SEEDS LTD

Clover House, Boston Rd., Sleaford, Lincolnshire, NG34 7HD
Tel: 01529 415555 Fax: 01529 413333 dennis.pell@entseeds.co.uk www.entseeds.co.uk
Soil Association P5679. Agricultural seed producers for cereals, peas, beans, grass and forage crops for resale direct to farmers and grounds throughout England and Wales.

GLEADELL AGRICULTURE LTD

Lindsey House, Hemswell Cliff, Gainsborough, Lincolnshire, DN21 5TH
Tel: 01427 421223 Fax: 01427 421230 brian.wilburn@gleadell.co.uk www.gleadell.co.uk
Organic grain marketing specialists. Soil Association no. P596. Organic marketing company committed to serving and promoting organic farming since 1986. Market specialists for all types and grades of certified organic cereals and pulses.

GOODACRE, JM & A

Old Manor Farm, Sewstern, Grantham,
Lincolnshire, NG33 5RF
Tel: 01476 860228 Fax: 01476 860228
Soil Association G4146. Potato specialist business offering several different varieties for sale, and contract growing and grading services.

JACK BUCK GROWERS

Oak House, Holbeach Bank, Spalding, Lincolnshire, PE12 8BL
Tel: 01406 422615 Fax: 01406 426173 www.jackbuck.co.uk
Soil Association P5546. Growers, packers and processors of speciality vegetables.

MELROW SALADS

Geest Ltd, West Marsh Rd., Spalding, Lincolnshire, PE11 2BB
Tel: 01775 761111 Fax: 01775 763011 niall.cameron@geest.co.uk
We source and supply organic fresh produce (avocados, tomatoes, peppers, beetroot) to major multiple retailers.

NEWFARM ORGANICS

JF & J Edwards & Sons, Soulby Lane, Wrangle, Boston, Lincolnshire, PE22 9BT
Tel: 01205 870500 Fax: 01205 871001
newfarmorganics@zoom.co.uk www.newfarmorganics.co.uk
We produce food that is organic and truly traceable. We specialise in growing potatoes, cauliflowers, cabbage, cereals and beans. We also produce quality beef from our Lincoln Red x suckler herd.

NU-TREL PRODUCTS LTD

Park Farm, Kettlethorpe, Lincoln, Lincolnshire, LN1 2LD
Tel: 01522 704747 Fax: 01522 704748 www.nutrelgroup.co.uk
Soil Association I3022. Manufacturers of speciality fertilisers for use in organic crop production.

OLIVER SEEDS

The Old Wood, Skellingthorpe, Lincoln, Lincolnshire, LN6 5UA
Tel: 0800 056 1122 Fax: 01522 507319
Soil Association P7038. Seed merchants. Grass mixtures, maize, fodder crops, green manure, amenity grass, wild flowers to farmers, and landscaping. Own production, mixing, warehousing, supported by technical team on phone and on-site.

OMEX AGRICULTURE

Bardney Airfield, Tupholme, Lincoln, Lincolnshire, LN3 5TP
Tel: 01526 396011 Fax: 01526 396001 andye@omex.com www.omex.co.uk
Manufacture and application of tailor-made suspension fertilisers plus a range of foliar-applied crop health promoters and crop nutrients.

SINCLAIR HORTICULTURE LTD, WILLIAM

Firth Rd, Lincoln, Lincolnshire, LN6 7AH
Tel: 01522 537561 Fax: 01522 513609 info@william-sinclair.co.uk www.william-sinclair.co.uk
Manufacturers of compost, lawn care, fertilisers, bark and mulches.

SWEDEPONIC UK LTD
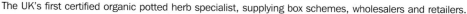

Spalding Rd., Bourne, Lincolnshire, PE10 0AT
Tel: 01778 424224 Fax: 01778 421200 mark@swedeponic.co.uk
The UK's first certified organic potted herb specialist, supplying box schemes, wholesalers and retailers.

UTOPIA UK

Enterprise Way, Pinchbeck, Spalding, Lincolnshire, PE11 3YR
Tel: 01775 716800 Fax: 01775 716808 sales@utopiauk.com www.utopiauk.com
Importation and supply of fresh exotic / tropical fruit and vegetables to the UK multiple retailers. Organic products include pineapple, papaya, mango, citrus, sweet potato, asparagus and other exotics.

WORLDWIDE FRUIT LTD
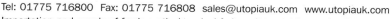

West Marsh Rd., Spalding, Lincolnshire, PE11 2BB
Tel: 01775 717000 Fax: 01775 717001
mark.everett@worldwidefruit.co.uk www.worldwidefruit.co.uk
Major fruit importer and UK pip/soft fruit producer servicing all of the major multiple retailers; specialists in fruit ripening. Year-round supply of apple, pear, kiwi, avocado and dates.

NORTHAMPTONSHIRE

ALPRO UK
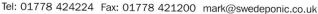

Altendiez Way, Latimer Business Park, Burton Latimer, Northamptonshire, NN15 5YT
Tel: 01536 720600 Fax: 01536 725793 commercialuk@alpro.be www.alprosoya.co.uk
Europe's leading manufacturer of dairy-free alternatives to milk, cream, yoghurt and desserts.

GOODNESS FOODS

South March, Daventry, Northamptonshire, NN11 4PH
Tel: 01327 706611 Fax: 01327 300436 lesley.cutts@goodness.co.uk www.goodness.co.uk
Soil Association P1636. We carry a fantastic range of organic foods, thousands of products including frozen and chilled foods. We deliver throughout the the UK. Phone for details or look at our websites: trade www.goodness.co.uk, or retail www.GoodnessDirect.co.uk.

GRANOVITA UK LTD

5 Stanton Close, Finedon Rd. Industrial Estate, Wellingborough,
Northamptonshire, NN8 4HN
Tel: 01933 273717 Fax: 01933 273729 kate.percival@granovita.co.uk www.granovita.co.uk
GranoVita UK manufactures a wide range of vegetarian products, many of which are organic. Our range includes the following organic products; breakfast cereals, sauces, soya drinks, pâtés, desserts, and a great deal more. Organic certifying bodies: QC&I, Organic Farmers & Growers (UK2), and the Soil Assn (UK5).

MARTLET NATURAL FOODS

10-14 Meadow Close, Ise Valley, Wellingborough, Northamptonshire, NN8 4BH

Tel: 01933 442022 Fax: 01933 440815

Poducers and suppliers of retail and bulk organic products. Preserves, chutneys, cider and wine vinegars, honey, molasses, malt, sugar syrups, mincemeat, sauces. Also seaweed extract, biostimulants and fertilisers. Soil Association approved.

PHOENIX FOODS

Brakey Rd., Corby, Northamptonshire, NN17 5LU

Tel: 01536 200101 Fax: 01536 202218 sales@phoenixfoods.co.uk www.phoenixfoods.co.uk

Soil Association P3068. Manufacturer of dry powdered food stuffs: hot chocolate, drinks, custard powder etc.

THE SONORA FOOD COMPANY LTD

Stephenson Close, Drayton Fields Ind. Estate, Daventry, Northamptonshire, NN11 8RF

Tel: 01327 705733 Fax: 01327 703592 info@sonora.co.uk www.discoveryfoods.co.uk

Manufacturers of flour tortillas and corn chips to major high street retailers.

NOTTINGHAMSHIRE

INTERNATIONAL DIAMALT CO. LTD.

Maltkiln Lane, Newark-on-Trent, Nottinghamshire, NG24 1HN

Tel: 01636 614730 Fax: 01636 614740

maltextracts@diamalt.co.uk www.diamalt.co.uk/organic.htm

Manufacture of liquid organic malt extract, dried organic malt extract, organic barley syrup and organic diastatic malt extract. Supplying the food and beverage industry with products in 15kg plastic buckets to 26 tonne tanker loads.

ONIONS (FARMS), P J

Shelton Lodge, Nr. Newark, Nottinghamshire, NG23 5JJ

Tel: 01949 850268 Fax: 01949 850714

Organic cereal and pulse storage, drying and cleaning. TASCC-registered food standards bagging line available to bag out of bulk storage.

THE SOUTH MIDLANDS

BEDFORDSHIRE

CATLIN, DAVID

Church Farm, Church Lane, Flitton, Bedfordshire, MK45 5EL

Tel: 01525 860277 Fax: 01525 861452 farmercatlin@aol.com

Organic vegetable and asparagus grower and wholesaler supplying local and national box schemes.

JORDANS (CEREALS) LTD, W

Holme Mills, Biggleswade, Bedfordshire, SG18 9JY

Tel: 01767 318222 Fax: 01767 600695 www.jordanscereals.co.uk

Jordans have been producing natural cereals for 30 years and their organic range combines superior quality, exceptional taste and support for British farming. Organic Food Awards 2004 Breakfast Cereals Highly Commended.

PRATT, S H & CO (BANANAS) LTD

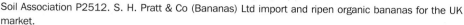

Laporte Way, Luton, Bedfordshire, LU4 8EN
Tel: 01582 436503 Fax: 01582 436570 bricelamarque@shpratt.com
Soil Association P2512. S. H. Pratt & Co (Bananas) Ltd import and ripen organic bananas for the UK market.

BUCKINGHAMSHIRE

DUDLEY, J C & CO LTD

Cheyney House, Francis Yard, East Street, Chesham, Buckinghamshire, HP5 1DG
Tel: 01494 792839 Fax: 01494 792875 sales@jcdudley.co.uk www.jcdudley.co.uk
Soil Association P4449. Importers/agents dealing in organic fruit juice concentrates, NFC fruit juices and purées, along with frozen elderflowers and frozen and dehydrated cranberries, blueberries and lingonberries.

THE ORGANIC WINE COMPANY

PO Box 81, High Wycombe, Buckinghamshire, HP13 5QN
Tel: 01494 446557 Fax: 01494 446557 afm@lineone.net
Importers and wholesalers, including mail order by the case, of organic wines, beers, spirits, juices, and olive oils. Established over 18 years, with a range of over 300 lines.

SYNERGY

Synergy House, Hillbottom Road, Sands Industrial Estate,
High Wycombe, Buckinghamshire, HP12 4HJ
Tel: 01494 492222 info@synergyflavours.com www.synergyflavours.com
Organic flavours and extracts.

GLOUCESTERSHIRE

THE AUTHENTIC BREAD CO

Unit 2, Strawberry Hill Business Park, Strawberry Hill,
Newent, Gloucestershire, GL18 1LH
Tel: 01531 828181 Fax: 01531 828151
breadbaron@authenticbread.co.uk www.authenticbread.co.uk
Established producer of high quality organic bakery and Christmas products. Everything from bread to pasties are lovingly hand-made in our Gloucestershire bakery. Winners of 6 Soil Association Good Food awards. Soil Association symbol no. P1912. Organic Food Awards 2004 Puddings Winner.

COTSWOLD HEALTH PRODUCTS LTD

Unit 5/8 Tabernacle Rd., Wotton-under-Edge, Gloucestershire, GL12 7EF
Tel: 01453 843694 Fax: 01453 521375 sales@cotsherb.co.uk www.cotsherb.co.uk
Soil Association no. P1926. Importers of herbs and spices.

DAIRY CREST LTD

Oldends Lane, Stonehouse, Gloucestershire, GL10 2DG
Tel: 01453 435543 Fax: 01453 435812 john.middleton@dairycrest.co.uk www.dairycrest.co.uk
Dairy Crest process organic dairy products, produced from raw milk, to suit market requirements, including organic cream and butter.

GLOUCESTERSHIRE

DAYLESFORD CREAMERY

Daylesford Creamery, Daylesford, Nr. Kingham,
Gloucestershire, GL56 0YG
Tel: 01608 658005 Fax: 01608 658009
j.schneider@daylesfordcreamery.com www.daylesfordorganic.com
Celebrated for craftsmanship and taste: we make award winning organic cheeses the traditional way, aged for full flavour and using milk from our own organically raised Friesians. Organic Food Awards 2004 Cheese Commended.

ECOTRICITY

Axiom House, Station Road, Stroud, Gloucestershire, GL5 3AP
Tel: 01453 756111 Fax: 01453 756222 info@ecotricity.co.uk www.ecotricity.co.uk
Green electricity supplier. Dedicated to building clean new energy sources that won't contribute to global warming. Ecotricity matches the standard price of your local electricity supplier, so it shouldn't cost you more than 'normal' polluting electricity.

FUTURA FOODS UK LTD

Wynchfield House, Calcot, Nr. Tetbury, Gloucestershire, GL8 8YJ
Tel: 01666 890500 Fax: 01666 890522 info@futura-foods.com www.futura-foods.com
Soil Association P1642. Danish manufacturing and dairy trading organisation. Selling and developing organic dairy products for UK retail/wholesale sectors. Marketed under 'Futura Organic' label. Organic Food Awards 2004 Cheese Commended.

THE GOURMET MUSHROOM COMPANY

Haymes Farm, New Rd., Southam,
Cheltenham, Gloucestershire, GL52 3NX
Tel: 01242 238021 Fax: 01242 237614 sales@haymesfarm.co.uk www.haymesfarm.co.uk
18-acre organic farm supplying organic brown or chestnut and white mushrooms, portabello, oyster, enoki and shiitake mushrooms. We supply box schemes, multiples and local retailers. Organic spent mushroom compost is available in large commercial quantities to other organic farmers.

GRAINFARMERS PLC

Unit 3, Compton Business Cenre, Compton Abdale,
Cheltenham, Gloucestershire, GL54 4LD
Tel: 01242 890003 Fax: 01242 890516
andrew.trump@grainfarmers.co.uk www.grainfarmers.co.uk
Trading arable produce, we will help you sell your produce or source the feed ingredients you need.

HOBBS HOUSE BAKERY

Unit 6, Chipping Edge Estate, Hatters Lane,
Chipping Sodbury, Gloucestershire, BS37 6AA
Tel: 01454 321629 Fax: 01454 329757
trevor@hobbshousebakery.co.uk www.hobbshousebakery.co.uk
Soil Association P1632. A traditional craft bakery producing award-winning breads. Three retail outlets, and supplies to outlets within 50-mile radius.

HOSIERS LTD

Damery Works, Woodford, Berkeley, Gloucestershire, GL13 9JR
Tel: 01454 261522 Fax: 01454 260127 andrewelliott@hosiersltd.co.uk
Genuine demerara organic molasses.

JUST WHOLEFOODS

Unit 16 Cirencester Business Est., Elliott Road, Love Lane, Cirencester,
Gloucestershire, GL7 1YS
Tel: 01285 651910 Fax: 01285 650266 info@justwholefoods.co.uk www.justwholefoods.co.uk
Manufacturers of award-winning vegetarian organic products, including confectionery (VegeBears),
instant soup mixes, stuffing mixes, etc. We also manufacture for other companies under contract, pro-
viding the products are vegetarian.

KITCHEN GARDEN PRESERVES

Unit 15, Salmon Springs Trading Estate, Cheltenham Road,
Stroud, Gloucestershire, GL6 6NU
Tel: 01453 759612 Fax: 01453 755899
info@kitchengardenpreserves.co.uk www.kitchengardenpreserves.co.uk
We produce a range of hand-made jams, chutneys, marmalades and condiments. We have been category winners in the Organic Food Awards three times in the last five years. We supply independent delicatessens, farm shops, box schemes and hamper companies. Organic Food Awards 2004, 2006.

MELCOURT INDUSTRIES LTD

Boldridge Brake, Long Newton, Tetbury, Gloucestershire, GL8 8RT
Tel: 01666 502711 Fax: 01666 504398 mail@melcourt.co.uk www.melcourt.co.uk
Soil Association I1222. Melcourt are specialist manufacturers of growing media products derived from
sustainable forest residues. We supply professional growers and the landscape industry with bark and
wood-derived mulches, soil ameliorants and play surfaces.

SHIPTON MILL LTD

Long Newnton, Tetbury, Gloucestershire, GL8 8RP
Tel: 01666 505050 Fax: 01666 504666 enquiries@shipton-mill.com www.shipton-mill.com
We are a small flour mill in the heart of the Cotswolds producing stoneground organic flours for the
craft baker, as well as supplying the home baker through our friendly mail order service. Members of
the Soil Association.

SUNSHINE CRAFT BAKERY

The British School, Slad Road, Stoud, Gloucestershire, GL5 1QW
Tel: 01453 752592
Bake and supply organic bread, cakes and savouries (vegetarian) for our own shop and Cheltenham
Nutrition Centres.

HERTFORDSHIRE

ALCOHOLS LTD

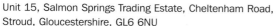

Charringtons House, The Causeway, Bishop's Stortford, Hertfordshire, CM23 2EW
Tel: 01279 658464 Fax: 01279 757613 peter.mckay@alcohols.co.uk www.alcohols.co.uk
Alcohols Ltd. produce organic gin and vodka and market organic alcohol, supplying in bulk and packed.

BROUGHTON PASTURES ORGANIC FRUIT WINE CO

The Silk Mill, Brook St., Tring, Hertfordshire, HP23 5EF
Tel: 01442 823993 Fax: 01442 823993 organicfruitwine@aol.com www.broughtonpastures.co.uk
The UK's formost producer of organic fruit wines. Available in several delicious flavours including mead,
ginger wine and a sparkling elderflower wine made in the traditional 'Methode Champenoise'. Look out
for our new range of Fairtrade Organic wines and our delicious Fairtrade organic liqueurs. Phone or
email for local outlets. Soil Association no. P1652.

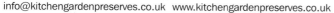

CEREAL PARTNERS

2 Albany Place, 28 Bridge Road East, Welwyn Garden City, Hertfordshire, AL7 1RR
Tel: 01707 824400 Fax: 01707 824569 aline.spittal@uk.nestle.com www.cerealpartners.co.uk
Cereal Partners UK manufacture a wide range of ready-to-eat breakfast cereals and include organic
within the portfolio.

EQ WASTE MANAGEMENT

Appspond Lane, Potters Crouch, St. Albans, Hertfordshire, AL2 3NL
Tel: 0870 560 2060 Fax: 01727 867866 sales@eqwaste.com www.eqwaste.com
OrganEQ's peat-free range of composts and soil blends are produced from a sustainable botanical
source providing a high quality supplement for the horticultural and agricultural markets. Delivery available nationwide.

HACIENDA DOS OLIVOS UK

Fourways Cottage, Hemel Hempstead Rd., Dagnall,
Berkhamsted, Hertfordshire, HP4 1QR
Tel: 01442 843861 amrcreighton@tiscali.co.uk www.dosolivos.com
Supplier of highest quality organic manzanilla table olives. Grown and produced on private estate
south-west of Seville, Spain. Available in various flavours. Spanish certified (CAAE N° 001177).

THE NATURAL COFFEE COMPANY

Arabica House, Ebberns Rd., Apsley, Hemel Hempstead, Hertfordshire, HP39RD
Tel: 01442 256625 Fax: 01442 248614 louise@naturalcoffee.co.uk www.naturalcoffee.co.uk
Coffee roaster. We offer a selection of organic and fairtrade coffees; retail and catering. We provide the
individual, the wholesalers and we roast & pack to order.

PLANT HEALTH CARE

121 High St., Berkhamsted, Hertfordshire, HP4 2DJ
Tel: 01442 864431 Fax: 01442 870148 info@planthealthcare.co.uk www.planthealthcare.co.uk
Manufacturers and suppliers of Soil Association approved liquid organic fertilizers, based on all plant
extracts. We supply 5 different analyses; 9:2:2, 9:2:7, 8:3:3, 6:5:6 and 4:2:8. We also supply bacterial and fungal products.

OXFORDSHIRE

BRITISH BAKELS

Granville Way, off Launton Rd., Bicester, Oxfordshire, OX26 4JT
Tel: 01869 247098 Fax: 01869 242979 bakels@bakels.com www.bakels.com
Ingredient supplier. Manufacturers of organic cake mixes, scone mixes, muffin mixes, bread improvers,
crumb softeners and baking powders. National distribution.

FINE LADY BAKERIES LTD

Southam Road, Banbury, Oxfordshire, OX16 7RR
Tel: 01295 227600 Fax: 01295 271430 info@finelady.co.uk
Fine Lady Bakeries Ltd produce a range of organic bread and rolls for both the retail and sandwich
making industries. Soil Association Licence No P1543.

MUTCHMEATS LTD

Newclose Lane, Witney, Oxfordshire, OX29 7GX
Tel: 01993 772972 Fax: 01993 776239
Abattoir. Private kill facility.

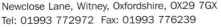

HERTFORDSHIRE / OXFORDSHIRE

RED KITE FARMS

Southend Farm, Turville Heath, Henley On Thames, Oxfordshire, RG9 6JR
Tel: 01491 638155 Fax: 01491 638633 clare@redkitefarms.com www.redkitefarms.com
Mixed organic farm with 400 dairy cows and 1,650 acres. Small on-farm milk processing unit.

ROWSE HONEY LTD

Moreton Avenue, Wallingford, Oxfordshire, OX10 9DE
Tel: 01491 827400 Fax: 01491 827434 rowse.honey@rowsehoney.co.uk www.rowsehoney.co.uk
Importer and processor of organic honey from Argentina, New Zealand and Brazil. Also importer and processor of organic pure Canadian maple syrup. Soil Association no. P2375.

WEST MIDLANDS

HEREFORDSHIRE

ACONBURY SPROUTS LTD

Unit 4, Westwood Industrial Estate, Pontrilas,
Hereford, Herefordshire, HR2 0EL
Tel: 01981 241155 Fax: 01981 241386 info@aconbury.co.uk www.aconbury.co.uk
A speciality food business, growing and supplying fresh ready grown organic beansprouts, sprouted seeds and pulses, including alfalfa, broccoli, radish, leek, mung bean, aduki bean, chickpea, sunflower sprouts and greens, snow pea shoots, and wheatgrass for juicing, sold throughout the UK and Ireland in organic, whole food, health food retailers & vegetable box companies. Ideal as nutritious salad and sandwich ingredients. Fresh wheatgrass, kits, seeds and juicers, also available via mail order. Alternative email and website: philippa@aconbury.co.uk and www.wheatgrass-uk.com.

BATCHLEY MILL ORGANIC FEEDS

Grendon Bishop, Bromyard, Herefordshire, HR7 4TH
Tel: 01885 483377 Fax: 01885 483321
Soil Association P628. The first animal feed business to have SA standard. Organic feeds for most classes of farm livestock.

BIOSPHERE ORGANICS

2 Wynns Green Cottages, Burley Gate,
Hereford, Herefordshire, HR1 3QT
Tel: 01432 820082 Fax: 01432 820088
biosphere-organics@supanet.com www.biosphere-organics.supanet.com
Growers, importers and wholesalers of fresh fruit, vegetables, herbs and spices. We can supply frozen products in bulk. Suppliers to packers, processors, box schemes, restaurants, shops, caterers throughout the UK. Certification by various IFOAM listed overseas certification bodies. Soil Association certification applied for.

EPIKOUROUS UK

2 Wynns Green Cottages, Burley Gate,
Hereford, Herefordshire, HR1 3AT
Tel: 01432 820082 Fax: 01432 820088 biosphere-organics@supanet.com www.epikourous.gr
Greek certified (DIO Greece No. 411-5/481-3/04) grower and processor of organic olives, olive oil, feta cheese and wines from Greece. Wholesale quantities only.

GEIMA UK

2 Wynns Green Cottages, Burley Gate, Hereford, Herefordshire, HR1 3QT
Tel: 01432 820082 Fax: 01432 820088 paulburgess@geima.it www.geima.it
Italian certified growers (Ecocert Italia CDD.OP.C728) of organic citrus (oranges, blood oranges, mandarins, clementines, lemons) and melons. Selling whole or mixed pallets into the UK.

HAYGROVE FRUIT

Redbank, Ledbury, Herefordshire, HR8 2JL
Tel: 01531 631797 Fax: 01531 634069 packhouse@haygrove.co.uk www.haygrove.co.uk
Soil Association Grower code G6412, Processor code P5435 . Fresh fruit and frozen bulk juice sales from organic fruits. Haygrove Organic production in UK, South Africa and Hungary.

JAMES' GOURMET COFFEE CO LTD

Unit 7, Cropper Row, Haigh Ind. Est., Alton Rd.,
Ross on Wye, Herefordshire, HR9 5LA
Tel: 0870 787 0233 Fax: 01989 566244
enquiries@jamesgourmetcoffee.com www.jamesgourmetcoffee.com
Discerning, ethical, passionate coffee specialists. Great coffee! Traditional service.

MEE, J R

Springfield Farm, Steensbridge, Leominster, Herefordshire, HR6 0LU
Tel: 01568 760270 Fax: 01568 760418
Farmers and packers of high grade table birds (chickens and turkeys) for sale to wholesalers and retailers – also at our farm gate.

PAKUCHO (UK)

21 Audley Crescent, Hereford, Herefordshire, HR1 1BW
Tel: 01432 271930 info@pakucho.co.uk www.pakucho.co.uk
Importing naturally pigmented organic cotton from Peru – wholesale & retail. I am involved with the product design and destribution in the UK. Coloured cotton from a fair trade project based in Peru that is helping to preserve almost extinct varietites of cotton. Pakucho introduces coloured cotton with a series of men's and woman's T-shirts. Certified by Skal, Netherlands, No. 5051.

PAUL RICHARDS HERBAL SUPPLIES

The Field, Eardisley, Herefordshire, HR3 6NB
Tel: 01544 327360 Fax: 01544 327360 paul.herbs@ntlworld.com
Soil Association PR10M. Fresh herbal tinctures (echinacea and many others), herbal oils and ointments (comfrey, calendula/hypericum, chickweed, horse chestnut). Wholesale, retail, mail order, own label. Contract herb grower and herbal product supplier.

RAPUNZEL UK

2 Wynns Green Cottages, Burley Gate, Hereford, Herefordshire, HR1 3QT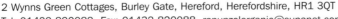
Tel: 01432 820082 Fax: 01432 820088 rapunzelorganic@supanet.com www.rapunzel.com.tr
Swiss certified (IMO No. TR7116) Turkish processor of dried fruits, nuts, olives, seeds, dried legumes, dried vegetables, alll available diced, sliced, powdered. Rapunzel is a 100% organic processing factory. Whole or mixed containers.

THE SEPTEMBER ORGANIC DAIRY

Whitehill Park, Weobley, Herefordshire, HR4 8QE
Tel: 01544 312910 Fax: 01544 312911
sales@september-organic.co.uk www.september-organic.co.uk
Soil Association P4691. Manufacturers of award winning organic ice cream in a range of unusual flavours available for home, retail, catering and wholesale. Member of the Soil Association Organic Farms Network.

HEREFORDSHIRE

STEPHENS, TP
Newton Court, Newton, Leominster, Herefordshire, HR6 0PF
Tel: 01568 611721 tps1@dialstart.net
Soil Association G7479. Organic cider makers.

SUNNYBANK VINE NURSERY

Journey's End, King Street, Ewyas Harold, Hereford, Herefordshire, HR2 0EE
Tel: 01981 240256 vinenursery@hotmail.com www.vinenursery.netfirms.com
Specialist producer of vines for both eating and wine. Plants grown without sprays or artificial fertilisers. Growing collection of seedless and disease-resistant varieties.

WELSH FRUIT STOCKS

Llanerchir, Bryngwyn, via Kington, Herefordshire, HR5 3QZ
Tel: 01497 851209 Fax: 01497 851209 sian@welshfruitstocks.co.uk www.welshfruitstocks.co.uk
Propagators of top quality soft fruit plants, including organic strawberry plants, raspberry canes, black/red/white currant bushes, gooseberry bushes, jostaberry bushes. Mail order gardeners' list and growers' list available.

WESTON'S CIDER

The Bounds, Much Marcle, Ledbury,
Herefordshire, HR8 2NQ
Tel: 01531 660233 Fax: 01531 660619 marketing@westons-cider.co.uk www.westons-cider.co.uk
Soil Association P1776. Westons have been producing cider since 1880. The organic cider was winner at the Organic Food Awards in 1998 and 2003. Producers of Organic Vintage Cider and Organize, the non-alcoholic nutrient drink. Organic Food Awards 2004 Cider Winners.

SHROPSHIRE

BEAFRESH LTD

Unit 2C, Archers Way, Knights Way, Battlefield Enterprise Park, Shrewsbury,
Shropshire, SY1 3AB
Tel: 01743 465060 Fax: 01743 465060
Vegetable processors. Specialists in preparing vegetables for the catering trade.

BELTON CHEESE CO LTD

Belton, Whitchurch, Shropshire, SY13 1JD
Tel: 01948 662125 Fax: 01948 662269 info@beltoncheese.co.uk www.beltoncheese.co.uk
Soil Association registered manufacturer of organic Cheddar, Cheshire, Lancashire, Wensleydale, Caerphilly, Double Gloucester and Red Leicester.

GET REAL (ORGANIC FOODS) LIMITED

Shotton Farm, Shotton Lane, Harmer Hill, Shrewsbury, Shropshire, SY4 3DN
Tel: 01939 210925 info@get-real.co.uk www.get-real.co.uk
Manufacturers of organic meat-free pies and ready meals for major retailers, independent health food stores and via by mail order.

GREENVALE AP LTD

Warrant Rd., Stoke Heath, Market Drayton, Shropshire, TF9 2JJ
Tel: 01630 637444 Fax: 01630 638939 post@greenvale.co.uk www.greenvale.co.uk
Package and trade organic potatoes and make organic dehydrated potato flake, sell organic potato seed.

HEREFORDSHIRE / SHROPSHIRE

GROCONTINENTAL LTD

Whitchurch Business Park, Shakespear Way, Whitchurch, Shropshire, SY13 1LJ
Tel: 01948 666600 hughjones@grocontinental.co.uk www.grocontinental.co.uk
Ingredients and fruit sorting. Multi-temperature storage and distribution with associated added value services; ingredient sorting; blast freezing and re-packing.

THE ORGANIC SMOKEHOUSE

Clunbury Hall, Clunbury,
Nr. Craven Arms, Shropshire, SY7 0HG
Tel: 01588 660206 Fax: 01588 660206
info@organicsmokehouse.com www.organicsmokehouse.com
Multi-award-winning artisan smokehouse. Dedicated organic smokehouse specialising in smoking salmon, various types of cheese, butter and salt. Smoking is carried out without mechanical intervention using traditional 'draft' method. Soil Association licence no. P8263. Organic Food Awards 2004, 2006.

SHROPSHIRE SPICE COMPANY

Unit 10 The Green Ind. Estate, Clun, Craven Arms, Shropshire, SY7 8LG
Tel: 01588 640100 Fax: 01588 640900 office@shropshire-spice.co.uk www.shropshire-spice.co.uk
Soil Association P4316. Manufacturers of dried stuffing mixes: sage & onion, parsley & thyme, celery & leek, garlic herb & mushroom which we supply to the multiples, wholesalers and retail outlets.

SWIFT, RICHARD C – BAKER & CONFECTIONER

Central Bakery, High St., Clee Hill, Nr. Ludlow, Shropshire, SY8 3LZ
Tel: 01584 890003 Fax: 01584 891317 swifts@bakery.co.uk www.swifts.bakery.co.uk
A traditional family craft bakery offering a range of five different organic breads, including organic white, brown, honey and sunflower, sunflower and soya and 100% rye. All hand-crafted.

STAFFORDSHIRE

BESTFOODS UK LTD – FOOD INGREDIENTS

Wellington Road, Burton-On-Trent, Staffordshire, DE14 2AB
Tel: 01283 511111 Fax: 01283 510194 jean.cattenach@unilever.com www.unilever.com
Bestfoods Ingredients specialise in the production of stocks and bouillons for manufacturers of prepared savoury foods. Licensed products include organic vegetable bouillon and organic light bouillon.

BROTHERS BREWING COMPANY LTD

1 Park Lodge House, Bagots Park Estate,
Abbots Bromley, Staffordshire, WS15 3ES
Tel: 020 8859 0606 Fax: 01283 840417 pam@brothersbrewing.co.uk www.freedombeer.com
Freedom Lager was set up in 1995 as Britain's first ever micro-brewed lager. Since then it has gained a Soil Association award for excellence. Freedom is owned by Dirty Pretty Things screenwriter Steven Knight along with brothers Michael and Richard. Not only is Freedom Lager 100% organic, it is vegan certified. It is brewed to the German purity laws, using no chemical ingredients. In an issue of *Arena* magazine, Freedom Lager was chosen as one of the best sixteen lagers in the world, describing it as "worryingly drinkable". Freedom are now brewing a pilsner version at their brewery in Abbots Bromley on a site which has its own pure limestone spring water, filtered over millions of years through layers of natural alabaster.

SHROPSHIRE / STAFFORDSHIRE

EARTHOIL PLANTATIONS LTD

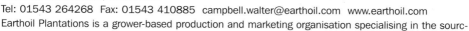

Unit 3, Shires Industrial Estate, Essington Close,
Lichfield, Staffordshire, WS14 9AZ
Tel: 01543 264268 Fax: 01543 410885 campbell.walter@earthoil.com www.earthoil.com
Earthoil Plantations is a grower-based production and marketing organisation specialising in the sourcing and supplying of certified organic essential and vegetable oils.

GLENNANS LTD

Units 4-12, Bridge Street Ind. Estate, Trinity Rd., Uttoxeter, Staffordshire, ST14 8ST
Tel: 01889 567338 Fax: 01889 562701 enquiries@glennans.co.uk www.glennans.co.uk
Soil Association P2184. Snack manufacturer specialising in batch-fried potato crisps, vegetable crisps (parsnip, beetroot, carrot and sweet potato), croutons, crackers and tortillas.

THE KERRYGOLD COMPANY LTD

Barnfields Ind. Estate, Sunnyhills Rd., Leek, Staffordshire, ST13 5SP
Tel: 01538 399111 Fax: 01538 399918 sales@kerrygold.co.uk www.kerrygold.com
Soil Association P5200. Pre-packed natural cheese and grated cheese for retail and industrial applications.

MOORLAND GREEN WASTE

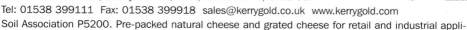

Cresford Farm, Caverswall Lane, Dilhorne, Staffordshire, ST10 2PH
Tel: 01782 397907 Fax: 01782 392928 anne@annewagstaff.wanadoo.co.uk
Producers of organic compost, mulches, soil improver, top soil.

PHYTONE LTD

Third Avenue, Centrum 100, Burton on Trent, Staffordshire, DE14 2WD
Tel: 01283 543300 Fax: 01283 543322 info@phytone.co.uk www.phytone.co.uk
Soil Association P5468. Supplier of a range of organic products including dried herbs and spices, vegetables and fruit juice concentrates and powders, caramel syrup and powder, malt extract, molasses and vanilla.

REGENCY MOWBRAY CO LTD

Hixon Industrial Estate, Hixon, Staffordshire, ST18 0PY
Tel: 01889 270554 Fax: 01889 270927 sales@regencymowbray.co.uk www.regencymowbray.com
Soil Association P4570. Manufacturer of organic food ingredients: organic fruit preparations for yoghurt and ice cream, organic flavourings, organic purées and sauces, natural flavourings for use in organic products.

STAFFORDSHIRE ORGANIC CHEESE

New House Farm, Acton, Newcastle Under Lyme, Staffordshire, ST5 4EE
Tel: 01782 680366 Fax: 01782 680366 d.deaville@virgin.net
Makers of traditional hand-made, hand-pressed cheeses from organic cows milk. Also makers of Whitmore organic sheeps milk cheese.

WOOTTON ORGANIC

Ramshorn, Farley, Oakamoor,
Staffordshire, ST10 3BZ
Tel: 01538 703228 Fax: 01538 709900 wholesale@woottonorganic.co.uk www.daylesford.com
Specialists in the finest organic meats: beef, lamb, venison, pork and poultry. In our organically certified on-site abattoir our Master Butcher prepares cuts fresh to order and will happily discuss specific requirements.

STAFFORDSHIRE

WARWICKSHIRE

CHARLECOTE MILL

Hampton Lucy, Warwick, Warwickshire, CV35 8BB
Tel: 01789 842072 john@charlcotemill.co.uk www.charlecotemill.co.uk
Soil Association P1555. Watermill producing wholemeal flour, including organic.

CITADEL PRODUCTS

32 St. Andrews Crescent, Stratford-Upon-Avon, Warwickshire, CV37 9QL
Tel: 01789 297456 Fax: 01789 297456 info@citadelpolytunnels.com www.citadelpolytunnels.com
Manufacturers of polytunnel greenhouses for over 30 years. Suitable for horticulture, livestock housing, storage etc.

KITCHEN GARDEN

Waverly Centre, Coventry Rd., Cubbington, Warwickshire, CV32 7UJ
Tel: 01926 851415 Fax: 01926 851997
manager@kitchen-garden.co.uk www.kitchen-garden.co.uk
OF&G registered. Range of organic condiments, herbs, spices, nut butters, herbal teas, essential oils. Established 10 years.

WELLESBOURNE WATERMILL

Kineton Road, Wellesbourne, Warwickshire, CV35 9HG
Tel: 01789 470237 hamilton.a@btconnect.com
Traditional water-powered mill that produces organic and non-organic wholemeal stoneground flour and organic and non-organic plain white flour, semolina and bran.

WEST MIDLANDS

FOREVER LIVING PRODUCTS

7 Bradmore Close, Solihull, West Midlands, B91 3ZB
Tel: 0121 713 2084 sarah@discoveraloe.co.uk www.discoveraloe.co.uk
Aloe Vera is the main ingredient in all our products. From topicals to drinks, cosmetics to cleaning products, weight management to supplements. We are the world's largest grower of aloe vera, which is grown organically and is pure and natural as certified by the International Aloe Science Council. Our bee products are also produced using ecologically responsible procedures.

MOODY LTD., JACK

Holly Bush Farm, Warstone Rd., Shareshill,
Wolverhampton, West Midlands, WV10 7LX
Tel: 01922 417648 Fax: 01922 413420
markbeasley@jackmoodylimited.co.uk www.jackmoodylimited.co.uk
Soil Association I4369. Producer of soil conditioners/compost. Centralised composting of green materials for the production of compost, soil conditioner, mulch and top dressing, supplied nationwide. All products accredited to BSI PAS 100.

A.R. PARKIN LTD

Unit 8, Cleton Street Business Park, Cleton Street, Tipton, West Midlands, DY4 7TR
Tel: 0121 557 1150 Fax: 0121 522 4086 enquiries@arparkin.co.uk www.arparkin.co.uk
Soil Association licence number P2508. Manufacturer and supplier of organic seasoning blends, ingredients, herbs, spices, peppers and crumbs.

WARWICKSHIRE / WEST MIDLANDS

phoenix Organics Ltd

Wholesalers of quality organic produce

Specialist suppliers of organic fruit and vegetables to independent retailers, box schemes and caterers. Customer service, attention to detail and reliable produce are our priorities.

Contact details:-

Tel: 01886 880713
Fax: 01886 880743
E-mail: phoenixorganics@btconnect.com
Web: www.phoenixorganics.ltd.uk

WORCESTERSHIRE

ELYSIA NATURAL SKIN CARE

27 Stockwood Business Park, Stockwood, Nr. Redditch, Worcestershire, B96 6SX
Tel: 01386 792622 Fax: 01386 792623 enquiries@drhauschka.co.uk www.drhauschka.co.uk
Elysia distributes the Dr Hauschka skin care range, holistic products using organically grown herbs and plants from certified biodynamic farms. The products and ingredients are not tested on animals.

FERTILE FIBRE

Tenbury Wells, WR15 8LT
Tel: 01584 781575 Fax: 01584 781483 sales@fertilefibre.fsnet.co.uk www.fertilefibre.com
Soil Association I1408. Organic Coir compost. We supply seed, multi-purpose and potting composts, plus Coir blocks, and fertilisers. Trade and mail order services available.

GORSEHILL ABBEY CHEESE

Gorsehill Abbey Farm, Collin Lane, Broadway, WR12 7PB
Tel: 01386 852208 Fax: 01386 858570 cheese@gorsehillabbey.co.uk www.gorsehillabbey.co.uk
Dairy farm producing a wide range of award-winning soft, semi-soft and harder cheeses.

PHOENIX ORGANICS LTD

Pullen's Farm, Bromyard Rd., Cradley, Nr. Malvern, Worcestershire, WR13 5JN
Tel: 01886 880713 Fax: 01886 880743
phoenixorganics@btconnect.com www.phoenixorganics.ltd.uk
We are wholesalers of organic fruits and vegetables, specialising in sales to box schemes, independent retail outlets, farm shops, caterers, processors and other non-supermarket outlets.

PRIMAFRUIT LTD

Enterprise Way, Vale Business Park, Evesham, Worcestershire, WR11 1GT
Tel: 01386 425000 Fax: 01386 425001 www.primafruit.co.uk
Importer of fresh organic fruit including grapes, stone fruit, berries, top fruit and citrus supplies to the industries. Committed to the organic market, growers, customers and consumers.

RED DEER HERBS LTD

Earl's Croome, Worcester, WR8 9DF
Tel: 01386 750734 enquiries@reddeerherbs.co.uk www.reddeerherbs.co.uk
RDH import and grow herbs for the food manufacturing industry. We will supply from 1kg to 1tonne. M&S, Sainsbury, Waitrose, Asda, Tesco sell products with our herbs. Deliveries nationally and throughout Europe.

THE NORTH-EAST

CO. DURHAM

ACORN DAIRY

Archdeacon Newton, Darlington, Co. Durham, DL2 2YB
Tel: 01325 466999 Fax: 01325 464567 organic@acorndairy.co.uk www.acorndairy.co.uk
Process organic milk from own farm delivering to doorsteps in and around the Darlington area with organic bread, eggs, cheeses, youghurts, butter, fruit juices. Poultry once a month.

NAFFERTON ORGANICS

Nafferton Farm, Stocksfield, Northumberland, NE43 7XD
Tel: 01661 832246 Fax: 01661 832246
info@ naffertonorganics.co.uk www.naffertonorganics.co.uk
We supply organically grown vegetables wholesale to box schemes and also supply to local customers via farm gate sales.

SMALES, LC & SON

Thornton Farm, Berwick-Upon-Tweed, Northumberland, TD15 2LP
Tel: 01289 382223 Fax: 01289 382018 janesmales@lcsmales-son.co.uk www.lcsmales-son.co.uk
Organic Farmers & Growers UKF040517. Produce, store and dry organic cereals. Registered organic seed producer. Cater for all orders large and small.

TYNE & WEAR

BLENDEX FOOD INGREDIENTS LTD

Hetton Lyons Industrial Estate, Hetton Le Hole, Tyne & Wear, DH5 0RG
Tel: 0191 517 0944 Fax: 0191 526 9546 blendex@blendex.co.uk www.blendex.co.uk
Blenders of organic herbs and spices for the food industry, specifically meat, poultry and bakery. Soil Association certified no. P1654.

F.M. (FOODS) LTD (TROPICAL WHOLEFOODS)

50 Southwick Ind. Estate, Sunderland, Tyne & Wear, SR5 3TX
Tel: 0191 548 0050 Fax: 0191 516 9946 info@fmfoods.co.uk www.fmfoods.co.uk
Soil Association P4707. Importation of Fairtrade and organic dried fruit and vegetables. Packing of imported products into retail display packs. Processing of imported products into snack bars, for own and private label.

WORCS / DURHAM / TYNE & WEAR

ITALYABROAD.COM
14 Lambert Square, Newcastle-upon-Tyne, Tyne & Wear, NE3 4PB
info@italyabroad.com www.italyabroad.com
Importer of italian organic food and wine from pasta to extra virgin olive oil, the finest Italian produce available online at italyabroad.com.

PUMPHREYS COFFEE LTD
Bridge St., Blaydon, Tyne & Wear, NE21 4JH
Tel: 0191 414 4510 Fax: 0191 499 0526
sales@pumphreys-coffee.co.uk www.pumphreys-coffee.co.uk
Soil Association P4547. Roasters and blenders of the finest quality coffees and teas to the wholesale, retail and catering sectors, established 1750.

TWINING, R & CO LTD
Earl Grey Way, North Shields, Tyne & Wear, NE29 6AR
Tel: 0191 296 0000 www.twinings.com
Soil Association P4121. 295-year-old tea manufacturer. Offers a wide variety of organic tea and infusions.

EAST YORKSHIRE

AARHUS KARLSHAMN UK LIMITED
King George Dock, Hull, HU9 5PX
Tel: 01482 701271 Fax: 01482 709447 steve.tate@aarhusunited.com
Importing, processing and packaging, organic extra virgin olive, safflower, sesame and sunflower oils, palm oil (and fractions) certified by the Soil Association, licence no. P966.

CRANSWICK COUNTRY FOODS
Inglemire Lane, Cottingham, Hull, HU16 4PJ
Tel: 01482 848180 Fax: 01482 876146 jim.brisby@cranswick.co. uk
Producers of fresh pork, sausage, cooked meats.

HUMBER VHB
Common Lane, Welton, Brough, HU15 1UT
Tel: 01482 661600 Fax: 01482 665095 sales@humbervhb.com www.humbervhb.com
Humber VHB are growers and packers of glasshouse grown tomatoes (including speciality), cucumbers, peppers and herbs for the retail market and local box schemes.

HUMDINGER LTD
Gothanburg Way, Sutton Fields Industrial Estate, Hull, HU7 0YG
Tel: 01482 625790 Fax: 01482 625791 paul.sangwin@humdinger-foods.co.uk
Packaging company packing for major brands within the wholefoods industry.

HURRELL AND MCLEAN (HURRELL'S)
Beverley Road, Cranswick, Driffield, YO25 9PF
Tel: 01377 271400 Fax: 01377 271500 nick@hurrells.fsbusiness.co.uk www.hmseeds.co.uk
Specialise in supply of organic farm seeds, forage/grass and combinable crops.

MOTHERHEMP LTD.

Springdale Farm, Rudston, Driffield, YO25 4DJ

Tel: 01262 421100 www.motherhemp.com

MotherHemp produces a quality range of organic hemp food products. Hemp's claim as a super food lies in its balance of essential fatty acids and high quality protein. The range includes: hemp pasta and pesto, Hemp Ice (a dairy-free ice cream), hemp oil and seeds. MotherHemp products will be of interest to anyone on a lactose-free, dairy-free, vegan, low sugar and low gluten diet.

SPRINGDALE CROP SYNERGIES LTD

Springdale Farm, Rudston, Driffield, YO25 4DJ

Tel: 01262 421100 Fax: 01262 421101 info@springdale-group.com www.springdale-group.com

Soil Association P7844. Seed merchant/advisor. Agronomy-based crop development business offering buy-back contracts and advice on organic crops. Supplier and trader of organic seeds and the only UK registered specialist organic oilseed supplier.

YORKSHIRE HEMP LTD

PO Box 120, Driffield, YO25 9YS

Tel: 01924 375475 Fax: 01924 374068 info@yorkshirehemp.com www.yorkshirehemp.com

A complete range of German certified hemp foods such as hemp seeds, hemp oil, shelled hemp seeds, hemp flour, hemp pasta to independent health food shops along with bulk hemp to the baking and food manufacturing industry. Certification: DE-013-OKO-Kontrollstelle D-NW-D-13-2352-B/C.

NORTH YORKSHIRE

AGGLOMERATION TECHNOLOGY LTD

Unit 7, Monkswell Park, Manse Lane, Knaresborough, HG5 8NQ

Tel: 01423 868411 Fax: 01423 868410 paul.cannings@aggtech.co.uk

Agglomeration (granulation) of sweet and savoury powdered ingredients and products (soups, gravy, chocolate drinks etc) and spray crystallisation of real chocolate.

COUNTRY PRODUCTS LIMITED

Unit 11A, Centre Park, Marston Business Park, Tockwith, York, YO26 7QF

Tel: 01423 358858 Fax: 01423 359858 mail@countryproducts.co.uk www.countryproducts.co.uk

Soil Association P1987. Contract packer. Wholesalers and contract packers of high quality food products, especially wholefoods and organic products.

FARNDALE FREE RANGE LTD

Hill Houses, Farndale, Kirkbymoorside, YO62 7LH

Tel: 01751 430323 Fax: 01751 430323 barry@farndale.com www.farndale.com

We produce SA organic eggs to the highest standard, which we deliver to discerning local shops in North Yorkshire, Cleveland and Teeside. We also design websites and provide computer services.

GREENVALE FARMS LTD

Leeming, Northallerrton, DL7 9LY

Tel: 01677 422953 Fax: 01677 425358 marketing@rooster.uk.com

Soil Association I809. Organic fertilisers. Greenvale produce organic pellets and fertilisers for garden centres, horticulture and agriculture.

THE KERFOOT GROUP LTD

Mawson House, The Bridge, Askew, Bedale, DL8 1AW

Tel: 01677 424881 Fax: 01677 422560 packed@kerfootgroup.co.uk www.kerfootgroup.co.uk

Soil Association P5494. Blending, packaging and distribution of vegetable oils to the food, pharmaceutical, technical and pet food industries.

KIRK, GA & SON

The Abattoir, Nunnington, York, YO62 5UU

Tel: 01439 748242 Fax: 01439 788546 ashberrygrangefarm@hotmail.com

We are a small country abattoir able to slaughter any animals, and will deliver (if a volume) by arrangement.

MERCER, HARVEY

Unit 15 Claro Court Business Centre,
Claro Road, Harrogate, HG1 4BA

Tel: 01423 528822 Fax: 01423 529977 enquiries@harveymercer.com www.harveymercer.com

Soil Association P7691. Producerss of Hearty's brand of soy based foods and snacks. These are healthy, vegetarian and often organic and gluten-free.

NEWFIELDS ORGANIC PRODUCE

The Green, Fadmoor, Kirkby Moorside,
North Yorkshire, YO62 7HY

Tel: 01751 431558 Fax: 01751 432061

Farm producing winter vegetables, potatoes, carrots, parsnips, onions, cabbages, swedes, beetroot, parsley, leeks, sprouts, broccoli, cauliflower, celeriac and lettuce. Organic Food Awards 2004 Fresh Fruit and Veg Commended.

R & R TOFU LTD

5 Rye Close, York Road Industrial Park, Malton, North Yorkshire, YO17 6YD

Tel: 01653 690235 info@clearspottofu.co.uk www.clearspottofu.co.uk

Manfacturers and packers of organic tofu and organic tofu products.

STAMFREY FARM ORGANIC PRODUCE

Stamfrey Farm, West Rounton,
Northallerton, North Yorkshire, DL6 2LJ

Tel: 01609 882297 Fax: 01609 882297 info@clottedcream.org

Traditionally made clotted cream using milk from our own dairy herd. Low fat organic yoghurt.

STEENBERGS ORGANIC ENGLISH TEA

PO Box 48, Boroughbridge, YO51 9ZW

Tel: 01765 640088 Fax: 01765 640101 enquiries@steenbergs-tea.com www.steenbergs-tea.com

Organic and Fairtrade single estate loose leaf teas in kraft or aluminium canisters. Great for food halls, delis and tea connoisseurs everywhere. Assam, Darjeeling, Green and Earl Grey. Guest organic teas starting shortly, including Chinese green tea.

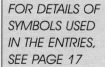

FOR DETAILS OF SYMBOLS USED IN THE ENTRIES, SEE PAGE 17

STEENBERGS ORGANIC PEPPER & SPICE

The Spice Factory, Barker Business Park,
Melmerby, Nr. Ripon, HG4 5NE
Tel: 01765 640088 Fax: 01765 640101 sophie@steenbergs.co.uk www.steenbergs.co.uk
Organic barbeque ribs. Full range of organic pepper, spice and herbs packed in glass, stainless steel, gift boxes and bulk (including seasonings) for food producers. Blends hand-produced in North Yorkshire to our own recipes – from curry powders through to sausage and bacon seasonings. Many of our products are sourced direct from farmers all around the world to ensure freshness and provenance. Wholesale available, packed for retail (including retail support) or bulk for food producers. Traditional Portuguese sea salt also available.

SUNFLOURS

The Hutts Mill, Grewelthorpe, Ripon, HG4 3DA
Tel: 01765 658534 Fax: 01765 658903 info@sunflours.com www.sunflours.com
Soil Association P1495,. We are organic and specialist flour producers and retailers. We mill, blend and supply many types of flour including a large range of gluten-free flour.

TAYLORS OF HARROGATE

Pagoda House, Prospect Rd., Harrogate, HG2 7LD
Tel: 01423 814000 Fax: 01423 814001 www.bettysandtaylors.co.uk
Tea blenders and coffee roasters.

UNITRITION

Olympia Mills, Barlby Rd, Selby, YO8 5AF
Tel: 01757 244111 Fax: 01757 244088 www.unitrition.co.uk
Soil Association registered. Oilseed crusher. Unitrition are specialist oilseed crushers and raw material upgraders, supplying crude oils and expeller cakes to food and agricultural industries.

WESTLER FOODS LTD

Amotherby, Malton, YO17 6TQ
Tel: 01653 693971 Fax: 01653 600187 trevor.newbert@westler.com www.westlerfoods.com
We manufacture the Chesswood range of organic meals in easy open cans: vegetable curry and vegetable hot pot.

YORKSHIRE FARMHOUSE EGGS LTD.

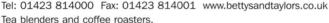

Village Farm, Catton, Thirsk, YO7 4SQ
Tel: 01845 578376 Fax: 01845 578660
enquiries@yorkshirefarmhouse.co.uk www.yorkshirefarmhouse.co.uk
We produce and pack organic eggs ro the highest standards, under the Soil Association and OF&G accreditation schemes. Eggs sold in most multiples and local catering and wholesale businesses.

SOUTH YORKSHIRE

POTTS BAKERS

Stanley Road, Stairfoot, Barnsley, S70 3PG
Tel: 01226 249175 Fax: 01226 249175 potts.bakers@care4free.net www.pottsbakers.co.uk
Soil Association P4477. Bakers of organic bread, cakes and puddings for independent and multiple retailers.

NORTH / SOUTH YORKSHIRE

THE REAL BREAD BAKEHOUSE LTD

Rear of 36 Cat Lane, Sheffield, S2 3AY

Tel: 0114 249 5459 Fax: 0114 281 7965 jcoatman@blueyonder.co.uk

Soil Association P4265. Hand-made organic bread for wholesale to retail outlets (or individuals who order above a minimum quantity and can collect). Deliveries to Sheffield, Nottingham, Leicester, Leeds, Manchester and London.

WEST YORKSHIRE

ELYSIUM NATURAL PRODUCTS LTD

Unit 12, Moderna Business Park, Mytholmroyd, Halifax, HX7 5QQ

Tel: Fax: 01422 884629 elysiumproducts@aol.com

Distribute organic foods: veg in jars, seeds, pulses, cakes, honey, biscuits, tortilla chips, juices, pet food, sweets, chocolate, health bars, gluten-free goods across the whole organic range.

FERREIRA DAC

Rose Cottage, Little Smeaton, Pontefract, WF8 3LF

Tel: 01977 621586 Fax: 01977 621586 ferreiradac@yahoo.co.uk

Exclusive suppliers of hand made Gourmet Organic sauces, pastas, antipasti, extra virgin olive oils, and vinegars from Parma Italy.

FYFFES GROUP LTD

Wakefield 41 Ind. Park, Kenmore Rd., Wakefield, WF2 0XE

Tel: 01924 826446 Fax: 01924 820109 dellam@fyffes.com www.fyffes.com

Ripening bananas, preparing and packing bananas. Distributing bananas to wholesalers and retailers.

GREEN & ORGANIC FESTIVALS

PO Box 41, Ilkley, West Yorkshire, LS29 0DF

Tel: 07812 159392 Fax: 01943 602803 info@go-shows.co.uk www.go-shows.co.uk

All-year-round nationwide organiser of festivals promoting organic and natural products. Dedicated to the environment, Green & Organic Festivals aim to bring together local people with a passion for natural healthy living, face to face with businesses and other organisations working hard to provide supplies and information you can trust. Visit our website for details of events local to you.

HAWORTH SCOURING COMPANY

Cashmere Works, Birksland St, Bradford, BD3 9SX

Tel: 01274 846500 Fax: 01274 846501 timw@haworthscouring.co.uk

Organic washing (scouring) of wool to commercial standards (quantities from 100kgs upwards.)

MONKHILL CONFECTIONERY

Monkhill Works, Ferrybridge Rd., Pontefract, West Yorkshire, WF8 2JS

Tel: 01977 466641 richard.adam@csplc.com

We manufacture and distribute Kernels Organic Popcorn made using traditional popcorn pans in sweet and salted variants.

FOR DETAILS OF
SYMBOLS USED
IN THE ENTRIES,
SEE PAGE 17

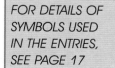

SOUTH / WEST YORKSHIRE

THE ORGANIC & NATURAL PRODUCTS FAIR
Organiser's Office, 44 Middleton Rd., Ilkley, West Yorkshire, LS29 9DZ
Tel: 01943 608642 michellehoggard@hotmail.co.uk
The Organic and Natural Products Fair is held at The Clarke Foley Centre, Cunliffe Rd., Ilkley, West Yorkshire LS29 9DZ every 2nd Sunday of the month. This is an opportunity for predominantly northern quality producers to sell, trial, meet and network with a regular customer base. Alternative contact details for organisers: Michelle Hoggard mobile 07747 782888; Kevin Good 28 Ash Grove, Ilkley, West Yorkshire LS29 8EP, telephone 01943 604590, mobile 07990 703671, email kr.good@googlemail.com.

SUMA WHOLEFOODS

Lacy Way, Lowfields Business Park, Elland, HX5 9DB
Tel: 0845 458 2291 Fax: 0845 458 2295 sales@suma.coop www.suma.co.uk
Soil Association P968. The UK's largest independent wholesaler, of organic, fair trade & natural foods. We also have extensive ranges of special diet and environmentally friendly products. Suppliers of RSPB wildlife friendly foods. Please contact us for more information & our catalogue. Organic Food Awards 2004 Store Cupboard Staples Winner.

THE NORTH-WEST

CHESHIRE

DUCKWORTH FLAVOURS

Astmoor Road, Runcorn, Cheshire, WA7 1PJ
Tel: 0161 886 0226 Fax: 0161 848 7331 www.duckworth.co.uk
Manufacturer of organic fruit juice compounds. Supplier of organic fruit juices. Manufacturer of food flavourings suitable for use in organic products.

GOODLIFE FOODS LTD
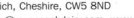
34 Tatton Court, Kingsland Grange, Warrington, Cheshire, WA1 4FF
Tel: 01925 837810 Fax: 01925 838648 enquiry@goodlife.co.uk www.goodlife.co.uk
Manufacturer of frozen vegetarian foods. Soil Association P2241.

RAVENS OAK DAIRY

Burland Farm, Wrexham Road, Burland, Nantwich, Cheshire, CW5 8ND
Tel: 01270 524624 Fax: 01270 524724 info@ravensoakdairy.com www.butlerscheeses.co.uk
Soft cow Brie and fresh cow cheese.

THE SALT COMPANY

Worleston, Nantwich, Cheshire, CW5 6DN
Tel: 01270 611112 Fax: 01270 611113 sales@thesaltcompany.co.uk www.thesaltcompany.co.uk
Importer of Red Sea salt for use in the organic industry. Packer of salt for manufacturing and retail use.

URENBIO

Woodpark, Neston, South Wirral, Cheshire, CH64 7TB
Tel: 0151 353 0330 Fax: 0151 353 0251 fruitworld@uren.com www.uren.com
Soil Association P1723. Urenbio imports, distributes and stocks a wide range of organic ingredients for food manufacturing: fruits, vegetables, beans, seeds, nuts, honey, oils, etc. We also re-clean and pack in our store in Whitchurch, Shropshire.

CUMBRIA

BOCM PAULS LTD

Penrith Industrial Estate, Penrith, Cumbria, CA11 9EH
Tel: 01275 378384 Fax: 01275 373828 mike.thompson@bocmpauls.co.uk www.bocmpauls.co.uk
Soil Association P4688. BOCM Pauls manufacture approved feeds for dairy cows, youngstock, beef, sheep, pigs and poultry. The products are supported by specialist management services for organic producers in England, Wales, Scotland and Northern Ireland.

HARLEY FOODS LTD

Blindcrake Hall, Blindcrake, Cockermouth, Cumbria, CA13 0QP
Tel: 01900 823037 Fax: 01900 828276
Importer of organic dried fruits, nuts, beans, pulses, herbs, spices, plus a large variety of ingredients for the wholesaler and manufacturer. We also source products on demand.

LANCASHIRE

COMMERCIAL FREEZE DRY LTD

45 Roman Way, Longridge Rd., Ribbleton, Preston, Lancashire, PR2 5BD
Tel: 01772 654441 Fax: 01772 655004
gh@commercialfreezedry.co.uk www.commercialfreezedry.co.uk
Soil Association P2697. Freeze drying on a commission dry or product sourced basis of any organic products. Meat, dairy, fruit, vegetables, all handled.

ECOS PAINTS

Unit 34, Heysham Business Park, Middleton Rd., Heysham, Cumbria, LA3 3PP
Tel: 01524 852371 Fax: 01524 858978 mail@ecospaints.com www.ecospaints.com
Organic odourless solvent-free paints, varnishes and other related products.

ENVIROSYSTEMS (UK) LTD/GREENLANDS NUTRITION LTD

  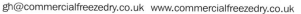

Pasture View, Barton Cross Park, Barton,
Preston, Lancashire, PR3 5AX
Tel: 01772 860085 Fax: 01772 866077 sales@envirosystems.co.uk www.envirosystems.co.uk
EnviroBed™ heat-treated bedding is affordable and hygienic and ensures clean, healthy livestock. From the beginning our respect for animals has been our inspiration for making the best products in the field to improve animal welfare and their environment. EnviroSystems also specialise in production of biological additives for bedding and slurry. Our bedding and associated products provide animals with the support necessary to maintain optimal health and wellbeing. EnviroSystems (UK) Ltd and its associate company Greenlands Nutrition offer innovative solutions in areas of environmental welfare, animal nutrition and sustainable farming systems.

LEHMANN SFI LTD, GUY

Alston House, White Cross, South Road, Lancaster, Lancashire, LA1 4QX
Tel: 01524 581560 Fax: 01524 581562 sales@guylehmann.com www.guylehmann.com
Specialists in supply of organic bulk dry mustard ingredients. Bulk organic wine, spirit and speciality vinegar. Organic sunflower, millet, linseed, caraway, pumpkin. All UK and Europe – minimum delivery: dry goods 25kg, liquids 1000ltrs.

NUTRIMATE LIMITED

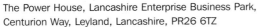

The Power House, Lancashire Enterprise Business Park,
Centurion Way, Leyland, Lancashire, PR26 6TZ
Tel: 01772 641181 Fax: 01772 641178 nutrimate@aol.com
NutriMate mineral and TTL plus liquid for trace elements, excellent nutrient utilization and reduced leeching in all growing conditions. NutriMate and TTL plus are naturally occurring organic chelation agents that improve growth dramatically wherever they are applied. Excellent on light soils.

OLVERSON LTD, NORMAN

Kershaw's Farm, Smithy Lane, Scarisbrick,
Ormskirk, Lancashire, L40 8HL
Tel: 01704 840392 Fax: 01704 841096 sales@redvelvet.co.uk www.redvelvet.co.uk
Farming. Prepacking and beetroot processing. Soil Association P2631. Vegetables.

PENNINE ORGANICS LTD

The Poultry Farm, Square Lane, Catforth, Preston,
Lancashire, PR4 0HQ
Tel: 01772 690261 Fax: 01772 690985
martin@pennineorganics.co.uk www.pennineorganics.co.uk
Pelleted, crumbled, micro poultry manure. Liquid feeds – plant 6:2:4, tomato 4:2:6. Liquids mixed to your own specification.

SAKER VEGERTARIAN FOODS LTD

Canteen Mill, Burnley Road, Todmorden, Lancashire, OL14 7DR
Tel: 01706 818189 Fax: 01706 818189 bdb1205691@hotmail.co.uk
Small, long established wholesale bakers, supplying the north of England. We specialise in organic breads and sugar-free cakes. We also produce vegan and vegetarian savouries, flapjacks and crumbles.

STAVELEY'S EGGS LTD

Coppull Moor Farm, Preston Road, Coppull, Nr. Chorley, Lancashire, PR7 5EB
Tel: 01257 791595 Fax: 01257 794700 eggs@staveleys.sagehost.co.uk www.staveleyseggs.co.uk
Organic egg production and distribution, Lion quality standards and RSPCA Freedom Food standards, wholesale deliveries, most places to shops etc. Eggs in pre-packs to Organic Food Federation standards.

ISLE OF MAN

MANN SPECIALITY FOODS

Kere-Volley, Cordeman Saint Marks, Ballasalla, Isle of Man, IM9 3AJ
Tel: 01624 851971 Fax: 01624 852418 raratcliffe.honey@manx.net
Import and distribution of organic honey.

GREATER MANCHESTER

ANTONELLI BROTHERS LTD

The Bakery, Weymouth Rd., Eccles, Greater Manchester, M30 8FB
Tel: 0161 789 4485 Fax: 0161 789 5592 info@antonelli.co.uk www.antonelli.co.uk
Soil Association P6011. The UK specialist maker of ice cream cones. Organic sugar and Smoothy Waffle cones stocked, others made to order with 8 weeks notice. Main stockists are Yeo Valley in Devon (home of Rocombe Ice Cream) and September Dairy Ice Cream in Herefordshire. Direct deliveries can be arranged.

ECO-INTERIORS OF CHORLTON

9 Hazel Court, Dudley Rd., Whalley Range, Manchester, Greater Manchester, M16 8DS
Tel: 0161 861 8219 scorble@yahoo.co.uk
Painters, decorators and floor sanders. We provide a high quality painting and decorating service using only organic, solvent-free products from recognised sources. We also sand floors and varnish and treat garden fences/sheds.

LEES, JW & CO, (BREWERS) LTD

Greengate Brewery, Middleton Junction, Greater Manchester, M24 2AX
Tel: 0161 643 2487 Fax: 0161 655 3731 giles.dennis@jwlees.co.uk www.jwlees.co.uk
Soil Association P7505. Brewers.

MARBLE BEERS LTD

73 Rochdale Rd., Manchester, Greater Manchester, M4 4HY
Tel: 0161 819 2694 Fax: 0161 819 2694 www.marblebeer.co.uk
Organic and vegan brewery, situated within Marble Arch Inn, producing four regular ales plus seasonals. Beer is available through Marble Arch and other free houses around the country on request.

ORGANIC 2000 LTD

Unit D27, New Smithfield Market, Openshaw, Greater Manchester, M11 2WJ
Tel: 0161 223 4944 Fax: 0161 223 4955 info@ organic2000.co.uk www.organic2000.co.uk
Umbrella co-operative. Largest and longest established organic fruit and vegetable wholesaler in the north-west and beyond. We supply box schemes and retail outlets, sourcing extensively from local producers. We offer an extensive list of fruit, veg, dairy products and more, including imported goods. Fair trade goods are supported. Deliveries available.

ORIGINAL ORGANICS

E15/16 New Smithfield Market, Whitworth St., Openshaw,
Manchester, Greater Manchester, M11 2WJ
Tel: 0161 220 7788 Fax: 0161 220 9906 originalorganics@hotmail.com
We work with local producers of fresh organic food and import when necessary to generate a comprehensive list of fruit, veg, milk, cheese, eggs, butter and sprouted seeds offered to shops, box schemes, caterers. Delivery possible.

MERSEYSIDE

ASSOCIATED BRITISH PORTS GARSTON

Dock Rd., Garston, Liverpool, Merseyside, L19 2JW
Tel: 0151 427 5971 Fax: 0151 494 3232 garston@abports.co.uk www.abports.co.uk
Soil Association P6728. ABP Garston is fully experienced in the handling, storage and distribution of organic agribulk products.

NORTHERN IRELAND

BULRUSH HORTICULTURE

Newferry Rd., Bellaghy, Magherafelt, Co. Londonderry, Northern Ireland, BT45 8ND
Tel: 028 7938 6555 Fax: 028 7938 6741 bulrush@bulrush.co.uk www.bulrush.co.uk
Soil Association I2467. Suppliers and manufacturers of organic substrates for use in the horticulture industry.

SCOTLAND

ABERDEENSHIRE

ABERDEENSHIRE

FEARNS
Redford Farm, Garvock, Laurencekirk, Aberdeenshire, AB30 1HS
Tel: 01561 378861 allan@fearns.uk.com www.fearns.uk.com
Swede grown, washed and packed for various outlets.

GRAMPIAN COUNTRY FOOD (BANFF) LTD
Tannery St., Banff, Aberdeenshire, AB45 1FR
Tel: 01261 815881 Fax: 01261 818387 cbarrie@gcfg.com www.gcfg.com
Soil Association P7487, CMI organic standards. Processors of whole chickens.

HOWEGARDEN, A DIVISION OF TRUXPLUS LTD
Auchturless, Turriff, Aberdeen, Aberdeenshire, AB53 8EN
Tel: 01888 511808 Fax: 01888 511841 info@truxplushowegarden.co.uk
Commercially pack organic produce for the wholesale market and primary pack for major supermarket chains. Specialise in locally grown produce.

KINNAIRDY ORGANICS
Mains Of Kinnairdy, Bridge Of Marnoch, Huntly,
Aberdeenshire, AB54 7RX
Tel: 01466 780856 Fax: 01466 780856 johns@kinnairdyorganics.freeserve.co.uk
Producers of organic cereals and pulses, manufacturer of organic animal feeds. Mobile: 07803 142167.

SALMAC SALES LTD
4 Albyn Terrace, Aberdeen, Aberdeenshire, AB10 1YP
Tel: 01224 626261 Fax: 01224 626206 info@salmac.co.uk www.salmac.co.uk
Salmac is the only supplier of Shetland organic salmon approved by the main organic certifying authority in the UK, the Soil Association. The salmon is also certified by Ecocert Sas for French customers.

UNITED FISH PRODUCTS
Greenwell Place, Aberdeen, Aberdeenshire, AB12 3AY
Tel: 01224 854444 Fax: 01224 854333 chreea@ufp.co.uk www.iaws.ie
Soil Association P3007. UFP manufactures 'organic fish meal' to Soil Association standards from local fish trimmings. The company is accredited to the Femas standard and can assure safe, pure and traceable fish meal.

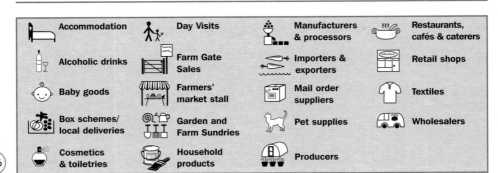

Accommodation	Day Visits	Manufacturers & processors	Restaurants, cafés & caterers
Alcoholic drinks	Farm Gate Sales	Importers & exporters	Retail shops
Baby goods	Farmers' market stall	Mail order suppliers	Textiles
Box schemes/ local deliveries	Garden and Farm Sundries	Pet supplies	Wholesalers
Cosmetics & toiletries	Household products	Producers	

ANGUS

SKEA ORGANICS

East Mains Farm, Auchterhouse,
Dundee, Angus, DD3 0QN
Tel: 01382 320453 Fax: 01382 320454 enquiries@ skeaorganics.co.uk www.skeaorganics.co.uk
Soil Association SP7982. We are a family business and leading growers and suppliers of organic seed
potatoes. We supply growers of all sizes throught the UK and Ireland as well as in a number of other
European countries. Our range of almost 30 varieties is selected for organic farming as well as being
selected for taste and a wide range of cooking methods. We also supply a range of vegetables and
ware/consumption potatoes of most of our 30 seed varieties. These are supplied throughout the year
from early potatoes in June of cold stored potatoes in May.

FIFE

ST. ANDREW'S ABATTOIR CO LTD

Largo Road, St Andrews, Fife, KY16 8NH
Tel: 01334 477313 Fax: 01334 477966
Run by butchers to service butchers. Cattle, sheep, pigs. Traditionally dressed by craftsmen. Chilling
facilities second to none. Deliveries throughout Fife, Lothian and Tayside. Casualty slaughter outside
business hours: 01382 553745.

HIGHLAND

AQUASCOT GROUP LTD

Fyrish Way, Alness, Highland, IV17 0PJ
Tel: 01349 884481 Fax: 01349 884176 www.foodfirst.co.uk
A Highland based manufacturer of fresh and frozen fish products. Scottish organic salmon is a key raw
material from which the company continues to base its new product development.

EDINBURGH SMOKED SALMON CO LTD

1 Strathview, Dingwall Business Park, Dingwall, Highland, IV15 9XD
Tel: 01349 860600 Fax: 01389 860606 essco@btconnect.com
Soil Association P6793. Smoked salmon company specialising in high quality consistent products with
a degree of innovation.

MILLERS OF SPEYSIDE

Strathspey Ind. Estate, Grantown on Spey, Highland, PH26 3NB
Tel: 01479 872520 Fax: 01479 872892 info@millersofspeyside.co.uk www.millersofspeyside.co.uk
Millers of Speyside are a small private abattoir situated in the Highlands of Scotland. Suppliers of qual-
ity beef, lamb and pork to the catering and retail trade.

NATURAL VEGETABLE COMPANY

Clachandreggy, Torbreck, Inverness, Highland, IV2 6DJ
Tel: 01463 250440 Fax: 01463 709515 maggie.natveg@btinternet.com
Growing salad produce for sale to local hotels and restaurants in addition to box scheme run by oth-
ers. Produce includes salad, tunnel grown summer crops, herbs and other more common veg.

POYNTZFIELD HERB NURSERY

Black Isle, By Dingwall, Highland, IV7 8LX

Tel: 01381 610352 Fax: 01381 610352 info@poyntzfieldherbs.co.uk www.poyntzfieldherbs.co.uk

BDAA 326. We are biodynamic growers of over 400 varieties of herbal plants and seeds, especially medicinals. Not importers, we export mainly to EU countries.

TIO LTD (THIS IS ORGANICS)

13 Greshop Road, Forres, Highland, IV36 2GU

Tel: 01309 696040 Fax: 01309 696060 mail@tio.co.uk www.tio.co.uk

Growers, packers and importers of organic root vegetables. Supply wholesale and multiple markets.

LANARKSHIRE

BLACKMOUNT ORGANICS

8 The Wynd, Biggar, Lanarkshire, ML12 6BU

Tel: 01899 221747 Fax: 01899 221518 orgmeat@aol.com www.scottishorganicmeats.com

BDAA 275. Family-run business dedicated to the supply of finest Scottish produced organic and biody-namic beef, lamb, pork and poultry. Sausages and bacon also available. Wholesale and mail order.

BROUGHTON ALES

Broughton, Biggar, Lanarkshire, ML12 6HQ

Tel: 01899 830345 Fax: 01899 830474 beer@broughtonales.co.uk www.broughtonales.co.uk

Soil Association P4734. Brewers of organic ales: Border Gold organic ale, Angel organic lager, Waitrose organic ale and Marks & Spencers organic ale and lager. All products available in 500ml bottles.

CRAIGTON PACKAGING

43-45 Scott's Road, Paisley, Lanarkshire, PA2 7AN

Tel: 0141 887 0244 Fax: 0141 887 5462 info@craigton.com www.craigton.com

Specialist contract bottling and packing company. Three expert business areas: bottling fine alcohol; packing, assembly and QA services to print and publishing industry; and wrapping bagging and filling operations. Services the UK and international customers.

THE NATURAL FRUIT & BEVERAGE COMPANY LIMITED

Viewfield Park, Viewfield Road, Coatbridge, Lanarkshire, ML5 5QS

Tel: 01236 429042 Fax: 01236 424234 gerry@nfbc.biz

Manufacturer of organic fruit juices.

SCOBIE & JUNOR

1 Singer Rd., Kelvin Industrial Estate, East Kilbride, Lanarkshire, G75 0XS

Tel: 01355 237041 Fax: 01355 576343 info@scobie-junor.co.uk www.scobiesdirect.co.uk

Suppliers of organic ingredients, and blended organic products for the meat and bakery industry.

100% ARABICA LTD

Schoolhouse, Lamington, Lanarkshire, ML12 6HW

Tel: 0131 208 3883 Fax: 08700 521515 buycoffee@100arabica.com www.100arabica.com

Gourmet and speciality coffee from Cafe Britt, organic shade-grown Costa Rican coffee, organic shade-grown 'Pachamama' Peruvian coffee.

HIGHLAND / LANARKSHIRE

LOTHIAN

BONALY FARM DAIRY

8 Dryden Rd., Loanhead, Lothian, EH20 9LZ
Tel: 0131 440 0110 Fax: 0131 440 1012
Soil Association P7338. Process and deliver to Edinburgh and surrounding area fresh organic milk and cream. Also suppliers of other dairy products, both organic and non-organic.

THE CALEDONIAN BREWING CO LTD

42 Slateford Road, Edinburgh, Lothian, EH11 1PH
Tel: 0131 337 1286 Fax: 0131 313 2370 www.caledonian-brewery.co.uk
Soil Association P903. Britain's first licensed organic brewer. Caledonian brews the world-renowned Golden Promise organic beer, available in most UK supermarkets.

DODS OF HADDINGTON

Backburn, Letham Rd., Haddington, Lothian, EH41 4NN
Tel: 01620 823305 Fax: 01620 824406
Soil Association SP6841. Dods of Haddington Limited established 1782, are growers and producers of agricultural seeds for the organic farmer and grower.

MACRAE HOLDINGS

Macrae Edinburgh, 50A West Harbour Road, Granton, Edinburgh, Lothian, EH5 1PP
Tel: 0131 552 5215 Fax: 0131 552 7521 donna.mccalman@macrae.co.uk www.macrae.co.uk
A processor of ready-to-eat seafood products, including organic Scottish smoked salmon, organic salmon pâté, organic trout pâté, organic hot smoked trout fillets and organic Scottish salmon gravelax. Licence P5868. Deliveries to UK and EEC.

NAIRN'S OAT CAKES

90 Peffermill Road, Edinburgh, Lothian, EH16 5UU
Tel: 0131 620 7000 Fax: 0131 620 7750 info@nairns-oatcakes.com www.nairns-oatcakes.com
Nairn's produce a range of oat cakes and oat biscuits. All of Nairn's products are wheat-free and contain no hydrogenated fat, no artificial colourings, flavourings or preservatives and no GM ingredients. They are suitable for vegetarians and vegans and for anyone with an allergy to nuts.

ORGANIC WORLD (SCOTLAND) LTD

Block 3, Unit 8, Whiteside Industrial Estate,
Bathgate, Lothian, EH48 2RX
Tel: 01506 632911 Fax: 01506 652444 trading@organic-world.co.uk www.organic-world.co.uk
We are primary wholesalers of organically grown fruit and vegetables supplying throughout Scotland and Northern England. We also have a retail shop on our premises where the public can buy fruit and vegetables, chilled, dairy and grocery products, all from organic production. Open Monday–Friday 8.30am–5.00pm.

PATERSON ARRAN LTD

The Royal Burgh Bakery, Livingston, Lothian, EH54 5DN
Tel: 01506 431031 Fax: 01506 432800 enquiries@paterson-arran.com www.paterson-arran.com
Producers of organic shortbread, oatcakes and biscuits, marmalades, preserves and chutneys.

SEAVEG

55 Wallace Cresent, Roslin, Lothian, EH25 9LN

Tel: 0131 440 4104 maire@seaveg.co.uk www.seaveg.co.uk

We supply a range of quality Seaveg,including Dulse, wakame, Kombu, Carragheen & Mixed SeaSalad. Our Seaveg is wild (non-farmed), hand harvested and all locally sourced from the unspoilt Atlantic shores of West Donegal. We supply retail and wholesale customers and aim to keep our prices as low as possible and our product as natural and unprocessed as possible.

SIMMERS OF EDINBURGH LTD

90 Peffermill Road, Edinburgh, Lothian, EH16 5UU

Tel: 0131 620 7000 Fax: 0131 620 7750

info@simmersofedinburgh.co.uk www.nairns-oatcakes.com

Producers of organic oat cakes and biscuits.

SIMPLY ORGANIC

19/21 Dryden Vale, Bilston Glen, Lothian, EH20 9HN

Tel: 0131 448 0440 belindaandchristine@simplyorganic.co.uk www.simplyorganic.co.uk

Simply Organic are an award-winning, all-organic company. We produce fresh organic convenience products including soups, pasta sauces and ready meals all of which are suitable for vegetarians, under the Simply Organic brand.

ISLE OF MULL

ISLAND BAKERY ORGANICS

Tobermory, Isle of Mull, PA65 6PY

Tel: 01688 302223 Fax: 01688 302378 organics@islandbakery.co.uk www.islandbakery.co.uk

Soil Association P6294. Producers of award-winning organic biscuits, first launched in September 2001. Available in delicatessens, organic stores, food halls and farm shops across the UK. See our website for more information.

ORKNEY ISLANDS

THE ORKNEY SALMON COMPANY LTD

Crowness Crescent, Hatston, Kirkwall,

Orkney, Orkney Islands, KW15 1RG

Tel: 01856 876101 Fax: 01856 873846 enquiries@orkneysalmon.co.uk www.orkneysalmon.co.uk

Soil Association SP2924. The pure waters off the coast of Orkney, where the North Sea and the Atlantic Ocean collide, are the ideal natural environment for raising organic salmon. Soil Association approved. See also www.aquascot.com.

STOCKAN & GARDENS

25 North End Road, Stromness, Orkney Islands, KW16 3AG

Tel: 01856 850873 Fax: 01856 850213

info@stockan-and-gardens.co.uk www.stockan-and-gardens.co.uk

Soil Association P1905. Manufacturer of traditional oatcakes.

PERTH & KINROSS

HIGHLAND SPRING LTD

Stirling St., Blackford, Auchterarder, Perth & Kinross, PH4 1QA

Tel: 01764 660500 Fax: 01764 660501 www.highland-spring.com

Soil Association G5068. Highland Spring is the UK's leading producer of natural mineral water. In 2001 Highland Spring became the first British brand of natural mineral water to achieve organic status for its catchment area, granted by the Soil Association.

MAINS OF MURTHLY

Mains of Murthly, Aberfeldy, Perth & Kinross, PH15 2EA

Tel: 01887 829899

Produce top quality organic lamb and beef in a continuous 12 month supply, all finished in perfect condition for the consumer.

STIRLINGSHIRE

GLENSIDE ORGANICS

2/4 Bandeath Ind. Estate, Throsk, Stirling, Stirlingshire, FK7 7XY

Tel: 01786 816655 Fax: 01786 816100 info@glensideorganics.co.uk www.glensidefarming.co.uk

Glenside's fertility farming system uses the Albrecht soil analysis, natural soil conditioning fertilisers and seaweed products optimising farm resources in the profitable production of quality crops and healthy livestock.

STRATHCLYDE

GREENCITY WHOLEFOODS

23 Fleming St., Glasgow, Strathclyde, G31 1PQ

Tel: 0141 554 7633 sales@greencity.co.uk www.greencity.co.uk

Soil Association P2370.Wholesaler and distributor of wide range of vegetarian wholefoods, including many organic, Fairtrade and vegan products. Also stock organic wines and beers and eco-friendly cleaning products.

INGRAM BROTHERS LTD

12 Lawwmoor Place, Dixons Blazes Ind. Estate, Glasgow, Strathclyde, G5 0YE

Tel: 0141 429 2224 Fax: 0141 429 2227

Soil Association P3006. Manufacturers of bakery ingredients including organic icings, toppings, marzipan and icing sugar. Wholesaler of organic sugar and cocoa powder.

WESTERN ISLES

WEST MINCH SALMON LTD

Gramsdale Factory, Gramsdale, Benbecula, Western Isles, HS7 5LZ

Tel: 01870 602081 Fax: 01870 602083 wmsltd@zetnet.co.uk

Soil Association SG6059 (production), SP5504 (processing). Producers of organic farmed Atlantic salmon.

WALES

CARMARTHENSHIRE

BLACK MOUNTAIN FOODS LTD

Beechwood, Llandeilo, Carmarthenshire, SA19 2HR
Tel: 01558 823424 Fax: 01558 823734 mynydddu@aol.com www.blackmountainfoods.co.uk
Soil Association G1802. Specialise in the distribution of organic meat to retailers in London and the
south of England. We are now expanding our operation to include the distribution of organic cheese,
vegetables and other products.

CALON WEN ORGANIC MILK CO-OPERATIVE

Unit 4, Whitland Industrial Estate, Whitland, Carmarthenshire, SA34 0HR
Tel: 01994 241481 Fax: 01994 241482 info@calonwen-cymru.com www.calonwen-cymru.com
Calon Wen is a fast-growing dairy co-operative currently owned by 20 family farms across Wales, supplying key organic dairy businesses and producing our own branded milk and butter. We believe in ethical trade, providing premium quality products with a universal appeal. The milk and dairy products you
buy from comes from organic milk from our cows, milked by us. All refreshingly simple; if you would
like to know more about us or our products, please do not hesitate to call.

CALON WEN ORGANIC FOODS

Unit 4, Whitland Industrial Estate, Spring Gardens,
Whitland, Carmarthenshire, SA34 0HR
Tel: 01994 241368 Fax: 01994 241063 orderline@calonwen-cymru.com www.calonwen.co.uk
Calon Wen Organic Foods deliver fresh organic fruit, vegetables and dairy products direct to retailers,
wholesalers and households across Wales and the Borders. We buy as much as possible from local
Welsh farms, we ensure all our growers receive a fair price and we pride ourselves our excellent service.

DUNBIA

Teify Park, Llanbydder, Carmarthenshire, SA40 9QE
Tel: 01570 480284 Fax: 01570 480260 www.dunbia.com
Abattoir. Lamb slaughtering and processing. Beef, slaughtering only.

FRANKLANDS FARM FEEDS

Unit 23 Anthony's Way, Cillefwr Ind. Estate, Johnstown, Carmarthen,
Carmarthenshire, SA31 3RB
Tel: 01267 222422 Fax: 01267 237479
amorrey@countrywidefarmers.co.uk www.countrywidefarmers.co.uk
Producers of approved non-organic ruminants coarse mixtures. SA 16, 18 and 20 are non-mineralised
mixes designed for a variety of ruminant feeding situations. Bags or bulk throughout south and mid-Wales.

KITE WHOLEFOODS

Y Cadw, 38 Fford Aneurin, Pontyberem, Carmarthenshire, SA15 5DF
Tel: 01269 871035 Fax: 01269 871035
enquiries@kitewholefoods.co.uk www.kitewholefoods.co.uk
Soil Association P5857. Producing award-winning and highly acclaimed organic mayonnaise in retail
and catering packs.

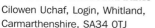   

LLANBOIDY CHEESEMAKERS
Cilowen Uchaf, Login, Whitland,
Carmarthenshire, SA34 0TJ
Tel: 01994 448303 Fax: 01994 448303 sue@llanboidycheese.co.uk
Soil Association P7158. Award-winning Cilowen Organic Cheese made on the farm in west Wales using local organic milk. Milk is pasteurised on-farm and cheese hand-made in traditional way, hard-pressed slowly and matured in its own natural rind to produce a distinctly different truckle cheese. 'Best New Organic Cheese' & Gold Medal, British Cheese Awards 2001. 'Best New Cheese Marketed in UK', World Cheese Awards 2001. Suitable for vegetarians. Organic Food Awards 2004 Cheese Commended.

PENCAE MAWR TRADITIONAL FARM FOODS

Pencaemawr, Llanfynydd, Carmarthen,
Carmarthenshire, SA32 7TR
Tel: 01558 668613 organic.chutney@ntlworld.com
As a diversification from our organic farm, we produce certified organic chutneys and preserves using locally produced ingredients wherever possible. Small batches and long cooking times give our chutneys a depth of flavour not possible with mass-produced products.

CEREDIGION
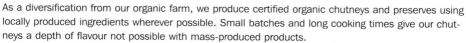

HOLDEN, PH & RM
Bwlchwernen Fawr, Llangybi, Lampeter, Ceredigion, SA48 8PS
Tel: 01570 493244 pholden@soilassociation.org
Soil Association symbol no. HO9WW. Established 1973. Ayrshire dairy herd of 60, 6 x beef cross Welsh Black, 12 acres of oats, 12 acres of carrots. Farmed at 720 feet.

THE KNOBBLY CARROT FOOD COMPANY
Unit 18, Llanbed Business Park, Tregaron Rd., Lampeter, Ceredigion, SA48 8LT
Tel: 01570 422064 Fax: 01570 422064 sales@theknobblycarrot.co.uk www.theknobblycarrot.co.uk
Manufacturers of fresh organic soups, ready to eat salads and sandwich fillings available to retailers and foodservice. Our real food products are healthy, convenient and delicious. Soil Association certified.

ORGANIC FARM FOODS

Llambed Enterprise Park, Tregaron Rd., Lampeter, Ceredigion, SA48 8LT
Tel: 01570 423099 Fax: 01570 423280 www.organicfarmfoods.co.uk
Widest range of fresh fruit and vegetables available for supermarkets, wholesalers, retailers and processors.

RACHEL'S ORGANIC DAIRY
Unit 63, Glanyrafon Industrial Estate, Aberystwyth, Ceredigion, SY23 2AE
Tel: 01970 625805 Fax: 01970 626591 enqs@rachelsorganic.co.uk www.rachelsorganic.co.uk
Organic dairy products, made solely from fresh liquid milk, organic fruit, organic sugar and live cultures. No flavours, colours, preservatives or stabilisers used. Soil Association certified. Nationwide coverage.

TROPICAL FOREST PRODUCTS
P.O. Box 92, Aberystwyth, Ceredigion, SY23 1AA
Tel: 01970 832511 Fax: 01970 832911 mail@tropicalforest.com www.tropicalforest.com
Soil Association no. P923. Importers, packers and sellers of exotic honey. We have a particular interest in promoting the produce of traditional regional artisans. Our Zambian and Tanzanian honey and wax carry Soil Association approval.

CLWYD

CALYPSO SOFT DRINKS LTD

Spectrum Business Park, Wrexham Industrial Estate,
Wrexham, Clwyd, LL13 9QA
Tel: 01978 668400 Fax: 01978 668430 www.calypso.co.uk
Calypso manufactures and markets Calypso Organics – a range of children's organic juice drinks in 250ml cartons – to both multiple retail and foodservice. Made with natural mineral water, three flavours are available: tropical, orange and forest fruits.

WILLIS LTD, JH

Gresford Bank, Gresford, Wrexham, Clwyd, LL12 8UT
Tel: 01978 852220 Fax: 01978 853737 transport@jhwillisltd.co.uk www.jhwillisltd.co.uk
Transport. We carry ex-farm organic milk for OMSCO, Calon Wen, South Caernarvon and Dairy Farmers of Britain.

FLINTSHIRE

ALEMBIC PRODUCTS LTD

River Lane, Saltney, Nr. Chester, Flintshire, CH4 8RQ
Tel: 01244 680147 Fax: 01244 680155 sales@alembicproducts.co.uk www.alembicproducts.co.uk
Manufacturer of variety of organic mayonnaises and dressings.

GLAMORGAN

SUNSCOOP PRODUCTS LTD

Units K1/K3 Coedcae Lane Ind.Estate, Pontyclun, Glamorgan, CF72 9HG
Tel: 01443 229229 Fax: 01443 228883 nuts@sunscoop.co.uk
Manufacturers of natural and processed nut products for retail outlets and the industrial sector.

GWENT

ABERGAVENNY FINE FOODS

Castle Meadows Park, Abergavenny, Gwent, NP7 7RZ
Tel: 01873 850001 Fax: 01873 736988 sales@abergavenny.uk.com
Producers and importers of a wide range of organic dairy products including fresh and aged cheeses in both brand and private label formats. Supplying wholesale, independent and multiple stores.

FARMHOUSE FREEDOM EGGS
Great House, Gwehelog, Monmouthshire, Gwent, NP15 1RJ
Tel: 01291 673129 Fax: 01291 672766 david@freedomeggs.co.uk www.freedomeggs.co.uk
We produce organic eggs in pre-packs for retail and on trays for the catering trade. We also supply mayonnaise, pickled eggs and egg products.

G COSTA & CO LTD

Prince Of Wales Industrial Estate, Abercarn, Gwent, NP11 5AR
Tel: 01495 244721 Fax: 01495 244626 www.gcosta.co.uk
We manufacture an extensive range of quality sauces for the retail, industrial and catering sector. We can offer an array of pack formats from sachets, bottles, jars, catering to bulk formats. Soil Association approved.

CLWYD / FLINT / GLAM / GWENT

GWYNEDD

THE ANGLESEY SEA SALT COMPANY LTD

Brynsigncyn, Anglesey, Gwynedd, LL61 6TQ

Tel: 01248 430871 Fax: 01248 430213 enq@seasalt.co.uk www.seasalt.co.uk

Halen Mon is pure, hand-harvested sea salt from the Atlantic waters around Anglesey. Organically certified, it is available in pure, white flakes, hand mixed with warm organic spices, gently smoked over Welsh oak, and, new for 2007, blended with Tahitian vanilla for a luxurious, sweet-tasting flake. The company is also showing a range of salt gifts beautifully presented in gift boxes finished with tissue paper and ribbon, and bath and shower products too.

WELSH LADY PRESERVES

Y Ffor, Pwllheli, Gwynedd, LL53 6RL

Tel: 01766 810496 Fax: 01766 810067

info@welshladypreserves.com www.welshladypreserves.com

Soil Association P5669. A family business producing a premium quality range of organic jams, marmalades and meal accompaniments designed for the grocery, delicatessen and gift markets. We offer bespoke private-label production services.

POWYS

COMPOST TECHNOLOGY LTD

Trewern, Welshpool, Powys, SY21 8EA

Tel: 01938 555456 superdugextra@aol.com www.compost-technology.co.uk

Manufacturers of organic composts. Delivery to UK except N. Ireland and offshore.

EARTHBOUND ORGANICS

The Toll House, Dolau, Llandrindod Wells,
Powys, LD1 5TL

Tel: 01597 851157 sales@earthbound.co.uk www.earthbound.co.uk

Hand-made organic skin care products sold online.

GOOD FOOD DISTRIBUTORS

35 Ddole Road Industrial Estate, Llandrindod Wells, Powys, LD1 6DF

Tel: 01597 824720 info@gfd.org.uk www.goodfooddistributors.co.uk

Soil Association P5894. Free delivery service, wholefoods in bulk and pre-packs, free own name labelling service and contract mixing. 100% vegetarian and GMO-free products. Vast range of products listed in our free price list.

GRAIG FARM ORGANICS

Dolau, Llandrindod Wells, Powys, LD1 5TL

Tel: 01597 851655 Fax: 01597 851991 sales@graigfarm.co.uk www.graigfarm.co.uk

Award-winning organic meats, fish and other organic foods available by mail order, internet, retail outlets. Organic Retailer of the Year 2001/2. Winner Soil Association Home Delivery/Internet Service Award 2004; Livestock supplies through producer group of 200 farmers across Wales and the borders. Organic Food Awards 1993–2006.

Associations

including certification bodies, education, clubs,
R&D, publications and other services

ABERDEEN BIODYNAMIC LAND TRUST

Beannachar, Banchory-Devenick, Aberdeen, Aberdeenshire, AB12 5YL
Tel: 01224 869138 richard@beannachar.org www.biodynamic.org.uk/ABLT.htm
Community Land Trusts. Purchase of agricultural land to hold in trust for biodynamic or organic food production, and support for businesses renting that land.

THE ACORN CENTRE

Todhurst Site, North Heath, Pulborough, West Sussex, RH20 1DL
Tel: 01798 873533 Fax: 01798 873533 michellewykes@aldingbournetrust.co.uk
Training centre for adults with learning disabilities. We grow our own organic vegetables, which are sold through our farm shop. Other organic produce also available. Coffee shop. Soil Association G2586, P5118.

AGROFORESTRY RESEARCH TRUST

46 Hunters Moon, Dartington, Totnes, Devon, TQ9 6JT
Tel: 01803 840776 mail@agroforestry.co.uk www.agroforestry.co.uk
Research charity producing books and information on fruits, nuts and agroforestry; also plants, seeds and rootrainers.

ALDINGBOURNE COUNTRY CENTRE

Blackmill Lane, Norton, Chichester, West Sussex, PO18 0JP
Tel: 01243 542075 Fax: 01243 544807 acc@aldingbournetrust.co.uk www.aldingbournetrust.co.uk
Aldingbourne Country Centre is a sheltered training centre for adults with learning difficulties. A wide range of organic products are produced on the 1.7 hectare site, and these are available on the menu in the cafe, from the site shop and at local farmers' markets. The centre has conference facilities for hire, a woodland walk and conservation area, and also specialises in horticulture (bedding/herbaceous plants, hanging baskets), furniture restoration and hand-made art and craft products. For further details contact Linda Thompson or Matt Swanson.

APPLIED RURAL ALTERNATIVES

10 Highfield Close, Wokingham, Berkshire, RG40 1DG
Tel: 0118 962 7797
Education of the general public in organic farming and growing issues by visits, meetings and publication of papers. Send SAE for details and programmes.

AVON ORGANIC GROUP

c/o 3 Dubbers Lane, Bristol, BS5 7EL
Tel: 0117 935 4261 membership@avonorganicgroup.org.uk www.avonorganicgroup.org.uk
Monthly meetings on organic gardening, local food and environmental themes. Visits to members' allotments. Sale of produce. Run organic orchard on Horfield Allotment site.

BELLA HERBS

Brocton Leys, Brocton, Stafford, Staffordshire, ST17 0TX
Tel: 01785 663868 beverleysquire@aol.com
We have a two-acre organic garden licensed by the Soil Association, where we run leisure courses in organic gardening. We are also producers of vegetables, fruit and herbs.

BIODYNAMIC AGRICULTURAL ASSOCIATION (BDAA)

Painswick Inn Project, Gloucester St., Stroud, Gloucestershire, GL5 1QG
Tel: 01453 759501 office@biodynamic.org.uk www.biodynamic.org.uk
With links across the world, BDAA promotes the unique biodynamic approach to organic agriculture, operates the Demeter Symbol (UK6), publishes a journal, sells books and offers training courses and workshops.

A–B

BORDEAUX QUAY

V-Shed, Canons Way, Bristol, BS1 5UH
Tel: 0117 906 5550 Fax: 0117 906 5567
kath.cockshaw@bordeaux-quay.co.uk www.bordeaux-quay.co.uk
Restaurant, brasserie, bar, deli, bakery and cookery school in a converted warehouse on Bristol's harbourside. European cooking using local regionally sourced organic ingredients.

BRYMORE SCHOOL FARM TRUST

Brymore School, Cannington, Bridgwater, Somerset, TA5 2NB
Tel: 01278 652428 Fax: 01278 653244
We are a secondary school of agriculture, horticulture and engineering with a mixed farm enterprise. We sell beef and table birds through farmers' markets, and pork, lamb and free range eggs privately.

CAMPHILL OAKLANDS PARK

Horticulture, Oaklands Park, Newnham on Severn, Gloucestershire, GL14 1EF
Tel: 01594 516550 Fax: 01594 516550 kaigarden@onetel.com www.oaklandspark.org.uk
Biodynamic Agricultural Association 101. Working community with people with special needs. Involved with regional biodynamic land training (2 years), vegetables, herbs and fruit for wholesaling and box scheme. Some meat available for box scheme customers. Above contacts are for wholesale; box scheme contacts are: 01594 516344/510365, anna@bergamot.basil.freeuk.com and www.bergamot.basil.freeuk.com.

CANON FROME COURT

Canon Frome Court, Canon Frome, Ledbury, Herefordshire, HR8 2TD
Tel: 0870 765 0711 membership@canonfromecourt.org.uk www.canonfromecourt.org.uk
Organic (uncertified) farming community comprising 18 households living in Georgian house and stable block set in 40 acres of park and farmland. Cows, goats, sheep, chickens, bees, arable fields, orchard and 2-acre walled garden. WWOOFers and potential community members welcome.

CAPEL MANOR COLLEGE

Bullsmore Lane, Enfield, Middlesex, EN1 4RQ
Tel: 020 8366 4442 enquiries@capel.ac.uk www.capel.ac.uk
Soil Association G7651. An organic sheep flock with Lincoln Longwoods and Suffolks. Sell organic hay, lamb and breeding stock. The farm is managed by Capel Manor College, which specialises in horticulture and associated land-based industry courses.

CENTRE FOR ALTERNATIVE TECHNOLOGY

Machynlleth, Powys, SY20 9AZ
Tel: 01654 705950 Fax: 01654 702782 info@cat.org.uk www.cat.org.uk
Soil Association L09WW. Established in 1974, the Centre for Alternative Technology is Europe's leading eco-centre, with information on renewable energy, environmental building, energy efficiency, organic growing and alternative sewage systems. Services include a visitor centre open 7 days a week, practical and informative publications, a mail order service of 'green' books and products, educational services for schools, consultancy for individuals and businesses, residential courses, membership and a free information service.

CLYNFYW COUNTRYSIDE CENTRE

Clynfyw, Abercych, Boncath, Pembrokeshire SA37 0HF
Tel: 01239 841236 Fax: 01239 841236 jim.clynfyw@virgin.net www.clynfyw.co.uk
Soil Association G4192. A residential, all-access countryside activity, education, arts and respite care holiday centre set on a working organic farm. Animals include Welsh Black cattle and Saddleback pigs. Member of the Soil Association Organic Farms Network.

B–C

COMMONWORK

Bore Place, Chiddingstone, Edenbridge, Kent TN8 7AR
Tel: 01732 463255 Fax: 01732 740264 info@commonwork.org www.commonwork.org
Conference and study centre with organic, wildlife and permaculture gardens on commercial organic farm. Residential accommodation for groups undertaking their own training and development work. Environmental/arts education programme and organic farm/food study days offered to schools and community groups by Commonwork, plus hands-on vocational training in organic farming for people of all abilities, and seasonal open days for the public. Commonwork also runs a development education centre (global education) from Maidstone, going out to schools, youth and community groups.

COMMUNITY COMPOSTING NETWORK

67 Alexandra Road, Sheffield, South Yorkshire, S2 3EE
Tel: 0114 258 0483 Fax: 0114 258 0483 ccn@gn.apc.org www.communitycompost.org
We are the national network providing support and representation for community groups that are in some way involved in the sustainable management of organic waste resources and community composting.

COMPASSION IN WORLD FARMING

Charles House, 5A Charles Street, Petersfield, Hampshire, GU32 3EH
Tel: 01730 264208 Fax: 01730 260791 sarah@ciwf.co.uk www.ciwf.co.uk
Compassion In World Farming is an international farm animal welfare organisation that has campaigned since 1967 to bring about the abolition of all factory farming systems, live animal exports and the cruelty suffered by farm animals as a result of intensive farming. CIWF works to acheive its aims through legal routes, hard hitting campaigning, public education and vigorous political lobbying.

COSWINASAWSIN

The Duchy College, Rosewarne, Cambourne, Cornwall, TR14 0AB
Tel: 01209 722100 Fax: 01209 722159
Coswinsawsin grows a variety of crops including field vegetables, sugar beet, potatoes, and cereals. Farm trail, educational visits, open days and farm walks are all available by arrangement with the office. Coswinsawsin Farm is an important resource for the newly created Organic Studies Centre at the Duchy College, Rosewarne, and is the most westerly of the Elm Farm Research Centre demonstration farms network. Member of the Soil Association Organic Farms Network.

COUNTRY SMALLHOLDING MAGAZINE

Fair Oak Close, Exeter Airport Business Park, Clyst Honiton, Devon, EX5 2UL
Tel: 01392 888481 editorial.csh@archant.co.uk www.countrysmallholding.com
Monthly magazine for smallholders, small farmers and anyone interested in small scale livestock, poultry keeping, growing crops, food, and all matters relating to self-sufficiency.

CRAIGENCALT ECOLOGY CENTRE

Craigencalt Farm, Kinghorn, Fife, KY3 9YG
Tel: 01592 891567 Fax: 01592 891567 cfec@free.uk.com www.cfec.org.uk
The Craigencalt Farm Ecology Centre is used by schools and adult groups for ecological studies, weekend study groups, and by various craft/arts persons. Visitors are welcome to take part, walk, bird watch, chat to members, even pitch in with the various projects underway.

DEER PARK FARM

Forty Acre Lane, Kermincham, Holmes Chapel, Crewe, Cheshire, CW4 8DX
Tel: 01477 532188 Fax: 01477 544638 martin.steer@lineone.net
Organic lamb (whole and half) available to order. Steer Ethelston Rural Ltd. Rural Chartered Surveyors are specialists in environmental and organic land management. Member of the Soil Association Organic Farms Network.

C–D

DEMETER COMMITEE OF THE BDAA
17 Inverleith Place, Edinburgh, Lothian, EH3 5QE
Tel: 0131 624 3921 fionajmackie@hotmail.com www.biodynamic.org.uk
Inspection, certification, and information service for biodynamic production.

DEPARTMENT FOR ENVIRONMENT, FOOD AND RURAL AFFAIRS (DEFRA)
Nobel House, 17 Smith Square, London, SW1P 3JR
Tel: 020 7238 6000 Fax: 020 7238 6609 organic.standards@defra.gsi.gov.uk www.defra.gov.uk
Defra has taken over responsibility for UK organic standards, previously monitored by UKROFS.

DERBY COLLEGE
Broomfield Hall, Morley, Ilkeston, Derbyshire, DE7 6DN
Tel: 0800 028 0289 eileen.swann@derby-college.ac.uk www.derby-college.ac.uk
Soil Association registered. Full-time and part-time courses in organic horticulture. Licensed producers of beef, lamb, cereal, and vegetables. Contact 'Course Student Services'.

DIGMYPLOT.CO.UK
digmyplot@hotmail.co.uk www.digmyplot.co.uk
Website detailing the organic growing of vegetables and fruit on an allotment. Raised beds, companion planting: a natural approach. Website completely changed on the first of every month. Interesting ideas and tips for everybody.

DORSET WILDLIFE TRUST
45 High St., Toller Pocorum, Dorchester, Dorset, DT2 0DN
Tel: 01300 320573 www.dorsetwildlife.co.uk
Soil Association G898. We run as a farmed nature reserve, producing fat and store lambs and suckled calves/store cattle.

EARTHWORM HOUSING CO-OP LTD
Wheatstone Leintwardine Shropshire SY7 0LH
Tel: 01547 540461 Fax: Contact: Hil Mason
Suppliers of willow for basket making, hurdles etc, venue for low cost hire for camps, courses, meetings. Demonstration wetland system and organic/veganic gardens. WWOOF host farm.

EAST MALLING RESEARCH
New Rd, East, Malling, Kent, ME19 6BJ
Tel: 01732 843833 Fax: 01732 849067 jean.fitzgerald@emr.ac.uk www.eastmallingresearch.com
We carry out research projects on organic apples and strawberries and plan to include more top and soft fruits in our organic demonstration area.

ECLIPSE SCIENTIFIC GROUP LTD
Medcalfe Way, Bridge Street, Chatteris, Cambridgeshire, PE16 6QZ
Tel: 01354 695858 Fax: 01354 692215 sales@esglabs.co.uk www.esglabs.co.uk
Eclipse offers a comprehensive technical support service, providing expert consultancy through to high quality chemical, microbiological and analytical research and testing services.

THE ECOLOGIST
Unit 18, Chelsea Wharf, 15 Lots Rd., London, SW10 0QJ
Tel: 020 7351 3578 Fax: 020 7351 3617 editorial@theecologist.org www.theecologist.org
The dangers of globalisation, the real reasons behind climate change, the threat of corporate power, the risks of GM food, the truth about global cancer – just some of the issues covered regularly by *The Ecologist*.

D–E

ECOLOGY BUILDING SOCIETY

7 Belton Rd., Silsden, Nr. Keighley, West Yorkshire, BD20 0EE
Tel: 0845 674 5566 (local rate) Fax: 01535 650780 info@ecology.co.uk www.ecology.co.uk
A mutual building society providing ethical savings accounts and green mortgages for run-down properties in need of renovation or conversion, and ecological self-build projects.

ECOPRODUCE LTD

2 New Cottages, Bill Hill Park, Wokingham, Berkshire, RG40 5QU
Tel: 020 7870 3756 info@ecoproduce.com www.ecoproduce.com
EcoProduce is an online marketplace for all organic and eco-friendly products. Our online auction system allows sellers to register and list their products at no cost, and buyers to purchase directly from producers.

ECOTRICITY

Axiom House, Station Road, Stroud, Gloucestershire, GL5 3AP
Tel: 01453 756111 Fax: 01453 756222 info@ecotricity.co.uk www.ecotricity.co.uk
Green electricity supplier. Dedicated to building clean new energy sources that won't contribute to global warming. Ecotricity matches the standard price of your local electricity supplier so it shouldn't cost you more than 'normal' polluting electricity.

ELM FARM RESEARCH CENTRE

Hamstead Marshall, Newbury, Berkshire, RG20 0HR
Tel: 01488 658298 Fax: 01488 658503 elmfarm@efrc.com www.efrc.com
EFRC provides agricultural and policy research, education and training courses, a farm trail, organic, OCIS and in-conversion advisory service, organic demonstration farm network, soil analysis, publications, consultancy and producer groups. Member of the Soil Association Organic Farms Network.

ELMWOOD COLLEGE FARM

Cupar Muir, Cupar, Fife, KY15 5RN
Tel: 01334 658900 Fax: 01334 658888 pmckinnon@elmwood.ac.uk www.elmwood.ac.uk
The farm is part of Cupar-based Elmwood College. We provide a wide range of courses including agriculture, conservation, gamekeeping, equine, animal care and plant operation, plus a range of short courses. We are part of the Soil Association Organic Farms Network.

EMBSAY CHILDREN'S CENTRE

Embsay Children's Centre, Pasture Road, Embsay, Skipton, North Yorkshire, BD23 6RQ
Tel: 01765 793286 cm@embsaychildrenscentre.co.uk www.embsaychildrenscentre.co.uk
Founded in 1992, we provide pre-school education and flexible day-care for children from eight weeks, and also offer out of school care for children once they move on to school. We and our parents recognise the value of good quality, home-cooked, organic food.

EMERSON COLLEGE

Hartfield Road, Forest Row, East Sussex, RH18 5JX
Tel: 01342 822238 Fax: 01342 826055 mail@emerson.org.uk www.emerson.org.uk
Soil Association & Demeter registered. Emerson College runs a three year, full-time training in Biodynamic Organic Agriculture, as well as short courses in biodynamics. Students at the college run a commercial biodynamic market garden through spring and summer.

THE ENGINE SHED

19 St. Leonard's Lane, Edinburgh, Lothian, EH8 9SD
Tel: 0131 662 0040 Fax: 0131 667 5319 engineshed@aol.com www.engineshed.org.uk
Training centre for adults with learning disabilities. Training in catering setting towards employment.
Five production workshops: café, bakery, outside catering, food processing and wholefood shop.

ENGLISH ORGANIC FOODS PLC
The Old Vicarage, 226 Ashbourne Rd., Turnditch, Derbyshire, DE56 2LH
Tel: 01773 550173 Fax: 01773 550855
Organic matching agency.

ETHICAL CONSUMER
Unit 21, 41 Old Birley St., Manchester, Greater Manchester, M15 5RF
Tel: 0161 226 2929 Fax: 0161 226 6277 mail@ethicalconsumer.org www.ethicalconsumer.org
Ethical Consumer is the leading consumer organisation for those concerned about the environment, animal welfare, buying organic and fair trade. *Ethical Consumer* magazine and www.ethiscore.org help you buy the most ethical products available. Also www.corporatecritic.org.

THE ETHICAL INVESTMENT CO-OPERATIVE LTD
12 St Nicolas Drive, Richmond, North Yorkshire, DL10 7DY
Tel: 0845 458 3127 ian@ethicalmoney.org www.ethicalmoney.org
Winner of the award for 'Best IFA' in the Guardian/Observer Consumer Finance Awards 2001, 2002 and 2003 – a firm of independent financial advisers dedicated to ethical and socially responsible investment. The advisers in the co-op have extensive experience in all aspects of financial planning, especially ethical investment. Clients range from concerned individuals to charities, trade unions, small businesses and NGOs.

FARMS FOR CITY CHILDREN
Nethercott House, Iddesleigh, Winkleigh, Devon, EX19 8BG
Tel: 01837 810573 ffcc@nethercott-house.freeserve.co.uk www.farmsforcitychildren.org
Educational Charity. Farms For City Children runs three organic farms where urban children come to stay and help the farmers. They learn to work together for the common good and gain a sense of achievement.

FEDERATION OF CITY FARMS AND COMMUNITY GARDENS
The GreenHouse, Hereford Street, Bristol, BS3 4NA
Tel: 0117 923 1800 Fax: 0117 923 1900 admin@farmgarden.org.uk www.farmgarden.org.uk
FCFCG supports and represents city farms, community gardens and similar community-led growing initiatives in the UK. We provide advice on a wide range of topics including funding and budgeting, community involvement, animal husbandry, horticulture, land management and legal issues. We arrange training and networking events for our members, and represent the movement at a national level.

FIRST LEARNING DAY NURSERY
50 Sheep Walk, Shepperton, Middlesex, TW17 0AJ
Tel: 01932 260600 admin@firstlearning.co.uk
The first and only certified organic children's day nursery in the UK, offering quality childcare for babies from 3 months to pre-school children aged 5 years. Part or full time places. Head office: 3 Union Court, Richmond, Surrey TW9 1AA, tel: 020 8939 2288.

THE FOOD COMMISSION
94 White Lion Street, London, N1 9PF
Tel: 020 7837 2250 enquiries@foodcomm.org.uk www.foodcomm.org.uk
The Food Commission is the UK's leading independent food watchdog, campaigning for healthier, safer food. Publishes the award winning *Food Magazine*. Call or write for a free copy.

FOOD MAGAZINE
The Food Commission, 94 White Lion Street, London, N1 9PF
Tel: 020 7837 2250 Fax: 020 7837 1141 enquiries@foodcomm.org.uk www.foodcomm.org.uk
The magazine of The Food Commission reports on genetic engineering, additives, pesticides, food irradiation, food labelling and animal welfare. Sample copies available. For general enquiries, news and submissions: enquiries@foodcomm.org.uk; press enquiries: press@foodcomm.org.uk.

FRIENDS OF THE EARTH
26-28 Underwood St, London, London, N1 7JQ
Tel: 0808 800 1111 Fax: 020 7490 0881 info@foe.co.uk www.foe.co.uk
Environmental pressure group. Friends of the Earth's 'Real Food' campaign asks the government to reform farming and food production to enable farmers to manage the countryside sustainably and provide high quality food for a fair income.

GARDEN ORGANIC – THE ORGANIC KITCHEN GARDEN
Audley End House, Saffron Walden, Essex, CB11 4JF
Tel: 01799 522148 Fax: 024 7663 9229 enquiry@hdra.org.uk www.gardenorganic.org.uk
HDRA, the organic organisation, runs the walled kitchen garden at Audley End House, an English Heritage property. The 2-acre walled gardens include heritage vegetables, vinery and fruit house. For opening hours please see website.

GARDEN ORGANIC – YALDING ORGANIC GARDENS
Benover Rd., Yalding, Nr. Maidstone, Kent, ME18 6EX
Tel: 01622 814650 Fax: 01622 814650 enquiry@hdra.org.uk www.gardenorganic.org.uk
Yalding Organic Gardens trace the course of garden history through 16 landscaped displays, illustrating the organic techniques used to maintain them. Shop for browsing and organic café for refreshments.

GENEWATCH UK
The Mill House, Manchester Rd., Tideswell, Buxton, Derbyshire, SK17 8LN
Tel: 01298 871898 Fax: 01298 872531 mail@genewatch.org www.genewatch.org
Policy research group. Research and analysis on GM crops and foods. Up-to-date information on latest developments and their implications.

GREEN BOOKS LTD
Foxhole, Dartington, Totnes, Devon, TQ9 6EB
Tel: 01803 863260 Fax: 01803 863843 sales@greenbooks.co.uk www.greenbooks.co.uk
Besides publishing *The Organic Directory*, we have a wide range of other books on organic living, including *The Organic Baby & Toddler Cookbook* and *Gaia's Kitchen: Vegetarian Recipes For Family And Community*. Also books on eco-building, organic gardening, green politics and economics, etc. Mail order and trade catalogues available on request.

GREEN CUISINE LTD
Penrhos Court, Kington, Herefordshire, HR5 3LH
Tel: 01544 230720 Fax: 01544 230754 daphne@greencuisine.org www.greencuisine.org
Soil Association E2051. Runs courses on food and health and offers consultations and natural therapies. The company also produce books and educational material. See also Penrhos Ltd and The Penrhos Trust.

THE GREENHOUSE
42-46 Bethel St., Norwich, Norfolk, NR2 1NR
Tel: 01603 631007 www.greenhousetrust.co.uk
An educational charity providing solutions to environmental problems. The building houses an organic, vegetarian/vegan licensed café and shop (open for Sunday lunch 12 to 3.30) plus meeting rooms and herb garden. Acts as a resource centre offering meeting space, offices and other facilities to local and regional voluntary groups.

GREEN ISP
Suite 3, Premier Hous Lockhill Mills, Holmes Rd., Sowerby Bridge, HX6 3LF
Tel: 0845 058 0659 sales@greenisp.net www.greenisp.net
Provide environmentally guided internet services, providing broadband, unmetered dial-up, 0845, email and web space, solar-powered office, advanced solar web hosting. Features and links on green issues.

GREENPEACE UK
Canonbury Villas, London, N1 2PN
Tel: 020 7865 8100 Fax: 020 7865 8200 info@uk.greenpeace.org www.greenpeace.org.uk
International environmental organisation which fights abuse to the natural world.

GROUNDWORK BLACK COUNTRY
Dolton Way, West Midlands, DY4 9AL
Tel: 0121 530 5500 Fax: 0121 530 5501 bc@groundwork.org.uk www.groundwork-bc.org.uk
Building sustainable communities through joint environmental action, training, education and community links, open days.

HEALTH FOOD BUSINESS MAGAZINE
The Old Dairy, Hudsons Farm, Field Gate Lane, Ugley Green, Essex, CM22 6HJ
Tel: 01279 816300 Fax: 01279 816496 info@targetpublishing.com www.targetpublishing.com
Health Food Business trade magazine is sent free of charge to all registered, named buyers of natural organic foods, drinks, toiletries, herbals and dietary supplements. Serves UK and Eire.

HEDGEHOG HILL ORGANIC NURSERY SCHOOL
42 High St., Greens Norton, Northamptonshire, NN12 8BA
Tel: 01327 323012 organicschools.limited@virgin.net
Organic children's day nursery and nursery school.

HERTFORDSHIRE ORGANIC GARDENERS
c/o 15 Bishops Rd., Welwyn, Hertfordshire, AL6 0NR
Tel: 01438 798593 hogs@btinternet.com
Members of HDRA. Gardening group.

HOLME LACY COLLEGE
Holme Lacy, Herefordshire, HR2 6LL
Tel: 01432 870316 Fax: 01432 870566 holmelacy@pershore.ac.uk www.pershore.ac.uk
Holme Lacy College is host to 'Project Carrot', which aims to create a leading European centre for sustainable agriculture and land management on its 600 acre farm and woodland estate. Member of the Soil Association Organic Farms Network.

HOPE TRUST (HOSPITALFIELD ORGANIC PRODUCE ENTERPRISE TRUST)
The plot next to Hospitalfield House, The Westway, Arbroath, Angus, DD11 4NH
Tel: 07837 862174 enquiries@ hopegardentrust.org.uk www.hopegardentrust.org.uk
We are a registered charity and provide horticultural training to adults with learning disabilities. We are certified as organic with the Soil Association. Open weekdays 2pm–4pm. Bus stop outside Hope on the Arbroath to Dundee route. Car park facilities at Hope.

THE HORTICULTURAL CORRESPONDENCE COLLEGE
Little Notton Farmhouse, 16 Notton, Lacock, Chippenham, Wiltshire, SN15 2NF
Tel: 01249 730326 Fax: 01249 730326 info@hccollege.co.uk www.hccollege.co.uk
Home study courses in garden and horticulture-related subjects, including a Soil Association approved organic gardening course. Also organic arable farming.

IMPACT PUBLISHING LTD
12 Pierrepont Street, Bath, Somerset, BA2 5SJ
Tel: 01225 446666 Fax: 01225 339494 info@impactpublishing.co.uk www.impactpublishing.co.uk
Publish 'Green Essentials', a series of practical organic gardening guides produced in association with the Soil Association and the HDRA, just £2.99 each.

INSTITUTE OF RURAL SCIENCES

Institute of Rural Sciences, University of Wales, Aberystwyth, Ceredigion, SY23 3AL
Tel: 01970 624471 Fax: 01970 622238 organic@aber.ac.uk www.organic.aber.ac.uk
Soil Association certified research/demonstration farm. BSc, PgCert and PgDipl in organic agriculture
with student bursary support available, sponsored by Waitrose and Horizon Organic Dairy. Extensive
DEFRA and EU-funded organic research programme.

INTERNATIONAL FEDERATION OF ORGANIC AGRICULTURAL MOVEMENTS, (IFOAM)

Charles-de-Gaulle-Str. 5, 53113, Bonn, Germany.
Tel: +49 (0) 228 926 5010 Fax: +49 (0) 228 926 5099 headoffice@ifoam.org www.ifoam.org
IFOAM is the world umbrella organisation of the organic agriculture movement, with 750 members. It
offers publications like the directory *Organic Agriculture Worldwide* and the magazine *Ecology And
Farming*, and organises international conferences and workshops.

INTERNATIONAL SOCIETY FOR ECOLOGY AND CULTURE

Foxhole, Dartington, Totnes, Devon, TQ9 6EB
Tel: 01803 868650 Fax: 01803 868651 info@isec.org.uk www.isec.org.uk
ISEC is a non-profit organisation concerned with the protection of both biological and cultural diversity.
Our emphisis is on education for action: moving beyond single issues to look at the more fundamental
influences that shape our lives.

IPSWICH ORGANIC GARDENERS GROUP

Baboushka, 223 Mersea Road, Colchester, Essex, CO2 8PN
Tel: 01206 570859 tetley@macunlimited.net www.irene.org.uk
Gardening group affiliated to the HDRA, meeting once a month September to May, speaker each
month. Bi-monthly newsletter, discount seeds and bulk purchasing scheme. Also attend local events to
promote organic gardening.

IRISH ORGANIC FARMERS AND GROWERS ASSOCIATION (IOFGA)

Main St., Newtownforbes, Co. Longford, Ireland.
Tel: (+353) 043 42495 Fax: (+353) 043 42496 iofga@eircom.net www.iofga.org
IOFGA is a company limited by guarantee, open to farmers, growers, consumers and others interested
in the production of healthy food and the protection of the environment. IOFGA operates an inspection
and certification scheme, publishes a magazine, *Organic Matters*, and other practical information for
organic farmers and growers. Details of IOFGA-registered producers, processors, wholesalers and those
offering box delivery and market stalls are available directly from IOFGA.

JIGSAW ENVIRONMENTAL

Main Street, Gisburn, Clitheroe, Lancashire, BB7 4HN
Tel: 01200 415979 gisburnproject@hotmail.com
We aim to support the long term development of people with disabilities and those disadvantaged
through economic or social exclusion. Organic horticulture is the platform from which we deliver
accredited horticultural training. Best environmental practice is also a key component of the site and
the project as a whole.

THE KINDERSLEY CENTRE AT SHEEPDROVE ORGANIC FARM

The Kindersley Centre, Sheepdrove Organic Farm, Warren Farm, Lambourn, Berkshire, RG17 7UU
Tel: 01488 674737 Fax: 01488 72285
pippa.regan@thekindersleycentre.com www.thekindersleycentre.com
Sustainable, organic and environmentally sound, The Kindersley Centre combines exceptional surroundings with the most advanced technology and attentive service. Set at the heart of award-winning
Sheepdrove Organic Farm, the centre is housed within a beautiful, eco-friendly building, surrounded by
fields and woodlands. A range of meeting places and adaptable seating for up to 200 people.

H-K

THE KINGCOMBE CENTRE

Lower Kingcombe, Toller Porcorum, Dorchester, Dorset, DT2 0EQ

Tel: 01300 320684 Fax: 01300 321409

nspring@kingcombe-centre.demon.co.uk www.kingcombe-centre.demon.co.uk

Residential study centre in converted farm buildings beside the river Hooke. Offers courses and holidays in a wide range of subjects for adults and children, fit and disabled. Day visits for schools and guided walks.

LACKHAM COLLEGE

Lacock, Chippenham, Wiltshire, SN15 2NY

Tel: 01249 443111 Fax: 01249 444474

A range of qualifications both part-time and full-time: City & Guilds Organic Gardening, Certificate in Organic Horticulture, National Certificate in Organic Horticulture, HND & HNC in organic crop production.

LAKEWOOD CONFERENCE CENTRE

Rhodyate, Blagdon, Bristol, Somerset, BS40 7YE

Tel: 01761 463366 Fax: 01761 463377 info@lakewoodcentre.co.uk www.lakewoodcentre.co.uk

A new contemporary conference centre with stunning views over lakes close to Bristol, Bath, M5. Purpose-designed with state of the art audio visual equipment. Local, fresh and organic food.

LAND HERITAGE

Summerhill Farm, Hittisleigh, Exeter, Devon, EX6 6LP

Tel: 01647 24511 Fax: 01647 24588 landheritage@hotmail.com www.landheritage.org

Land-based charitable trust. Seeks to protect and preserve small family farms creating organic tenancies; promotes community supported agriculture schemes; supplies educational packs raising awareness of organic farming; publishes material and provides conversion advice.

LOW LUCKENS ORGANIC RESOURCE CENTRE

Low Luckens, Roweltown, Carlisle, Cumbria, CA6 6LJ

Tel: 01697 748186 lowluckensorc@hotmail.com www.lowluckensfarm.co.uk

The Organic Resource Centre is located in 220 acres of organically managed farmland. The centre provides self catering accommodation, a range of events and courses and educational access. Organic meat and vegetables available.

MAGDALEN FARM

Magdalen Farm, Winsham, Chard, Somerset, TA20 4PA

Tel: 01460 30144 Fax: 01460 30177 www.themagdalenproject.org.uk

Soil Association Registered (G932) mixed farm, beef sucklers, pigs, field veg, polytunnels and cereals, selling vegetables and meat via box scheme and farm gate sales. Residential education centre. Member of the Soil Association Organic Farms Network.

MENTRO LLUEST

Llanbadorn Fawr, Aberystwyth, Ceredigion, SY23 3AU

Tel: 01970 612114 Fax: 01970 612114 mentro.lluest@talk21.com

Soil Association G3081. Mentro Lluest teaches skills to people with special needs within a framework of organic growing, environmental sustainability and social cohesion. We specialise in producing salad, seasonal vegetables and herbs.

NATIONAL FARMERS' RETAIL AND MARKETS ASSOCIATION

PO Box 575, Southampton, Hampshire & Isle of Wight, SO15 7BZ

Tel: 0845 230 2150 justask@farma.org.uk www.farmersmarkets.net

A farmers' market is one in which farmers, growers or producers from a defined local area are present in person to sell their own produce direct to the public. All products sold should have been grown, reared, caught, pickled, baked, smoked or processed by the stall holder.

K-N

THE NATIONAL INSTITUTE OF MEDICAL HERBALISTS

Elm House, Mary Arches St., Exeter, Devon, EX1 6AH
Tel: 01392 426022 Fax: 01392 498963 nimh@ukexeter.freeserve.co.uk www.nimh.org.uk
Professional body of practising medical herbalists. Offers details/information on all aspects of western herbal medicine and how to source a qualified practitioner. Details on education and research available. All members have undergone a rigorous four-year training.

NEAL'S YARD REMEDIES COURSES

4 Bedale St., Borough Market, London, SE1 9AL
Tel: 020 7940 1404 Fax: 020 7940 1401
courses@nealsyardremedies.com www.nealsyardremedies.com
Alongside our highly successful natural cosmetics and medicine business, Neal's Yard Remedies runs courses in natural medicine, aromatherapy, flower remedies, nutrition, herbalism and homoeopathy. The courses are run in our purpose-built teaching studio in Covent Garden; many encompass a visit to our herb farm and new factory in Dorset.

THE NETHERFIELD CENTRE

Netherfield Place Farm, Netherfield, Nr. Battle, East Sussex, TN3 9PY
Tel: 01424 775615 Fax: 01424 775616 simon@thenetherfieldcentre.co.uk
The Netherfield Centre for Sustainable Food and Farming runs education courses, training and networking for those interested in sustainable agriculture. The Netherfield Centre is located on an organic farm and linked to a network of farms sharing a cutting room and marketing meat locally.

NORFOLK ORGANIC GROUP

25 St Mildred's Road, Norwich, Norfolk, NR5 8RS
mail@norfolkorganic.org.uk www.norfolkorganic.org.uk
Local group of Soil Association and HDRA. We aim to promote the organic movement in Norfolk by increasing public awareness of organic methods of farming and gardening.

THE NORTH WALES ORGANIC GROWERS AND PERMACULTURE GROUP

Pen-y-Bryn, Talwrn, Llangefni, Ynys Mon, Gwynedd, LL77 7SP
Tel: 01248 750029
Group of members who put newcomers to the area in touch with existing organic growers and permaculturists.

OLIVER, E M & R J H

Blacklands, Crowhurst, Battle, East Sussex, TN33 9AB
Tel: 01424 830360 Fax: 01424 830360 architects@mnroliver.fsbusiness.co.uk
Architects (RIBA) to environment-conscious designs.

ORGANIC CENTRE WALES

University of Wales, Aberystwyth, Ceredigion, SY23 3AL
Tel: 01970 622248 Fax: 01970 622238 organic@aber.ac.uk www.organic.aber.ac.uk
Operated in partnership with Soil Association, Elm Farm Research Centre, IGER, UWA and ADAS. Advice and demonstration. Dissemination of information on organic farming at all levels from producers, to consumers, through training courses, advice, demonstration farms, discussion groups, publications and website.

ORGANIC FARMERS AND GROWERS LTD (OF&G)

Elim Centre, Lancaster Rd., Shrewsbury, Shropshire, SY1 3LE
Tel: 0845 330 5122 Fax: 0845 330 5123 info@organicfarmers.org.uk www.organicfarmers.org.uk
We carry out inspection and certification of organic production, processing and a wide range of other organic enterprises. For more information, please contact us.

N–O

THE ORGANIC FARM SHOP

Abbey Home Farm, Burford Road, Gloucestershire, GL7 5HF

Tel: 01285 640441 Fax: 01285 644827 info@theorganicfarmshop.co.uk www.theorganicfarmshop.co.uk

Soil Association G1715, R5253. Cookery courses, educational visits, woodland walk. Our own vegetables, meat, eggs and soft fruit, a vast range of organic food, textiles and environmentally friendly skin care, bodycare, books and magazines. Large meeting room, yurt and hut for hire, greenfield camping. Member of the Soil Association Organic Farms Network.

ORGANIC FOOD FEDERATION (OFF)

31 Turbine Way, Eco Tech Business Park, Swaffham, Norfolk, PE37 7XD

Tel: 01760 720444 Fax: 01760 720790 info@orgfoodfed.com www.orgfoodfed.com

EC-listed certification body for the organic food industry, certifying producers, processors, caterers and importers. UKAS-accredited for producing and processing. Also able to offer certification against our private standards for cosmetics and acquaculture. Authorised by DEFRA under the member state code UK4. Representation and lobbying at Government, EU and Non-Government level. Personal service offered at all times, with telephones answered between 9.00–5.30 on weekdays.

ORGANIC GARDENING

Mortons of Horncastle Ltd., Media Centre, Horton Way, Horncastle, Lincolnshire, LN9 6JR

Tel: 01507 523456 mortons@mortons.co.uk www.mortons.co.uk

The UK's only all-organic monthly gardening magazine. Practical hands on advice on every aspect of the garden – vegetables, fruit, herbs, ornamentals, wildlife.

ORGANIC HOLIDAYS

Tranfield House, 4 Tranfield Gardens, Guiseley, Leeds, West Yorkshire, LS20 8PZ

Tel: 01943 870791 lindamoss@organicholidays.com www.organicholidays.com

Guide to holiday accommodation on organic farms/smallholdings and to B&Bs, guest houses and small hotels where organic produce is used according to availability.

ORGANIC LIFE MAGAZINE

GMC [PUB] 86 High St., Lewes, East Sussex, BN7 1XN

Tel: 01273 477374 jamesbl@thegmcgroup.com www.gmcpubs.com

Organic Life Magazine is a national monthly magazine with a difference. We bring you the latest news and features on all that's best in organic, ethical and fair trade living, all on 100% recycled paper.

ORGANIC & NATURAL BUSINESS MAGAZINE

The Old Dairy, Hudsons Farm, Fieldgate Lane, Ugley Green, Essex, CM22 6HJ

Tel: 01279 816300 Fax: 01279 816496 kathryn@targetpublishing.com www.organic-business.com

Organic & Natural Business Magazine reports authoritatively on developments within the organic and wider natural food, healthy eating and fair trade markets. Committed to servicing the needs of multiple retail buyers, farm shops, convenience and grocery stores, delis and other food service retailers.

ORGANIC SCHOOLS LIMITED

42 High St., Greens Norton, Northamptonshire, NN12 8BA

Tel: 01327 358444 organicschools.limited@virgin.net

Operates organic children's day nurseries and nursery schools in the UK.

ORGANIC STUDIES CENTRE

Duchy College, Rosewarne, Cambourne, Cornwall, TR14 0AB

Tel: 01209 722155 Fax: 01209 722159 j.burke@cornwall.ac.uk

Soil Association G4694. Organic agricultural research and demonstration and training. Arable/field vegetables demonstration farm, farm walks, trials and demos. R&D, including farmers' participatory studies in all sectors of organic agricultural production.

ORGANIC TRADE SERVICES

Northorpe House, Northorpe, Donington, Lincolnshire, PE11 4XY
Tel: 07974 103109 info@organicts.com www.organicts.com
The organic industry portal on the internet. Marketplace, news, newsfeeds, directory, discussion information and more. News and trade offers via email.

ORGANIC TRUST LTD

Vernon House, 2 Vernon Avenue, Clontarf, Dublin 3, Ireland.
Tel: 00 353 1 8530271 Fax: 00 353 1 8530271 organic@iol.ie www.organic-trust.org
Organic inspection and certification service. Publication of quarterly professional journal, educational services and information.

ORGANICA LP

Nerine House, PO Box 434, St. George's Esplanade, St. Peter Port, Guernsey, Channel Islands, GY1 3ZG
Tel: +44 1481 739584 Fax: +44 1481 701619
info@organica-guernsey.com www.organica-guernsey.com
Worldwide consultants in marketing of organic farm produce.

THE PENRHOS TRUST

Penrhos Court, Kington, Herefordshire, HR5 3LH
Tel: 01544 230720 Fax: 01544 230754 martin@penrhos.co.uk www.penrhostrust.org
Charity for the restoration of historic farm buildings regenerated with organic and ecological small businesses. Education: conservation, food heritage, organic food production.

PERMACULTURE MAGAZINE

Permanent Publications, The Sustainability Centre, East Meon, Petersfield, Hampshire, GU32 1HR
Tel: 0845 458 4150 Fax: 01730 823322 info@permaculture.co.uk www.permaculture.co.uk
Permaculture Magazine – solutions for sustainable living, published quarterly. *Earth Repair Catalogue* of over 500 books, videos, tools and products available free and online at www.permaculture.co.uk.
Alternative telephone number: 01730 823311.

PHYTOBOTANICA (UK) LTD

Greens Barn, Greens Lane, Lydiate, Merseyside, L31 4HZ
Tel: 01695 420853 info@phytobotanica.com www.phytobotanica.com
Producers of the first certified organic essential oils in the UK (lavender, peppermint, roman chamomile, german chamomile) and organic hydrosols. On-farm commercial hydrodistillation facilities and conference centre for educational days (e.g. aromatherapy and holistic therapies).

PLANTS FOR A FUTURE

The Field, Higher Penpol, St. Veep, Lostwithiel, Cornwall, PL22 0NG
Tel: 01208 873554 www.pfaf.org
Day visits and tours, courses on woodland gardening, permaculture, nutrition, research, information, demonstration and supply of edible and otherwise useful plants. Plants for a Future is a registered charity researching and demonstrating ecologically sustainable vegan organic horticulture in the form of woodland gardening and other permacultural practices.

POSITIVE NEWS

5 Bicton Enterprise Centre, Clun, Shropshire, SY7 8NF
Tel: 01588 640022 Fax: 01588 640033 office@positivenews.org.uk www.positivenews.org.uk
Quarterly newspaper covering organics and organic farming, green energy and green building, health, peace, recycling, new economics, national and international news, including book reviews. Magazine, *Living Lightly on the Earth*, free to subscribers.

O–P

PROPER JOB

Crannafords Ind Park, Chagford, Devon, TQ13 8DJ
Tel: 01647 432985 Fax: 01647 432985 compost@properjob.eclipse.co.uk www.properjob.ik.com
Community business. Holistic co-op, changing 'waste' into resources, especially composting, collecting compostables, education/consciousness raising. Organic veg production and sale in our community shop/café. Setting up training in related issues. Organic collection round.

PROSPECTS TRUST

Snakehill Farm, Reach, Cambridge, Cambridgeshire, CB5 0HZ
Tel: 01638 741551 Fax: 01638 741873 prospect@farming.co.uk www.prospectstrust.org.uk
Soil Association registered. Charitable trust, working together with people with learning disabilities. Provision of training, work experience and work opportunities in organic market gardening and horticulture for people with learning disabilities.

QUARTIER VERT

85 Whiteladies Rd., Bristol, BS8 2NT
Tel: 0117 973 4482 Fax: 0117 974 3913 info@quartiervert.co.uk www.quartiervert.co.uk
Restaurant, cookery school, bakery, catering. Simple European traditional cooking using local organic ingredients.

RAGMANS

Ragmans Lane Farm Lower Lydbrook Gloucestershire GL17 9PA
Tel: 01594 860244 Fax: 01594 860244 info@ragmans.co.uk www.ragmans.co.uk
We have a comprehensive programme of permaculture and sustainable land use courses. We produce comfrey cuttings and roots for sale by mail order. We offer farm tours by appointment, a campsite, and a bunkhouse available for hire for parties up to 16 people.

RARE BREEDS SURVIVAL TRUST

National Agricultural Centre, Stoneleigh Park, Kenilworth, Warwickshire, CV8 2LG
Tel: 024 7669 6551 Fax: 024 7669 6706 enquiries@rbst.org.uk www.rbst.org.uk
Registered charity for the conservation of rare and endangered livestock breeds.

RECKLESS ORCHARD

The Barn, The Street, Olveston, Bristol, Gloucestershire, BS35 4DR
Tel: 01454 618181 Fax: 01454 618181 contact@recklessorchard.com www.recklessorchard.com
A small innovative landscape architecture practice which promotes and encourages the planting and maintenance of both traditional and new orchards. We work for private and commercial clients. We have a special interest in nature conservation and wildlife. Our designs are both evocative and provocative.

REDFIELD COMMUNITY

Buckingham Rd., Winslow, Buckinghamshire, MK18 3LZ
Tel: 01296 713661 Fax: 01296 714983 info@redfieldcommunity.org.uk www.redfieldcommunity.org.uk
Redfield is an intentional community. We grow and raise our own organic produce as well as running courses and offering accommodation for groups.

REGIONAL CENTRE FOR ORGANIC HORTICULTURE

RCOH, School Farm, Dartington, Nr. Totnes, Devon, TQ9 6EB
Tel: 01803 400999 Fax: 01803 408168 info@dartingtontech.co.uk www.dartingtontech.co.uk
Based on the Dartington Hall Estate near Totnes in south Devon, established as a training centre under the guide of its parent company Dartington Tech, to promote horticultral training throughout South Devon. It is a thriving commercial operation with 6.5 acres of Soil Association certified land producing a variety of fruits and vegetables both in the field and under glass. We supply a range of products throughout the year and welcome enquiries in relation to both training and sales.

P–R

351

THE RESPONSIVE EARTH TRUST

Plasdwbl Biodynamic Farm, Mynachlog Ddu, Clynderwen, Pembrokeshire, SA66 7SE
Tel: 01994 419352
Plasdwbl Biodynamic Farm is a charitable trust run for the benefit of students wishing to gain practical experience in biodynamic farming and gardening. We have a Welsh Black herd and two Jersey milkers. The farm is 40 hectares, and on 4 hectares we grow vegetables and forage. We make our own butter, cheese and bread. Demeter cert. no. 111.

RESURGENCE MAGAZINE

Ford House, Hartland, Bideford, Devon, EX39 6EE
Tel: 01237 441293 Fax: 01237 441203 satish@resurgence.org www.resurgence.org
Resurgence Magazine brings together leading writers and educationalists to present topics of vital importance to our world including ecology, climate change, sustainable development, organic living, human scale education and conflict resolution.

RIVERSIDE COMMUNITY SOCIAL ENTERPRISE LTD

South Riverside Community Development Centre, Brunel St., Riverside, Cardiff, Glamorgan, CF11 6ES
Tel: 029 2019 0036 Fax: 029 2025 0549 ken@riversidemarket.org.uk www.riversidemarket.org.uk
Riverside Community Market Association is a social enterprise run with the aim of improving access to fresh, local and organic produce. The company runs a weekly farmers' market and a community food growing project.

ROBERT OWEN COMMUNITIES

Lower Sharpham Barton Farm, Ashprington, Totnes, Devon, TQ9 7DX
Tel: 01803 732502 Fax: 01803 732502 sharphamfarm@roc-uk.org
Day centre for people with learning disabilities. Dairy, beef, sheep, laying birds and vegetables. Produce milk, meats, eggs and veg.

RUSHALL FARM

Scratchface Lane, Bradfield, Berkshire, RG7 6DL
Tel: 0118 974 4547 jst@rushallfarm.org.uk www.rushallfarm.org.uk
Rushall Farm is a mixed organic farm situated in the heart of the beautiful Pang valley. It has cattle, sheep, and woodland, and grows a range of cereal crops. It is also home to the John Simonds Trust, an educational charity that promotes a love and understanding of farming and the countryside.

RUSKIN MILL COLLEGE

The Fisheries, Horsley, Gloucestershire, GL6 1PL
Tel: 01453 837500 Fax: 01453 837506 www.ruskin-mill.org.uk
Biodynamic Agricultural Association 245. Part of special needs further education college with biodynamic market garden and mixed farm, and fish farm. Café and shop; crafts, exhibitions, workshops, concerts, storytelling and talks.

SAWDAY PUBLISHING, ALASTAIR

The Home Farm Stables, Barrow Gurney, Bristol, Somerset, BS48 3RW
Tel: 01275 464891 Fax: 01275 464887 andreea@sawdays.co.uk www.sawdays.co.uk
Publisher producing and selling guides to Special Places to Stay across Europe and in India and Morocco. Most owners use home-grown, local or organic produce. Also produces the Fragile Earth Book series, sets of mini-essays on environmental and social themes. See also www.specialplaces-tostay.com and www.fragile-earth.com.

R–S

who, what, where, when and why organic?

Soil Association
the heart of organic food & farming

for all the answers and tempting offers go to www.whyorganic.org

- Mouthwatering offers on organic produce
- Seasonal recipes
- Expert advice on your food and health
- Order more copies of the Organic Directory
- Join the Soil Association and support our work

SCOTTISH AGRICULTURAL COLLEGE

Craibstone Estate, Bucksburn, Aberdeen, Aberdeenshire, AB21 9YA
Tel: 01224 711072 Fax: 01224 711293 david.younie@sac.co.uk www.sac.ac.uk/consultancy/organic
Licensed producer of organic crops, beef and sheep. Advice, research, and education – SAC provides
advice on organic farming (including telephone Helpline 01224 711072) to Scottish farmers, education and vocational training, and multi-disciplinary research across most aspects of organic farming.

SCOTTISH ORGANIC PRODUCERS ASSOCIATION (SOPA)

Scottish Organic Centre, 10th Avenue, Royal Highland Centre, Inglisten, Edinburgh, Lothian, EH28 8NF
Tel: 0131 333 0940 Fax: 0131 333 2290 info@sopa.org.uk www.sopa.org.uk
SOPA primarily offer an organic certification service to farmer producers. SOPA is the leading Scottish
organic sector body.

SEA SPRING PHOTOS

Lyme View, West Bexington, Dorchester, Dorset, DT2 9DD
Tel: 01308 897766 Fax: 01308 897735 sales@seaspringphotos.com
The slide library contains many images of certified organic products and scenes on organic agricultural
and horticulutural holdings.

SMALLHOLDER BOOKSHOP

Stoke Ferry, Kings Lynn, Norfolk, PE33 9SF
Tel: 01366 500466 bookshop@lodgecottage1.freeserve.co.uk www.smallholder.co.uk
Mail order publisher. Books and videos on smallholding, livestock, poultry, organics, growing, environ-
ment and general rural interests.

SMALLHOLDER MAGAZINE

3 Falmouth Business Park, Blickland Water Rd., Falmouth, Cornwall, TR11 4SZ
Tel: 01326 213333 Fax: 01326 318749 liz.wright1@btconnect.com www.smallholder.co.uk
Smallholder Magazine covers all aspects of livestock and crops plus up to date news for both organic
and non-organic but has an organic sympathy – targeted at the small farmer and those exploring niche
markets.

SOIL ASSOCIATION

South Plaza, Marlborough St., Bristol, BS1 3NX
Tel: 0117 314 5000 Fax: 0117 925 2504 info@soilassociation.org www.soilassociation.org
The Soil Association is a membership organisation with charitable status, founded in 1946. It encourages an ecological approach to agriculture and offers organic cultivation as the sustainable long-term
option above chemical farming. Mail order book catalogue, bookshop, information packs, publications
and magazine Living Earth. Its subsidiary the Soil Association Symbol Scheme is an EC-approved certification body which inspects and licenses commercial food producers, processors and other manufacturers to the highest organic standards, and acts as the consumer's guarantee of organic quality.

SOIL ASSOCIATION LTD. (SA CERT)

South Plaza, Marlborough St., Bristol, BS1 3NX
Tel: 0117 314 5000 Fax: 0117 925 2504 info@soilassociation.org www.soilassociation.org
Soil Association Limited is the largest of the UK certification bodies, and currently inspects and certi-
fies over 70% of UK licensed organic producers and processors. We certify to the Soil Association
Standards for Organic Food and Farming, which are well respected worldwide. The well known Soil
Association Organic Symbol, featured in this book and displayed on much organic food and packaging,
is widely recognised and trusted by consumers.

SOMERSET FOOD LINKS

Units 10 & 11, Bridge Barns, Long Sutton, Nr. Langport, Somerset, TA10 9PZ
Tel: 01458 241401 Fax: 01458 241228 enquiries@foodlinks.org.uk www.somerset.foodlinks.org.uk
County food links project established 1999 to encourage thriving local food economy by supporting
Somerset businesses (producers, processors, retailers, caterers, accommodation providers), schools
and community groups. Advice to local food businesses (including direct marketing, co-operation, public procurement), advice to community food growing projects, social enterprise development, advocacy,
lobbying and awareness raising. Mobile: 07968 428047.

STOCKBRIDGE TECHNOLOGY CENTRE LTD

Cawood, Selby, North Yorkshire, YO8 3TZ
Tel: 01757 268275 Fax: 01757 268996 robjacobson@stc-nyorks.co.uk
STC Ltd provides contract R&D, technology transfer and related services in all aspects of organic field
and glasshouse vegetable production: specialisms include variety evaluation, fertility inputs and
pest/disease control.

STROUD COMMUNITY AGRICULTURE LTD

48c High St., Stroud, Gloucestershire, GL5 1AN
Tel: 0845 458 0814 info@stroudcommunityagriculture.org www.stroudcommunityagriculture.org
A community co-operative which runs a farm business. The farm grows vegetables and has pigs and
cattle. Anyone can become a member and get a weekly veg bag with an option to buy meat also.
Membership tel: 01453 840037.

SUGARBROOK FARM

Mobberley Rd., Ashley, Nr. Altrincham, Cheshire, WA14 3QB
Tel: 0161 928 0879 mail@sugarbrookfarm.co.uk www.sugarbrookfarm.co.uk
Soil Association G4603. Bed and breakfast with en-suite facilities from £25 per person, close to
Manchester airport and Tatton Park. Sheep and arable farm welcoming educational access under
Countryside Stewardship i.e. free visits.

SUSTAIN

94 White Lion St., London, N1 9PF
Tel: 020 7837 1228 Fax: 020 7837 1141 sustain@sustainweb.org www.sustainweb.org
Sustain – the alliance for better food and farming – advocates food and agriculture policies and practices that enhance the health and welfare of people and animals, improve the working and living environment, promote equity and enrich society and culture.

THE SUSTAINABLE LIFESTYLES RESEARCH CO-OP LTD

The Office, Pond Cottage East, Cuddington Rd., Dinton, Aylesbury, Buckinghamshire, HP18 0AD
Tel: 01296 747737 mikegeorge.lara@btinternet.com
Organic Food Federation no. 0071/01/981. Free range eggs, seasonal vegetables and fruit, especially
Victoria plums. Occasional lamb, mutton (Jacobs sheep). Selling at Tring Farmers' market and from farm
stall. Full public access to 70 acres. Farm walks through woodland to the riverside. Run by volunteers.

TRIODOS BANK

Brunel House, 11 The Promenade, Bristol, BS8 3NN
Tel: 0800 328 2181 Fax: 0117 973 9303 mail@triodos.co.uk www.triodos.co.uk
Triodos Bank's unique Organic Saver Account offered in partnership with the Soil Association gives you a
secure and rewarding way to target your savings to organic enterprises. We provide full banking services
for organic food and farming enterprises, including current and investment accounts, overdrafts and loan
facilities. As Europe's leading ethical bank we have financed a wide range of organic businesses over
many years and understand the needs and dynamics of the sector. Contact us for more details.

S-T

ULSTER WILDLIFE TRUST

John McSparran Memorial Hill Farm, Glendun, Cushenden, Co. Antrim, Northern Ireland, BT44 0PZ
Tel: 028 2176 1403 Fax: 028 2176 1403 ulsterwt@glendunfarm.fsnet.co.uk
Soil Association G6697. Farming together with wildlife in a progressive and sustainable manner, producing lamb and beef from traditional and native breeds. Native trees are also produced in our nursery.

UNITED WORLD COLLEGE OF THE ATLANTIC

St. Donats Castle, Llantwit Major, Vale of Glamorgan, Glamorgan, CF61 1WF
Tel: 01446 799012 Fax: 01446 799013 estate@uwcac.uwc.org www.atlanticcollege.org
Soil Association G5656. An international 6th form College with a 20-hectare farm unit producing organic lamb and beef.

UNSTONE GRANGE ORGANIC GARDENING FOR HEALTH

Crow Lane, Unstone, Nr. Chesterfield, Derbyshire, S18 4AL
Tel: 01246 412344 Fax: 01246 412344 admin@unstonegrange.co.uk www.unstonegrange.co.uk
We provide gardening opportunities for volunteers from all over Derbyshire: people with learning disabilities, mental health issues, single parents, retired, people changing careers or downshifting. Others are well and want to stay well, or want to learn about organic horticulture. We run an OCN-approved organic horticulture course.

UPPER RED HOUSE FARM

Llanvihangel, Monmouth, Gwent, NP25 5HL
Tel: 01600 780501 Fax: 01600 780572
Soil Association G4969. Tir Gofal. The farm is mainly pasture with some arable, producing forage and spring cereals with emphasis on conservation and educational visits to study environment and wildlife. Educational visits, all ages welcome, but booking essential.

WARRINER SCHOOL FARM

The Warriner School, Bloxham, Banbury, Oxfordshire, OX15 4LJ
Tel: 01295 720777 Fax: 01297 721676 www.atschool.eduweb.co.uk/warriner
A mixed 16-hectare farm based at the Warriner School, a secondary comprehensive at Bloxham in Oxfordshire. A further 24 hectares are rented nearby. The farm is a purpose-built educational resource. It provides a practical, relevant and realistic experience of farming, the rural environment and land use to students from Warriner and other schools. Member of the Soil Association Organic Farms Network.

U–W

THE WESSEX ORGANIC MOVEMENT (WORM)

Tel: 0845 330 3953 Fax: 0845 330 3953 sec@wessexorganic.org.uk www.wessexorganic.org.uk
Soil Association, HDRA, BTCV. We hold talks and visits to promote and educate farmers, producers or consumers about organic methods and to network information, and set up projects to meet their needs.

WESTHOPE COLLEGE

Westhope College, Craven Arms, Shropshire, SY7 9JL
Tel: 01584 861293 www.westhope.org.uk
Soil Association No. G4886. Adult education weekend and weekly courses, C&G exams. Depth of the country, organic food.

WHITEHOLME FARM

Whiteholme, Roweltown, Carlisle, Cumbria, CA6 6LJ
Tel: 016977 48058 whiteholmefarm@hotmail.com www.whiteholmefarm.co.uk
Whiteholme Farm is an organic livestock farm situated in the north-east of Cumbria. Home reared organic beef, lamb and pork is prepared at our on-farm butchery from traditional breeds and sold to local customers through direct sales and farmers' markets. Accomodation, education and farm walks are all available. Member of the Soil Association Organic Farms Network.

WHOLESOME FOOD ASSOCIATION

1 Ball Cottage, East Ball Hill, Hartland, Devon, EX39 6BU
Tel: 01237 441118 sky@wholesome-food.org.uk www.wholesomefood.org
Provides a low cost alternative to organic certification for the small scale grower and small farmer. We operate a unique 'peer review' verification system backed by our 'open gate' growing policy, which enables customers to visit growers' premises by appointment. We welcome producers, processors, suppliers, distributors and supporters who support local, chemical-free food production.

WILTSHIRE COLLEGE – LACKHAM

Lackham Park, Lacock, Chippenham, Wiltshire, SN15 2NY
Tel: 01249 466800 Fax: 01249 444474 wiltscoll@ac.uk www.wiltscoll.ac.uk
We offer a range of FE & HE courses in organic horticulture at National Certificate/Diploma and National Award in Organic Horticulture. For further details visit the website or telephone 01249 466873.

WOMENS ENVIRONMENTAL NETWORK

PO Box 30626, London, E1 1TZ
Tel: 020 7481 9004 Fax: 020 7481 9144 info@wen.org.uk www.wen.org.uk
Educational environmental charity, educating women and men who care about the environment from a women's perspective. Projects include local food, women's food growing groups, health, real nappies and waste prevention.

WOODBROOKE QUAKER STUDY CENTRE

1046 Bristol Rd., Selly Oak, Birmingham, West Midlands, B29 6LJ
Tel: 0121 472 5171 Fax: 0121 472 5173 kathleen@woodbrooke.org.uk www.woodbrooke.org.uk
Set in ten acres of organically managed gardens, Woodbrooke is a residential Quaker education centre, also offering conference facilities and general accommodation. Guests enjoy organic food grown on the premises.

THE WORLD LAND TRUST

Blyth House, Bridge St., Halesworth, Suffolk, IP19 8AB
Tel: 01986 874422 Fax: 01986 874425 info@worldlandtrust.org www.worldlandtrust.org
A UK-based, international conservation charity working to preserve the world's most biologically important and threatened lands. The Trust has helped purchase and protect more than 300,000 acres of habitats rich in wildlife in Belize, Costa Rica, the Philippines, South America and the UK. For a unique, eco-friendly gift, save an acre of rainforest for £25.

WORLDLY GOODS

10-12 Picton St., Bristol, BS6 5QA
Tel: 0117 942 0165 Fax: 0117 942 0164 wg@eco-logicbooks.com www.eco-logicbooks.com
Specialise in wholesale/trade sales of books that provide practical solutions to environmental problems, permaculture, organic gardening etc. Contact us for free catalogue.

WWOOF (WORLD WIDE OPPORTUNITIES ON ORGANIC FARMS)

PO Box 2675, Lewes, East Sussex, BN7 1RB
Tel: 01273 476286 Fax: 01273 476286 hello@wwoof.org www.wwoof.org.uk
WWOOF helps volunteers find host farms worldwide to be able to experience organic growing, meet like-minded people, exchange skills and get into rural areas. Help in exchange for bed and board.

YORKSHIRE ORGANICS

Bog House Farm, Mickleby, Saltburn, North Yorkshire, TS13 5NA
Tel: 01947 840075 jenny@yorkshireorganics.freeserve.co.uk
A producer group aiming to promote organic awareness in Yorkshire. We hold quarterly meetings which are farm walks, talks and socials and publish a quarterly newsletter.

W–Y

INDEX

D-F

F–H

H–L

R–S

S–W

FUTURE EDITIONS OF *THE ORGANIC DIRECTORY*

Please contact us if:

- You think your company or organisation should be included in *The Organic Directory*
- You want the details of your entry to be amended
- You know of a company or organisation that you think should be included in *The Organic Directory*
- You have suggestions as to how we can improve *The Organic Directory*

In all cases, please email Clive Litchfield at: organiceco@aol.com

or write to him c/o Green Books Ltd, Foxhole, Dartington, Totnes TQ9 6EB.

There is no charge for inclusion in *The Organic Directory*, although we also accept paid advertising in the printed version.

THE ORGANIC DIRECTORY ONLINE

You can find *The Organic Directory* online at the Soil Association's website:

www.whyorganic.org